The Holt
MODERN
BIOLOGY
Program

MODERN BIOLOGY
Otto, Towle, and Bradley

Annotated Teacher's Edition to the Modern Biology Text
Biology Investigations   Otto, Towle, and Otto
Annotated Teacher's Edition to Biology Investigations
Laboratory Investigations   Otto, Towle, and Otto
Test Masters in Biology

Supplements to Modern Biology

Human Physiology   Morrison, Cornett, Tether, and Gratz
Living Things   Teter, Edwards, Fitzpatrick, and Bain
Modern Health   Otto, Julian, Tether, and Nassif
Modern Sex Education   Julian, Jackson, and Simon

Other Basic Texts in Life Science

MODERN BIOLOGY

James H. Otto
Albert Towle
James V. Bradley

HOLT, RINEHART AND WINSTON, PUBLISHERS
NEW YORK · LONDON · TORONTO · SYDNEY

James H. Otto was a biology teacher and head of the Science Department at George Washington High School, Indianapolis, Indiana.

Albert Towle is a professor of biology and supervisor of biology student teachers at California State University, San Francisco, California.

James V. Bradley is a biology teacher at Lake Forest High School, Lake Forest, Illinois.

Editorial Development William N. Moore, Roger R. Rogalin, M. Jean Young
Editorial Processing Margaret M. Byrne, Regina Chilcoat, Shelley L. Feiler
Art and Production Vivian Fenster, Fred C. Pusterla, Robin M. Swenson, Annette Sessa, Beverly Silver, Anita Dickhuth, Dorina Virdo
Product Managers John W. M. Cooke, Laura Zuckerman
Advisory Board Rhenida Bennett, John W. Griffiths, Henry May, David J. Miller, Douglas A. Nash, Jonathan Permar, George Salinger, John Taggart
Consultant John Matejowsky
Researchers Pamela Floch, Gerard LaVan

Photo and art acknowledgments appear on page x.

ISBN 0-03-056031-4
1234   032   9876543

Content Critics

Unit	Reviewer
1	Michael W. Berns Professor and Chairman Department of Developmental and Cell Biology University of California, Irvine
2	John B. Jenkins Department of Biology Swarthmore College
3	Bruno J. Kolodziej Department of Microbiology Ohio State University
4	Margaret Balbach Department of Agriculture Illinois State University
5	Jeffrey A. Butts Department of Biology The University of North Carolina at Charlotte
6	Warren F. Walker, Jr. Department of Biology Oberlin College
7	Claude A. Villee, Jr. Andelot Professor of Biological Chemistry Harvard Medical School
8	Eugene P. Odum Director, Institute of Ecology University of Georgia

Teacher Critics

Unit	Reviewer
1, 2	Rosalie Morris Teacher, Elmont Memorial High School Elmont, New York
3, 4	Joyce G. Greene Teacher, Boulder High School Boulder, Colorado
5, 6	Robert F. Patton Director, Dallas Environmental Science Center Seagoville, Texas
7, 8	Jerry Resnick Assistant Principal, Science Department Sheepshead Bay High School Brooklyn, New York

v

Preface

MODERN BIOLOGY begins with a discussion of the unique properties of living organisms that set them apart from the nonliving. The presentation of molecular and cellular biology follows, and gives a background for the concepts of reproduction and genetics. Understanding the continuity of life and the transmission of characteristics to offspring by hereditary determiners gives meaning to organic variation and scientific classification. Units dealing with microbiology, multicellular plants, invertebrate animal life, the vertebrate animals, and human biology follow in logical sequence. The final unit serves as a fitting climax and an overview of the entire biology course. This last unit begins with an overview of the sphere of life on this planet. It then narrows the focus of the relationship of organisms to their physical environment and with other organisms. Finally it deals with the place of the organism itself.

The authors of MODERN BIOLOGY have always believed that the learning process should involve a mastery of certain fundamental concepts at the beginning of the course in biology. From these initial understandings, the progression from cell to protists, to plants and animals, and finally to the human will come naturally. In this systematic approach to the study of biology, the student discovers unity in the organisms.

The approach and methodology that have evolved successfully in thousands of secondary school classrooms and laboratories have been preserved in MODERN BIOLOGY. These features have been tested and proved effective by thousands of science teachers. The many professional biologists making significant contributions in the research laboratories who have learned from earlier editions of this text are evidence of the value of such an approach.

As in previous editions, this tenth revision of MODERN BIOLOGY has been updated in all areas in which new knowledge is significant to the high school student. The authors have attempted to maintain the readability at a level proportionate to the average student. The Appendix includes a four-kingdom system of classification with major characteristics.

In the sections of MODERN BIOLOGY dealing with evolution, scientific data have been used to present this material as theory rather than fact. The information presented allows for the widest possible interpretation that can be applied to any set of values, either religious or scientific. Every effort has been made to present this material in a nondogmatic manner.

A special feature of MODERN BIOLOGY is the two inserts. The *Human Body* helps students to understand the structure of their own bodies. The *Frog Anatomy* is a valuable reference tool for the study and dissection of the frog.

In each unit, careers that cover a diversity of interests and educational requirements are presented. It is recognized that these are not all the careers available to students, but they indicate the range of opportunities in the field of biology.

A list of interesting and challenging activities is offered at the end of each unit. Also at the end of each unit is a list of related books and articles.

The questions at the end of the chapter relate directly to the chapter objectives. Each question in Questions for Review can be answered using information from the text. The section called Applying Concepts is designed to extend thoughts on biology topics beyond the text.

The Facts & Figures sections feature unusual facts about biology that make learning biology more interesting.

The present authors are indebted to the late Truman J. Moon, whose successful texts BIOLOGY FOR BEGINNERS and BIOLOGY were the predecessors for this book. The many letters and comments from students, teachers, and parents have been appreciated and further suggestions from teachers are invited. The authors have tried to maintain authority in MODERN BIOLOGY.

To The Student: How To Use This Book

The proper use of your textbook will help to make the study of biology easier and more enjoyable. MODERN BIOLOGY has several features that will be of great help in getting the most out of your study of biology. Follow this simple guide to learn how.

Part I Vocabulary

In biology you will be exposed to a new language, the language of biology. MODERN BIOLOGY helps you to grasp more easily the new vocabulary of this language.

A. Look at the bottom of page 2. The word *biology* is in **boldface italics.** *Biology* is an important term. Each boldface italic word is defined in the Glossary at the back of the book and is included in Biologically Speaking at the end of the chapter. *Biology* is also defined on page 3 of your textbook.

B. Look at the middle of page 8. In the left-hand margin is the prefix *micro-.* This prefix can help you understand what the word *microscope* means. Note that the word *microscope* is in italics only. It is an important word to know but it does not appear in Biologically Speaking. It is a word with which you are probably familiar or is not a word emphasized in the chapter.

C. Now that you know *micro-* means "small" and *biology* is "the study of life," what do you think the word *microbiology* means? If you do not know, look in the Glossary.

Part II Major Concepts

A. Look at page 2 again. At the top of the page, on the left, is a list of objectives. After you study the chapter, you will be able to perform all these objectives. If you have already done Part I of this exercise, you are already able to perform objective A.

B. Look at the top of page 6. The main idea of this paragraph is in **boldface.** What objective does it refer to?

C. Look at the middle of page 8. The rest of Chapter 1 will deal with "Important Tools of the Biologist." Look at the boldface heads of the next few sections. What is the main tool of the biologist? *Microscope* is the answer. Titles of sections and the way they are organized help you to learn the major concepts of each chapter.

D. Look in the Index (page 743 and following pages) under *microscopes.* Is there somewhere else in the book you can find out more about microscopes? The Index will tell you the page numbers where you can find out more about microscopes. The Index will also give you a list of related topics.

CONTENTS

Frog Insert art by John Murphy

Human Body insert courtesy of W. B. Saunders Company

Unit Opening Photographs
1. Patricia Peck
2. L. Grillone, © J. Gennaro, Photo Researchers Inc.
3. Manfred Kage, © Peter Arnold, Inc.
4. Derek Fell
5. Stephen Dalton © 1979, Photo Researchers
6. M. Austerman, © Animals Animals
7. from *The Mitchell Beazley Atlas of the Body and Mind*, © Mitchell Beazley Publishers Limited 1976. Published 1976 in the USA by Rand McNally and Company, Chicago. Reproduced by permission of the publishers.
8. Bob Campbell, Bruce Coleman

All other photographs are acknowledged on the page on which they appear.

Cover and title page: A nudibranch mollusk of the genus *Glaucus* eating a "tentacle" of a hydrozoan of the genus *Porpita*. (Animals Animals, © Oxford Scientific Films) For more information on nudibranchs turn to page 378.

> *Sometimes, in the course of the modulation of relations between animals, there are inventions that seem to have been thought up on the spur of the moment, like propositions to be submitted for possible evolution. Some are good-humored, even witty. Certain Australian surf bathers, several years ago, were stung by tiny creatures that turned out to be nudibranchs armed with the stingers of Portuguese men-of-war. Having fed on jellyfish, the Glaucus community had edited their meal and allowed the stinging cells to make their way to the surface of their new host, thus creating, for the time, a sort of instant hybrid with, allowing for some asymmetry, the essential attributes of each partner.*

From **THE LIVES OF A CELL** by Lewis Thomas. Copyright © 1971 by the Massachusetts Medical Society. Copyright © 1974 by Lewis Thomas. Used by permission of Viking Penguin Inc.

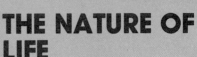

THE NATURE OF LIFE

Biology is a science that deals with living things. Learning about life does not always have to be done in a laboratory. The earliest humans certainly had to know many things about biology in order to survive. And they must have used one of the most important techniques still used in science today: *Observation.*

You already know many things about life. Living things differ from nonliving things. Living things differ from one another. Yet all living things are alike in many ways. In your study of biology you will explore the living state using many techniques and tools of science. Perhaps people will never be able to explain life, but scientific investigations can bring a better understanding of the beautiful and marvelous condition that is life.

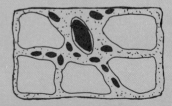

1

The Science of Life

A **DEFINE** biology.
B **DEMONSTRATE** the use of the scientific method.
C **DESCRIBE** the limits and application of science.
D **IDENTIFY** the parts of a light microscope.
E **EXPLAIN** the limitations of the light microscope.
F **EXPLAIN** the advantages of the electron microscope.

1–1 | Do you think these early humans had any knowledge of biology?

Biology: A Science

Biology developed from the human need to understand events and solve problems. Early humans learned where to go to seek food and how to stalk animals. Imagine the daily routine of a small band of early humans as shown in the picture above. Perhaps they spent the nights in the shelter of a cave. But during the day, their activities centered around obtaining food. After much trial and error, they learned to work together. The killing of a large animal would have marked a successful day. But the hunt may have taken many days and involved long hikes and no food. At these times the people must have eaten all kinds of plants and small animals. Certainly many were poisoned by animal bites or by eating some kinds of plants. They may have become very ill or even died without knowing why. But by observation and communication people recognized certain plants and animals as poisonous. Knowledge of biology, then, became very important in the lives of the human. People have always tried to learn more about themselves and other living things for practical reasons. Human survival depends on it. The study of *biology* (BI-ahl-uh-jee) grew out of this necessity.

The word *biology* comes from two Greek words. *Bios-* means "life," and *-logos* means "thought" or "science of." The word *science* may be defined as "a body of knowledge and the methods of gaining that knowledge." **Biology is the study of life.** It includes logical, scientific methods by which biologists today are adding to our knowledge.

Information about biology, as other sciences, is being recorded at a great rate. More biological knowledge has been gained in the past quarter century than in the twenty centuries before! What brought biology, and science in general, to this golden age? Let's look at some answers.

Superstition and Prejudice Replaced by Science

People have always tried to explain things they did not understand. Many events were explained only by guess-work or as superstition and magic. Perhaps you believe a person's life is shaped by the positions of stars and planets. Has anyone ever found evidence for this idea? Once people believed that mud in ponds turned into eels, fish, and frogs. You may laugh at this idea now, but it has taken science several centuries to overcome this type of thinking. Science, based on fact and logic, is replacing superstition.

Scientific investigation usually leads to more investigation. When one problem is solved, the answer points to new problems for investigation. You might picture scientific knowledge as a tiny point of light in a sea of darkness. Through many centuries, scientists of many nations have added knowledge to widen this "circle of light." As the circle grows, more places on its outer edge become available for investigation. In other words, the more people learn, the more they realize how much more can be learned.

Science Is a Universal Effort

The acceptance of scientific thought has changed people's ways of thinking. During the Middle Ages, ignorance and superstition blocked the search for questioning and understanding. Scientists began to break through these walls with the coming of the Renaissance.

In the sixteenth century Andreas Vesalius of Belgium rebelled against the methods of medieval medicine. At that time it was customary for a professor to read while an assistant cut up an animal for students to observe. But Vesalius wanted to do his own dissections to show and explain the parts of an animal to his students. His observations led him to question many ideas that were then considered to be facts. Vesalius' work showed the value of making firsthand observations. He established a scientific study of *anatomy*, an important branch of biology.

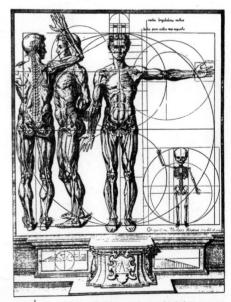

1-2 | One of the first branches of biology was the study of anatomy. *(The Bettmann Archive, Inc.)*

This is only one great moment in the history of biology. During your reading you will find that **modern biology has grown from the work of people of all nations.**

The Limits of Science

In the Middle Ages, "scientific truths" were handed down from earlier times. These "truths" were not to be questioned, much less disproved. People who dared to disagree were ridiculed, attacked, and sometimes killed. Even a generation ago, science was believed to be much more exact than it is now known to be. **Today, people no longer think of any scientific answer as a final one. They know that ideas may have to change in the light of new discoveries.**

Ideas about the different sciences have also been changing. At one time, clear lines were drawn between the fields of science. Today the lines are gone. **All sciences are related.** Perhaps you believe that chemistry and biology are separate sciences. *Chemistry* is the science of the makeup of materials and how they can change. You will discover, in your study of the living condition, that chemistry is very important. For example, digestion of food, growth, and even why children resemble their parents, all result from chemical activity. Physics, too, is important to the biologist. *Physics* is the science of materials and motion. It deals with such things as mechanics, heat, electricity, light, sound, and atomic energy. But without a knowledge of physics, the changes in matter and energy involved in life could not be completely understood.

1–3 I Exobiology is a new science. Are conditions right on Jupiter for life as we know it? *(NASA)*

Advances in chemistry and physics have made it possible to build more efficient rockets. The rockets carry satellites to orbit the earth. And the information sent back from the satellites has changed many concepts about the earth. It has been learned that the earth is slightly flattened at the poles and bulges at the equator. Its crust varies in thickness. The knowledge gained from the satellites has enabled probes to be sent far out into space. What conditions exist on other bodies? Could life exist on any? There is a new field of biology that deals with these questions. It is called *exobiology*. Because of the methods used, exobiology involves biology combined with chemistry, physics, and earth science.

exo = outer

Pure and Applied Science

It is often said that there are two kinds of science—**pure science,** or basic research, and **applied science.** In pure science, research is done for the sake of knowledge itself. Applied science makes practical use of this knowledge. For example, much pure science research has been done on how one plant could be grown from another. As you may already know, a cutting may be made from a geranium plant, and the new plant will produce flowers exactly like the first plant. But such cuttings from a pine tree won't grow! Scientists have wondered why. For many years biologists have tried to do this very thing. Some biologists removed tiny sections from a pine needle and discovered that these small parts of a pine needle could be kept alive in the laboratory. Then, they observed that these tiny sections would grow. It was even more surprising when the tiny growing parts formed roots and new pine needles. These were the beginnings of what soon became trees. In this way applied science has helped to develop new forests with only the best trees.

1-4 | The cut stem will grow into a complete plant that will bear the same kind of flower as the plant from which it was taken. *(top: Ted Vaughn, Grant Heilman; bottom: Runk, Schoenberger, Grant Heilman)*

1-5 | New trees can be cloned from small pieces taken from a pine needle of a single tree. *(left: Courtesy of Crown Zellerbach; right: Courtesy of Weyerhauser Company)*

STEPS OF THE RESEARCH METHOD

Define the Problem

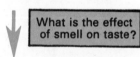
What is the effect of smell on taste?

Gather Information

Your FIVE Senses

Form Hypothesis

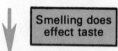
Smelling does effect taste

Prove or Disprove by Experimentation

EXPERIMENT   CONTROL

Collect Data

DATE ..... TIME	DATE ..... TIME ....
First Trial: Apple Onion Potato	First Trial: Apple Onion Potato
Second Trial:	Second Trial:

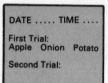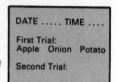

Conclusion

The sense of smell does effect what you taste

1–6 | Steps of the research method used in a controlled experiment.

Scientific Methods

There is no one scientific method. **A scientific method can be thought of as a logical, orderly way to solve a problem or answer a question.** It is this logic and order that makes scientific methods different from ordinary, hit-or-miss approaches. Remember, though, that scientific methods are not magic. Even the best planned experiment can fail. Yet failure itself may lead to final success. By careful study of each result, a new direction may be found.

Several methods are used in science, depending on the nature of the problem. Perhaps the most important, especially for your biology course, is a *research method*.

A Research Method

The steps in this research method are logical and orderly. In fact, they are simply a system of common sense.

- *Define the problem.* You can't solve a problem unless you see that one exists. For example, how does a root absorb water from the soil? What controls your heartbeat? Well planned experiments can answer each of these questions. But in science, every answer raises new questions. Successful research leads to new research and new knowledge.

- *Collect information on the problem.* Scientists must build on the work of other scientists. Otherwise science could not advance beyond what one person could learn in one lifetime. Before beginning an experiment, the scientist studies all important information that has to do with the problem. Often it turns out that someone has already answered many of the questions involved. For this reason, a library of scientific papers, journals, and books is an important part of a research center. Your textbook and laboratory guide, along with other reading, will serve you in the same way in this course.

- *Form a hypothesis.* The available information may not fully explain the problem. The researcher must then begin to experiment. At this point, a **hypothesis** (hi-POTH-eh-sis) is needed. The hypothesis is a sort of working explanation or trial answer.

  The hypothesis gives the experimenter a point toward which to aim. But no matter how reasonable the hypothesis seems, it cannot be accepted until supported by a large number of testings. The research worker must be open-minded enough to change or drop a hypothesis if the evidence does not support it.

- *Experiment to test the hypothesis.* The scientist must set up an experiment that will either support or disprove the hypothesis. This means that the experiment must test *only* the condition involved in the hypothesis. All other factors must be removed or otherwise accounted for. The one factor tested is called the **experimental factor.**

Usually a second experiment called the **control** is done along with the first experiment. In the control experiment, all factors *except the one to be tested* are the same as in the first experiment. In this way, the control shows the importance of the missing or added experimental factor.

■ *Observe and record data from the experiment.* Everything about the experiment should be recorded accurately. How was it planned and set up? Under what conditions was it carried out? What happened *during* the experiment? And finally, what were the results? The record may include notes, drawings, tables, graphs, or other forms of information. These records are the *data*. In modern research, data are often processed by computer.

■ *Draw conclusions*. Data have value only when valid conclusions are drawn from them. Such conclusions must be based *entirely* on facts observed in the experiment. If other experiments continue to support the hypothesis, it may come to be called a **theory.** A good theory explains the facts and also predicts new facts.

A Controlled Experiment Using the Research Method

When you have a cold, your nose is stuffed up. This affects your sense of smell. You might have also noticed that your food has little or no taste. This could lead you to wonder if your sense of smell affects how you taste things. You can try to find an answer to your question by doing a simple controlled experiment.

First, define the problem you want to solve involving smell and taste. You can define a problem by asking a question. *What is the effect of smell on taste?*

The next step should be to go to the library. Much has been written on the effect of smell on taste. Still, you may not find an exact answer to the question. But, based on knowledge from reading, you form a hypothesis: Smelling does affect taste. This hypothesis must now be supported or disproved by experiments.

An experiment can be done using small pieces of onion, apple, and potato. Two people are needed for this experiment. One person conducts the experiment, while the other (the subject) is tested. The subject is blindfolded so that the onion, apple, and potato can't be identified by sight. The nose of the subject is held to block out any smell. The person conducting the experiment gives the blindfolded person a piece of either onion, apple, or potato. What does the subject taste? Record the results. Repeat this several times using the onion, apple, and potato in any order. The subject rinses his or her mouth between each taste so that the different tastes don't mix.

Now, do the same test with the potato, apple, and onion but this time the subject's nose is not held. This will serve as the *control*. Record the results.

To draw conclusions, compare the results from your notes of the experiment and control. Very likely you will conclude that *the sense of smell does affect what you taste.*

But this conclusion raises several other questions. For example, why could you taste sweetness? To what degree does smelling affect taste? Would other people react in the same way? If you were told what you were eating would it affect the results? These are only a few questions that a simple experiment raises. A hypothesis that has strong support usually leads to many more questions.

Important Tools of the Biologist

Early Microscopes

By logical and organized study, early biologists learned many things about life. But they were limited by what they could actually see. Perhaps the most important tool used in biology is the microscope. The development of this instrument allowed biologists to study living things in greater detail than ever before.

It is hard to say who actually invented the microscope. Even a single-lens magnifying glass is really a *simple microscope.* And single lenses that could magnify ten to twenty times were being used in the Middle Ages.

micro = small

The first known *compound microscope* was made about 1590 by the Janssen brothers, two Dutch eyeglass-makers. Their microscope had *two* lenses, one mounted at each end of a tube-within-a-tube barrel. One lens magnified the already enlarged image of the other. The microscope was focused by sliding the tubes back and forth. Galileo used another early compound microscope to study biological materials as early as 1610.

Some years later, a Dutch merchant named Anton van Leeuwenhoek (LAVE-in-HOOK) began grinding lenses as a hobby. He is said to have made about 250 different simple microscopes. Each was designed for examining a specific thing. For example, one microscope had a tube for holding

1-7 | Early microscopes: (a) compound microscope made by the Janssen brothers; (b) Galileo's microscope; (c) one of van Leeuwenhoek's simple microscopes; (d) a microscope used over a hundred years ago. *(The Bettmann Archive, Inc.)*

a small fish in front of the lens. When van Leeuwenhoek held the lens to his eye, he saw blood surging through vessels in the fish's tail. Another of his microscopes was built for examining pond water. Through it, he saw a swarm of microscopic animals, which he described as "cavorting beasties." This must have been a surprise, because the tiny life forms he observed were too small to be seen with the naked eye. Improvements allowed van Leeuwenhoek's microscopes to magnify by about three hundred times. In a very real sense, this Dutch merchant's hobby opened up one of the most important fields of modern science—*microbiology*.

The Modern Compound Microscope

Compound microscopes have improved steadily since the time of the Janssen brothers. More powerful lenses and finer mechanical parts have been developed. Since modern microscopes use ordinary light, such instruments are called *light* microscopes. A light microscope may have its own light source. Or it may simply have a mirror that reflects available room light through the lenses.

A light microscope contains several lenses. One lens is the *eyepiece* at the top of the microscope. Other lens sets are contained in *objectives*. Microscopes have from one to four objectives. Different objective lenses give different magnifying powers. The microscopes used in most high schools magnify about 100 times (100X) at low power. At high power, they may magnify by 430 times (430X) or 440 times

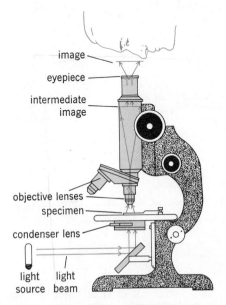

1-8 | Passage of light rays through the compound microscope allows the specimen to be viewed clearly.

(440X). At these enlargements, the smallest living units of plants and animals called *cells* may be seen clearly. Many microscopic plants and animals may also be seen. But smaller cell structures and very small living things, such as bacteria, need more magnification. Special objectives can give enlargements of 1,000 to 1,500 times, depending on the eyepiece used.

In microscopic study, the unit of measurement commonly used is the micrometer or **micron** (μm). It is equal to 0.000001 meter or about 1/25,000 inch. These units are needed to describe very small specimens. For example the single-celled organisms bacteria range from 0.5 to 2 μm.

Limits of Light Microscopes

Lenses could be made that would give enlargements greater than 1,500X. Yet no light microscope magnifies

Careers

The research biologist has a Ph. D. degree and post-doctoral experience working with other research scientists.

Electron microscope technicians are often hired to prepare specimens, operate the microscope, and take photographs for researchers. The technicians usually have a college degree in biology and special training in the use of electron microscopes.

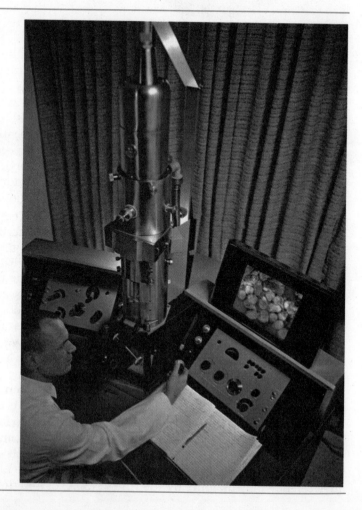

1–9 | A biologist using an electron microscope. Notice that the image of the specimen appears on a screen. (*Courtesy Parke, Davis & Co.*)

much more than this. Why not? The answer lies not in lenses or other microscope parts, but in the nature of light itself.

There are two important factors to consider when an image is enlarged. One is the microscope's **magnification,** or how much it enlarges an image. The other factor is **resolution,** or the microscope's capability to deliver a visible image with clear details. Magnification and resolution are closely related.

Each set of lenses bends the light rays in such a way that the rays are spread apart. This spreading forms the *magnified image* that reaches the eye. The more the light rays are bent and spread, the greater the magnification. But this bending and spreading of light rays affects resolution in a different way. Look at a picture in your text. Without magnification, the picture is clear, and the details are sharp. If you view it through a reading glass, you see that the picture is made up of many small dots. If you used stronger and stronger lenses, the dots appear farther and farther apart. Finally, so few dots are visible in the field that the picture itself is lost. In other words, **higher magnification brings lower resolution.**

The Electron Microscope

A new and very different kind of instrument has opened up worlds that no microscope could reach. The **electron microscope** does not use ordinary light. An electron microscope uses a stream of electrons. With the invention of the electron microscope, the problem of resolution with the light microscope was solved. Details of cell structure could be studied. Particles called viruses could be observed. These viruses are even 1,000 times smaller than most bacteria. One problem with this type of microscope, though, is that the material to be studied has to be sliced very thin. Living cells cannot be observed with this kind of electron microscope.

A newer model of the electron microscope makes an image of the *surface* of the object. It is capable of very high magnification. It is called a *scanning electron microscope.* This has been a useful addition to the biologists' tools. With this electron microscope three-dimensional figures can be observed. See figure 1-10 (bottom). Relatively large figures can also be seen.

In this chapter, you have studied some of the methods and tools that biologists use in their work. And as always with science, new techniques have answered many questions, but these answers have brought about many more questions.

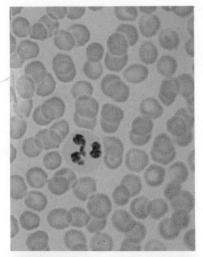

1-10 | Blood cells observed (a) through a light microscope (about 1,000X); (b) through a scanning electron microscope (about 5,000X) *(top: Carolina Biological Supply Co.; bottom: Manfred Kage, Peter Arnold)*

Summary

Science is a body of knowledge and the methods of gaining that knowledge. Biology is the science of living things.

Pure science is basic research. Applied science makes practical use of the knowledge gained by pure science. All branches of science are related. A research method of science involves a problem and the orderly way in which an answer may be found. After gathering information about the problem, a hypothesis can be formed. But testing is needed to see if the hypothesis is correct. Observations of the experiments are carefully recorded before conclusions can be made. Sometimes experiments show that a particular hypothesis was not correct. Then more questions and more hypotheses come to mind.

Through science, much information can be gained. This information often changes many of our ideas. The compound and electron microscopes, for example, have changed many ideas about living things.

Biologically Speaking

biology	experimental factor	magnification
pure science	control	resolution
applied science	theory	electron
hypothesis	micron	microscope

Questions for Review

1. Give examples of scientific achievements that show science as a universal effort.
2. Describe steps of a research method used in science.
3. People often think that all scientific research is done in the laboratory. Why is the library important?
4. What is the purpose of a control in an experiment?
5. Distinguish a hypothesis from a theory.
6. What is the difference between pure and applied science?
7. Name the structures through which light passes as it passes through a light microscope.
8. Distinguish between magnification and resolution as they relate to a light microscope.
9. Describe the difference in the pictures obtained from an electron microscope and a scanning electron microscope.

Applying Concepts

1. Discuss ways progress in biology has paralleled the perfecting of the microscope.
2. Outline a controlled experiment that tests one factor.
3. Discuss advantages of an electron microscope in relation to the limitations of a light microscope.

A **DISTINGUISH** between living and nonliving organisms.
B **LIST** the characteristics of living things.
C **NAME** the five stages in the life span of an organism.
D **EXPLAIN** why organisms must be able to adapt to their environment.
E **COMPARE** biogenesis and spontaneous generation.
F **EXPLAIN** the roles of Redi and Spallanzani in the theory of abiogenesis.
G **DESCRIBE** Pasteur's experiment that proved the principle of biogenesis.

2–1 | Name the living and nonliving things. (© Ernest Wilkinson, Animals Animals)

The Living and the Nonliving

Look at the nature photograph above. Can you easily separate the living from the nonliving things in the scene? The animals and the plants are *organisms.* Organisms are *complete and entire living things.* **Organisms are made of substances organized into living systems.** You probably said that the water and rocks are *nonliving.* Their substances are organized very differently from the substances of the organisms. But what about the fallen logs? Certainly they were once living, but now they are nonliving.

Clearly the living and nonliving conditions are different. Yet they are closely related. When you compare the trees and the logs, you can see that the substances of both come from nonliving soil, air, and water. When an organism dies, its substances return to the nonliving state. What, then, *is* the difference between living and nonliving? What is meant when it is said that something is *alive?* Let's look at the ways in which living things are alike. These characteristics of living things are used by biologists to define *life.*

13

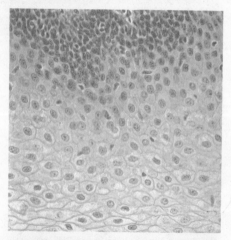

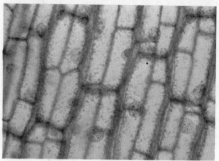

2-2 | The basic units of all living things are cells. (a) human skin cells (250X); (b) leaf cells (120X). *(a: Manfred Kage, Peter Arnold; b: Ward's Natural Science Establishment)*

Facts & Figures

A blue whale can grow from an egg, weighing 0.000035 of an ounce, to 29 tons in 23 months.

proto = first

Characteristics of the Living Things

Organisms Organize Protoplasm

All living things have a complex system of substances organized in a special state of chemical activity. This system is referred to as *protoplasm.* Substances are organized in this way only in living things. In other words, **only organisms organize protoplasm.**

Protoplasm is not a definite living substance. In fact, protoplasm is not a definite substance in the way that water, salts, sugars, and acids are substances. Water, for example, has a definite composition. The composition of protoplasm differs in all living things. In fact, protoplasm even differs in the different *parts* of an individual. The makeup of any bit of protoplasm is changing constantly.

Protoplasm, itself, is not "alive." The substances that it is made of are not living. Protoplasm is mostly water containing salts and food substances the organism needs to live. Yet, when these substances are organized into a system by an organism, the state of chemical activity called the *living condition* is established.

Organisms Constantly Use Energy

In order for chemical activities to occur, energy is used. Since life is a state of constant chemical activity, it needs a constant supply of energy. All life's energy ultimately comes from the sun. It is stored in the complex chemical substances called *foods.* Plants and animals both break down stored foods and release this energy. As you will soon learn, energy is used to support the many life processes. **Life continues only as long as energy is supplied and put to use by an organism.**

Organisms Are Made of Cells

All organisms are made of cells. Some are made of billions of cells, some just a few cells. There even are organisms that are made of only *one* cell. This is why biologists often call the cell the *common unit of life.* In this course you will study many different organisms. In every case, from bacteria to the seed plants, from ameba to the human, you will be dealing with cells. **Cells are the basic units of living things.**

Parts of the cell may remain after an organism dies. The wood of a table, for example, has cell walls, but it is not alive. Just because the cell walls are present doesn't prove a living condition. It only shows that a living condition once existed. **Cells are produced only by organisms and are never organized by nonliving materials.**

Perhaps you have heard about viruses. Viruses are *not* cells. Biologists say that they are *subcellular.* That is, they are less complex than cells in their makeup. Yet they have certain chemical properties that are found only in living cells. Are viruses organisms? Are they really living? Or are they a link between the living and nonliving states? You will explore these questions when you study viruses in Chapter 16.

sub = **under, below**

Organisms Are Capable of Growth

All organisms grow larger, at least during part of their lives. You may think of some nonliving things, such as icicles and crystals, that appear to grow. But this kind of growth is very different from the growth of living things.

An icicle grows larger as more and more water freezes on its surface. A crystal grows larger in much the same way. Icicles and crystals grow only as more material of the same kind is added to their surfaces.

The growth of organisms is quite different. A tree doesn't grow by collecting more "tree" on its surface. Nor do you grow by attaching more of "you" to your skin. Your growth involves a complex series of chemical processes. During these processes you take in food, which is then chemically changed. Then the cells in your body organize the food substances to form more of "you."

Most people stop growing at around 21 years of age. But does this mean that all growth has stopped? No, they have only stopped growing *larger.* They are still growing in another way. Throughout the living condition, all organisms constantly replace the materials of which they are made. This growth by replacement continues as long as the organism lives.

Organisms Have a Life Span

Life is activity. As long as an organism is alive, it is growing either in size or by replacement. When conditions no longer favor this activity, life ends. **All organisms have a fairly definite period of life, which is called the *life span.***

The life span of any organism may be divided into five stages. These stages are (1) beginning, (2) growth, (3) maturity, (4) decline, and (5) death. After an organism is formed, it goes through a period of rapid growth. This growth period may last for minutes, weeks, months, or years, depending on the organism. As the organism grows larger, the rate of growth decreases. Finally maturity is reached. During maturity, growth is reduced to repair and replace the organism's substances. At last the organism reaches a point at which it can no longer repair or replace all damaged or worn-out materials. This marks the period of decline, which ends in death.

Five Stages of Life Span

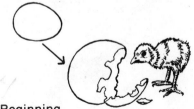

Beginning

Growth

Maturity

Decline

Death

2–3 | The five stages in the life span of a chicken.

3 weeks

5 yr.

30 yr.

70 yr.

500 yr.

1000 yr.

∞

2–4 | The life spans of different organisms vary greatly.

Facts & Figures

The bristlecone pine tree in California may live more than 5,000 years.

How long can an organism live? The answer differs greatly for different organisms. Certain insects live only a few weeks. Five years is old for some fish. A horse may reach an age of thirty or more. A white oak may live five hundred years. Certain kinds of California redwood trees would be young at that age and might live for thousands of years. For human beings, the average life span in the United States is about seventy years. Perhaps in a few generations this span will be lengthened.

A definite life span is a characteristic of all living things. But why does life have this limit? If an organism could continue to organize and replace its substances, couldn't it go on living forever? Perhaps it could, if certain changes could be avoided. But scientists are only beginning to learn about the processes involved in these changes.

In a way organisms, or parts of organisms, *do* live forever. In your study of biology you will deal with many one-celled organisms such as bacteria. A bacterium is microscopic, which means it is so small it can only be seen with the aid of a microscope. A bacterium may be formed and reach maturity in a half hour or less. At this point, it splits into two bacteria, which then grow and repeat the process. In this way, a bacterium never dies of old age. The same is true for amebas and other one-celled organisms.

Organisms Reproduce

Even an ameba or a single bacterium has a definite life span. All organisms have a life span. They must reproduce if life is to continue. Reproduction may occur in many ways. A bacterium reproduces by splitting. In some cases, parent organisms form special cells for reproduction. In other cases, a part of the parent organism may break off and the piece may grow on its own. However, all forms of reproduction are alike in principle. In each, either a mass of protoplasm divides or a small part of a mass of protoplasm develops from the parent. An elephant develops from a bit of living matter no larger than a pinhead. The substance of this matter comes from both parents. The resulting organism can live and grow for a lifetime. **Only living things produce offspring.**

Organisms Produce Similar Organisms

If you were shown a picture of a baby bear and asked to describe how it would appear in two years, you probably could answer. You could tell what a bear looks like and how large bears usually grow. Very likely your description would fit almost any full-grown bear. But how can you be sure that a baby bear won't grow up to look like a horse, or even a tree?

2–5 | A mother bear with her offspring. *(Leonard Lee Rue III, Bruce Coleman)*

The answer lies in the expression "like produces like." Mature plants and animals are expected to be like their parents in both form and size. Have you ever wondered why this is so?

There are many ways in which mature organisms will not be like their parents. You may not be able to recognize these differences among grown bears. But consider the brothers and sisters in the same human family. You will at once see many differences. These differences are called **variations.**

It is a characteristic of living things that **organisms produce organisms similar to themselves. No two offspring are exactly alike, nor are they exactly like their parents.**

Organisms Are Affected by Their Environment

All organisms must use energy in order to stay alive. The **environment** plays a key role in an organism's ability to obtain energy. Factors in the environment both support life and threaten it.

Exactly what is the environment? **An organism's environment is its surroundings.** The environment includes physical factors such as weather, air, light, soil, and so on. But it also includes all the many life forms that share the physical environment.

The physical environment differs greatly from place to place. Consider the differences between a hot desert and rainy forest. As conditions differ, so do the life forms. Desert plants and animals could not survive in the rainy forest, nor could rainy forest life survive in the desert. Organisms have special characteristics that enable them to live in a specific environment.

Facts & Figures

The longest recorded human life has been 125 years.

2–6 | Could these plants live in one another's environments? *(top: Manuel Rodriguez; bottom: Entheos, EPA-Documerica)*

An organism may be well suited to its physical environment. Even so, the organism must compete with other living things around it. Sometimes it competes for food or for other things necessary to life. For example, a young tree on the forest floor must compete with many other plants for growing room. Organisms must also compete with natural enemies. For instance, robins are a constant threat to worms and caterpillars. But hawks, crows, and cats in turn present a constant threat to robins.

Organisms Can Adapt to Their Environment

Conditions in an environment change from time to time. Sometimes the changes are sudden, as when there is a fire, a storm, or a long dry period. Other changes may take place over a very long time. These include such things as changes in climate, changes in soil, and the steady wearing down of mountains and hills.

If organisms are not suited to a new condition, they can no longer survive. In order to survive they must do one of two things. They must either move to a better environment, or they must change. A change in the organism cannot occur in one generation, it occurs over many generations.

The characteristic of *variation* allows organisms to survive changing conditions. Many of the differences, or variations, of offspring have little effect on the survival of the offspring. Only rarely does a variation give an organism a better chance of surviving. But if such a variation is passed on to the next generation of offspring, they will have a better chance of surviving. Over a long period of time, all organisms of that type may have the helpful characteristics. **The process in which a species slowly or rapidly becomes better suited to survive is called *adaptation*.**

When speaking of adaptation, people often say that an

2–7 | In what ways is this whitetailed deer adapted to its environment? *(Stephen J. Krasemann, Peter Arnold Inc.)*

organism changes to fit its environment. This does not happen. Plants and animals do not change *in order* to survive. They survive *because* change has taken place.

The northern white-tailed deer did not develop long legs in order to run fast. Instead, deer that had long legs could run fast and so they survived. In turn, they produced offspring that also had long legs and could run fast. Deer with short legs could not run as fast. Often these deer did not survive long enough to produce offspring that would also have short legs. Today, the northern white-tailed deer have the helpful characteristic of long legs. Whether or not the variations are helpful, the possibility of variation is a characteristic of the living condition.

Organisms Can Respond to Their Environment

A living organism is able to respond to conditions outside itself. This function of living systems is referred to as *irritability.* An organism responds to a *stimulus* from the environment. A *stimulus* is a factor or environmental change capable of producing activity in an organism. The stimulus may be light, temperature, water, sound, pressure, the presence of chemical substances or food sources, or a threat to life. The organism's *response* is the way it reacts to a stimulus.

Different organisms respond in very different ways. For example, a plant may have a growth response. This happens when a root pushes toward water or a stem grows unevenly and bends toward light. Animals can react in more complex ways. Sight, hearing, taste, touch, and smell are responses to conditions in the environment. More complex responses include fleeing from or fighting an enemy, hunting for food, and seeking or building shelter.

Nonliving substances may change as conditions within the environment change. For example, water freezes or turns to steam at different temperatures. But only living organisms can respond to a stimulus for survival value.

2–8 | In what way have these plants responded to their environment? *(Daniel Wasp)*

Life Comes from Life

The Principle of Biogenesis

As you have learned, the life of every organism comes from its parents or parent. Does life ever spring from nonliving matter? No evidence of this happening has been found. It seems that *life comes only from life.* Biologists call this the principle of **biogenesis** (by-oh-JENN-uh-siss). Though all the evidence argues for it, biogenesis actually is a fairly new idea.

bio = life
gen = to be produced, be born, become

Belief in Spontaneous Generation

From ancient times until less than a century ago, most people believed that certain nonliving materials could change directly into living organisms. A closely related belief was that one life form could give rise to a completely different form. For example, a tree could produce a lamb or a goose. This type of belief is called *spontaneous generation* or *abiogenesis.*

a = without

Many stories of spontaneous generation had to do with smaller animals such as insects and worms. The stories were told because people in early times had little knowledge of how such animals grew and developed. One of the strangest stories came from the Belgian doctor Jean van Helmont some three centuries ago. According to van Helmont, a dirty shirt placed in a container of wheat would produce mice in 21 days. The mice would be formed in the fermenting wheat. The human sweat in the shirt would supply an "active principle" needed for the process.

There were many other ideas about spontaneous generation. For example, frogs and fish were thought to develop in clouds and to fall to earth with rain. It was also believed that flies came from the dead, decaying bodies of animals

2-9 | Spontaneous generation myths: Frog and fish from mud, geese from barnacles, mice from wheat.

such as horses. These flies really came from maggots that hatched from eggs laid in the body. But because no one had seen the eggs being laid, the belief was not questioned for centuries.

Redi Attacks Spontaneous Generation

Until the late nineteenth century, most scientists accepted the idea of spontaneous generation without question. There was no real evidence for this idea. In those times, people often drew conclusions that were not supported by facts. But a seventeenth-century Italian scientist, Francesco Redi (RAY-dee) demanded proof. Could decaying fish change into flies? Redi said no. Flies came from eggs laid by flies. The decaying meat was nothing more than food for the maggots.

In 1668, Redi tested his hypothesis in an experiment. He placed bits of veal, snake, fish, and eel in four different clean jars. He then did the same with four other jars. One set of jars, which today would be called the *control set*, was left open. The other set, which would be called the *experimental set*, was tightly sealed. In any investigation, one experiment is not enough to prove or disprove a hypothesis.

2–10 | Redi's first experiment to disprove spontaneous generation.

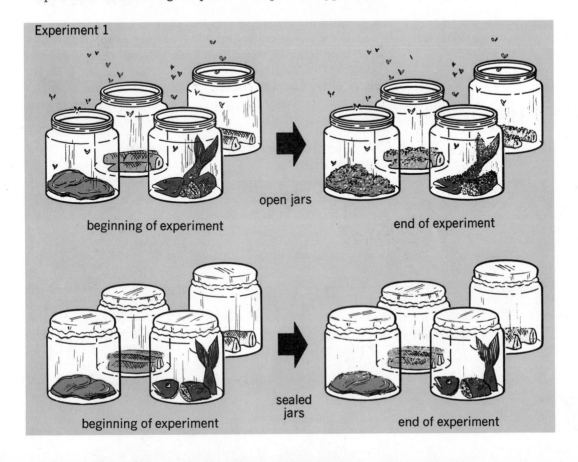

Experiment 1

beginning of experiment — open jars — end of experiment

beginning of experiment — sealed jars — end of experiment

This is why Redi used four jars for each set. In the control set Redi wanted to show what usually happens when meat is left out in the open. In the experimental set he wanted to see what would happen if air was kept out of the jars. The exclusion of outside air was his *experimental factor.*

Flies soon gathered inside the open jars and laid eggs. In a short time, maggots appeared in all of the open jars. Several weeks later, Redi opened the sealed jars. He found rotten meat but no maggots. From this evidence, Redi concluded that maggots hatch from eggs laid by flies and are not produced by spontaneous generation.

If Redi had stopped there, his point would not have been proved. There was actually no *control* in this experiment. Remember, the experimental factor was the exclusion of air. Those who believed in spontaneous generation would have said that air was needed as an "active principle." Air could not enter the sealed jars. So Redi's first experiment really involved not one, but two experimental factors: air and flies.

Redi did a second experiment. He filled four jars with the same materials as before. But this time he covered the jars with only a fine cloth. Air could pass through the cloth but flies could not. As the meat decayed, flies laid eggs on the cloth, but no maggots appeared in the meat.

This second experiment gave strong proof that flies come only from flies and not from rotting meat. But the supporters of spontaneous generation continued in their belief. What was true of flies might not be true of such animals as worms. Though flies came only from flies, other organisms might still arise by spontaneous generation.

The Microscope and Spontaneous Generation

By the eighteenth century, the microscope had become a widely used tool of science. Biologists were viewing all sorts of microscopic organisms that had not been visible

2-11 | Redi's second experiment. His critics noted that the first experiment did not allow air into the sealed jars.

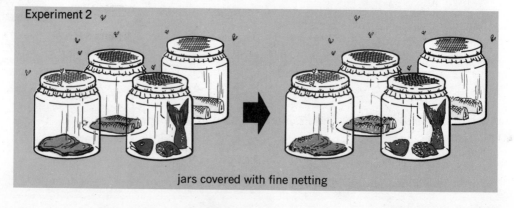

Experiment 2

jars covered with fine netting

before. Samples of broths and sugar solutions were seen to be swarming with bacteria, yeasts, molds, and other organisms. From where had these organisms come? Some scientists supported spontaneous generation as the only possible answer. Another group argued that the organisms could come only from other organisms.

The English scientist John Needham supported the idea of spontaneous generation. Needham boiled a meat broth for a few minutes in loosely sealed flasks. After a few days, he viewed the broth with a microscope and found it teeming with microscopic organisms. He repeated the experiment with other meat and vegetable broths. The results were the same. Needham claimed that boiling had destroyed all life in the broths. And since the flasks were sealed, he said, the organisms present after standing must have formed by spontaneous generation.

Spallanzani Questions Needham's Conclusions

About 25 years after Needham's experiments, Lazzaro Spallanzani of Italy led an attack against the conclusions Needham had drawn. Spallanzani felt that Needham had not boiled the broths long enough to destroy all life and had not sealed the flasks tightly enough. If so, the organisms found later in the broths could have come from organisms that survived the boiling. Or they could have come from organisms that entered the flasks from the air. In any case, Spallanzani hypothesized that the organisms had not come from spontaneous generation.

Spallanzani then did a series of experiments. He boiled some seeds in water for a short time and placed the broth in glass flasks. He then completely sealed each flask by melting the glass together at the top. All the flasks were placed in boiling water for one hour and then removed. After several days, Spallanzani opened each flask and looked for evidence of life in the broth. None of the broths contained living organisms.

To Spallanzani, this experiment proved that the organisms found by Needham could not come from spontaneous generation. But this evidence did not satisfy Needham's supporters. They claimed that boiling for an hour had destroyed the "active principle" of the broth. This, they said, was why spontaneous generation had not taken place.

Spallanzani felt certain that no "active principle" was destroyed by boiling. To prove this, he did a second series of experiments.

Spallanzani reasoned that if boiling destroyed some "active principle," longer boiling would destroy *more* of the "principle." Thus, he boiled one set of flasks for half an

Needham's Experiment

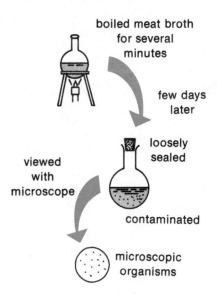

Spallanzani's Experiment

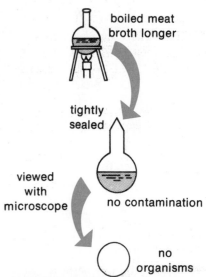

2–12 | Needham's experiment to prove spontaneous generation and Spallanzani's experiment to disprove spontaneous generation.

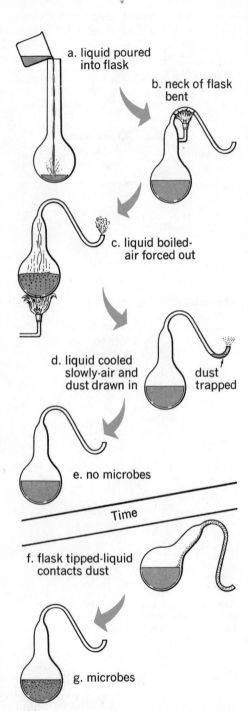

a. liquid poured into flask

b. neck of flask bent

c. liquid boiled- air forced out

d. liquid cooled slowly-air and dust drawn in

dust trapped

e. no microbes

Time

f. flask tipped-liquid contacts dust

g. microbes

2-13 | Pasteur experimented with swan-necked flasks to disprove spontaneous generation.

hour, another for an hour, a third for an hour and a half, and a fourth for two hours. After boiling, the flasks were loosely sealed and carefully marked. Spallanzani could have left the flasks completely open. After all, he was not trying to show that organisms could enter the flasks from the air. His experiment was meant only to prove that boiling did not destroy an "active principle" needed for spontaneous generation.

After eight days, Spallanzani checked the broths in each set. Living organisms were present in all of the broths. But Spallanzani was surprised when he noted the numbers of organisms in the broths. In all but one kind of broth (which was made with corn) *the broths boiled longest contained the most organisms!* What had happened? Spallanzani concluded that, in all but the corn broth, longer boiling dissolved more seed or egg yolk. In other words, the broths boiled longest offered the richest food supply for organisms.

Clearly, heating did not destroy an "active principle" in seed broths. In fact, heating made the broths better suited for the growth of microscopic organisms. Yet the supporters of spontaneous generation did not give up in the face of this evidence. The argument went for another 50 years. Then, at last, it was settled by a young scientist just beginning his brilliant life's work.

Pasteur Defeats Spontaneous Generation

It was Louis Pasteur, the nineteenth-century French chemist, who finally laid to rest the theory of spontaneous generation. Pasteur carried out several experiments that provided evidence clearly defeating the supporters of spontaneous generation.

In his first series of experiments, Pasteur used several liquids that would support growth of bacteria and other organisms. Each liquid was sealed in a flask and boiled long enough to kill all organisms present. Pasteur then took the flasks to several places where the air contained different amounts of dust. In flasks opened along dusty roads, great numbers of organisms grew within a few days. Flasks opened on hills and mountains showed much less growth of organisms. These results supported Pasteur's belief that bacteria and other organisms were present in the air with dust.

Pasteur set out to find support for his hypothesis under the more controlled conditions of his laboratory. He prepared a liquid containing sugar and yeast and poured it into flasks. He heated the long neck of each flask and bent it into an S-shape somewhat like a swan's neck. The liquid was then boiled for several minutes, forcing air out of the flask. As the liquid slowly cooled, air returned to the flask through the neck.

Throughout the experiment, air moved into the flasks. But water and dust particles from the air settled in the trap formed by the swan's-neck curve. Thus, no organisms appeared in the sugar liquid even though it was in constant contact with the outside air. On the other hand, a flask could be tipped so that the liquid came in contact with the trapped dust. If this was done, great numbers of organisms were present in the liquid within a few days.

No argument could stand against Pasteur's simple experiment. It was clear that boiling had not destroyed the ability of the liquid to support organisms. Nor had the flasks kept out any "active principle" that might be in the air. Both the liquid and the air would support the growth of bacteria and other organisms. However, these organisms had to come from outside the flask, not from spontaneous generation within it.

The theory of spontaneous generation, accepted for centuries without any real evidence, was defeated. From Pasteur's time to the present, all experiments have supported biogenesis: Life comes only from life.

Summary

The differences between living and nonliving things involve their organization and changes. One single characteristic does not define life. Organisms use energy and they grow. Organisms have similar structures; they are all made of cells. Organisms also have a definite life span, and they reproduce similar organisms. In response to the environment, organisms are able to adapt to changes. Nonliving things do not have *all* these characteristics by which life is recognized.

People have wondered about the origin of living things. In the past, many people believed in abiogenesis. That is, they believed that nonliving things would produce living organisms. This theory has been replaced by a belief in biogenesis, which means *all life comes from life.*

Biologically Speaking

organism	adaptation
protoplasm	irritability
life span	biogenesis
variation	spontaneous generation
environment	

Questions for Review

1. What is the biological concept of an organism?
2. List the main characteristics of living things.
3. Give a definition of protoplasm in relation to modern biological concepts.
4. In what way is growth by living things different from growth by nonliving things?
5. List the five stages in the life span of an organism.

6. Explain the relationship between variations and adaptations.
7. State the theory of biogenesis.
8. Give examples of myths based on belief in spontaneous generation.
9. Describe Redi's experiments to disprove spontaneous generation.
10. How did Spallanzani refute Needham's support of spontaneous generation?
11. Describe Pasteur's contribution to the belief in biogenesis.

Applying Concepts

1. Describe how Redi's experiments conform to modern scientific practice. Why was his second experiment of special importance?
2. Explain how Pasteur accounted for all variable factors in his experiments disproving spontaneous generation of microorganisms.
3. Discuss various ways in which living organisms respond to external stimuli.

3–1 l Wheat plants store energy from the sun. *(Grant Heilman)*

The Chemical Basis of Life

Matter, Energy, and Life

Matter **is the material of which everything, living and nonliving, is made.** But, the living condition requires energy. Energy is obtained from the food an organism needs. From where does this energy come? How are matter, energy, and life related? Think of a single wheat plant. What chemical materials does it take from the soil and air? How does it get the energy from the sun? How is this energy stored? What do animals do with this energy when they eat wheat as food? How does this food become part of the body?

Scientists understand many of the changes in matter and energy involved in the living condition. And yet many changes are not understood. Your study of biology will become more interesting when you understand more about matter and energy.

What Is Matter?

Perhaps you already know some facts about matter and changes in matter. **Matter is anything that occupies space and has mass.** Matter includes all solids, liquids and gases.

These states of matter may seem quite different to you, but they are all alike in certain ways.

Solid matter has particles that are packed closely together. Yet even in a solid such as lead, the particles vibrate constantly and have space between them. In *liquid matter*, the space between particles is much greater. The particles vibrate more actively and move freely as a liquid. In *gaseous matter*, the particles are much farther apart and move even more freely than in solid or liquid matter. You cannot see some gases, such as those making up the air. But in other gases, such as chlorine, when the particles are close enough together, they appear greenish. Carbon monoxide, a deadly gas, cannot be seen or smelled. One gas, called hydrogen, is the least dense gas. Yet even hydrogen has mass and occupies space.

Changes in Matter

The difference between solids, liquids, and gases is caused by the amount of activity of particles and the space between the particles. Matter can be changed by changing particle spacing and activity. These changes occur often and are called **physical changes.** Water is a good substance to use to show physical changes. At or below the freezing point, water is in a solid form called ice. If the ice is heated, it changes from solid matter to liquid water. Continued heating causes the particles to vibrate rapidly and spread farther apart. At the boiling point, liquid water changes to steam, a gas. Solids, liquids, and gases are *states of matter.* **In a physical change, the states of matter have changed but no change has occurred in the particles that make up the matter.**

Chemical change is different from physical change. In a chemical change matter actually changes *from one substance to another*, not simply to a different state. For example, when wood burns, a chemical change takes place. The matter of the wood is changed into very different substances. Some of these are gases, which are given off into the air. In fact, one of these gases is steam, or water in the gaseous state. It may surprise you to learn that burning wood gives off water. Wood is formed by a series of complex chemical changes in a living tree. The tree used many different substances from the soil and air to grow. One of these substances was water.

Energy and Energy Changes

Energy from the sun supports life and takes part in all life activities. Energy is involved in all matter and all changes in matter. Remember the example of the physical change from ice to liquid water and gaseous steam? Heat was used

3–2 | The solid, liquid, and gaseous states of matter. What characteristics of each state are illustrated?

to make the change. Heat is energy. **Energy is something that is capable of doing work or causing change.**

There are two types of energy. *Kinetic energy* is energy in action, energy that actually is doing work or causing change. A moving car or running water are forms of kinetic energy. Kinetic energy also takes the form of *radiant* energy. Such radiation includes electric waves, radio waves, heat, visible light, and rays such as X rays. Energy from the sun radiates toward the wheat plants in the picture at the beginning of this chapter.

The other type of energy is *potential energy.* As the name suggests, this means that it is possible for the energy to do work or cause change. But such work or change is not actually taking place. **Chemical Energy is one form of potential energy.** If you look again at the photograph of growing wheat plants at the beginning of the chapter, you may be able to imagine potential energy becoming *stored chemical energy* in the wheat. In this case radiant energy from the sun is stored as chemical energy.

Potential energy and kinetic energy are closely related. One form can be changed to the other. The kinetic energy in the form of radiation is used by the wheat plants in their living condition. Some of this energy is used and some is stored as potential energy. Matter, then, can store energy. Scientists have used the same principle in developing solar batteries. The sun's energy is captured and stored as potential energy in the batteries. It can then be used as electricity to perform work.

Coal is another example of stored energy. The energy stored in coal originally came from the sun. In the form of coal, it remains potential energy until the coal is burned. Then the stored energy is released as heat and light, two forms of kinetic energy. Something is needed to start the coal burning. This is called *activation energy.*

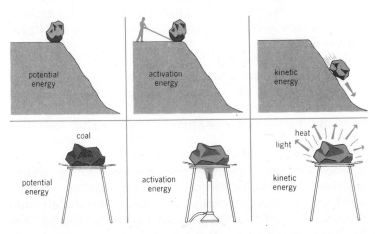

3-3 | In both cases, potential energy is converted into kinetic energy by activation energy.

The Particles of Matter

There are more than one half million words in the English language. Yet the spellings of these words come from the 26 letters of the alphabet. In much the same way, all the matter of the world is formed from 92 natural **chemical elements.** Like letters of the alphabet, these elements may be combined in many different ways. The elements form the many substances that make up all living and nonliving matter in the world.

Most of the natural elements are quite rare. Less than 15 elements make up 99 percent of the matter of the earth. In their combined states, elements form many familiar substances, such as water. If the elements are a chemical alphabet, the substances are words that are "spelled" with only a few letters.

The smallest unit of an element is called an *atom.* **All matter is made of these tiny particles called atoms.** Atoms are rearranged into different combinations *in ordinary chemical changes.*

A symbol is often used to represent an atom of an element. In most cases, the symbol is the first letter or letters of the element's name. For example, the symbol *C* represents one atom of the element carbon. *Ca* stands for calcium and *Cl* for chlorine. *H* represents one atom of hydrogen, and *O* stands for an oxygen atom. Some chemical symbols come from old Latin names for elements. For example, *Na* represents sodium (natrium) and *Fe* for iron (ferrum).

The Structure of Atoms

All atoms are made of the *same kinds* of particles. For example, an oxygen atom is made of exactly the same kinds of particles as an iron atom. What makes the two atoms different is that these particles are present in different numbers and arranged in different ways. The same thing is true for all the atoms of the known elements. Each element has a unique atomic structure.

Let's look at the structure of atoms. The smallest and simplest atom is the element hydrogen. It has a center called the **nucleus.** Inside the nucleus of the hydrogen atom is a single particle called a *proton.* The proton has a positive (+) electrical charge. Moving around the nucleus of the hydrogen atom is a single, very small particle called the *electron.* Compared to the proton, the electron has almost no weight. But the electron does carry a negative (−) electrical charge. The charges of the proton and the electron balance. Thus, the atom as a whole has no charge. The hydrogen atom is neutral.

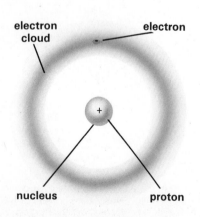

3–4 | Model of the hydrogen atom.

The second simplest element is helium. Its nucleus has two protons. Two electrons move around the nucleus. An oxygen atom has eight protons and eight electrons. The largest natural atom is uranium. Uranium atoms have 92 protons and 92 electrons. One form of uranium is used as a fuel in atomic power plants.

The number of protons in the nucleus is called the **atomic number.** The atomic number determines what element the atom is. There are 92 atomic numbers in the series of natural elements. The 92 elements range from hydrogen (atomic number 1) to uranium (atomic number 92).

The electrons constantly move around the nucleus of an atom in the same way as planets move in a solar system. They do not follow clear, regular paths, but they do move at given distances from the nucleus. These different distances are called *energy levels.*

The first energy level can hold one electron in the hydrogen atom or two electrons in the helium atom. Then there is a gap out to the second energy level, where as many as eight electrons may orbit. Up to 18 electrons also may occupy the third energy level. In larger and larger atoms, the electrons are arranged in more and more complex ways.

Look at the nucleus of the ordinary hydrogen atom in figure 3-4. The nucleus contains one proton (+). Look at the nucleus of the helium atom in figure 3-5. Notice that the nucleus has two protons. But it also contains two *neutrons* (N). The neutron is the third kind of particle found in atoms. The nuclei of all atoms other than hydrogen contain one or more neutrons in addition to the protons. Neutrons have about the same mass as protons but have no electrical charge. The neutron adds to the mass of an atom but does not affect its chemical activity. **The total number of protons and neutrons of an atom is the *atomic mass.*** The atomic mass of the ordinary hydrogen atom is one. This is because it has one proton. It has no neutrons. Consider the helium atom. Its *atomic number* is two because it has two protons in its nucleus. But its *atomic mass* is four. This is because its nucleus has two neutrons and the two protons. Now you should be able to look at the model of the ordinary oxygen atom in figure 3-6 and determine its atomic mass.

Let's consider carbon, one of the other elements important to all living things. Ordinary carbon atoms have six protons and six neutrons. Carbon, then, has an *atomic mass* of 12, with the *atomic number* of 6. Do you know how many electrons are in the carbon atom? If a uranium atom has an atomic mass of 238 and has 92 protons, how many neutrons are present? If you can answer these questions, you are ready to understand more important differences in atomic structure.

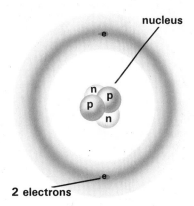

3–5 | Model of the helium atom.

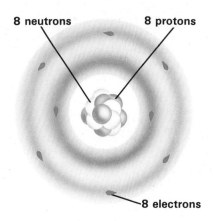

3–6 | Model of the oxygen atom.

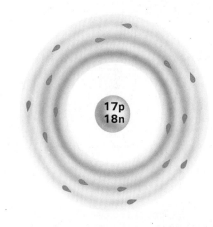

3–7 | Model of the chlorine atom showing different energy levels.

iso = equal
topos = place

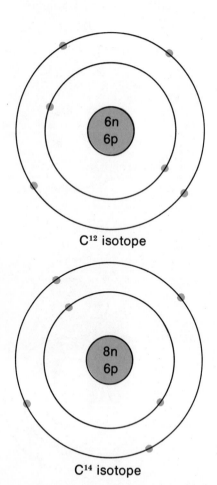

C^{12} isotope

C^{14} isotope

3–8 | The isotope carbon-14 has eight neutrons while ordinary carbon-12 has six neutrons.

Isotopes

Perhaps you have noticed references to "ordinary" atoms of an element. There are atoms that are not "ordinary." Some elements have atoms that are different. The difference is in the number of *neutrons* present. All atoms of a given element have the same number of protons and the same number of electrons. But the number of neutrons may vary. **This is why different atoms of the same element may have different atomic masses.** These different atoms of the same element are called *isotopes.*

You have seen that ordinary carbon has six protons and six neutrons. It is known as carbon-12. The isotopes of carbon may have five, six, seven, or eight neutrons. Carbon-14 has eight neutrons. It is still carbon because it has six protons. As you will see later, this isotope has been very important in biological research. Another isotope of great importance in research is oxygen-18. Oxygen-18 has ten neutrons. Ordinary oxygen is oxygen-16, with eight neutrons. An isotope, then, has a different number of neutrons than an element.

Compounds

Early chemists discovered that some substances contain only one element, while others are made of two or more elements. **A substance in which two or more different elements are combined chemically is called a *compound.*** If you think of elements as letters of a chemical alphabet, then compounds are the words they form. Just as a symbol stands for each element, a *formula* stands for a compound. Perhaps you already know that H_2O is the formula for water. This formula shows that water is made of two atoms of hydrogen and one atom of oxygen.

Table salt has the formula NaCl, which is called sodium chloride. It is made of one atom of sodium and one atom of chlorine. The formula for cane sugar is $C_{12}H_{22}O_{11}$. There are 12 carbon atoms, 22 hydrogen atoms, and 11 oxygen atoms.

The following important concepts will help you as you learn more about compounds:

1. Under certain conditions, *most* elements will combine with one or more other elements. Such elements are said to be *chemically active.* Certain other elements show almost no chemical activity. They are called *inert* elements. Inert elements include helium, neon, argon, krypton, xenon, and radon.

2. Each element has its own *combining capacity* for joining with other elements. For example, the chemical proper-

ties of hydrogen allow it to combine with certain other elements, such as oxygen. But there are other elements with which hydrogen cannot combine.

3. In forming compounds, elements combine in *definite proportions*. In forming water, for example, two atoms of hydrogen always combine with one atom of oxygen.

4. A compound has *its own properties*. These properties are not the same as the properties of the elements making up the compound. For example, water has its own properties, and these properties are not the same as those of hydrogen and oxygen.

Covalent Bonding

What holds the two hydrogen atoms and one oxygen atom together to form water? It is a force called a *chemical bond.* To understand how such bonds work, you need to look more closely at electron activity. **The chemical activity of an atom depends upon the number of electrons and the way in which they are arranged. Most important are the electrons at the highest energy level, farthest from the nucleus.**

In water, for example, atoms *share* electrons at the highest energy level. **The shared electrons orbit both atomic nuclei. This sharing of electrons is known as a *covalent bond.*** Certain atoms share one pair of electrons, each atom supplying one electron. The energy needed to break a covalent bond and separate the atoms is called *bond energy.*

You will be able to understand covalent bonding and bond energy if you look at figure 3-9. The energy levels are represented by the circles. Remember that the first energy level can hold two electrons. The second energy level can hold eight electrons. A hydrogen atom has only one electron. The oxygen atom has two electrons in its first energy level and six in its second energy level. In water, the electrons of hydrogen and oxygen are shared, forming *covalent bonds.* Two atoms of hydrogen share their electrons with one atom of oxygen. When this happens, the second energy level of oxygen has its maximum number of eight electrons. At the same time, by sharing, the first energy level of the hydrogen atoms have their maximum number of two electrons.

Atoms that share electrons in covalent bonding form units of matter called **molecules.** One *molecule* of water is H_2O. A molecule is the smallest part of a substance that still has the characteristics of that substance. In other words one water molecule (H_2O) can become steam. A water molecule can also be broken down, or decomposed, into the

con = with
valentis = made strong

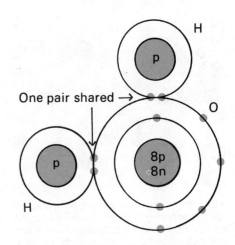

3-9 | A representation of the electrons being shared in the covalent bonds of a water molecule (H_2O).

elements hydrogen and oxygen. Only by combining again chemically will the hydrogen and oxygen become water.

Diatomic Molecules

As you have seen, molecules are formed by atoms that share electrons in covalent bonding. But some molecules are made of two atoms of the same element. Hydrogen atoms, for example, very often tend to share electrons with other hydrogen atoms. They are then called *diatomic molecules.* A molecule of hydrogen is represented as H_2. The bond in this molecule is a *single bond*. That is, two hydrogen atoms share one pair of electrons.

Ionic Bonding

You have seen already how atoms of *different* elements combine to form molecules by covalent bonding. A very different kind of bond involves a *transfer* of electrons between atoms. Some atoms tend to give up electrons. Such atoms are called *electron donors*. Other atoms tend to gain electrons and are called *electron acceptors*. **The transfer of one or more electrons from one atom to another forms an *ionic bond.*** Compounds involving ionic bonds are quite different from those involving covalent bonds.

Ionic bonds form an *ionic compound*. One ionic compound is sodium chloride, or table salt (NaCl). You may know that table salt is in the form of crystals. Under a hand lens, these crystals appear as small cubes. Are salt crystals made of molecules? The answer is no because covalent bonding is not involved here. When atoms carry positive or negative electric charges, they are called *ions.* A salt crystal is made of great numbers of sodium and chlorine ions. Each sodium ion carries a positive charge, while each chlorine ion has a negative charge. Because of their opposite charges, sodium and chlorine ions are attracted to each other and held together in the crystal. This kind of bonding is *ionic*, not covalent.

Atoms are usually neutral. The positive charges of the protons in an atom usually exactly balance the negative charges of the electrons. Thus, the atom as a whole carries no charge. How then do ions and ionic bonding arise?

As you learned before, the ionic bond involves an electron *transfer*, rather than a sharing. The sodium atom has 11 protons and 11 electrons, and so it is neutral. The chlorine atom, with 17 protons and 17 electrons, is also neutral. But the sodium atom is an electron donor. That is, it tends to *give up* an electron. When the sodium atom gives up an electron, its outermost energy level is full with eight electrons. The chlorine atom, an electron acceptor, tends to *gain* an electron. When the chlorine atom gains an electron, its outermost energy level is full with eight electrons.

di = two

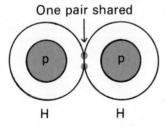

One pair shared

H   H

3–10 | A representation of the electrons being shared in the covalent bonds of the diatomic hydrogen molecule (H_2).

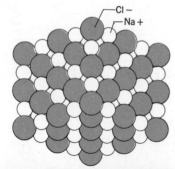

Cl –
Na +

3–11 | (top) A model of some sodium chloride crystals. (bottom) A photo of sodium chloride crystals (20X). The sodium and chloride ions are held together in the crystals by ionic bonds. Why is this not called a molecule? *(bottom: Runk, Schoenberger, Grant Heilman)*

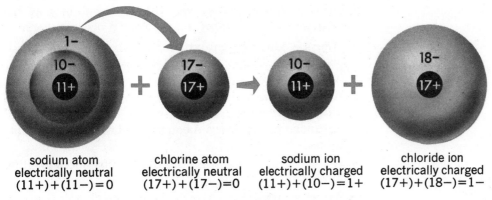

sodium atom	chlorine atom	sodium ion	chloride ion
electrically neutral	electrically neutral	electrically charged	electrically charged
$(11+)+(11-)=0$	$(17+)+(17-)=0$	$(11+)+(10-)=1+$	$(17+)+(18-)=1-$

3–12 | A representation of the formation of sodium and chloride ions.

When the outermost energy level is full, the atom reaches a more *stable* condition. So, while an atom may be electrically neutral from the start, it may reach an even more stable condition by bonding with another atom. In the sodium atom, the outermost level could be filled by either gaining seven electrons or by lending one electron. In the chlorine atom, the outermost level could be filled by either gaining one electron or lending seven. But what really happens is that only one electron is transferred. The transfer of one electron from the sodium atom to the chlorine atom makes both atoms stable.

But the transfer of an electron from sodium to chlorine changes the electric charge on both atoms. With 11 protons and only 10 electrons, the sodium atom becomes an ion with a charge of $+1$. And the chlorine ion, with 18 electrons and only 17 protons, has a charge of -1.

Ions are found throughout the earth, a water planet. They are very important to living things. Plants absorb ions from the water in the ground. For example, the cells of plant roots may take in potassium ions. The concentration of the potassium ions inside the cell may be many times greater than the concentration in the water in the soil.

Mixtures

A **mixture** occurs when two or more substances are mixed together with no chemical change taking place. If you were to stir sugar into water, you would be making a mixture. There is no bonding of atoms, and no new molecular or ionic substance is formed. A mixture can best be described by comparing its properties with those of a compound.

1. The substances that form a mixture are blended together physically, but are not joined chemically. This is what happened when the sugar was stirred in the water.

2. The substances in a mixture can be separated by physical means. If you let the water evaporate, the sugar would remain.

3. The substances that form a mixture can be added in different amounts. One or two teaspoons of sugar could be added to the water. A compound has definite proportions.

4. A mixture has the properties of the substances forming it.

5. When a mixture is formed, there is no chemical action involving energy changes in the formation of a new substance.

Solutions and Suspensions

There are several kinds of mixtures. For example, one substance may be dissolved in another. This kind of mixture is called a **solution.** The dissolved substance is called the *solute;* the substance in which it is dissolved is called the *solvent.*

A solution is formed when molecules or ions of a solute are spread evenly through molecules of a solvent. When you add sugar to water, the sugar crystals dissolve in the water. That is, sugar molecules separate from the crystals and spread evenly among the water molecules. In this case, water is the solvent and sugar is the solute. At a given temperature, a given amount of water can dissolve only a given amount of sugar. When no more sugar will dissolve, it is said that the solution is *saturated.*

Water is the most important solvent for life. It makes up the largest part of protoplasm and dissolves the many essential substances needed for life. It is in water that the chemical reactions of life occur. Reactions associated with living organisms and the environment occur in solutions. Because most substances dissolve in water it is often known as the *universal solvent.*

Most ionic compounds, such as sodium chloride, dissolve easily in water. The ion pairs separate and spread through the solvent. This splitting of ion pairs is called *dissociation.* Dissociation of sodium and chlorine ions can be represented as follows:

$$Na^+Cl^- \xrightarrow{\text{water}} Na^+ + Cl^-$$

Another kind of mixture involves particles that are much larger than ions or molecules. This kind of mixture is called a **suspension.** You can form a suspension by stirring starch into water. The starch particles will spread through the water and may remain separated for some time. After a while, however, the particles will settle to the bottom. They do this because the force of gravity is stronger than the force that holds them in suspension. It is the size of the particles that determines whether they will be dissolved or only suspended.

Colloidal Systems

Many substances break into very large molecules or groups of smaller molecules when mixed with water. These particles are larger than the molecules that form solutions, but smaller than the particles in suspensions. Gelatin is such a substance. It is called a **colloid** (KAHL-oyd). When dissolved in water, the particles of gelatin spread apart. Because of their small size, the particles remain suspended as do molecules or ions in solutions.

kolla = glue
oid = like

Protoplasm is a *colloidal suspension*. In cells, large molecules or groups of molecules remain spread apart in water. In this form protoplasm is in a *sol* state. The suspended particles remain separated by water molecules much as the gelatin dissolved in warm water.

The chemical reactions of life occur in protoplasm in the sol state. As you know, a gelatin suspension can "set." In this form it is called a *gel*. The colloidal suspension of protoplasm can do the same thing. In the gel condition the large molecules actually surround the water molecules. But the chemical reactions of living protoplasm cannot take place in this state. The cell would be dead. You see the formation of the gel state when you fry an egg. The colloidal suspension of the egg white changes to a solid, or gel, form.

Inorganic Compounds: Building Materials of Life

Only 18 of the 92 natural elements will be discussed at this time. These 18 elements and their compounds are by far the most common substances in the makeup of living organisms. They supply the greater part of materials needed in the chemical activities of life.

If there were no life on earth, the elements and the **inorganic** compounds of the earth would remain. Inorganic compounds are quite different from those formed by living organisms. Yet the natural elements and inorganic compounds of the earth are the raw materials from which life builds more life.

Oxygen, as molecular oxygen, makes up nearly 21 percent of the mixture of gases in the atmosphere. Oxygen is necessary for most living things.

3–13 | Which of the above photos shows gelatin in the *sol* state? Which shows gelatin in the *gel* state? *(both: Matthew Stettler)*

Table 3-1 ELEMENTS ESSENTIAL TO HUMANS

ELEMENT	AMOUNT IN BODY (69.3-kilogram, 154-pound, person)	
oxygen	45.5 kg	(100.1 lbs)
carbon	12.6	(27.72)
hydrogen	7	(15.4)
nitrogen	2.1	(4.62)
calcium	1.05	(2.31)
phosphorus	0.7	(1.54)
potassium	0.25	(0.54)
sulfur	0.2	(0.35)
sodium	0.1	(0.23)
chlorine	0.1	(0.23)
magnesium	0.04	(0.077)
iron	0.0027	(0.006)
manganese	0.002	(0.0045)
iodine	0.03 gm	(0.00006)
silicon fluorine copper zinc	minute traces	

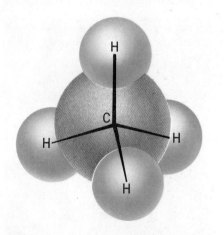

3-14 | The arrangement of the carbon and hydrogen atoms making up the methane molecule.

Water is the most abundant inorganic compound. It is also the most abundant compound in organisms. Water forms from 65 to 95 percent of the substance of every living thing. It is the chemical source of hydrogen and some of the oxygen needed by living things. Protoplasm itself is made of materials dissolved or suspended in water. Water is the medium in which dissolved materials are taken in from the environment. It is the medium of transport for foods, minerals, and other substances in living systems. Water is necessary for life on earth.

Carbon dioxide is an inorganic compound that supplies carbon as well as oxygen. Chemical products of organisms contain carbon. Thus, directly or indirectly, carbon dioxide is necessary to all life.

Mineral compounds supply the other elements needed for life. Minerals may come from the soil, or they may be dissolved in water, or found as salts in sea water.

Human beings cannot directly use carbon dioxide and many of the necessary minerals. They cannot build their bodies directly from carbon dioxide, minerals, and water. Like nearly all animals, people must rely on the green plants as a link to these inorganic compounds. The plants organize such compounds into the complex foods people use as energy sources and building materials.

Organic Compounds: Products of Life

All living organisms produce *organic* compounds quite unlike the inorganic substances of the earth. Scientists once thought that *only* organisms produced organic compounds, which explains the term *organic*. Today it is known that this is not so. In fact, many organic compounds used today are synthetic products of industry.

Whether synthetic or made by living organisms, all organic compounds have one thing in common. They all contain carbon. Several things about carbon make it the key element in organic compounds. The electron structure of a carbon atom allows it to form four covalent bonds with other atoms. And these bonds may be single, double, or triple depending on how many electron pairs are shared with other atoms. Carbon atoms can also link with each other. They can form rings or long chains. The carbon groups form a "backbone" to which atoms of other elements attach. In this way, they form very large, complex organic molecules.

Organic chemists have learned exactly how the atoms

are arranged and bonded in thousands of organic molecules. A **structural formula** is a map of the atoms and bonds in a molecule. A close look at a structural formula in figure 3-15 will give you a good idea of how organic molecules are put together. The carbon atoms may form rings in one part of the molecule and a branching chain in another part. The lines stand for bonds. The carbon atoms form bonds with each other, with hydrogen atoms, and with OH molecules. Each carbon atom forms four single bonds, or two single bonds and one double bond.

A **molecular formula** can be used to represent a molecule. The molecular formula for cholesterol is $C_{27}H_{45}OH$.

The building of organic molecules by living organisms is known as **biosynthesis.** Biochemists are greatly interested in learning how biosynthesis works. Somewhere in this process the key to how life continues may be found.

Carbohydrates

One important group of organic compounds are the **carbohydrates.** Carbohydrates are made of carbon, hydrogen, and oxygen. The proportion of hydrogen atoms to oxygen atoms is two to one, as in water. Examples of carbohydrates are *sugars*, *starches*, and *celluloses*. These substances are found in all plant cells.

Sugars are organized in plants, but as foods they provide the basic fuel for animal life as well. There are several types of sugars. Simple sugars, or **monosaccharides (MON-uh-sack-uh-rides),** may contain either five or six carbon atoms. Three simple sugars are well known and important in biology. *Glucose*, made by green plant cells, is the main cell fuel in both plants and animals. *Fructose* and *galactose* are also made in the green plant cell, using the

carbo = carbon
hydra = water

mono = one
sakcharon = sugar

3-15 | Structural formulas of three different monosaccharides. All three molecules have the same numbers of carbon, hydrogen, and oxygen atoms. But each has a different arrangement of these atoms. Both chain and ring forms are shown for each monosaccharide.

glucose   galactose   fructose

energy from the sun. They are quite similar to glucose. All three have six carbon atoms and the molecular formula $C_6H_{12}O_6$. However, their structural formulas are different.

Certain plants combine two molecules of simple sugar to form one molecule of a double sugar, or **disaccharide.** Disaccharides have the molecular formula of $C_{12}H_{22}O_{11}$. One molecule of water is given off in the process. This is why the reaction is called **dehydration synthesis.**

In a process much like dehydration synthesis, a glucose molecule and a fructose molecule combine. The product is *sucrose,* common table sugar taken from sugar cane or sugar beets. Glucose and galactose molecules combine to form *lactose,* or milk sugar.

Starches are complex carbohydrates made of glucose units in chains. Starches are *polysaccharides.* Each glucose unit in a starch has six carbon atoms, but a molecule of water has been removed. Figure 3-16 shows the formation of a disaccharide with the removal of an H and an OH. This permits the C-O-C bonding to form the larger molecule. Dozens to many thousands of glucose units join in this way to form a starch molecule.

Cellulose molecules are even larger and more complex than those of starches. In cellulose, long chains of glucose units are bonded side by side. This gives cellulose fibers great strength. Cellulose is formed in the cell walls of plants and give the plant support. You are familiar with cellulose in the forms of wood, paper, cotton, and many other plant products.

When animals use carbohydrates for food, the molecule is first broken apart to again form simple sugars. One molecule of water is needed to do this. This process is called **hydrolysis.** Note that hydrolysis is the opposite of *dehydration synthesis.*

Corn and potato plants produce starches, as do rice, wheat, and other grains. Animal starch, or *glycogen,* is produced in the liver and stored in the liver and muscles.

lysis = loosing or releasing

de = away
hydra = water

3–16 | The *dehydration synthesis* of maltose from two molecules of glucose.

glucose   glucose   maltose   +   water

Maltose   Water

HO– glucose –O– glucose –OH + $\underset{H}{\overset{H}{\diagdown}}$ O $\longrightarrow$ HO– glucose –OH + HO– glucose OH

3-17 | A model showing the *hydrolysis* of maltose

When extra fuel is needed, the liver breaks down this starch to glucose. Athletes take advantage of this knowledge. Long distance runners, for example, may eat larger amounts of carbohydrates than usual several days before a contest. The chemical energy stored as glycogen can then be used during the race.

Lipids

The **lipids** (LIP-idz) make up a second major group of organic compounds. The most common lipids are *fats, oils,* and *waxes.* Like the carbohydrates, lipids are made of carbon, hydrogen, and oxygen. In lipids, however, the ratio of hydrogen atoms to oxygen atoms is much greater than two to one. **The body can release much more energy from a given amount of fat than from the same amount of carbohydrate.** This is because the molecules of fat have more bonds. The potential energy, then, is much greater in fats than in carbohydrates.

In forming a *fat* molecule, one molecule of *glycerol combines* with three molecules of *fatty acid.* This is another example of dehydration synthesis. The removal of H from the glycerol and OH from a fatty acid forms the water molecule. This permits the C-O-C bonding of the two molecules. One molecule of water is released as *each* fatty acid molecule joins the glycerol. In forming *one* molecule of fat, *three molecules* of water are released.

Could you put fat in some water, shake it, and turn it back into glycerol and fatty acids? No. But in the living system this very reaction takes place. When fat is used for energy in the body, *hydrolysis* occurs. Three water molecules combine with each fat molecule, breaking it apart. One molecule of glycerol and three molecules of fatty acid are formed. Energy is released.

Fats occur mainly in animal tissues and as butterfat in milk and other dairy products. Lipids that are liquid at room temperature are known as *oils.* You are familiar with such vegetable oils as corn, peanut, and soybean oils.

Waxes, such as beeswax are joined to an alcohol other than glycerol.

3-18 | The *dehydration synthesis* of a fat molecule from three fatty acid molecules and one glycerol molecule.

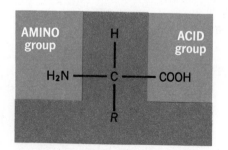

3-19 | The generalized formula for an amino acid. The *R* indicates any other molecule that could be attached.

poly = many

3-20 | The *dehydration synthesis* of a dipeptide. As water is removed the two amino acid molecules become linked by a peptide bond.

Proteins and Amino Acids

Proteins are the most common organic compounds in living cells. Proteins are very complex and exist in very many different forms.

Protein molecules are mainly made of carbon, hydrogen, oxygen, and nitrogen atoms. Sulfur is often present, as are iron and phosphorus. **The basic building blocks of protein molecules are *amino acids.*** There are about 20 common amino acids, each made of two basic groups of atoms.

Look at figure 3-19. You will see an amino group and an *acid* group on the amino acid. The amino group is made of two hydrogen atoms bonded to a nitrogen atom (-NH2). The organic acid group is made of a carbon atom joined to two oxygen atoms and a hydrogen atom (-COOH).

The amino acid units are joined together by the process of dehydration synthesis. The OH from an acid group of one amino acid joins to an H from the amino group of another amino acid. This forms one molecule of water and permits a C-N bonding of the two amino acids. The C-N bonding is called a *peptide bond.* Two amino acids joined by this bonding make a *dipeptide molecule.* Dipeptide molecules join together, forming chains called **polypeptides.** Each time a dipeptide joins the chain, one molecule of water is removed. Many protein molecules are made of a single long polypeptide chain.

The amino acids are the "letters" that make up the protein "words." Consider that a single protein molecule may contain as few as 50 or as many as 3,000 amino acid units. Proteins do not always have all 20 kinds of amino acids. Just as forming words with the letters in the alphabet, the possibilities of forming proteins from amino acids are fantastic. Finally, the amino acid units may be arranged in different ways. They may form branching chains, which is something that can't be done in forming words from an alphabet. There is almost no limit to the number of different proteins possible.

Different kinds of plants and animals may contain very different proteins. Members of the same species have many kinds of proteins in common. For example, certain kinds of

Di Peptide   Water   Amino Acid   Amino Acid

$$H-N-C-C-N-C-C-OH \;+\; O \;\longrightarrow\; H-N-C-C-OH \;+\; H-N-C-C-OH$$

Amino Acid   Amino Acid

3-21 | A model showing the *hydrolysis* of a dipeptide.

proteins are found in all human beings, but in no other organisms. Even within a species, however, the protein makeup varies. Every cell of your body contains as many as 2,000 different proteins. And some of your proteins are unlike those of any other person. In fact, it can be said that some proteins make people human, while others make people individuals.

The plant and animal proteins you take in as foods are different from your own proteins. You cannot use the protein of a hamburger directly. In your body these proteins are first broken down into amino acids. The process is hydrolysis. As each amino acid is removed from its protein chain, one molecule of water is needed. This breaks the peptide (C-N) bond. These "letters" of the "alphabet" can now be put into your own "words." You organize these amino acids into new polypeptide chains that match your own proteins.

Enzymes

An organism is a living chemical system in which substances are constantly changing. Molecules react with other molecules. Materials are organized and broken down. What starts these changes? What controls them? What keeps one change from interfering with another? The answer is *enzymes.* **Enzymes are proteins that act as catalysts.** That is, enzymes cause chemical changes to occur and affect the rate of change, but they are not part of the product.

Think about what happens when you open a bottle of soda pop. Bubbles of carbon dioxide are given off. If the bottle stands for a time, the drink goes "flat." You could control the rate of reaction. You could slow it down by putting on the cap and placing it in the refrigerator. You could speed it up by leaving off the cap and placing it in the warm sunshine. In these cases, you have been a catalyst. You have caused these reactions to take place. You have controlled the rate of change in the bottle of soda. But you are not part of this change. You have remained the same, but the contents of the bottle have changed.

Facts & Figures

Rocks are made of atoms, and may sometimes contain carbon atoms. But if the carbon is not from living things, they are not organic molecules.

3-22 | This model illustrates how an enzyme works on a specific substrate. The dipeptide undergoes hydrolysis to form two amino acids. Note that the enzyme remains unchanged in the process.

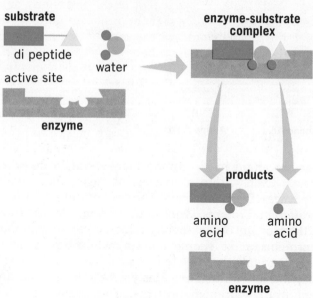

You could be a catalyst to many different kinds of reactions. But enzymes are *specific* in their actions. That is, each one has a certain job. For example, an enzyme in your saliva acts on the starches you eat. This enzyme acts *only* on starch. It causes hydrolysis to occur, changing starches to maltose sugar. If you chew a starchy food such as a cooked potato, you swallow some sugar. Other enzymes cause chemical changes in fats. Still others change proteins. Enzymes control all the chemical changes involved in the living condition.

Another important thing about enzymes is that they are not used up in the reaction. For example, once the enzyme in saliva causes a molecule of starch to change to maltose, it is free to act again. This enzyme brought about hydrolysis of a starch molecule, but it remains unchanged. Enzymes bring about these reactions at low temperatures. Some of the same reactions that happen in cells can be done in the laboratory without enzymes. But to do so would require heat. The temperature needed for the laboratory reactions would kill cells.

Exactly how enzymes work is not yet known. Many possible models of enzyme action are hypothesized. In one model, the enzyme is seen as being something like a piece of a puzzle. At one place on the enzyme molecule is an *active site*. This site fits a certain substance. The substance that the enzyme causes to react is called a *substrate*. Figure 3-22 shows the active site of an enzyme joining the substrate. Once formed, this *enzyme-substrate complex* reacts quickly, forming two molecules. As you can see in the model, the enzyme has not been changed. It is free to form another

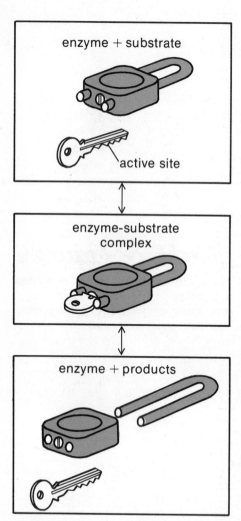

3-23 | One model for the action of an enzyme is the lock and key hypothesis. Only one *key* (enzyme) will fit the *lock* (substrate).

complex. With many enzyme molecules and many substrate molecules present, these reactions occur quickly. Do you think the results would be the same if you mixed the substrate and water in a test tube?

Often one chemical reaction in an organism involves several different changes. This calls for a group, or "team," of enzymes. This kind of group is called an *enzyme system*. Other molecules that are not proteins may also take part in the enzyme activity. Such molecules are known as **coenzymes.**

Summary

Both living and nonliving things are made of matter. All the matter on earth is made of 92 natural elements and their compounds. In physical changes, matter changes from one state to another. In chemical changes, matter actually changes from one substance to another. Energy is involved in all matter and all changes in matter.

The natural compounds are called inorganic compounds. Living organisms change these substances into organic compounds. Among important organic compounds are carbohydrates, lipids, and proteins.

Enzymes are proteins that act as catalysts. They cause chemical changes to occur and affect the rate of change. Enzymes work at low temperatures. They break apart food, and combine the molecules again in different ways.

Biologically Speaking

matter
physical change
chemical change
kinetic energy
potential energy
activation energy
chemical element
atom
nucleus
atomic number
atomic mass
isotope
compound
formula
covalent bond
bond energy
molecule
diatomic molecule
ionic bond
ion

mixture
solution
suspension
colloid
inorganic
organic
structural formula
molecular formula
biosynthesis
carbohydrate
monosaccharide
disaccharide
dehyration synthesis
hydrolysis
lipid
protein
amino acid
polypeptide
enzyme
coenzyme

Questions for Review

1. What is matter? What are the states of matter?
2. Describe the difference between physical and chemical energy.
3. Given an example of the conversion of potential energy to kinetic energy.
4. List the three particles of an atom and give their location and charge.
5. What are isotopes?
6. Distinguish between covalent and ionic bonding.
7. Explain the relationship of a solvent and a solute in a solution.
8. What is a colloid?
9. How is the present-day definition of *organic compound* better than the original definition?
10. Give examples of the three forms of carbohydrates.
11. What are the molecules that combine to form a fat molecule?
12. How does one protein differ from another?
13. What is an enzyme?

Applying Concepts

1. A certain atom has six protons and eight neutrons. How many electrons does it have? Diagram this atom.
2. Discuss the key position of carbon in the organization of organic compounds.
3. Discuss the vital role of enzymes in the chemical reactions occurring in organisms.
4. Explain the relationship between hydrolysis and dehydration synthesis in forming new protein from the protein an animal eats.

The Structural Basis of Life

A **DESCRIBE** the development of cell studies.
B **EXPLAIN** the cell theory.
C **LIST** the processes of a living cell.
D **IDENTIFY** the parts of a cell.
E **DESCRIBE** the functions of the parts of the cell.
F **EXPLAIN** cell specialization.
G **EXPLAIN** the difference in organization of prokaryotes and eukaryotes.
H **DESCRIBE** the levels of structure of organisms.

4-1 | Early microscopes. *(Courtesy of Bausch & Lomb)*

Units of Life

Early biologists learned many things about life, but they were limited by what they could actually see. With the development of lenses and microscopes, higher magnification was possible. Biologists could see new things. And even today, more discoveries are being made with tools such as the electron microscope. Not only can more things be seen, but it is better understood which elements and compounds are important to life. Where are these materials organized into a living thing? **The *cell* is the basic structural unit of life.** What is a cell? Let's begin to answer this question by looking at how cells were discovered.

The Discovery of Cells

More than three hundred years ago, the British scientist Robert Hooke observed some thin slices of cork through a microscope. In 1665, his report *Micrographia* told what he had seen. To his surprise, Hooke said, the cork was a mass of tiny cavities, similar to a honeycomb. They reminded

cella = small room

him of the small rooms in a monastery, which were called cells. So, Hooke called these cork structures *cells*.

Hooke did not realize that the most important part of the cells was missing. The empty shells he saw had once held active, living materials. But Hooke did not follow his discovery by studying plant or animal cells that still contained such materials. In fact, it was not until 1835 that another scientist discovered these substances.

A French biologist named Felix Dujardin (DOO-ZHAR-DAN) viewed living cells with a microscope and found what is now called **protoplasm.** Three years later, the German botanist Matthias Schleiden proposed that *all plants* are made of cells. The following year, Theodor Schwann, a German zoologist, stated that all animals also are made of cells. Twenty years later, Rudolf Virchow, another German biologist, published his observations. He had been working with disease and how disease affected living things. He concluded that cells can come only from other cells. He further stated that plant cells can only come from other plant cells, and animal cells can only come from other animal cells.

The work of Hooke and nineteenth-century biologists such as Dujardin, Schleiden, Schwann, and Virchow established the *cell theory*.

- The cell is the unit of structure and function of all living things.
- Cells come from other cells by cell reproduction.

Recent Cell Studies

The development of the light microscope has greatly added to the knowledge of cells. But as you learned in Chapter 1, the electron microscope, first developed in the 1930s, can magnify objects up to one million times. But biologists using the electron microscope were not able to see cell structures in action. Material to be observed had to be sliced very thin. It also had to be dried and stained. And no specimen could survive in the high vacuum of the electron microscope.

At the same time researchers were using the electron microscope, another group of scientists took a different approach. During the twentieth century, biochemists began to take a closer look at the proteins that make up living things. Cells were ground into a fine mixture. These mixtures were then placed in test tubes, which were then put in centrifuges. These machines rotate at speeds that produce hundreds of thousands of times the force of grav-

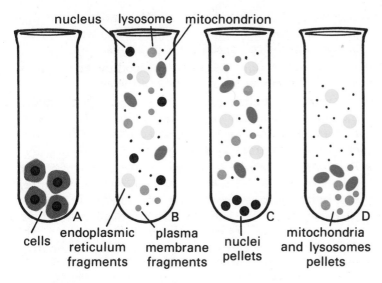

4-2 | (a) mixture of cells is placed in tube A. (b) shows the cell parts after grinding. (c) shows the nuclei formed pellets after centrifuging at low speed. The nuclei are removed and the tube is centrifuged again. (d) shows pellets of mitochondria and lysosomes after centrifuging at high speed. The pellets can be removed and further separated.

ity. Heavier particles would settle on the bottom of the tubes and the lighter particles at the top. Each layer contained different cell parts. They could then be removed and studied with the electron microscope.

Other biochemists treated living cells with radioisotopes, serving as *tracer elements*. Radioisotopes are isotopes that send off charged particles from their nuclei. The resulting *radioactivity* can be traced with special equipment. Then the cells were ground and spun down in the centrifuge. In this way, electron-microscope studies of the layers gave the scientists more information. Photographs taken showed a concentration of the tracer elements in certain parts of the treated cells. In the 1950s the electron-microscope studies and the biochemical studies were considered together. Because of these studies, chemical reactions can now be related to specific structures in the cells.

Processes of Cells

All life processes involve energy changes that take place in the cell. Each specialized cell part may be involved in one or more reactions. The following are processes that occur in living cells:

- *Nutrition.* Food molecules are necessary to supply both energy and building materials in cells. Some cells form their own food molecules. Others take them in from the environment.

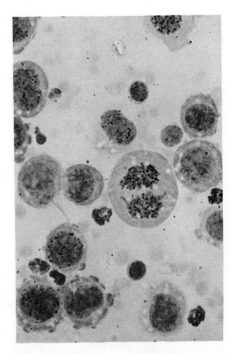

4-3 | Radioautograph of cells from a mouse tumor. DNA is labeled with radioactive tritium and appears as black dots in the nuclear material. *(Courtesy of Renato Baserga)*

- *Digestion.*   Many foods must be broken down into simpler forms in order for a cell to use them. Certain enzymes in the cell speed these reactions.
- *Absorption.*   A cell takes in water, food molecules, ions, and other necessary materials from the environment.
- *Biosynthesis.*   Cells organize many organic substances, including carbohydrates, fats, and proteins. This biosynthesis is necessary for growth and for the production of enzymes to control cell activity.
- *Respiration.*   *Cellular respiration* is the release of chemical energy when the bonds of certain organic molecules, especially glucose, are broken. The energy released is necessary to all cell activities. In most cells, O_2 is most often used and CO_2 is usually a waste product. The exchange of these gases between the cell and its environment is a process called *respiration.*
- *Excretion.*   Waste materials of cell activity are passed from the cell to the environment.
- *Secretion.*   Certain cells synthesize molecules of substances such as vitamins and hormones. When *secreted* (SE-KREE-ted), or passed out of the cell, these substances affect the activities of other cells.
- *Response.*   Cell activities may change in response to stimuli from the environment such as heat, light, pressure, or chemicals.
- *Reproduction.*   Cells divide from time to time. In a complex organism, such splitting results in more cells in the organism. In one-celled organisms, splitting simply produces more organisms.

Cell Structures

The Nucleus

Most cells have a large oval or spherical body near the center of the cell. This is the **nucleus. The nucleus is the control center for all cell activity.** Without its nucleus, a cell will not live very long.

The nucleus is surrounded by a thin, double *nuclear membrane.* This membrane separates the nuclear materials from other parts of the cell, but it is not really a solid barrier. Substances pass from the nucleus to the rest of the cell between the molecules of the nuclear membrane.

The nucleus contains a thick kind of protoplasm, rich in protein, called *nucleoplasm.* At least one **nucleolus** is also present. The nucleolus takes part in protein synthesis. Spread through the nucleoplasm are fine strands of *chro-*

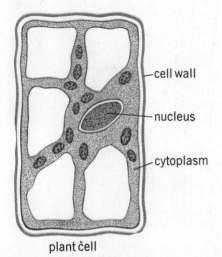

plant cell

4-4 | The plant cell and its three major parts: nucleus, cytoplasm, and cell wall.

matin material. This material is thought to be the active forms of the **chromosomes,** which control the activities of the cell.

chromo = color
soma = body

Cytoplasm

Cell materials outside the nucleus make up the **cytoplasm.** Under the light microscope, the cytoplasm, which fills most of the cell, looks like a clear, thick fluid. Cytoplasm is a *colloidal solution*. It often flows within the cell.

cyto = cell
plasma = anything formed or molded

Several organized structures called **organelles** are contained in the cytoplasm. The name *organelle* means "little organ." Some organelles can be seen through a light microscope. Others, because of their small size, were not seen until the electron microscope came into use.

Each kind of organelle seems to take part in a specific chemical activity. These chemical activities will be discussed later as the subject is presented, but first the structure, makeup, and location of the organelles will be discussed.

Endoplasmic Reticulum The cytoplasm contains a system of double membranes that tend to lie parallel to one another. This system, the **endoplasmic reticulum,** fastens to the cell membrane and the nuclear membrane. Biologists think that the endoplasmic reticulum may act as part of a system of canals referred to as the cytoplasmic *vacuolar system*. Along with other organelles, the endoplasmic reticulum forms a means for materials to pass through the cytoplasm. It also provides a surface to which enzymes and certain cell structures are attached.

endo = inside

At high power, an electron microscope shows many tiny, grainy structures attached to the endoplasmic reticulum. These are the **ribosomes.** The ribosomes contain enzymes that control protein synthesis. **The ribosomes are the protein factories of the cell.** They contain large amounts of RNA, a substance made in the nucleolus and closely related to DNA. These two substances, DNA and RNA, are important organic compounds called *nucleic acids*. These molecules direct what kinds of proteins are made in the ribosomes. You will learn how these molecules work in Chapter 7. Although ribosomes are among the smallest cell structures, their function is one of the most important.

Mitochondria The electron microscope also shows details of the rod-shaped organelles called **mitochondria** (MY-toe-KON-dree-uh). These are the centers of respiration in the cell. The mitochondria release the energy that supports all cell activities. A mitochondrion has two membranes,

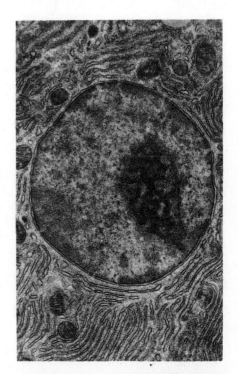

4–5 | Electron micrograph of the nucleus. The nucleolus is the dark mass within the nucleus (about 8,000X) *(Courtesy of Don W. Fawcett)*

4–6 | Electron micrograph of the endoplasmic reticulum lined with ribosomes. Part of the nucleus appears at the top.

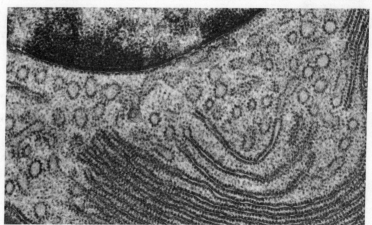

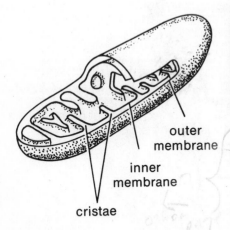

4–7 | A mitochondrion with its double-layered membrane.

mitos = thread

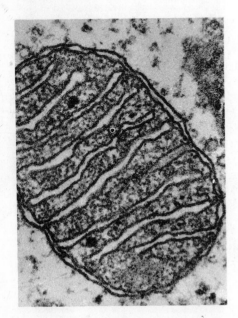

4–8 | Electron micrograph of a mitochondrion showing the outer and inner membranes and cristae.

each made of a layer of protein molecules and a layer of fat molecules. The inner membrane forms long inward folds at several points. These long folds, called *cristae*, increase the surface area of the membrane. Mitochondria contain enzymes that split organic molecules and transfer energy to other compounds. Energy is also released in the cell. **At least 95 percent of the energy in the cell comes from chemical activity in the mitochondria.** This energy is *not* produced by the cell. The cell merely converts energy from one form to another.

The mitochondria have other important functions. They help to control the amount of water, calcium, and other inorganic ions in the cytoplasm. They are involved in the breakdown of sugars, fatty acids, and amino acids. Thus, they release potential energy from these compounds and recycle many substances.

Lysosomes   The cytoplasm of most cells contains rounded organelles called *lysosomes.* They are somwhat smaller than mitochondria and have only a simple membrane. Lysosomes contain enzymes that cause the digestion of proteins. When a cell takes in large molecules, the lysosomes break these molecules into smaller molecules. The smaller molecules can then be used for building materials by the cell. In some cells even larger matter, such as bacteria, are taken in. The lysosomes then release their enzymes around the bacteria, destroying them. The enzymes of lysosomes also speed the breakdown of worn-out cells. When a cell dies, the lysosomes burst open and their enzymes break down the cell proteins. The products are then available for building new cells.

Golgi Apparatus   Another important cell organelle was first seen in 1898 by the Italian scientist Camillo Golgi. This

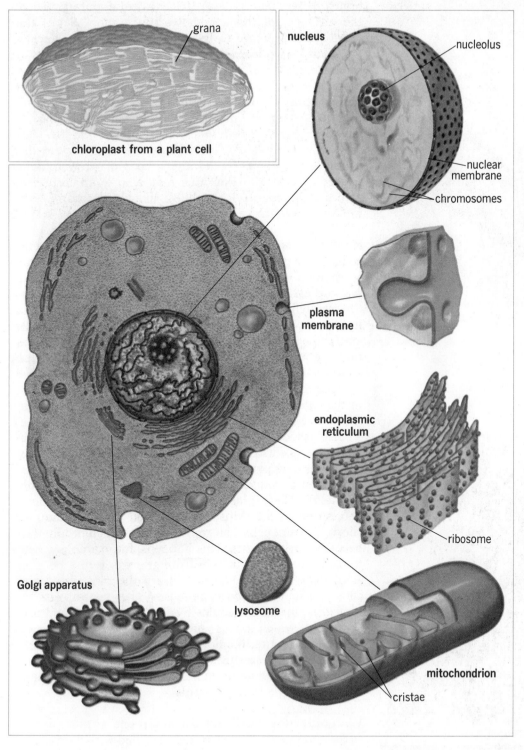

grana

chloroplast from a plant cell

nucleus

nucleolus

nuclear membrane

chromosomes

plasma membrane

endoplasmic reticulum

ribosome

Golgi apparatus

lysosome

mitochondrion

cristae

4–9 | Model of a typical animal cell and its organelles.

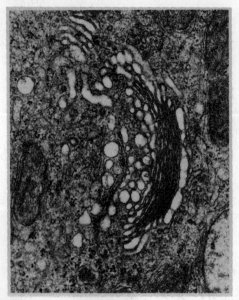

4-10 | Electron micrograph of Golgi apparatus (29,520X). (©L. V. Bergman and Associates)

leukos = white

organelle is called the **Golgi** (GOHL-jee) **apparatus.** Today, the electron microscope shows much more detail than Golgi could see. The Golgi apparatus looks like stacks of flattened sacs piled one on top of the other. The sacs are separated by membranes. The Golgi apparatus receives molecules of protein from the endoplasmic reticulum. Acting as a *protein packaging factory*, it wraps up large numbers of protein molecules into a single membranous envelope. This protein package then goes to the cell's surface for "export." This is how the cells secrete their hormones, enzymes, and other types of proteins when needed. The Golgi apparatus may also wrap certain enzymes into separate organelles, like the lysosomes, that remain inside the cell.

Plastids   **Plastids** are organelles found most often in plant cells. Some plastids act as chemical factories, while others serve mainly to store foods. The most familiar plastid is the **chloroplast,** which contains the green pigment **chlorophyll.** Chlorophyll is packaged between layers of protein and lipids in bodies called **grana.** Chloroplasts vary both in size and shape in different kinds of organisms. Their main function is forming carbohydrates, because they contain the enzymes necessary to this process. Energy from the sun is trapped and changed to chemical energy of carbohydrates in the chloroplast. Humans get energy when the carbohydrates are taken in as food.

Besides chlorophyll, some chloroplasts contain pale yellow pigments called **xanthophylls** (ZANTH-o-fills) and yellow orange pigments known as **carotenes.** Other plastids, often called **chromoplasts,** may produce red or blue pigments. These plastids give the color to some flower petals and to the skins of fruits such as the tomato and cherry. In some cells, chloroplasts lose their chlorophyll and become chromoplasts. This happens, for example, when a tomato ripens and changes from green to red.

Leucoplasts (LOO-ko-plasts) are the plastids of plant cells that serve as food storehouses. They contain enzymes that join glucose molecules by the process of dehydration synthesis, which forms starch molecules. This process sometimes occurs in chloroplasts, but leucoplasts are the main centers for storing starch. Starch does not dissolve in water. So it is not found in the nucleus or in the cytoplasm. It is stored *only* in the plastids.

Vacuoles   Plant cells often contain one or more cavities in the cytoplasm. These cavities are filled with fluid and are known as **vacuoles.** There is a *vacuolar membrane*, much like the plasma membrane, around each vacuole. This

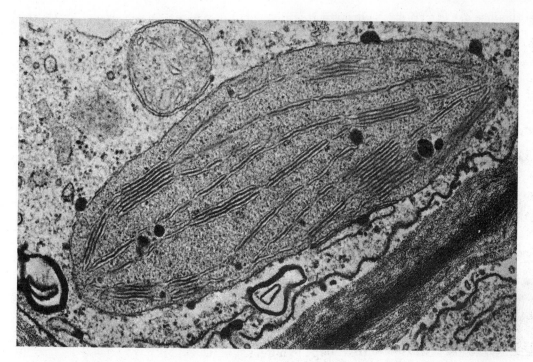

4–11 | Electron micrograph of grana in a chloroplast. (*Courtesy Myron C. Ledbetter, Brookhaven National Laboratory*)

membrane controls the movement of molecules between the vacuole and the rest of the cell. In some plant cells, the vacuole may be a large, central structure. As a plant cell grows, small vacuoles join and form a single large vacuole. Pressure from this vacuole may force the cell's outer membrane against the cell wall.

The fluid in plant vacuoles is mainly water. Ions of mineral compounds, sugar and protein molecules, and other organic materials are also present. Water-soluble pigments are found in the vacuoles of plant cells. The coloration of plants may be due to these pigments, which are not contained in chromoplasts. The most common of these pigments are the *anthocyanins* (AN-thuh-SY-uh-ninz). These are shades of scarlet, crimson, blue, purple, and violet. The beautiful colors of flowers, autumn leaves, the purple of the turnip top, and the reds of the radish and beet are caused by anthocyanins.

Other vacuoles may contain food materials and waste products. In many one-celled organisms, vacuoles are organelles that serve in getting rid of extra water.

The Nature of Membranes

The outer edge of the cytoplasm forms a *plasma membrane* or *cell membrane*. This membrane separates the cell from other cells and from surrounding fluids. Like the nuclear membrane, it is not a solid barrier. Molecules can pass

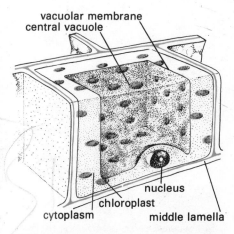

vacuolar membrane
central vacuole
nucleus
chloroplast
cytoplasm
middle lamella

4–12 | A representation of a typical plant cell. The central vacuole is completely surrounded by cytoplasm.

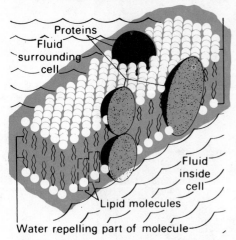

Water attracting part of molecule

Proteins
Fluid
surrounding
cell

Fluid
inside
cell

Lipid molecules

Water repelling part of molecule

4-13 | The plasma membrane is made of a double layer of lipid molecules embedded with protein molecules.

through it. However, the plasma membrane controls this traffic. **The plasma membrane allows some molecules to pass through but stops others.** For this reason, it is called a *selectively permeable membrane.*

All plasma membranes are not the same. Yet there is a general pattern of all plasma membranes. It is made of a double layer of *phospholipid* molecules. The phosphate part of these molecules is made of the elements phosphorus and oxygen. The lipid part is made of carbon chains of fat molecules. Protein molecules are embedded in the lipid layers.

The plasma membrane is not smooth. It is folded with indentations and bulges. This increases the amount of surface through which molecules may pass. The same kind of membrane forms wherever the cytoplasm borders another substance. Vacuoles are surrounded by membranes similar to the plasma membranes. If these membranes are damaged, cytoplasm may ooze through the opening for a short time, but other molecules will soon plug the opening.

The Cell Wall

Most plant cells are surrounded by a ***cell wall.*** This nonliving structure both protects and supports the cell. Where two cells meet, each builds a part of the cell wall between them. In a way, this wall is like a plaster wall that separates two rooms. A cell wall begins with a layer called the *middle lamella.* This structure contains jellylike substances called *pectin* (PECK-tin). Many fruits, including apples, contain large amounts of pectin. Pectin is released during cooking and forms a jelly as it cools. This is how jellies and jams are made.

Attached to the middle lamella are thin *primary walls,* formed by the cells on either side. The primary walls are

4-14 | Structure of a plant cell wall. (a) plant cell when plant is well watered. (b) plant cell when plant is wilted. In both cases the cell wall remains rigid.

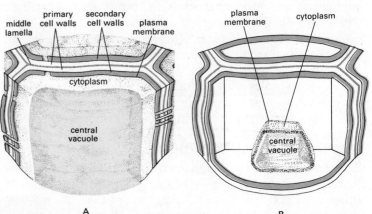

middle lamella

primary cell walls

secondary cell walls

plasma membrane

cytoplasm

central vacuole

plasma membrane

cytoplasm

central vacuole

A

B

made of cellulose and pectin. In soft plant structures such as leaves, flower petals, and soft fruits, these walls are fairly thin. In harder structures such as stems, the walls are thicker. This is what makes vegetables "crunchy" when you bite into them. Other cellulose layers make up the *secondary walls*. These firm, rigid walls may remain long after the cells are dead. Wood, for example, has very thick secondary walls. Since Hooke was looking at dead cells, what he saw were these secondary walls.

Cells Differ in Structure

By now you can see that cells are very complex things. And further, all kinds of cells are not alike. The plastids of plant cells, for example, are not found in animal cells.

Two groups of organisms show even greater cell differences from those just described. These are the bacteria and the blue-green algae. Bacteria are tiny cells that can cause some disease. They are also used in making such things as yogurt and cheese. Blue-green algae are found in moist, shady places on the land and even on the damp bark of trees. They are also found in stagnant ponds and puddles where they form a greenish slime on the surface. In water reservoirs, blue-green algae may grow and give the water a stagnant, "fishy" odor.

Bacteria and blue-green algae cells do not have a nucleus with a nuclear membrane. They have no mitochondria, chloroplasts, endoplasmic reticulum, Golgi apparatus, lysosomes, or vacuoles. The life processes of these simple cells are carried out without organelles. Since the bacteria and blue-green algae cells lack a nucleus, they are called **prokaryotes** (proh-KAR-ee-ohts). *Prokaryotes* means "before nucleus." This name separates them from the **eukaryotes** (yoo-KAR-ee-ohts), the cells containing nuclei. *Eukaryote* means "true nucleus." Each cell of a eukaryote has organelles, its small "factories." As you look at more complex organisms, you will see many ways that eukaryotic cells differ from each other.

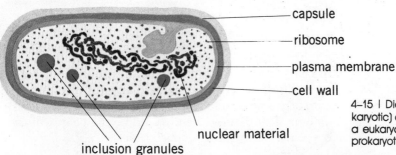

— capsule

— ribosome

— plasma membrane

— cell wall

nuclear material

inclusion granules

4–15 | Diagram of a typical bacterial (prokaryotic) cell. What structures can be found in a eukaryotic cell that cannot be found in a prokaryotic cell?

Levels of Structure

The simplest organisms are organized at only one level of structure. As organisms become more complex, their structures are organized in more complex ways. Let's look at the different levels of structure found in organisms.

Biologists think of a cell as the *first* level at which life is organized. The cell is the basic unit of structure of living things. **A complete living thing that is made of only one cell is said to be a *unicellular* organism.** Yeasts and amebas are examples of unicellular organisms.

Tissues

The more complex organisms are **multicellular,** or made of many cells. These cells are not simply grouped in a colony. They work closely together and depend on one another. They also show **cell specialization.** That is, there are different *kinds* of cells, each kind suited for a different activity.

A *tissue* is a group of cells in an organism that are alike in structure and activity. This is the *second* level at which structures are organized in living things. Your body contains many different tissues, such as muscle tissue, nerve tissue, bone tissue, and so on. Plants also have tissues. The skin of a potato, for example, is a kind of plant tissue.

Each kind of tissue has a special job. Muscle tissue provides motion. The cells in muscle tissue *specialize* at this job. However, they must also continue the chemical activities that keep them alive. They must take in some food and oxygen, form proteins and other organic compounds, and so on.

This specialization leads to another characteristic of multicellular organisms, which is *division of labor.* You can see how division of labor works in our own society. Doctors do not have to hunt or raise food because farmers do this job. Factory workers do not have to build their own houses because carpenters do this job. In the same way, the different kinds of cells in complex organisms divide their labor. Muscle cells can specialize in motion because other cells throughout the body supply them with food, oxygen, and other needs.

Organs

In more complex plants and animals, a *third* level of structure can be seen. **An *organ* is made of several tissues working as a unit to perform a certain activity.** You might think of an organ as a factory manufacturing speakers for stereo systems. The tissues, then, would be the people of the factory, each performing a special task.

unus = one

multus = many, much

Facts & Figures

Cells vary in size. A single cell of *Valonia,* a green alga, may weigh as much as 10 grams. In comparison, a single human liver cell would have a mass of 0.000001 (10^{-7}) grams.

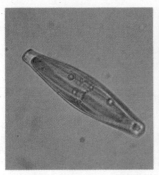 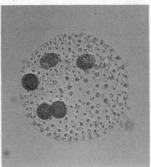 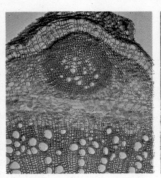 

A hand is an organ. It is made of skin, muscle, bone, blood, nerves, and other tissues. Your heart, stomach, and brain are other examples of organs. Plants, too, have organs. A plant stem, such as a tree trunk, is an organ made of wood, bark, and other tissues.

4-16 | Levels of organization. A unicellular organism (450X), a colonial organism (100X), seed plant tissue (60X), striated muscle tissue (210X). *(left two: Runk, Schoenberger, Grant Heilman; middle right: ©Manfred Kage, Peter Arnold; right: Alfred Owczarzak, Taurus Photo)*

Organ Systems

In higher organisms, especially animals, there is a *fourth* level of structure. This is the **organ system. An organ system is made of several organs working as a unit to perform a certain activity.** If an organ is compared to a factory, then an organ system would be like an assembly plant. Various components from many factories are put together to make your stereo set.

In your body, the *digestive system* is made of many organs. Each organ is involved in breaking down foods into molecules for your cells. Another organ system carries these molecules to all parts of your body. This is the *circulatory system*. It includes the heart, blood vessels, and lymph vessels. In complex animals, there is an organ system for almost every life activity.

Summary

The cell is the unit of structure and function in all living things. All cells come from other cells by cell reproduction. Thus, a knowledge of cells is important in biology. Modern tools and methods used by scientists have provided much information about what cells are and how they function. All cells are not alike, and they all do not have the same organelles. However, all life processes involve energy changes that take place in the cell.

Some organisms are made of a single cell. Others are made of many cells organized as tissues, organs, and organ systems. In these complex organisms, cells specialize in different activities. The different kinds of cells in an organism support one another through division of labor.

Biologically Speaking

cell	mitochondria	vacuole
protoplasm	lysosome	plasma membrane
nucleus	Golgi apparatus	cell wall
nucleolus	plastid	prokaryote
chromatin	chloroplast	eukaryote
chromosome	chlorophyll	unicellular
cytoplasm	grana	multicellular
organelle	xanthophyll	cell specialization
endoplasmic	carotene	tissue
reticulum	chromoplast	organ
ribosome	leucoplast	organ system

Questions for Review

1. In one sense Robert Hooke discovered cells; in another sense he did not. Explain.
2. Name the two principles of the cell theory.
3. List nine processes that characterize the living condition.
4. The nuclear membrane separates certain structures from the rest of the cell but it is not a barrier. Why is this important?
5. Describe the molecular makeup of the plasma membrane.
6. List the cytoplasmic organelles of the cell and give the function of each.
7. Describe the structure of the mitochondria.
8. Why are the chloroplasts referred to as carbohydrate factories?
9. Describe the various contents of cell vacuoles.
10. What are the main differences between prokaryotic and eukaryotic cells?
11. List the levels of biological organization from simple to complex.

Applying Concepts

1. In what respect is the cell the basic unit of life?
2. Do you believe that the mere presence in a test tube of all the vital substances composing protoplasm would result in a living condition? Give possible reasons supporting your opinion.
3. Discuss the specialization of cell content in regard to the various organelles.
4. Discuss why a unicellular organism is usually more versatile than one cell of a multicellular organism.

5–1 | This person must constantly make adjustments. *(Steve Firebaum, Bruce Coleman)*

The Cell and Its Environment

A **DEFINE** homeostasis.
B **DISTINGUISH** between a permeable and a selectively permeable membrane.
C **EXPLAIN** diffusion pressure.
D **EXPLAIN** the principle of diffusion through a membrane.
E **EXPLAIN** osmosis as it relates to the cell.
F **DEFINE** turgor pressure, cytolysis, and plasmolysis.
G **DESCRIBE** the behavior of cells in different solutions.
H **EXPLAIN** the principles of active transport.

Biological Balance

Have you ever climbed a mountain? Imagine yourself on a mountain, high above the ground. As you climb up, you constantly must make adjustments. With each step you must carefully keep your balance. You can not lean too far, or you will fall. As you move up the mountain, your body must constantly make adjustments to each new situation.

Perhaps you will never actually climb a mountain. However, like all living things, you will constantly make adjustments to new situations. Every organism faces changing conditions, both within itself and in its environment. An organism constantly must adjust to these changing conditions in order to survive. It must keep a balance between life activities and the conditions that affect it. This balance is called ***homeostasis.***

homeo = equal, to make like
stasis = standing

Homeostasis

Homeostasis occurs at all levels in living things. In many cases the entire organism adjusts to changes. These are behavioral changes. For example, a desert is quiet when the noonday sun beats down. But in the early morning or late

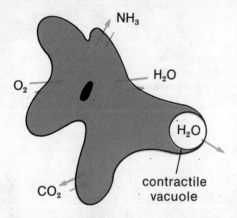

5-2 | Single cells also must be in a state of balance with the environment.

evening many animals come out of their hiding places. They search for food in the cooler parts of the day.

Homeostasis also occurs at the level of organs and organ systems. In the more complex animals, organs work together closely to keep the best internal environment. All organs depend on the action of the heart. The heart acts as a pump and supplies oxygen and food to all parts of the body. But it doesn't work alone, and heart action changes as a reaction to body changes. During exercise the heart beats faster because the tissues need more oxygen and more food. At the same time the faster heartbeat is also needed to remove extra cell wastes produced by greater activity. This is one way organs work together to keep homeostasis in the organism.

In multicellular organisms, the external environment of each cell is the surrounding fluid. But environmental changes are also important to unicellular organisms. One-celled organisms living in lakes, rivers, oceans, and even on land must also be in a state of homeostasis with the environment. If a pond organism were moved into the ocean, it would not be able to keep its internal environment constant. It would not be able to keep a balance in the salty ocean. Nor could a single muscle or nerve cell from your body live in pond water because many needed chemicals would not be provided. **A cell can keep its necessary balance only within limits of environmental changes.** Let's look at the ways in which cells maintain homeostasis.

The Plasma Membrane and Homeostasis

At the cellular level, homeostasis depends greatly on the movement of materials into and out of the cell. Foods, oxygen, and other materials are taken into the cell. Waste products and other substances pass out of the cell. All these materials must pass through the plasma membrane. The kinetic energy that moves molecules and ions causes them to bump into the membrane. Some materials pass through the plasma membrane, but not in large numbers. The rates at which certain substances pass through the plasma membrane vary. If a substance passes through a membrane, the membrane is *permeable* to that substance. If a membrane lets some substances pass but not others, it is *selectively permeable.* The plasma membrane is selectively permeable. How does the membrane stop some substances while letting others pass? There is no single answer. Several important factors are

1. *The structure of the plasma membrane itself.* As you learned in Chapter 4, the surface of the membrane is folded with many indentations. Also, there are spaces between the molecules that make up the membrane.

2. *The size of the particles.* The spaces between the molecules of the membrane might be large enough for small molecules to pass through, but too small for large molecules.

3. *The chemical makeup of the particles.* Water molecules pass freely through the plasma membrane. Gases such as O_2 and CO_2 pass freely through membranes. And larger molecules that can dissolve in lipids will also pass freely through the membrane. Alcohol is an example of such a molecule.

4. *Whether or not the particles are soluble in water.* The fluids that bathe cells usually are solutions of molecules and ions in water. Most substances that do not dissolve in water cannot pass through the plasma membrane.

5. *Conditions inside or outside the cell.* The amount and type of dissolved material in the cell or the outside environment may affect the membrane and molecules that are allowed to pass. Factors such as temperature and pressure will also affect a membrane's activity.

Diffusion

To better understand how substances pass through a cell membrane, you need to know more about molecules and their motion. In any substance, the molecules are constantly moving. This motion results from kinetic energy within the molecules themselves. Molecular motion is slight in solids, but much greater in liquids and gases. The movement of the molecules is *random*. That is, the molecules move in straight lines until they collide with other molecules. Then they bounce off each other and move in straight lines again until they collide with still other molecules. This kind of movement results in a gradual spreading out of the molecules. In the end, they will be spread evenly through any given space. This gradual, even spreading out of molecules is known as ***diffusion.***

As an example of diffusion, think of what happens if you open a jar of ammonia in a classroom. As soon as you open the jar, the ammonia molecules start diffusing into the air.

Facts & Figures

It is a property of substances that they will not all diffuse at the same rate. The sodium ion will diffuse at a greater rate than will the potassium ion.

5–3 | The diffusion of a solid in a liquid. Copper sulfate diffuses into water until a state of equilibrium is reached. This happens when the particles are equally distributed throughout the water.

Facts & Figures

Enzymes are large protein molecules. However, even proteins pass through cell membranes.

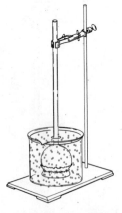

5-4 | Diffusion through a permeable membrane: The bulb of a thistle tube is filled with a sugar solution. It is covered tightly with a piece of muslin then placed in a jar of water. Water molecules (blue) move through the membrane into the sugar solution as sugar molecules (red) move through the membrane into the water in the jar.

Soon the people in the front of the room smell the ammonia. As diffusion continues, the smell of ammonia reaches those in the back of the room. Then the smell becomes stronger throughout the room. More and more ammonia molecules spread out in random motion among the molecules of gases in the air. Finally, a state of *equilibrium* is reached. The ammonia molecules, though still in motion, are spread evenly among the air molecules in the room.

As ammonia diffused into the air, air molecules also diffused into the ammonia jar. This fact leads to a basic law of diffusion. According to this law, **substances diffuse from areas of greater concentration to areas of lesser concentration.** You can see that this happened with both the air molecules and the ammonia molecules. Diffusion continued until the concentration of air and ammonia molecules was equal in all parts of the room.

Factors that Affect Diffusion

You have seen that substances diffuse from areas of greater concentration to areas of lesser concentration. *Concentration* also affects the *rate* at which substances diffuse. The greater the concentration, the more rapidly diffusion takes place. *Temperature* also affects diffusion. The higher the temperature, the greater the speed of molecular motion. Diffusion takes place from areas of higher temperature to areas of lower temperature. *Pressure* also speeds molecular motion. High pressure causes the molecules to be packed closely together. They bump into one another at a great rate. Low pressure allows the molecules to spread out, so they travel farther before they meet another molecule. Thus, diffusion takes place from areas of high pressure to areas of low pressure.

To conclude, the differences in molecular concentration, temperature, and pressure all affect diffusion. Together these differences result in the force called ***diffusion pressure.***

Diffusion Through a Permeable Membrane   How does a membrane affect the movement of molecules in diffusion? The answer depends on the nature of the membrane and the substances being diffused.

You can do a simple experiment with a *permeable* membrane of fine muslin (loosely-woven cloth). The bulb of a thistle tube is filled with sugar syrup. A piece of muslin is then tied tightly over the open end of the bulb. Finally, the bulb is placed in a jar of water.

Since muslin is permeable to both water and sugar molecules, two things happen. Water molecules will diffuse from the jar into the sugar syrup in the tube. At the same time, sugar molecules will diffuse from the tube into the water in the jar. Finally, the concentration of sugar and water molecules will be the same on both sides of the muslin. This is the equilibrium state. At the equilibrium state, the *diffusion pressure* is zero.

Diffusion Through a Selectively Permeable Membrane   The permeable muslin membrane had little effect on diffusion. What if the plasma membrane of a cell were as permeable as the loosely-woven cloth? The cell would not be able to regulate what comes into the cell and what goes out. Molecules of water and other substances could enter the cell easily. But at the same time, the molecules of the cell would diffuse into the environment. This does not happen in living cells. The plasma membrane is *selectively permeable*.

You can do another experiment much like the one with the muslin. However, instead of using muslin, tightly tie a selectively permeable membrane to the thistle tube. Sheep bladder or frog skin are good ones to use. You can see the beginning of this experiment in figure 5-5. Water molecules will diffuse from the jar of water into the thistle tube. At the same time, sugar molecules will diffuse from the thistle tube into the jar of water. The selectively permeable membrane, however, lets the sugar molecules through slowly. But at the same time, it lets water molecules pass through rapidly. After several hours, the level of the solution in the tube will rise. The level of the solution in the jar will fall.

As the solution rises in the tube, the force of gravity becomes important. Gravity pulls down on the solution in the tube. This, in turn, puts pressure on the inner surface of the selectively permeable membrane. When this pressure is equal to the diffusion pressure of the water molecules, equilibrium is reached and diffusion stops. Diffusion stops even though the concentration of water molecules remains greater in the jar than in the tube.

Osmosis: A Diffusion of Water

The experiment just described is an example of **osmosis** (ahs-MOW-sis). **Osmosis is the diffusion of water through a selectively permeable membrane from an area of greater concentration of water to an area of lesser concentration of water.** Notice that the word *osmosis* refers only to the diffusion of *water*. Thus, in this definition, the word *concentration* refers only to the concentration of water molecules.

Osmosis and the diffusion of other substances through the plasma membrane affects all living cells. Remember that diffusion is purely a physical process. Usually no cell

5-5 | Diffusion through a selectively permeable membrane: In this experiment a selectively permeable membrane separates the sugar solution in the thistle tube from the water in the jar. The water molecules rapidly move through the membrane into the sugar solution. The sugar molecules move through the membrane at a much slower rate. This results in a higher water level in the thistle tube.

energy is involved. The molecules move by their own kinetic (heat) energy. For this reason, it is said that diffusion is **passive transport.**

Osmosis and Plant Cells   Osmosis plays a very important part in the lives of organisms. Let's see how this process affects a (plant cell. Assume that the solution outside the cell is **hypotonic.** This means that the solution has a *lesser concentration of solutes* and a *greater concentration of water molecules* than does the cell content. Thus, there will be a net movement of water *into* the cell.)

hypo = less than, below

As water diffuses into the cell by osmosis, it builds up a pressure known as **turgor pressure.** Remember that a plant cell is surrounded by the cell wall. The cell cannot swell as the turgor pressure grows. However, the pressure does force the cytoplasm and plasma membrane firmly against the cell wall. This causes the cell to become stiff. At some point, the turgor pressure becomes equal to diffusion pressure of the water molecules outside the cell. A state of equilibrium is then reached, and diffusion stops. When equilibrium is reached, the total number of water molecules entering the cell equals the total number leaving the cell.

As long as there is enough water in the cell environment, turgor pressure will be maintained. This is especially important for soft plant tissues such as leaves, petals, and soft stems. Turgor pressure keeps such plant tissue stiff and firm. Without turgor pressure, the plant wilts.

Osmosis and Animal Cells   (Animal cells do not have cell walls. In animal cells, turgor pressure cannot build up to a point at which osmosis stops. Water simply continues to diffuse into the cells. The cells must get rid of some of this water. Otherwise, they would swell until they burst.)

Many one-celled organisms that live in fresh water have **contractile vacuoles.** These organelles act as tiny pumps constantly pushing water out through the cell membrane. **The contractile vacuole helps to keep a water-balance in the cells.** Without these structures, the cells would soon burst.

Fish and other water animals that breathe through gills also take in large amounts of water. In these animals, extra water is removed by excretion in the form of urine. In human beings, the kidneys, sweat glands, and lungs help to remove extra water.

In nature, water contains minerals and other dissolved substances. These solutes lower the concentration of water molecules, which results in a lower diffusion pressure. Distilled water, on the other hand, has a 100 percent concentration of water molecules. Distilled water has a

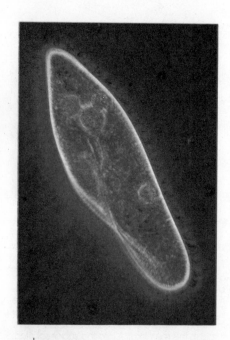

5–6 | The circles in this one-celled organism are contractile vacuoles (350X). *(Eric Graves, Photo Researchers)*

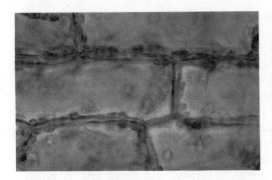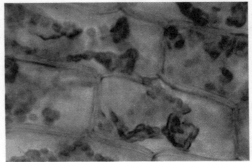

higher diffusion pressure than water containing solutes. If certain one-celled organisms are placed in distilled water, they will swell and burst. Their contractile vacuoles cannot overcome the rapid osmosis caused by the high diffusion pressure of distilled water. If you place a drop of blood in distilled water, much the same thing will happen. The blood cells will quickly swell and burst. This bursting of cells caused by pressure within them is called **cytolysis** (sy-TAHL-uh-sis).

5–7 | (left) Normal *Anacharis* cells in isotonic solution. (right) Plasmolyzed *Anacharis* cells in hypertonic solution. *(Phillip A. Harrington)*

cytos = cell
lysis = a loosening

Plasmolysis: Loss of Cell Turgor

Remember that a cell has no control over osmosis. The direction in which water diffuses depends only on the different concentration of water molecules inside and outside the cell. You have learned what happens when the solution outside the cell is hypotonic. What if the solution outside the cell has a *higher concentration of solutes* and a *lower concentration of water* than the cell content? The outside solution is then **hypertonic,** and water diffuses *out* from the cell into the environment. As outward diffusion continues, tugor pressure is lost and the cell content shrinks. This condition is called **plasmolysis** (plazz-MAHL-uh-siss).

hyper = more than, above, beyond

plasma = anything formed or molded

Cells in Isotonic Solutions   When the solution outside a cell has the *same concentration of solutes* and the *same concentration of water molecules* as the cell content, the solution is **isotonic.** Water molecules diffuse through the plasma membrane both in and out of the cell. The rate of diffusion is the same in both directions. The cell neither gains nor loses water.

iso = equal

Active Transport

So far you have been learning about *passive transport* of materials through the plasma membrane. You have seen

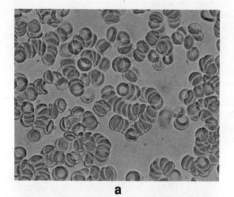

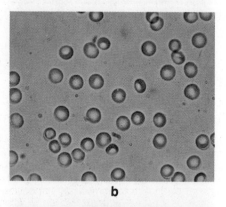

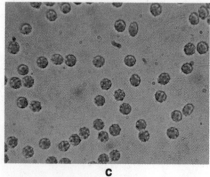

5–8 | Red blood cells in three solutions. (a) Normal red blood cells in isotonic solution. (b) Swollen red blood cells in hypotonic solution. Water pressure may burst the cells. (c) Shrunken red blood cells in hypertonic solution. *(Phillip A. Harrington)*

endo = inside

exo = outside

how diffusion pressure can cause molecules to pass through the membrane. No cell energy is needed for passive transport.

Many mineral salts and other substances form ionic solutions in water. The charged ions penetrate the membranes very slowly. Still, ions, such as sodium (Na^+) and potassium (K^+), play an important part in the chemical activities of the cell. A root cell, for example, may absorb mineral ions from solutions with a *lower* ion concentration than within the cell. How does this happen? According to the law of diffusion, such ions would move out of the cell and not into it. In marine organisms, certain cells may have concentrations of iodine thousands of times greater than the iodine concentration of sea water. Yet, these cells still absorb iodine from the water. How do they do this? **When the plasma membrane moves molecules against diffusion pressure, energy is needed. This is called** *active transport.*

It is not known exactly how the cell is able to do this. Such a "shuttle service" requires energy. Figure 5-9 shows a model of one hypothesis of how such a system might work.

Passage of Large Molecules Through the Plasma Membrane

Water molecules, ions, and other materials are small enough to pass through the plasma membrane. But large molecules such as lipids, amino acids, and even proteins pass through membranes. How does this happen?

The passage of large molecules and particles through the plasma membrane into the cell is known as *endocytosis.* Electron-microscope studies of cells often show that the plasma membrane folds inward, forming little pouches. The membrane then comes together, sealing the openings. Now, the large molecules and other particles that were in the pouches are in the cytoplasm as vacuoles. The formation of fluid-filled vacuoles at the surface of the cell is called *pinocytosis.*

Many cells manufacture protein molecules that will act as enzymes and hormones outside the cell. You may remember that the ribosomes make the proteins and the Golgi apparatus "packages" them. These packages of protein in the cytoplasm move to the plasma membrane. There, the plasma membrane folds inward and "cuts off" the protein package, releasing it to the outside. **The passage of large molecules through the plasma membrane to the outside of the cell is called** *exocytosis.* Lipids and many cell wastes are also discharged from cells by exocytosis.

Both endocytosis and exocytosis are activities of cells.

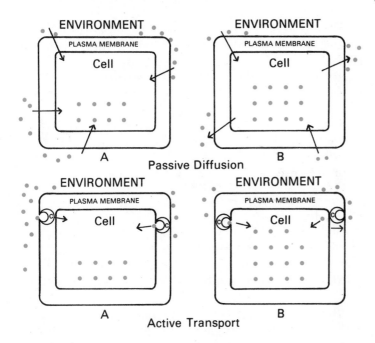

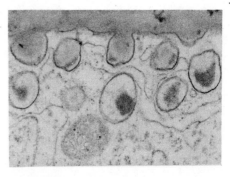

5-9 | Model to show passive diffusion and active transport. At equilibrium (B) of diffusion, molecules may move both ways. In active transport, carrier molecules (C) shuttle a molecule through the plasma membrane and into the cell. Then it returns to the environment to pick up another molecule for delivery to the cell.

5-10 | Electron micrograph showing the pouches that are formed by pinocytosis (66,300X). (Courtesy of Dr. Varien R. Tilton, Iowa State University)

They both need energy and are active transport processes.

Passive and active transport of materials through the plasma membrane are ways in which the cell maintains homeostasis.

Summary

To survive, an organism must maintain a state of balance between life activities and the conditions that affect it. An important factor in this balance is the movement of materials in and out of the cell. All this traffic must pass through the cell membrane.

The cell membrane is selectively permeable. Foods, water, wastes, and other materials can pass through the membrane. But the materials of the cell structures themselves are kept within the membrane.

The forces of diffusion control the movement of molecules and other particles through the membrane. Diffusion of water is called osmosis. No cell energy is used in diffusion. For this reason, movement of molecules by diffusion is called passive transport. In some cases, cells absorb ions against the force of diffusion pressure. Cell energy is used in this process, known as active transport. Large molecules cannot pass through membrane pores. Instead, they flow into pouches in the membrane and are sealed off. They then enter the cell as vacuoles.

Biologically Speaking

homeostasis
permeable
selectively permeable
diffusion
diffusion pressure
osmosis
passive transport
hypotonic
turgor pressure

contractile vacuole
cytolysis
hypertonic
plasmolysis
isotonic
active transport
endocytosis
pinocytosis
exocytosis

Questions for Review

1. What is homeostasis?
2. Distinguish between a permeable and a selectively permeable membrane.
3. What is a plasma membrane? What is its composition?
4. What is diffusion? What is the name for the balance that results from diffusion?
5. Describe the external factors that influence diffusion rates.
6. How is osmosis related to diffusion?
7. What is a hypertonic solution?
8. Describe the different results you would get if you put a plant cell and an animal cell in a hypertonic solution.
9. Distinguish between active and passive transport.
10. How are some cells able to bring in materials too large to enter by active or passive transport?

Applying Concepts

1. Discuss what might happen to a cell if the membrane were permeable to all molecules.
2. What factors determine whether or not a particle will permeate a plasma membrane?
3. What might happen to the cells of a freshwater plant if it were placed in salt water? Why would fresh water destroy a saltwater plant?

6

Photosynthesis, Respiration, and Cell Energy

A **COMPARE** photosynthesis and respiration.

B **EXPLAIN** the concept of autotrophs and heterotrophs.

C **EXPLAIN** the importance of ATP.

D **DESCRIBE** the function of chlorophyll.

E **DESCRIBE** the light reactions and dark reactions.

F **DISTINGUISH** between photosynthesis and chemosynthesis.

G **EXPLAIN** the stages in cellular respiration and fermentation.

6–1 | What is the source of this person's energy? *(HRW photo by Russell Dian)*

You and Energy

On a dark and cold winter morning an alarm clock rings. Barely awake, you reach over to turn off the alarm. The muscle cells in your arm use chemical energy to perform this task. Perhaps you felt only half awake when you arose to begin the day's activities. But awake or asleep, the many activities of your body use energy. Even when you are asleep the muscles of breathing and the beating of your heart constantly use energy. The energy came from the foods you ate. These foods directly or indirectly came from the radiant energy of the sun. In this chapter you will learn how this energy is trapped by green plants and stored in molecules that your body cells can use.

Energy and Life

You have learned about the potential energy that is in chemical bonds. **The energy living cells use is the potential energy stored in the simple glucose molecules. The energy comes from the sun.** How does the sun's energy become potential energy in the glucose molecule? How does a cell release this energy? You can begin to find answers to these questions by looking at two important cell processes.

1. **Photosynthesis** is a process that involves a series of chemical changes. The organic food molecule glucose is organized from inorganic CO_2 and water using the sun as an energy source. The radiant energy of light is changed to chemical energy and stored in the glucose molecules as potential energy. Photosynthesis occurs *only* in certain green plant cells.

2. **Respiration** is a process that also involves a series of chemical changes. But in respiration, the potential energy of glucose molecules is actually released and used by the cells. This occurs when the glucose molecule is taken apart. In the process CO_2 and water are released. Respiration goes on in *all* living cells.

Self-feeders and Other-feeders

auto = self
trophos = one who feeds

Organisms that organize organic food molecules from inorganic molecules are called *autotrophs*. Green plants are autotrophs.

You depend on green plant cells for food from which energy can be released. **Organisms, such as yourself, that are unable to synthesize organic food molecules from inorganic molecules are called *heterotrophs*.** The cow that eats grass in a pasture is also a heterotroph. Its dependence is direct. It gets its energy directly from the autotrophs. When your eat beef or drink milk from the cow, your dependence is indirect. This is because the energy has passed from the sun to the grass to the beef, and then to you. Animals are heterotrophs. As you can see, *all life depends on autotrophs.*

heteros = other

In the living world, matter is constantly recycled. Simple substances are organized into complex ones, and complex substances are broken down to simple ones. Look at figure 6-2. The autotroph (tree) puts O_2 and CO_2 together to form the organic food molecule glucose. Oxygen is given off in the process. The heterotroph (rabbit) uses the glucose and oxygen. During respiration the glucose is broken down in the rabbit's cells. Carbon dioxide and water are given off. These substances can be used again by the autotroph. Carbon dioxide and water, then, are recycled. But how is energy from the sun used? Some of the sun's radiant energy is used by the tree to form glucose. During respiration in the cells of the rabbit, some energy is used to break apart the glucose molecule. The total energy for the rabbit's cell, then, would be the potential energy in the glucose molecule *minus* the energy the cell used to break apart the molecule. *Energy is not recycled.* New energy must be supplied con-

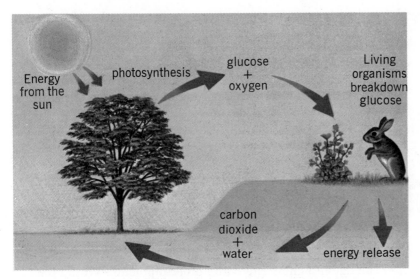

6-2 | Energy and living things.

stantly. This new energy comes from the sun through the process of photosynthesis. Heterotrophs then get energy from their food.

Photosynthesis: The Energy Storing Process

In a way, the word *photosynthesis* is self-explanatory. *Photo* means "light," and *synthesis* means the "building of a complex substance from simpler substances." In photosynthesis, the simple substances are carbon dioxide and water. The complex substance formed is glucose. Light energy is also required for photosynthesis, and oxygen is given off as a by-product. A simple chemical equation for photosynthesis can be written as follows:

$6CO_2 + 6H_2O + \text{light energy} = C_6H_{12}O_6 + 6O_2$
carbon + water + light energy = glucose + oxygen
dioxide

This equation gives only the most general idea of what happens. It shows a single reaction, but photosynthesis is actually a complex *series* of reactions. What happens in these reactions? Does carbon dioxide unite *directly* with water? Does the oxygen by-product come from the carbon dioxide, the water, or both? How is light energy changed into chemical bond energy? Biologists asked these and other questions for many years. Before you learn the answers, let's look at a few more key facts about photosynthesis.

Chlorophyll: An Energy Trap   What makes plants green is a key to how green plants make food. The importance of this green pigment is shown in the following example. If

photos = **light**
syn = **with**

thesis = **putting together**

Facts & Figures

More than 2,000 years ago Aristotle observed that sunlight was necessary for plants to become green.

6–3 | Plants contain color pigments other than green chlorophyll. The oriental maple contains the reddish-orange pigment carotene. (HRW Photo by Russel Dian)

you were to plant some bean seeds, water them, and keep them in total darkness, they would sprout. But they would be a pale yellow color rather than green. Left in the dark, they would soon wither and die. If you moved them to the light, these yellowish seedlings would begin to turn green. ***Chlorophyll* is the green pigment in plants.** Photosynthesis will not occur until the chlorophyll develops.

In photosynthesis, chlorophyll acts as an energy trap. Using the sun's radiant energy, chlorophyll acts as a *catalyst*. Remember that a catalyst is a substance that helps the reaction to occur but does not chemically enter into it. Plant cells may have other pigments such as yellow xanthophylls and orange carotenes. These *accessory pigments* also trap radiant energy from the sun. They may function to transfer energy to chlorophyll molecules.

What if carbon dioxide and water were mixed in a flask along with chlorophyll and other pigments? Would photosynthesis take place if the flask was placed in light? The answer is no. Chlorophyll alone is not enough. In some experiments where whole chloroplasts have been removed from cells, photosynthesis did occur. It seems that living cell processes are needed for photosynthesis to occur.

You have learned that in nature photosynthesis occurs only in green plant cells. Actually, the plant itself does not have to be green. Photosynthesis may take place in red or brown plants, such as certain seaweeds. But even these plants have the green pigment chlorophyll in their cells. It just happens that they have other colored pigments too. **Photosynthesis can take place only in the presence of chlorophyll, which traps the sun's energy.**

Conditions for Photosynthesis

Since light is the energy source for photosynthesis, light conditions have a great effect on the process. The energy from the sun travels to the earth in the form of rays of different wavelengths and energy. These rays are usually seen together as white light. But in a rainbow the different wavelengths are separated. Then they are seen as red, orange, yellow, green, blue, and violet. Together, these rays make up the ***visible spectrum.*** The various colors of light are made of different wavelengths. The longer the wavelength, the less energy. Red rays, for example, have the longest wavelength and the least energy of the visible rays. At the other end of the visible spectrum are the violet rays. They have the shortest wavelength and the highest energy.

Most land plants absorb the greatest energy from violet and blue rays, and somewhat less energy from red and orange rays. A little green and yellow light is absorbed, but

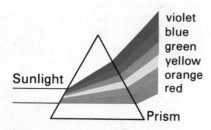

Sunlight

violet
blue
green
yellow
orange
red

Prism

6–4 | When sunlight passes through a prism, the *visible spectrum* can be seen.

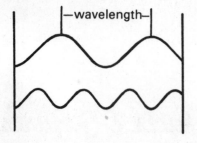

—wavelength—

6–5 | Energy in the visible spectrum travels in waves. The shortest wavelength has the greatest energy. Plants vary in the particular rays they absorb.

most of these wavelengths are reflected or pass through plant structures. The rays that are reflected are the ones that are seen. For example, green plants are green because they reflect light rays of that color band. This is why chloroplasts appear green or yellow-green.

All plants are not green. **The accessory plant pigments are adaptations to different living conditions.** They may function in trapping different wavelengths of light energy. In the ocean, for example, plants are living in different light conditions as compared to land plants. Seawater absorbs most of the red and violet rays. You know that when you dive into the water, the light becomes dimmer as you go farther beneath the surface. Water, then, lowers the total intensity of light. The accessory pigments may trap the wavelengths of light that penetrate the water. In shallow water, ocean plants absorb energy for photosynthesis mostly from blue, green, and yellow rays. They are brownish in color. Deepwater algae, living 20 meters (63 feet) or more underwater, use the blue and green rays for energy. Many of these are reddish in color. But they all have chlorophyll in addition to the other pigments.

6-6 | These two marine autotrophs live at different depths. Their pigments help them absorb different wavelengths of light energy. above: pink coralline algae on rocks; bottom: giant kelp. *(above: Douglas Faulkner; below: William E. Ferguson)*

ATP: Energy Storage

Light energy may enter the cell too fast for all of it to be stored in glucose by photosynthesis. There is a way in which this extra energy is held in reserve. Then it can be ready to be used in controlled amounts as the cell needs it. The substance that does this important job is the energy transfer compound *adenosine triphosphate*, or **ATP.**

ATP is organized in the cell mitochondria and released to all parts of the cell. Figure 6-7 shows an ATP molecule. Refer to this figure as you read about the structure of ATP.

In one part of the molecule, a unit of *adenine* is bonded

Facts & Figures

There are several different kinds of chlorophylls. They are called A, B, C, D, and E.

6-7 | A structural formula of an ATP molecule.

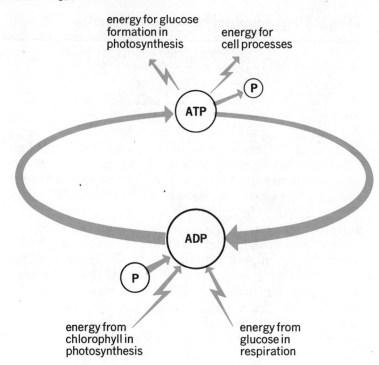

energy for glucose formation in photosynthesis

energy for cell processes

ATP

ADP

energy from chlorophyll in photosynthesis

energy from glucose in respiration

6–8 | ADP receives energy and attaches a phosphate molecule, changing to ATP. This energy is stored in the ATP molecule. If a phosphate is removed from ATP, forming ADP, the energy is released.

to a unit of *ribose*, a 5-carbon sugar. Together these two substances make *adenosine*. A short chain of smaller *phosphate* molecules is attached to the adenosine. ATP is called adenosine *tri*phosphate because it has *three* phosphates attached.

In building ATP, one phosphate is first bonded to adenosine. At this point, the molecule is *adenosine monophosphate*, or **AMP.** A second phosphate builds the molecule to **ADP,** or *adenosine diphosphate*. This phosphate is attached by a high-energy bond. A third phosphate, attached by a still higher energy bond, produces *ATP*.

Cells can only use energy in the form of a molecule of ATP. Think of an ATP molecule as A-P~P~P. The ~(P) indicates a high-energy bond. When the cell needs energy, an enzyme removes the last ~(P). The breaking of the chemical bond forms ADP and releases energy. You can consider the reaction as: A-P~P~P→ A-P~P + (P) + *energy*. A constant supply of ATP is *always* needed for energy. The ATP molecule is like a charged battery. When the cell changes ATP to ADP + (P), it uses the energy released. The ADP is like a discharged battery. In respiration, the cell uses energy stored in the food molecule to recharge the battery. This process can be represented by: energy + (P) + ADP→ATP. These changes occur over and over in a cell. Energy is stored in ATP, moved around the cell, and released as needed. **Living cells really run on ATP power.**

The Photosynthesis Process

For a long time biologists knew that oxygen was given off when photosynthesis occurred in green plants. Biologists already knew that light supplied the energy stored in glucose. But the idea that light energy split water molecules became known later. It was also found that chlorophyll plays an important part in this energy transfer. The reactions among water, light, and chlorophyll make up the first phase in photosynthesis. Since these reactions occur only in the presence of light, this phase of photosynthesis was named the *light reactions.*

The Light Reactions

In this first phase of photosynthesis, water (H_2O) is split into oxygen and hydrogen. The oxygen is given off as a waste material, but the hydrogen is used. These are complex reactions and the process seems long. But the whole series of light reactions occur in a fraction of a second. Still, it helps to describe these reactions as a series of steps, even though they take place at almost the same time. Refer to figure 6-10 as you read the following description.

6-9 | Photosynthesis: In the light reaction, energy and raw materials are used on the left; while the product is formed during the dark reaction at the right.

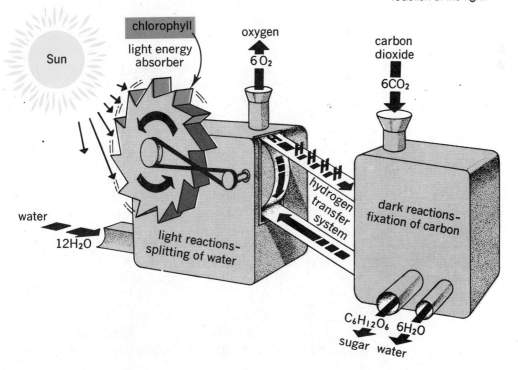

Sun

chlorophyll

light energy absorber

oxygen

$6 O_2$

carbon dioxide

$6CO_2$

water

$12H_2O$

light reactions- splitting of water

hydrogen transfer system

dark reactions- fixation of carbon

$C_6H_{12}O_6$ $6H_2O$

sugar   water

■ *Chlorophyll is energized.* Chlorophyll acts as an **energy carrier** in the light reactions phase. It is thought that light energy causes a sudden change in the atoms of chlorophyll molecules. Electrons are moved to a greater distance from the nucleus of the atom. This is to say that electrons move *from lower to higher energy levels.* Thus, kinetic light energy is trapped as chemical potential energy in the chlorophyll molecule. But this energy isn't stable like that stored in glucose molecules. Chlorophyll molecules in this state are said to be *energized*, or excited.

You might compare the energized chlorophyll molecule to a hot potato pulled out of a campfire. As the hot potato is passed from person to person, some of its heat warms the hands that hold it. Before long, the potato has cooled, but it is still a potato!

Similarly, the electron in an energized chlorophyll molecule can be transferred from one molecule to another in a series of reactions. At each transfer, some energy is lost from the chlorophyll molecule. The electrons of the chlorophyll molecule drop back to a lower energy level. Soon, the chlorophyll is no longer energized. It is ready to trap more light and again become energized. But what does the cell do with the energy from the transfer of electrons?

■ *Energy is stored in ATP.* Chloroplasts contain ADP. Some of the energy released by energized chlorophyll changes ADP to ATP in the chloroplasts. How does this happen? The excited electron of the energized chlorophyll is passed through a series of coenzymes. You learned in Chapter 3 that a coenzyme is a nonprotein molecule that works with an enzyme in controlling a reaction. Each time it is passed along, the electron of the chlorophyll molecule loses a little energy. But this energy is used to change low-energy phosphate groups to high-energy phosphate groups. The high-energy phosphate combines with ADP, changing it to ATP. Thus, radiant energy has been converted to chemical energy in the chloroplast of the plant cell. The chlorophyll molecule has lost its high-energy state and is ready to trap more light.

■ *Water molecules are split.* All the trapped light energy is not used to change ADP to ATP. Some of the energy in the excited chlorophyll molecules is used to break apart the bonds of water molecules. The water molecules are split into hydrogen ions (H^+) and hydroxide ions (OH^-).

■ *Hydrogen is trapped by NADP.* Chloroplasts contain a coenzyme known as NADP. NADP is a **hydrogen acceptor.** It combines readily with the hydrogen released by the

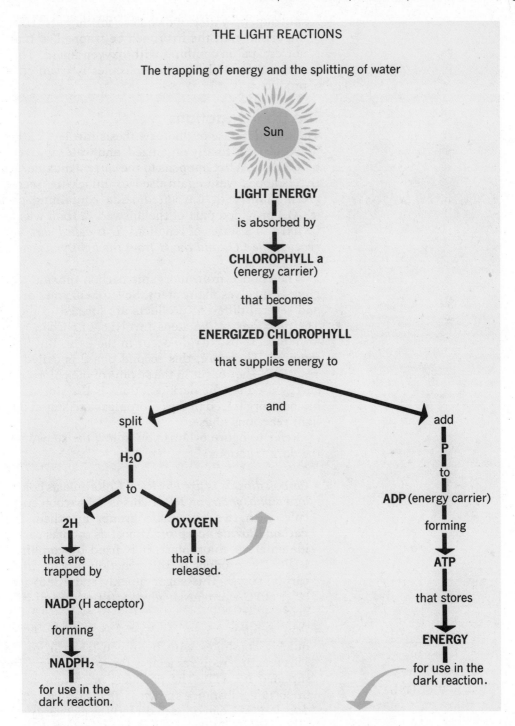

6-10 | The light reactions.

splitting of water molecules, forming $NADPH_2$. It is important that the hydrogen be trapped so that it does not escape or combine with oxygen again. The oxygen released from the water molecules is given off as a by-product.

The Dark Reactions

The second phase of photosynthesis involves carbon dioxide. Glucose is finally organized, and water is given off as a by-product. What happens to the carbon dioxide? Radioactive isotopes were again used to unlock the secret of the green plant cell. Carbon dioxide containing carbon-14 ($C_{14}O_2$) provided part of the answer. Carbon was found to be fixed in a series of reactions. *It is called carbon fixation because the CO_2 and the H from the light phase are used to make glucose.*

The change from inorganic carbon dioxide to organic glucose involves many steps. Several enzymes are needed, and several different products are formed in the process. The reactions of the steps involved in carbon fixation to form glucose usually do occur in the light. But light is not required. Therefore, this second phase is called the **dark reactions.** They occur in the stroma of the chloroplasts. The energy used for the dark reactions is the stored ATP. This has been organized in the chloroplast and stored during the light reactions phase.

Refer to figure 6-11 as you follow the steps involved in the dark reactions.

- *Carbon dioxide is fixed by RDP.* Chloroplasts contain *ribulose diphosphate,* or **RDP.** This is a 5-carbon sugar molecule, with two phosphate groups attached. RDP is a **carbon dioxide acceptor.** Almost as soon as carbon dioxide enters a chloroplast, it is fixed by combining with RDP. The product of this reaction is very unstable 6-carbon sugar. This sugar quickly splits into two molecules of PGA, or *phosphoglyceric* (FAHSS-foe-gli-SEHR-ick) *acid.*

- *PGA combines with hydrogen and forms PGAL.* PGA quickly combines with hydrogen taken from $NADPH_2$. This reaction requires a large amount of energy, which is supplied by ATP. The products are water and a very important substance known as **PGAL** or *phosphoglyceraldehyde.* PGAL can be used directly as an energy source for cell activity. In fact, plants supplied with PGAL can survive without photosynthesis or any other food source. For this reason, you could even think of PGAL, instead of glucose, as the main product of photosynthesis. So, some PGAL *is* used directly by the cell, but, in photosynthesis,

THE DARK REACTIONS

The fixing of carbon in a carbohydrate

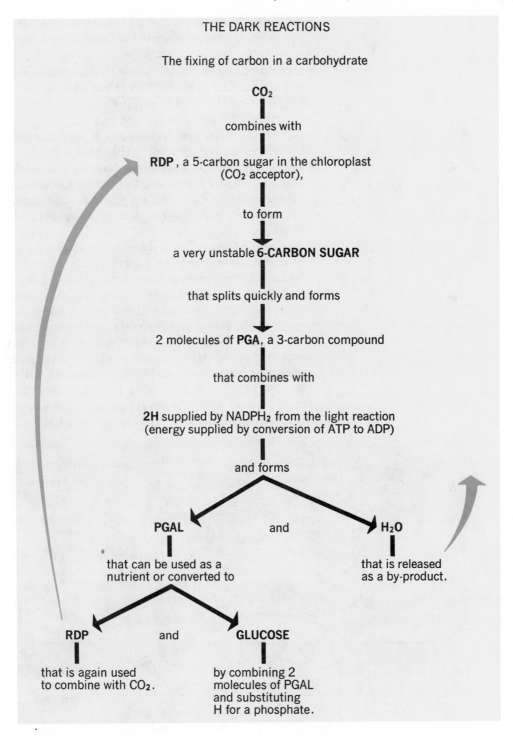

CO_2

combines with

RDP, a 5-carbon sugar in the chloroplast
(CO_2 acceptor),

to form

a very unstable **6-CARBON SUGAR**

that splits quickly and forms

2 molecules of **PGA**, a 3-carbon compound

that combines with

2H supplied by $NADPH_2$ from the light reaction
(energy supplied by conversion of ATP to ADP)

and forms

PGAL   and   **H_2O**

that can be used as a
nutrient or converted to

that is released
as a by-product.

RDP   and   **GLUCOSE**

that is again used
to combine with CO_2.

by combining 2
molecules of PGAL
and substituting
H for a phosphate.

6–11 | The dark reactions.

a cell produces much more PGAL than it needs. Much of the PGAL is changed into other products, mainly glucose, in further chemical reactions.

- *Other products of PGAL.* Some PGAL molecules are used in forming RDP. This RDP can then fix more carbon dioxide, starting the dark reactions cycle over again.

Other PGAL is changed to glucose. In this reaction, two PGAL molecules combine. The formula for PGAL is $C_3H_5O_3\sim(P)$. The symbol $\sim(P)$ stands for an attached phosphate group. This phosphate is removed and replaced by hydrogen in each of the two PGAL molecules. This results in $C_6H_{12}O_6$, or glucose. The simple sugar fructose, or fruit sugar, can also be produced from PGAL.

Simple sugars formed from PGAL may be combined by *dehydration synthesis* to form double sugars. One such sugar is table sugar, or sucrose ($C_{12}H_{22}O_{11}$). By dehydration synthesis, the simple sugars may also join in long chains to form starches and celluloses. Some plants also build PGAL molecules into oils such as corn oil.

You can think of photosynthesis as a bridge. Only by crossing the bridge can carbon dioxide, water, and light energy be organized into PGAL, glucose, and other organic compounds. Without this bridge, almost all life on earth would end. **Photosynthesis is the chemical link between the inorganic and organic worlds**

6–12 | Photosynthesis acts as a chemical bridge between the inorganic world and the organic world.

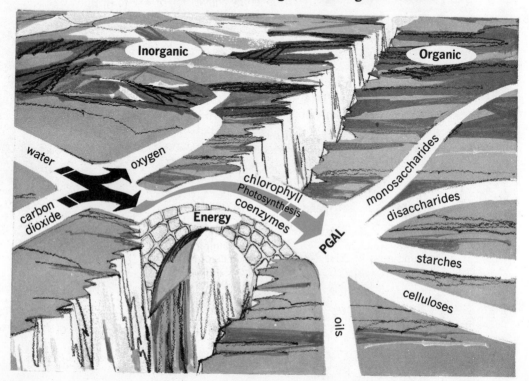

Chemosynthesis

There are other ways of crossing the bridge between the inorganic and organic worlds. Certain bacteria do *not* depend on photosynthesis. Some have enzyme systems that trap the energy released during *inorganic* chemical reactions. These organisms use this energy in splitting water molecules. The bacteria can organize their own carbohydrates *without using light energy*. This process is known as **chemosynthesis.**

chemo = with or by chemicals

These special bacteria build fats, proteins, and nucleic acids from the carbohydrates formed in chemosynthesis. Bacteria are sometimes thought of as low forms of life. However, in terms of cell chemistry, bacteria are well prepared for survival.

Respiration

Cellular respiration includes all the chemical reactions in which energy is released in support of cell life. These reactions include the breaking down of glucose and other foods and the transfer of energy to ATP. The exact reactions involved, products formed, and amount of energy released may vary. But respiration is necessary to the life of every cell.

When you think of respiration in your own body, you may think of breathing. But breathing is only an exchange of gases between your body and the surrounding air. The purpose of breathing is to allow blood to pick up O_2 from the air and deliver it to your cells. It is in the body cells that respiration takes place.

In Chapter 3 you learned about the bonds that hold atoms together in molecules. Chemical energy is stored in these bonds. When the molecules break down, the bonds are broken and their energy is released. The chemical bond energy in organic fuel molecules, such as glucose, was once light energy from the sun. This light energy was stored in the glucose during photosynthesis. So you see, **the chemical bond energy released in respiration first came from the sun.**

Just how is energy released? The answer is *oxidation.* Oxidation involves either the adding of oxygen or the removal of hydrogen from a molecule. In each case, *electrons are removed from the substance being oxidized.* Figure 6-13 shows a Brazil nut being burned. In this process, oxygen from the air is being added to the nut. The chemical bond energy is released as heat and light. Certainly, cells

6-13 | A burning Brazil nut demonstrates the large amounts of chemical bond energy that is released from food. *(HRW photo by John King)*

Facts & Figures

In 1786, Ingenhausz proved that carbon dioxide and light were used in photosynthesis. He also showed that in the dark, green plants gave off carbon dioxide and used oxygen.

an = without
aeros = air, the atmosphere

6-14 | Stage one of cellular respiration. Notice that two molecules of ATP are required for this reaction. Four molecules of ATP are formed. (P) indicates a high energy bond.

could not stand this sudden release of energy. **Respiration is a controlled process.** The cells or organisms get their energy by removing hydrogen from molecules. The respiration process takes place in many steps.

Stages of Cellular Respiration

Each step of respiration in a cell is controlled by enzymes. As energy is released, the cell's batteries are recharged by changing ADP to ATP. Glucose is the fuel most commonly used by organisms. Glucose is oxidized by the cell in two stages.

Anaerobic Stage The first stage is called *anaerobic* (an-a-ROH-bik) since it does *not* involve molecular oxygen. This stage occurs outside the mitochondria. As many as 12 enzymes are used in this series of reactions. The main result is that a glucose molecule is broken down to two 3-carbon molecules of *pyruvic acid*. *Two* ATP molecules supply the activation energy needed for this process. However, enough energy is released in splitting the glucose molecule to form *four* ATP molecules. Thus, there is a net gain of *two* ATP molecules. *Four* hydrogen atoms are also given off in the formation of *pyruvic acid*. These are joined to a coenzyme, *nicotinamide adenine dinucleotide*, or **NAD**, which is a *hydrogen acceptor*. The NAD then becomes $NADH_2$.

The energy released in this first stage of cellular respiration is about seven percent of the energy in the glucose molecule. The rest of its energy remains in the bonds of the pyruvic acid molecules.

Aerobic Stage The second stage of cellular respiration is called the *aerobic* stage since it requires molecular oxygen. In this stage, *pyruvic acid is broken down*. Water and carbon dioxide are given off, and energy is released. This stage involves two main series of steps.

$$2\,NAD + 4H \longrightarrow 2\,NADH_2$$

$$\underset{\text{energy}}{2\,ATP} \longrightarrow 2\,ADP + 2\sim(P) + \underset{\text{glucose}}{C_6H_{12}O_6} \longrightarrow \underset{\text{Pyruvic Acid}}{2\,CH_2 \cdot CH \cdot COOH} + 4H + 4\sim(P)$$

$$4\,ADP + 4\sim(P) \longrightarrow 4\,ATP$$

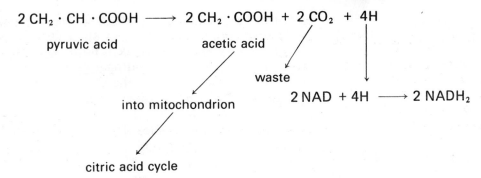

$$2 \, CH_2 \cdot CH \cdot COOH \longrightarrow 2 \, CH_2 \cdot COOH + 2 \, CO_2 + 4H$$

pyruvic acid   acetic acid

waste

into mitochondrion

$$2 \, NAD + 4H \longrightarrow 2 \, NADH_2$$

citric acid cycle

6–15 | The first step, stage two, of cellular respiration. The two molecules of the three-carbon pyruvic acid form two molecules of the two-carbon acetic acid. The four hydrogen atoms combine with two coenzyme molecules (NAD) to form two molecules of $NADH_2$. Two molecules of carbon dioxide are given off as a waste product. The two molecules of acetic acid enter a mitochondrion.

The pyruvic acid formed in the first stage is not a stable compound. In the presence of molecular oxygen, it breaks down without the energy of ATP. The 3-carbon pyruvate molecules become 2-carbon molecules called *acetic acid*. The carbon that is released combines with oxygen, forming carbon dioxide. This is some of the carbon dioxide that is given off as waste product of cellular respiration. Look at figure 6-15 and you will see that two molecules of carbon dioxide are given off and two molecules of acetic acid are formed. Two molecules of each result because one molecule of glucose formed two molecules of pyruvic acid in the first stage. At the same time, four atoms of hydrogen are released. As in the first stage, these combine with two molecules of NAD to form two molecules of $NADH_2$.

At this point, the acetic acid molecules enter a mitochondrion. Each acetic acid molecule joins a 4-carbon compound already present in the fluid of the mitochondrion. The new 6-carbon compound is *citric acid*. In the mitochondrion, a series of reactions occur. First, one carbon is removed from the 6-carbon citric acid. The carbon unites with oxygen, forming carbon dioxide. The next step removes another carbon, which combines with oxygen to form another carbon dioxide molecule. This leaves a four-carbon compound, which can unit with another acetic acid molecule to repeat the process. This is why these reactions in the mitochondrion are called the ***citric acid cycle.*** Each time the carbon dioxide forms in the citric acid cycle, four atoms of hydrogen are released. These are joined to coenzyme molecules of NAD to form $NADH_2$.

If you have counted all the hydrogen atoms that have come from the many reactions, you would know that 24 hydrogen atoms are produced by every molecule of glucose in cell respiration. These would form 12 molecules of $NADH_2$.

Hydrogen is a very reactive atom. In the cell it will be combined with oxygen to form water. But this cannot hap-

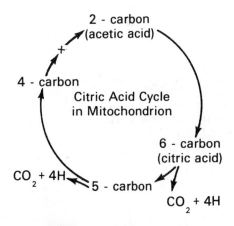

2 - carbon
(acetic acid)

4 - carbon

Citric Acid Cycle
in Mitochondrion

6 - carbon
(citric acid)

$CO_2 + 4H$

5 - carbon

$CO_2 + 4H$

6–16 | The citric acid cycle. This cycle shows what happens to one molecule of acetic acid. In cell respiration, two molecules of acetic acid are formed. Thus, for every molecule of glucose, four molecules of carbon dioxide and 16 atoms of hydrogen are given off in the citric acid cycle.

pen all at once. When the hydrogen atom combines directly with an oxygen atom to form a water molecule, it does so with explosive force. In the cell, however, this is *not* the reaction that takes place. Hydrogen goes through a chain of reactions. At each "link" in the chain, the hydrogen loses energy. The hydrogen is passed from $NADH_2$ to other special coenzyme molecules. These molecules are located on the inner membrane surface of the mitochondria in a series of reactions. At each step in this series, the electron of the hydrogenation passes through a series of reactions called the **electron transport chain.** Every two electrons passed along the chain releases enough energy to change three low-energy phosphates (ADP + P) to three high-energy phosphates (ATP). From one molecule of glucose that produces 12 molecules of $NADH_2$, 36 molecules of high-energy phosphates (ATP) would be formed. Once the electrons have been transported through this last series of reactions, they combine with hydrogen ions and oxygen atoms to form water. The role of oxygen in respiration is to get rid of the hydrogen. Twelve water molecules are formed from each molecule of glucose in cell respiration. Six of these water molecules are used in the reactions of the citric acid cycle. A net gain of six water molecules is produced from these reactions beginning with one molecule of glucose.

The equation for cellular respiration can be written as follows:

$$C_6H_{12}O_6 + 6O_2 \rightarrow 6CO_2 + 6H_2O + \text{energy (38 ATP)}$$
glucose + oxygen → carbon + water
dioxide

Uses of Cell Energy

The useful energy produced by one molecule of glucose in the first stage of cellular respiration was only two molecules of ATP. But the aerobic stage produced 36 molecules of ATP from each molecule of glucose. This is still only about 60 percent efficient. Much of the remaining energy is

6-17 | During the last series of reactions in cell respiration, 24 hydrogen electrons with high energy are passed along the electron transport chain. The energy of two hydrogen electrons changes three ADP to three ATP. At the end of the chain the final hydrogen acceptor combines the electrons with a hydrogen ion and with oxygen to form water.

Stages 1 and 2 of all respiration produces 24H and forms $12NADH_2 \rightarrow 12NAD + 24H$ electrons (high-energy).

Hydrogen acceptors in electron chain → energy (ADP→ATP)
energy (ADP→ATP)
energy (ADP→ATP)
Final H acceptor

$24 \text{ electrons} + 24H^+ \rightarrow 12H_2$

$12H_2 + 6O_2 \rightarrow 12H_2O$

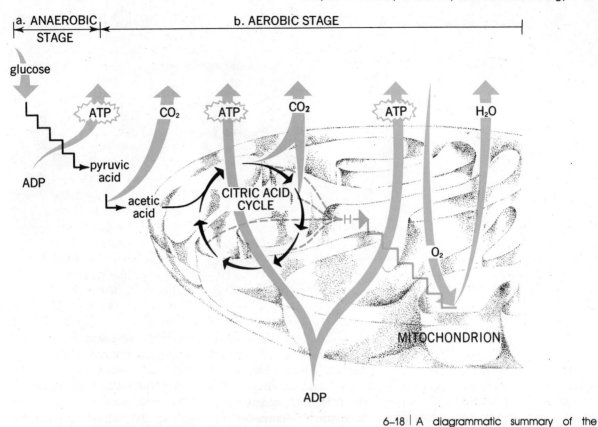

6–18 | A diagrammatic summary of the chemical changes that occur in cellular respiration.

generated as heat. The mitochondria, then, are like small heating units of the cell. In warm-blooded animals, this heat keeps the body temperature constant. The remaining energy, stored in ATP, can be released for use in many cell activities. It may be used in building starches, fats and oils, nucleic acids, and proteins. It may also support activities such as active transport, cell division, and muscle contraction. Many molecules of ATP are changed to ADP to release energy for muscle contraction when you reach over to turn off an alarm clock.

Fermentation

You can now understand why oxygen is necessary to get the most energy from glucose. But even without oxygen, some energy may be obtained from the first stage or anaerobic breakdown of glucose. Some organisms do get their energy in this way. Anaerobic respiration is called **fermentation.** This is not the same as the anaerobic stage of respiration previously mentioned. It is the same in that it too does not involve molecular oxygen. Fermentation does begin much the same way as cellular respiration. Glucose is broken

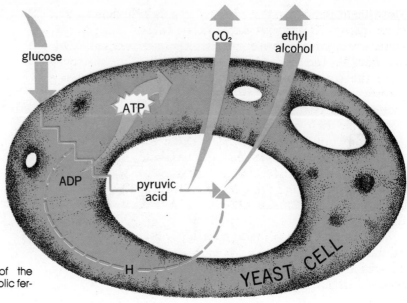

6-19 | A diagrammatic summary of the chemical changes that occur in alcoholic fermentation.

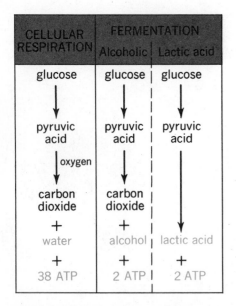

6-20 | A comparison of the end products and energy released in cellular respiration and alcoholic and lactic acid fermentation.

down to two pyruvic acid molecules, and a small amount of energy is released. From this point, the pyruvic acid may be broken down in *two* different ways.

In yeasts and certain other organisms, a carbon dioxide molecule is removed from pyruvic acid. The product formed is then broken down to the end product, ethyl alcohol. The process, known as **alcoholic fermentation,** can be represented as follows:

$$C_6H_{12}O_6 = 2C_2H_5OH + 2CO_2 + \text{energy (2 ATP)}$$

glucose = ethyl + carbon
          alcohol dioxide

Yeasts are mixed with sugar solutions to make alcohol. The organism doesn't have enzymes to break down the alcohol. And, as you have seen, anaerobic respiration is *not* an efficient use of glucose for making ATP. In fact, certain alcohols contain so much energy that they can be mixed with gasoline and burned. These alcohols are waste products of organisms such as yeast.

In animals tissues such as muscle, **lactic acid fermentation** may take place. Here, with no molecular oxygen present, pyruvic acid is changed to lactic acid as an end product. This process is represented by the following equation:

$$C_6H_{12}O_6 \rightarrow 2C_3H_6O_3 + \text{energy (2 ATP)}$$

glucose → lactic acid

Notice again that much less energy is released and stored in ATP during fermentation than during aerobic respiration. Most of the energy of the glucose remains in the chemical bonds of the fermentation end products.

Most life forms depend on photosynthesis, which occurs in green plants. During photosynthesis, carbon dioxide and water are organized into organic compounds, such as PGAL and glucose, the basic fuel for all cells. Thus, light energy from the sun is stored as chemical energy. The energy transfer compound ATP is the unit of stored energy for living things. Some autotrophs do not use the sun's energy. They make their own food by using energy stored in inorganic compounds. This process is chemosynthesis.

Cellular respiration in cells releases the energy stored in glucose. Glucose molecules are broken down, and their chemical bond energy is released. Some of this energy is given off as heat. Some is stored in ATP for use in cell activities.

The process of respiration constantly goes on in all cells. All living cells must have a constant supply of energy. Aerobic respiration requires oxygen. Anaerobic respiration occurs without oxygen and is called fermentation.

Summary

---

photosynthesis
respiration
autotroph
heterotroph
chlorophyll
visible spectrum
ATP
AMP
ADP
light reactions
energy carrier
hydrogen acceptor
dark reactions
RDP

carbon dioxide acceptor
PGAL
chemosynthesis
cellular respiration
oxidation
anaerobic
NAD
aerobic
citric acid cycle
electron transport chain
fermentation
alcoholic fermentation
lactic acid fermentation

Biologically Speaking

---

1. Describe the importance of photosynthesis to all life.

2. Define photosynthesis using words and the chemical formula.

3. Why are the heterotrophs dependent on the autotrophs for their lives?

4. Describe the importance of ATP to living things.

5. How does a molecule of ATP store and release energy?

6. What part does chlorophyll play in the process of photosynthesis?

Questions for Review

7. Outline the steps of the light reactions of photosynthesis.
8. Outline the steps in the fixation of CO_2 in the dark reactions.
9. Why are different plant pigments considered to be adaptive?
10. How is chemosynthesis different from photosynthesis?

11. What is the biological importance of respiration?
12. How does respiration occur without the presence of high temperature?
13. Define cellular respiration using a chemical equation.

14. Describe the two types of fermentation.
15. List several processes requiring cell energy.

Applying Concepts

1. Explain why chloroplasts appear green in color.
2. Describe the conditions that affect photosynthesis.
3. From where do cells derive their usable energy?

4. Why might photosynthesis and respiration be considered complementary processes?
5. Compare the processes of burning wood and cellular respiration. Be sure to include the end products of each of these processes.

7-1 | Life's spiral staircase. *(HRW Photo by Russell Dian)*

Nucleic Acids and Protein Synthesis

A **RECOGNIZE** the importance of protein synthesis.

B **DESCRIBE** the replication of DNA.

C **IDENTIFY** the chemical structure of DNA and RNA.

D **UNDERSTAND** the process of transcription of the DNA code.

E **STATE** the importance of the triplet code of RNA.

F **DESCRIBE** the role of RNA in protein synthesis.

G **LIST** the functions of proteins in living cells.

Protein Synthesis: A Universal Life Process

Every living cell contains proteins. The cell organelles are made largely of protein. As you learned in Chapter 4, protein molecules are found throughout the plasma membrane. Cytoplasm is a colloidal suspension of proteins. Enzymes, which are necessary to all cell activities, are protein molecules. The process of making the many different kinds of proteins is called **protein synthesis.** Since the living condition depends on exactly the right kind of proteins in the cell, protein synthesis is very important. The chemical information necessary to make proteins is passed on to each new generation of organisms.

Protein synthesis takes place in *all* cells. Every cell organizes its own protein molecules. Through the process of protein synthesis, cells build many different kinds of proteins. The parts of the same plant also have different proteins. Those in the trunk of a tree are quite different from the ones found in leaves. Your proteins are different from those of your parents. And proteins in the cells of your skin are different from those in the cells of your muscles or glands. You may have read in a newspaper about kidney transplants. Why do these transplants sometimes fail? Proteins in the new organ are not like proteins in the body to which they are transplanted. So, the new kidney cells cannot be kept alive by the body into which they are transplanted.

Every animal and plant has a different structure and different chemical reactions. This is because they have different kinds of proteins. There are many millions of different proteins in the living world. Proteins differ from one another because they are made of different combinations of amino acids. The 20 amino acids are like the letters of an alphabet. Many words can be made with 20 letters. They can be combined in many different ways. How are these amino acids put into proper sequence in cells? For years biologists wondered how this process was controlled. They knew that the protein "factories" of cells are the ribosomes. It is on these tiny bodies, attached to the endoplasmic reticulum, that proteins are actually formed. And it was also known that the control center for all cell activities is in the nucleus. But what substance in the nucleus acted as this control? How does this substance code the particular sequence from the nucleus to the ribosomes where the proteins are finally made? Answers to these questions came with one of the most important discoveries in the history of biology.

DNA

The Discovery of DNA

The cell nucleus contains many rod-shaped bodies called *chromosomes*. For a long time biologists thought that these structures somehow controlled cell activities. Biochemical studies showed that the chromosomes were made of the substances *protein* and *nucleic acid*. Remember that proteins are large molecules made of amino acids. *Nucleic acids* are also very complex biological compounds. They are made of phosphate groups, sugar groups, nitrogen-containing bases, and amino acids. A single nucleic acid molecule may have hundreds of thousands of individual atoms. But it was not known how these atoms were arranged in a nucleic acid molecule. Could either proteins or nucleic acids control all cell activity, including protein synthesis?

Research in the 1940s pointed to nucleic acid as the control substance. But its structure, the way the atoms are actually arranged, had still not been learned.

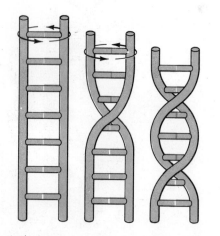

7-2 | The formation of a double helix can be compared to the twisting of a flexible ladder.

In 1953 an important discovery was made. Two young scientists were working with nucleic acids at Cambridge University in England. One was an American biologist, James D. Watson. The other was a British biophysicist, F. H. C. Crick. Together, they proposed a model of an important organic molecule. This molecule was **DNA,** or *deoxyribonucleic* (dee-ock-see-RY-boe-noo-KLAY-ick) acid.

de=away, without
oxy=oxygen

The Structure of DNA

You have already seen diagrams of structural formulas for several substances. Among these are the carbohydrates, lipids, proteins, and ATP. DNA is much larger than any of these. It is made of millions of atoms. Yet it is not large enough for its structure to be seen under an electron microscope. Searching for a pattern of this molecule was like looking for the solution to a puzzle. When Watson and Crick offered a model of DNA, it was just like providing the solution. Suddenly, the answers about the control of protein synthesis and other activities became clear.

Watson and Crick described the DNA molecule as being spiral in shape, and they called it a *double helix*. To understand this structure, imagine a rope ladder with metal rungs. If the ladder is twisted, a double helix is formed. Imagine, further, that the ladder is in two parts. Each part is made of a length of rope to which many half-rungs are attached. The whole ladder is formed by joining the half-rungs. The weakest part of the ladder is the middle part of the rungs where they are joined.

Look at figure 7-3 and you will see what units form the sides of the twisted ladder model. The rope parts are long strands made up of *sugar units* joined to *phosphate units*. The sugar unit is a 5-carbon sugar called *deoxyribose*. Attached to each deoxyribose unit is a nitrogen-containing base. This base forms a half-rung of the ladder. To make the ladder complete, each base is joined by weak hydrogen bonds to a base from the other strand of DNA.

Now let's consider the DNA model in more detail. The three-part unit of phosphate, deoxyribose, and base unit is called a **nucleotide.** Think of a DNA molecule as a double strand of nucleotides joined by their bases. Several thousand nucleotides may make up a single strand!

Notice that the model in figure 7-3 shows the nitrogen-containing bases in four different colors. Each color also has a different letter. Can you discover any pattern in the way these bases are joined?

There are four types of bases in DNA. Two are organic molecules known as **purines** (PURE-eens). *Adenine* (ADD-uh-EEN) and *guanine* (GWAHN-EEN) are the names of these purines. The other two are known as **pyrimidines** (pie-

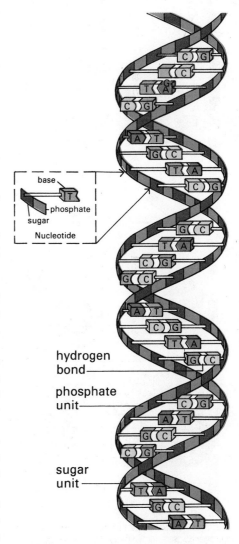

7–3 | Model of the double helix of DNA.

RIM-uh-DEENS). *Thymine* (THI-MEEN) and *cytosine* (SY-toe-SEEN) are the names of these pyrimidines. These four bases have the DNA code letters A, G, T, and C. **These nucleotide bases are part of a code system that controls protein synthesis.**

Did you find the bonding pattern in figure 7-3? The bases bond in only two combinations, adenine to thymine and guanine to cytosine. This is very important to a DNA code system. Let's see how this pattern of a DNA molecule can control protein synthesis.

Replication of DNA

One amazing thing about the DNA molecule is that it can build an exact copy of itself. This process is known as *replication,* and it is very important in explaining how cells reproduce more cells. Every cell has a code. **DNA replication allows the cell to pass its code from one generation to the next.** The DNA code must be replicated exactly. Future organisms must get the same code so they make correct proteins for that species. During replication, the weak hydrogen bonds between the bases of DNA break. DNA "unzips" its two halves. Then, each nucleotide attaches to the proper base: *adenine to thymine and guanine to cytosine.* Thus, two duplicate molecules of DNA are formed. Figure 7-4 shows this process.

Replication occurs every time a cell divides. A duplicate molecule of DNA goes into each new cell. **The exact structure of DNA carries its code to the new cell.** In the following section, you will see how this works.

RNA

The DNA of a eukaryote cell is in the nucleus. But proteins are synthesized in the ribosomes. How is the code of DNA delivered to the ribosomes? During the cell's activities, the DNA in the nucleus does another amazing thing. A strand of DNA codes the building of a near-copy of itself by a process called *transcription.* This near-copy is *ribonucleic acid,* or **RNA.** This molecule is most important in protein synthesis. How does RNA differ from DNA?

First, *ribose* is the sugar in RNA. It contains one more oxygen atom than the deoxyribose in DNA. Second, in RNA, the base thymine is replaced by another pyrimidine called *uracil.* The code letters for RNA, then, are A,G,U, and C. The third difference is that RNA usually remains a single strand, rather than a double strand like DNA.

As figure 7-5 shows, adenine always pairs with uracil in the RNA strand. Cytosine always pairs with guanine, just as in the DNA molecule.

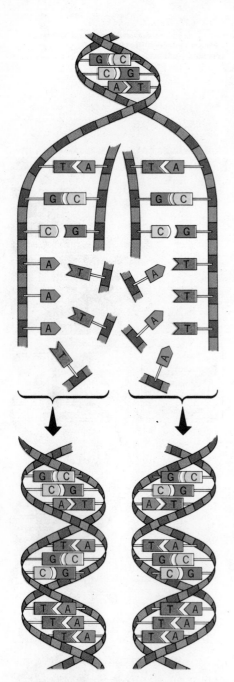

7-4 | Replication of a DNA molecule. DNA "unzips," and nucleotides then attach to the proper bases. Now there are two duplicated DNA molecules.

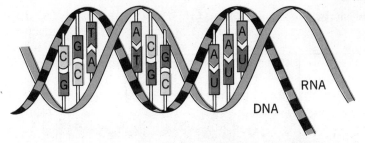

RNA

DNA

7-5 | DNA transcribing RNA. Once RNA is formed, the double helix "unzips" and RNA remains a single strand. What are the two places it may go?

You have seen how the DNA code controls both replication and transcription. But how do these processes control protein synthesis? DNA is in the nucleus, and proteins are organized in the ribosomes. The DNA code must be carried from the nucleus into the cytoplasm where the ribosomes are. This is the job of a single strand of RNA called **messenger RNA** (mRNA). A single strand of messenger RNA leaves the nucleus through the nuclear membrane. Some of it, though, may be stored in the nucleolus. When messenger RNA is in the cytoplasm, it is ready to direct the synthesis of protein. Let's see how the directions of DNA are delivered to the ribosomes by this messenger.

Three-letter Code Words in RNA

The four nucleotide bases of RNA are represented as A, G, U, and C. These bases make up the alphabet from which code words of RNA are formed. There may be thousands of bases on an RNA strand, and they may occur in any order. But you must remember that **the order on any particular messenger RNA is directed by the code on the single strand of DNA that forms it by transcription.**

It is not *single* bases that are important, but groups of three called *triplet codons.* Each base triplet on a messenger RNA is a three-letter code word. For example, in figure 7-5, the triplet code words on the messenger RNA formed by transcription are UUU, GCA, and ACG.

The four letters of the messenger RNA code can be combined into 64 different three-letter words. How do these words affect protein synthesis? What exactly is it that they code? The answer is the words code for *amino acids.* Remember that proteins are made of long chains of amino acid units. *Each triplet codon on a messenger RNA codes a specific amino acid.* Further, the **order of the triplet codons on a strand of messenger RNA codes the order in which amino acids will be put together to build a protein.** Each messenger RNA triplet codon always codes the same amino acid. But different messenger RNA molecules transcribed from different DNA molecules may have these triplet codons arranged in a very different order. This gives rise to many different proteins.

Facts & Figures

When DNA is heated to 70° C, hydrogen bonds between the base pairs adenine-thymine or guanine-cytosine break apart. DNA is said to be *denatured.* Its properties are then changed.

Middle position in code word

	U	C	A	G	
U	UUU ⎫ Phenylalanine UUC ⎭ UUA ⎫ Leucine UUG ⎭	UCU ⎫ UCC ⎪ Serine UCA ⎬ UCG ⎭	UAU ⎫ Tyrosine UAC ⎭ UAA Termination UAG Termination	UGU ⎫ Cysteine UGC ⎭ UGA Termination UGG Tryptophan	U C A G
C	CUU ⎫ CUC ⎪ Leucine CUA ⎬ CUG ⎭	CCU ⎫ CCC ⎪ Proline CCA ⎬ CCG ⎭	CAU ⎫ Histidine CAC ⎭ CAA ⎫ Glutamine CAG ⎭	CGU ⎫ CGC ⎪ Arginine CGA ⎬ CGG ⎭	U C A G
A	AUU ⎫ AUC ⎬ Isoleucine AUA ⎭ AUG Methionine initiation	ACU ⎫ ACC ⎪ Threonine ACA ⎬ ACG ⎭	AAU ⎫ Asparagine AAC ⎭ AAA ⎫ Lysine AAG ⎭	AGU ⎫ Serine AGC ⎭ AGA ⎫ Arginine AGG ⎭	U C A G
G	GUU ⎫ GUC ⎪ Valine GUA ⎬ GUG ⎭	GCU ⎫ GCC ⎪ Alanine GCA ⎬ GCG ⎭	GAU ⎫ Aspartic acid GAC ⎭ GAA ⎫ Glutamic acid GAG ⎭	GGU ⎫ GGC ⎪ Glycine GGA ⎬ GGG ⎭	U C A G

First position in code word

Third position in code word

7–6 | Dictionary of messenger RNA code words for amino acids. How do these indicate that DNA must also have three letter code words?

There are 64 possible three-letter code words or *codons* in messenger RNA. But there are only 20 common amino acids. Thus, several different codons may code the same amino acid. A few codons, though, do not code any amino acid. Instead, these seem to act as signals for the end of a protein chain. Such a codon may be thought of as the period at the end of a protein "sentence." Other codons may possibly act as signals for the beginning of a protein molecule.

Figure 7-6 shows the 64 possible three-letter code words on messenger RNA and the amino acid each codes. Look again at the strand of messenger RNA in figure 7-5. It has the codons UUU, GCA, and ACG in that order. Which amino acids do these triplets code?

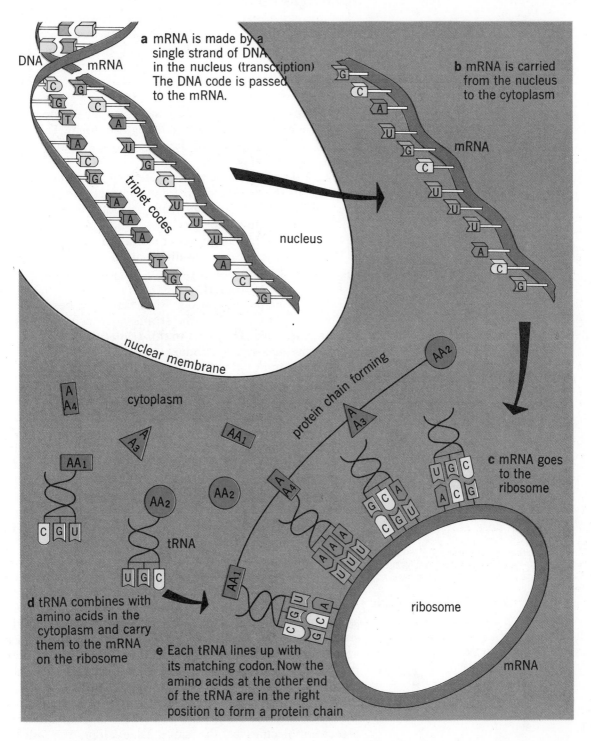

DNA   mRNA

a mRNA is made by a single strand of DNA in the nucleus (transcription) The DNA code is passed to the mRNA.

triplet codes

nucleus

nuclear membrane

b mRNA is carried from the nucleus to the cytoplasm

mRNA

c mRNA goes to the ribosome

cytoplasm

protein chain forming

AA₂

A AA₄

A AA₃

AA₁

AA₁

AA₂

AA₂

C G U

tRNA

U G C

A A₃

A A₄

AA₁

ribosome

mRNA

d tRNA combines with amino acids in the cytoplasm and carry them to the mRNA on the ribosome

e Each tRNA lines up with its matching codon. Now the amino acids at the other end of the tRNA are in the right position to form a protein chain

7–7 | The roles of DNA and RNA in protein synthesis.

Building Amino Acids into Proteins

Now you can answer the question about how RNA codes for protein synthesis. Once in the cytoplasm, messenger RNA acts as a pattern, or *template,* for the building of amino acids into proteins. Several protein molecules are organized at the same time along the messenger RNA strand. Let's look at this process.

It is thought that mRNA attaches to a ribosome at a point where a protein chain will begin to form. There are several such points on the RNA strand, each marked by special *initiator codons.*

The amino acids needed for protein synthesis are spread throughout the cytoplasm. In your body cells, for example, these amino acids have come from the food you have eaten. The individual amino acids are now picked up and brought to the template in the right order to make a specific protein. It is the combination of the different 20 amino acids that make up a different protein. This is the job of another type of RNA called *transfer RNA* (tRNA).

There is a special transfer RNA that attaches to each amino acid. At one end of the strand of transfer RNA is a triplet code word. **The bases in this triplet fit the bases in a specific messenger RNA codon.**

Look again at figure 7-6 on page 96 and find the names of the amino acids represented by a messenger RNA having codons of UUU, GCA, and ACG. They are phenylalanine, alanine, and threonine. These are the "instructions" to the ribosome to make a protein having these three amino acids put together in this particular sequence. The tRNA molecules attached to phenylalanine, alanine, and threonine must come together in this order. The triplet codes on the tRNA serve to do this. Remember that in RNA, uracil is substituted for thymine. The transfer RNA strands for this example would have to have the codes of AAA, CGU, and UGC.

These transfer RNA strands attached to the amino acids phenylalanine, alanine, and threonine are now attached to the template. When these amino acids are brought together, they attach to one another. The tRNA strands move off into the cytoplasm. The ribosome continues to move along the mRNA template. More tRNA strands, each with a specific amino acid, are attached. This process places each amino acid in the right position to be added to a chain until the protein is completed. The ribosome then releases the protein into the cytoplasm and the mRNA moves away.

A single ribosome builds only one protein molecule. However, several ribosomes may be building different protein molecules at the same time along the mRNA template. Further, it is thought that a strand of mRNA may act as a template more than once.

The Importance of DNA

DNA determines the makeup of structural proteins, enzymes, and all other proteins. In this way, DNA controls not only the physical makeup of cells, but their chemical activities as well. In fact, DNA controls the whole organism. DNA can replicate during cell division, passing all its instructions to the daughter cells. Its code is carried by messenger RNA to the ribosomes where specific proteins are synthesized. Protein synthesis involves several kinds of processes and types of nucleic acids. The processes bring together the specific number and kinds of amino acids to synthesize proteins. That way the daughter cells synthesize the same kind of proteins as the parent cell.

As you go on in biology, you will see the importance of DNA again and again. How do organisms grow? How does an organism keep its identity through its whole life? Why are organisms like their parents in some ways but different in others? DNA provides the answers to all these questions. You are you because of your DNA!

DNA Engineering

In the past few years, scientists have made many interesting discoveries. One of the most exciting discoveries was the ability to transplant genetic material. Scientists developed a technique to transplant strands of DNA from one cell to another. They removed pieces of DNA from one type of bacterium. They placed these pieces of DNA into another type of bacterium found in the human intestine. In this way, scientists actually changed the genetic makeup of a cell.

In 1976 the National Institutes of Health issued a set of guidelines. The guidelines were to be used by researchers studying DNA recombinations. Possible benefits as well as the hazards of recombinant DNA research were considered. Some recombinant DNA studies, such as with poisons produced by insects, snakes, and prokaryotes, are entirely banned by the National Institutes of Health guidelines.

Protein synthesis is a key process in the living condition. All living cells contain protein. DNA controls protein synthesis through a code of 64 base triplet "words." Transcription passes the code to messenger RNA.

Summary

Messenger RNA carries the code out into the cytoplasm. Here, the messenger RNA acts as a template for the building of proteins. Units of transfer RNA bring amino acids to the template. In the ribosome, the codons on the template are "read." With the help of transfer RNA, the amino acids are attached to one another in the proper order for forming the correct protein molecule.

Biologically Speaking

protein synthesis	replication	template
DNA	transcription	initiator codon
nucleotide	RNA	transfer RNA
purine	messenger RNA	
pyrimidine	triplet codon	

Questions for Review

1. Explain the importance of protein synthesis to all living things.
2. Describe the Watson-Crick model for DNA.
3. How is RNA formed from DNA?
4. What do the triplet codes of RNA determine?
5. In what three ways is RNA different in structure from DNA?
6. Explain the function of messenger RNA in protein synthesis.
7. How does transfer RNA contribute to protein synthesis?
8. What is the function of ribosomes?
9. Why is the specific sequence of amino acids important?
10. List several functions of proteins in cells.

Applying Concepts

1. If a certain protein is composed of 500 amino acids, how long is the DNA molecule?
2. Describe the chemical mechanisms by which DNA controls protein synthesis.
3. Explain why proteins are specific in individual organisms.
4. Why is replication an extremely important property of DNA?
5. Discuss why DNA is called the "key to life."

UNIT 1

Activities

1. Suggested topics for written library reports: early biologists, exobiology, problems of aging, and guidelines governing DNA research.

2. Follow the steps in a scientific research method and repeat Redi's experiments. Write a report on your conclusions.

3. Select a common compound. Make a large chart showing the molecular or ionic structure. Explain your chart to the class.

4. Make a bulletin board display for your room. You can cut out different cell parts from construction paper. Pin them to a diagram of a cell. Use string as "pointer lines," and label the cell parts.

5. Obtain some flower petals, leaves, and a piece of white potato. Make microscope slides to demonstrate plastids.

6. Ask your teacher if you can set up a diffusion demonstration for the class. You will need a beaker and a few crystals of copper sulfate. Fill a beaker with water and place it on a piece of white paper. At the start of the class, drop a few crystals of copper sulfate in the beaker. Observe the results immediately and compare them with the results at the end of the class period.

7. Make a large chart showing the reactions that are involved in cell respiration. Explain the chart to the class.

8. Make a rope-ladder model of the DNA molecule. Color the rope to indicate the sugar and the phosphate units. Color the wooden or metal rungs to indicate the organic bases. Show and explain your model to the class.

9. Read: Watson, James D. *The Double Helix.* New York, Atheneum Publishers, 1968. Make a report on the discovery of the DNA molecule.

Related Readings

Books

Berns, Michael W., *Cells*. Holt, Rinehart and Winston, New York, 1977. A complete discussion of the many cell types, how cells are studied, the parts of cells, aging and death of cells. Many good photographs are presented.

Eckehard, Munck, *Biology of the Future*. Franklin Watts, Inc., New York, 1974. Reviews recent biological developments and gives insights into vast frontiers of biology.

Pines, Maya, *Inside the Cell: The New Frontier of Medical Science*. U.S. Department of Public Health, Education and Welfare, Publication No. 79-1051. Discusses the structure and functions of the cell organelles.

White, Emil, *Chemical Background for the Biological Sciences*, Second Edition. Prentice-Hall, Inc., Englewood Cliffs, NJ, 1970. Presents and explains the chemical nature of life.

Articles

Brachet, Jean, "The Living Cell," *Scientific American*, September 1961. A good introduction to the study of the cell.

Frieden, Earl, "The Chemical Elements of Life," *Scientific American*, July 1972. Names the elements that make up living organisms, with an explanation of the elements' uses.

Galston, Arthur W., "The Membrane Barrier," *Natural History*, August-September 1974. A discussion of the cell membrane and the way materials move into the cell.

Gould, Stephen J., "On Heroes and Fools in Science," *Natural History*, August-September 1974. A look at how some scientists based their discoveries on facts while others relied on superstition.

Levine, R. P., "The Mechanisms of Photosynthesis," *Scientific American*, December 1969. Discusses the food-making process in plants.

Lodish, H. F. and James E. Rothman, "The Assembly of Cell Membranes," *Scientific American*, January 1979. This article discusses how a cell membrane grows and how the differences between its two sides are preserved.

Mazia, Daniel, "The Cell Cycle," *Scientific American*, January 1974. A fascinating account of cells and how they reproduce.

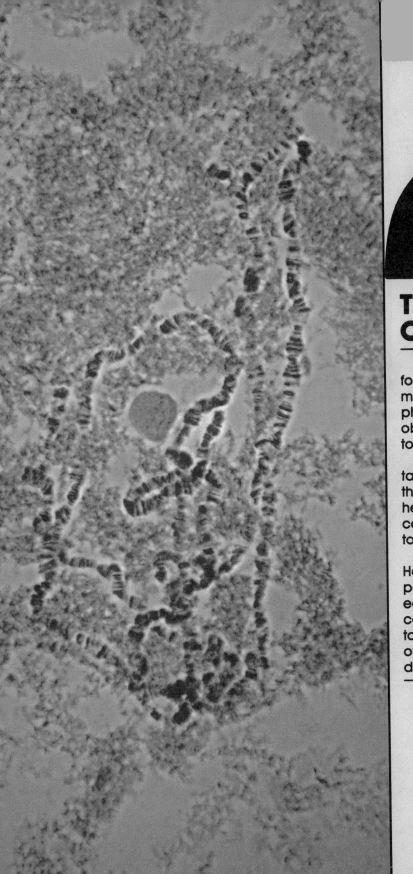

THE CONTINUITY OF LIFE

Prehistoric sharks, turtles, or fossil fern plants lived over 200 million years ago. Yet their physical characteristics are obvious in organisms alive today.

For this kind of continuity to take place, the chemical code that controls an organism's heredity must be passed from cell to cell and from generation to generation.

What is the chemical code? How are inherited characteristics passed from cell to cell? Why is each offspring not an exact copy of its parents? The answers to these questions lie in the study of genes, chromosomes, and cell division.

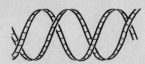

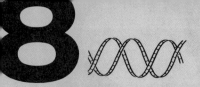

Cell Growth and Reproduction

A **EXPLAIN** cell division.

B **EXPLAIN** how a gene is related to DNA.

C **DISCUSS** how genes and chromosomes are related to each other.

D **NAME** and describe the phases of mitosis.

E **DISCUSS** sexual and asexual reproduction.

F **DEFINE** meiosis and its importance in sexual reproduction.

G **DESCRIBE** the major differences between mitosis and meiosis.

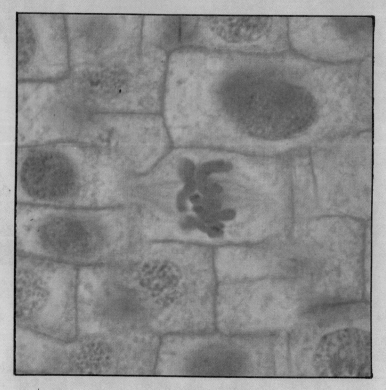

8–1 | Mitosis in the onion root tip. (© Lester Bergman and Associates, Inc.)

Limits to Cell Growth

All cells, even those of a tulip or a whale, are about the same size. They are so small that you usually need a microscope to see them. Whales are bigger than tulips because whales have more cells than tulips have.

Cells of plants and animals grow to a certain size, then divide. Sizes vary greatly but an average-sized animal cell, such as a red blood cell, is about eight microns (.0004 inches) in diameter. Why don't individual cells grow to a giant size? It seems reasonable that a microscopic cell could double or triple its size. The result would be an organism two or three times larger but with the same number of cells as before. Why doesn't this happen? The answer involves the cell's surface area (the outside of its cell membrane) and its volume.

The cell gets all its food and oxygen through the cell membrane. Its waste products, like carbon dioxide, must pass through this same membrane to leave the cell. As a cell grows, its contents increase in volume. Its surface area also increases, but not as much as its volume. **If a cell became too big, its surface area would be too small to allow enough**

cube of side s

area = $s \times s = s^2$

volume = $s \times s \times s = s^3$

s-length	a	v
1 cm	1 cm²	1 cm³
2 cm	4 cm²	8 cm³
3 cm	9 cm²	27 cm³
5 cm	25 cm²	125 cm³
6 cm	36 cm²	216 cm³

8–2 | The volume increases more than the surface area.

food or oxygen to enter or waste products to leave. The cell would die. This is why most *uni*cellular animals and plants are microscopic in size.

uni = one

Cell Division and Heredity

When a cell divides, it splits in two. The cell that divided is called the *parent cell*. The two cells that result are called *daughter cells*. The daughter cells have the same characteristics, or *traits*, as the parent cell. Parent cells pass their traits to the daughter cells. But how do the daughter cells inherit traits from the parent cells?

When a cell is going to divide, short, thick strands appear in the nucleus. These structures are called **chromosomes. Chromosomes contain the code for inherited traits of the organism. Through chromosomes this code is passed on to future generations of cells.**

Facts & Figures

The human body is thought to contain over 60,000 billion body cells.

chromo = color
soma = body

What Are Genes?   *Genes* are the units of heredity. **The code that determines the inherited characteristics, or traits, of an organism is called the *genetic code.*** The code is in the form of a long, spiraling molecule of DNA. Each hereditary trait, like the color of your eyes, your upright walk, the type of bark on a tree, and the shape of a leaf, is controlled by one or more genes. The strands of DNA in a chromosome may carry hundreds, perhaps thousands, of genes.

The genetic code is passed from parent cells to daughter cells through the process of cell division. Chromosomes divide during cell division so that daughter cells inherit the genetic code.

Facts & Figures

It is estimated that the human cell contains two to three million genes.

inter = between

Mitosis

Mitosis is a process of cell division that increases the number of body cells in an individual organism. During mitosis, the materials in the nucleus of the parent cell duplicate and divide into two identical sets. After this happens, the cytoplasm divides.

The Five Phases of Mitosis

Mitosis is one continuous process, but for convenience it is described as having five phases. These phases are illustrated in figures 8-3 through 8-8 (whitefish mitosis).

Interphase   The *interphase* is **not really considered part of cell division. It is actually the period between divisions.** Much of a cell's life is spent in this period.

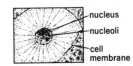

nucleus
nucleoli
cell membrane

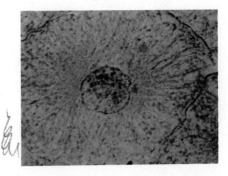

8-3 | Mitosis: Interphase. *(Carolina Biological Supply Co.)*

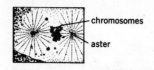

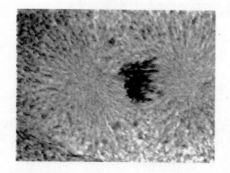

8-4 | Mitosis: prophase. *(Carolina Biological Supply Co.)*

centro = center
pro = first
meta = middle

Facts & Figures

After only 20 successive divisions, a single cell will produce 1,048,576 cells.

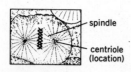

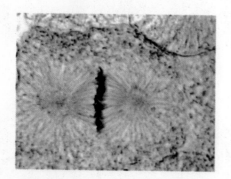

8-5 | Mitosis: metaphase. *(Carolina Biological Supply Co.)*

At this time genetic material called the **chromatin network** is spread throughout the nucleus like a fine network of thin threads. Dense round bodies called *nucleoli* are present in the nucleus. Just outside the nuclear membrane is a small oval area called the **centrosome.** The centrosome contains one or two smaller structures called *centrioles.*

When cell division is about to occur, the DNA replicates itself so that the DNA in each chromosome is doubled. The cell then contains two complete sets of genes located on the doubled chromosomes.

Near the end of interphase, the centrioles separate and start to move apart. The actual process of mitosis is about to begin.

Prophase   During early *prophase* there are clear signs that mitosis is starting. The nucleoli start to disappear. The centrioles move to opposite sides of the nucleus. Protein fibers called **astral rays** form around each centriole. The centriole and its rays together are called an **aster.**

During prophase the long threads in the nucleus grow shorter and thicker and become visible as chromosomes. The two strands of a chromosome are called **chromatids.** Each chromatid contains one strand of the replicated DNA. The two chromatids are held together at a single point called the **centromere.**

During late prophase both the nucleoli and the nuclear membrane have completely broken down and disappeared into the cytoplasm. The centrioles approach opposite sides of the cell. More protein fibers form between the two centrioles. Many of the fibers reach from one centriole to the other and form a structure called a **spindle.** Each end of the spindle is called a *pole.* The chromosomes move toward the middle of the spindle between the two poles.

Metaphase   During *metaphase* the chromosomes line up, beside each other, at the equator. Some protein fibers of the spindle extend from opposite poles and attach to the centromeres of the paired chromatids. The chromatids are short, thick, and coiled around one another.

Anaphase   During *anaphase* the joined chromatids separate from one another. They begin to move toward opposite poles. The chromatids appear to be pulled to opposite poles by a shortening of the protein fibers connected to their centromeres.

Anaphase ends when the chromatids reach the poles.

Telophase   During *telophase,* the last phase of mitosis, the chromosomes reach opposite poles and the cell membrane pinches inward. This pinching forms a groove, or furrow, around the equator. The furrow deepens until the two daughter cells separate.

As this separation process is occurring, the chromosomes begin to disappear, and the chromatin network reappears. The spindle fibers and asters disappear. New nucleoli appear, and the nuclear membrane is formed. The centrosome reappears. As telophase ends, the mitotic process is complete.

Differences Between Plant and Animal Mitosis

Mitosis in animal cells is what has been discussed so far.

In many ways, the description of animal mitosis applies to mitosis in plant cells. Plant cells, however, lack *centrioles*, which animal cells have. Also, plant cells develop a cell plate (wall) between the two daughter cells. Except for these differences, the process is alike for both plants and animals.

Cell Growth and Specialization

An organism increases in size because its cells multiply. However, there is more to growth than just cell division. As an organism develops, its cells become differentiated or more specialized. Specialized cells are cells that perform a specific function. For example, your muscle cells perform one function; they contract (shorten). There are specialized cells in plants that use energy to transfer salts from one cell to another. In all multicellular organisms, there are specialized cells to perform specific functions.

Remember that in mitosis each cell receives a complete genetic code. Why, then, can't each cell perform every function of the organism? The answer is that in a complex organism, each cell uses only some of its genes. In a plant, a root-hair cell has the genes to make the green pigment chlorophyll, but it does not use them. A nerve cell has the genes to become a muscle cell, but only functions as a nerve cell. Only the part of the code that pertains to the specialized cell is used by that cell.

Cell Division and Reproduction

Cell division has been discussed as a means of plant or animal growth. Now you will learn about cell division as a part of an organism's reproduction process.

There are two methods of reproduction. These are *asexual reproduction* and *sexual reproduction*. Cell division is an important step in both processes.

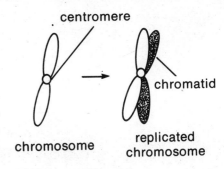

8–6 | Chromatid formation.

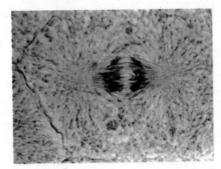

8–7 | Mitosis: anaphase. (*Carolina Biological Supply Co.*)

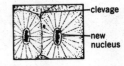

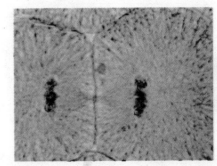

8–8 | Mitosis: telophase. (*Carolina Biological Supply Co.*)

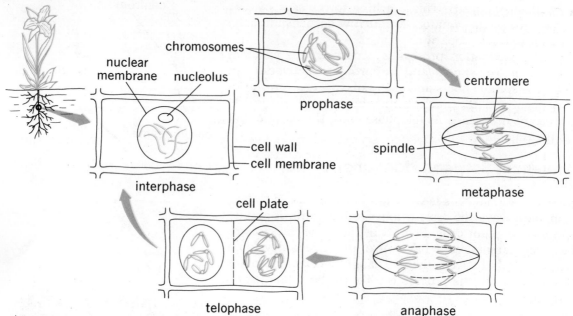

8-9 | Mitosis in a plant cell.

Asexual Reproduction

One method of reproduction is *asexual reproduction.* **Asexual reproduction means producing offspring from one parent.** The offspring is an exact copy of the parent because it has the same genes. Asexual reproduction occurs mainly in lower plants and animals, such as bacteria, molds, algae, and protozoa.

The process of asexual reproduction can occur in a number of ways. These include *binary fission, spore production, budding,* and *cloning.* In all these methods, the offspring forms through mitotic cell division.

- *Fission.* The simplest form of asexual reproduction occurs when an organism simply splits in two. Unicellular organisms such as bacteria, algae, and protozoa reproduce this way. This type of reproduction is called **fission.** If the two resulting cells are of equal size, this process is called **binary fission.**

- *Spore Production.* Some organisms, such as certain molds you see growing on old bread or rotting fruit, reproduce asexually by means of spores. **Spores** are extremely small asexual reproductive cells. Once formed, the spores are set free from the parent.

- *Budding.* In **budding,** a single cell forms a small bud, or knob. The bud pinches free from the parent cell. The parent cell can then form another bud. The buds may grow and become parent cells themselves.

bi = two

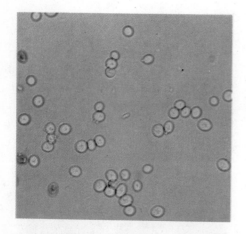

8-10 | These yeast cells are producing by budding. Under certain conditions, they will also form spores (450X). *(Runk, Schoenberger, Grant Heilman)*

- *Cloning.* **Cloning** is a method that can be used to reproduce certain plants. In one method a single cell, such as a leaf cell, can be placed in a nutrient. The cell multiplies. The resulting cells differentiate into roots, stem, and leaves. A complete plant develops from a single cell. The advantage to cloning is that an exact duplicate of the original is made every time.

But what about cloning people? It is not possible at this time, but some scientists believe it may be possible in the future. Complex organisms can't be cloned easily, because they have more very specialized cells.

Sexual Reproduction

Sexual reproduction in almost all cases involves two parents. In cases where both sexes are present in the same organism, self-fertilization is possible. Each parent contributes genes to the offspring. So each individual offspring has a different set of inherited traits from the parents. It is also different from all other members of its own species. **Organisms that reproduce sexually show a wide range of differences in traits within a species.**

Sexual reproduction involves the fusion of two specialized cells. These special sex cells are **gametes.** The female gamete in both animals and plants is called an **egg.** The male gamete is called a **sperm.** When male and female gametes unite, a fertilized egg, or **zygote,** is formed. The zygote can develop into a complete, mature organism. The cell division involved in sexual reproduction is called *meiosis.*

zygo = join
homo = same
logo = word

Meiosis

Chromosome Number

As you have already seen, in mitosis each new cell has the same number and type of chromosomes as the parent cell. Because of this, every body cell of a given organism has the same number of chromosomes as all the other cells. **In fact, all normal members of the same species have the same number of chromosomes in their body cells!**

By observing cells during division, scientists have determined that *chromosomes in the body cells always occur in pairs.* The two chromosomes of a pair are identical in form and in the way the genes are arranged. The chromosomes of such a pair are called *homologous chromosomes.*

Human body cells normally have 23 pairs of homologous chromosomes, or a total of 46 chromosomes. A cell with a complete set of homologous chromosomes is said to have the **diploid** chromosome number. Thus the diploid number for human beings is 46.

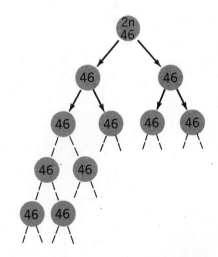

8–11 | The diploid number (2n) varies for different organisms. In humans 2n = 46. During mitosis the number of chromosomes remain constant as the cells multiply to form the body.

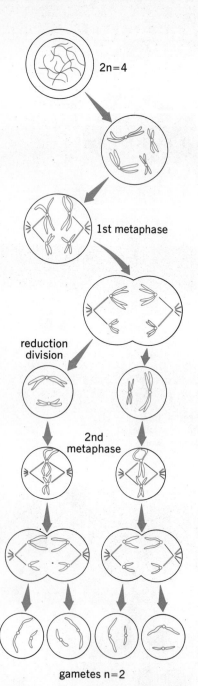

2n=4

1st metaphase

reduction
division

2nd
metaphase

gametes n=2

8-12 | Meiosis: The formation of gametes. One half of the chromosomes of a body cell goes into a gamete. The red chromosomes were contributed by the father, the blue chromosomes were contributed by the mother. If fertilization occurs, the chromosomes have passed from grandparent, to parent, to offspring.

Each gamete has half the number of chromosomes as the other cells of the body. This number, which is half the diploid number, is called the **haploid** number. Eggs and sperms are produced from cells with the diploid number. More complex plants and animals have organs that specialize in producing gametes. The cells of these organs are diploid but produce haploid gametes. How can this happen? The answer lies in a special kind of cell division that occurs in these organs to produce gametes. This special kind of cell division that reduces chromosome number is called **meiosis** (my-OH-suhs).

The Stages of Meiosis

The main function of meiosis is to form gametes with the haploid number of chromosomes. The diploid number is sometimes referred to as the *2n number*. The haploid number is the *n number*. In meiosis, the diploid (2n) number is reduced to the haploid (n) number.

Meiosis involves two separate cell divisions. Refer to figure 8-12 while reading the following discussion of meiosis. In this figure the red chromosomes represent chromosomes from the male parent. The blue chromosomes represent chromosomes from the female parent.

First Stage of Meiosis During *interphase I* the genetic material is in the form of chromatin network. When cell division is about to occur, DNA replicates itself.

During *prophase I* the fine threads of the chromatin network shorten and thicken, and chromosomes appear. Soon each chromosome can be seen to have two chromatids.

An important event of prophase now occurs. *Homologous chromosomes come together in pairs.* Each pair of homologous chromosomes consists of one chromosome contributed by each parent. Because a pair of chromosomes has a total of four chromatids, the homologous pair that has come together is called a **tetrad.**

The chromatids of homologous chromosomes come in close contact with one another. In fact, they twist around one another. This contact between homologous chromosomes is called **synapsis.** The newly formed tetrads move toward the middle of the cell.

During *metaphase I* the tetrads line up, one tetrad under another, in the middle of the cell.

During *anaphase I* the homologous chromosomes of each pair go to opposite poles of the cell. Notice that it is only the chromosomes that separate from one another. The chromatids of an individual chromosome do not separate.

During *telophase I* cell division is completed and two daughter cells result.

In summary, stage I of meiosis produces two daughter cells. **Each daughter cell contains only one chromosome of each pair that was in the parent cell. The total number of chromosomes present in each daughter cell is one half the number of chromosomes in the parent cell.**

Second Stage of Meiosis *There is no replication of DNA in the second stage of meiosis.* There is only the division of the cytoplasm and the separation of the two chromatids of each chromosome. The following are descriptions of the phases of meiosis II:

During *prophase II* the chromosomes become visible under a microscope and compact.

During *metaphase II* the chromosomes line up, one under another, in the middle of the cell.

During *anaphase II* the chromatids of each chromosome separate. The chromatids of each chromosome go to opposite poles of the cell.

During *telophase II* the cell division is complete, and four haploid daughter cells result.

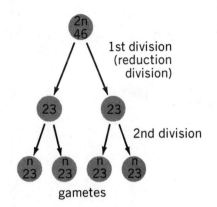

8–13 | Meiosis: The production of gametes from human body cells. Diploid number (2n) is reduced by one-half to the haploid number (n). In humans, 2n = 46, n = 23.

Egg and Sperm Development During Meiosis
The main difference between egg formation and sperm formation is in cytoplasmic division. Cytoplasm divides unequally in egg formation. One haploid cell, the **ootid,** receives most of the cytoplasm. It develops into a mature egg. The other three haploid cells, called **polar bodies,** die and are absorbed by the organism. The egg needs the extra cytoplasm in case it is fertilized and develops into a new organism. The larger egg cell can meet the extra requirements for nutrition in the developing organism.

There is little cytoplasm in each sperm cell. In sperm formation, the cytoplasm is divided equally. Four equal-sized gametes result from sperm formation. In animal cells, the sperm grows a "tail" and is ready to fertilize an egg.

Fertilization and Growth

When fertilization occurs, a zygote is formed. The zygote will then start the life cycle all over again. Through repeated mitotic cell divisions, a whole organism grows from this one cell. The zygote is much like any other cell. It contains the genetic code for the organism. But it can lead to the formation of a complex organism with specialized cells.

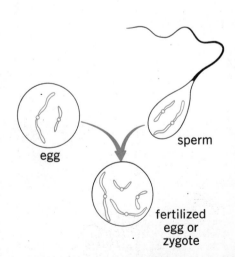

8–14 | Fertilization. The combining of the chromosomes of two haploid gametes restores the diploid condition.

Summary

Cells reach a certain size and then divide. Growth in plants or animals takes place by the cell division called *mitosis*. In mitosis cells split to produce daughter cells, which contain exactly the same *genes* (the same hereditary code). The daughter cells, therefore, are exactly like the parent cell from which they came.

Another kind of cell division, called *meiosis*, is involved in sexual reproduction. In meiosis special cells called *gametes* are produced. Each gamete contains only half of a full set of the heredity carriers called *chromosomes*. In sexual reproduction two gametes, one from each parent, unite to form a *zygote*. The new organism has a full set of chromosomes, half of which came from one parent and half from the other parent.

Biologically Speaking

chromosome	centromere	gamete
gene	spindle	egg
genetic code	metaphase	sperm
mitosis	anaphase	zygote
interphase	telophase	diploid
chromatin network	asexual reproduction	haploid
centrosome	fission	meiosis
centriole	binary fission	tetrad
prophase	spores	synapsis
astral ray	budding	ootid
aster	cloning	polar bodies
chromatid	sexual reproduction	

Questions for Review

1. Name the phases of mitosis and give a characteristic for each phase.
2. Explain how a gene is related to DNA.
3. Why is reduction division important in sexual reproduction?
4. How are genes related to chromosomes?
5. Distinguish between a chromosome and a chromatid.

6. What are the differences between sexual and asexual reproduction?
7. Use the term diploid (2n) and haploid (n) to describe the major differences between mitosis and meiosis.

Applying Concepts

1. Discuss how a cell in your body is related to the cells of your parents and your grandparents.
2. Why does sexual reproduction produce more diversity (individual differences) in organisms than asexual reproduction does?

Principles of Heredity

9-1 | Can you trace family relationships in this photo? *(The Bettmann Archive Inc.)*

The Study of Heredity

Two great influences, heredity and environment, make you what you are at this moment. Your *heredity* consists of those traits that you inherited from your parents. Recall from Chapter 8 that meiosis and fertilization are processes in which the parents' chromosomes are passed to their offspring. These chromosomes contain *genes*. Each gene controls a particular characteristic, or trait, such as eye color or height.

Environment is the other great influence in your life. Environment is all the outside forces that act on an organism. Your environment includes all the people, places, and things around you. It includes your school, home, food—everything from the outside that affects you.

Sometimes it is hard to separate the effects of heredity from the effects of environment. Your height, for instance, is affected partly by the genes that your parents passed to you. But it is also affected by the foods you eat. If you go hungry all your life, you will not grow as tall as if you are well fed. The idea of heredity is not a new one. But only since the early part of the 1900s have scientists understood

Facts & Figures

There are more than eight million ways the 23 chromosomes of a human mother and the 23 chromosomes of a human father can combine.

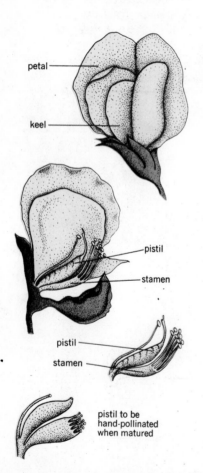

petal

keel

pistil

stamen

pistil

stamen

pistil to be
hand-pollinated
when matured

9–2 | If the stamens are removed before natural pollination occurs, the flower may be hand-pollinated when the pistil is mature.

how genes and chromosomes pass on hereditary traits. So only recently have people begun to understand the way in which parents pass their traits to their children.

Gregor Mendel: Pioneer of Genetics

The science of heredity is called **genetics.** The roots of modern genetics reach back to a small garden in nineteenth-century Austria. During his years as a high school teacher in the town of Brunn, Gregor Mendel kept a small garden plot at the monastery where he lived. Mendel was interested in heredity and used his garden for experiments with plants. He used several kinds of plants in his experiments, but his most important work was with pea plants.

Why did Mendel choose garden peas for his experiments? First, he had observed that they differed from each other in certain ways. They had contrasting pairs of the same traits. Some pea plants were short and bushy. Others were tall and climbing. Some produced yellow seeds. Some produced green seeds. Some had colored seed coats, and some had white. In all, Mendel identified seven different pairs of traits in which the plants differed.

The second reason that Mendel used pea plants had to do with the way they reproduce. You may know that the flower is the reproductive structure in seed plants. Each flower of a pea plant contains several *stamens*. These structures produce pollen grains, which form sperm nuclei. Each pea plant flower also has a structure called a *pistil*, which contains egg cells at its base. The transfer of pollen from stamens to pistil results in fertilization. This process is called *pollination*.

Pea plants normally carry on *self-pollination*. That is, pollen is transferred from stamens to pistil on the same flower or on flowers of the same plant. But Mendel's experiments also involved *cross-pollination*. In this process, pollen is transferred from one plant to the pistil of a different plant. Thus, egg and sperm come from different plants. You can see why this would be important in studying how contrasting traits are passed on in heredity. Mendel made sure of cross-pollination by removing the stamens from a young pea plant flower. Later, when the pistil of this flower matured, he transferred pollen to it from another plant.

Mendel's Experiments and Results

Mendel began his experiments by observing the results of self-pollination in pea plants. Generation after generation, the results were always the same. Seeds from tall plants always produced tall plants. Yellow seeds always produced plants that developed yellow seeds. The same was true for each trait in the seven contrasting pairs. The traits of the parent plant were always passed on to its offspring.

Mendel's next step was to see what would happen if he crossed two plants with contrasting traits. He selected tall and short plants. He made hundreds of crosses by transferring the pollen from the tall plants to the pistils of the short ones. When the seeds matured on the short plants, he planted them to find out the results of his cross. Would the offspring be short? Would they be tall? Or would they be of medium height, with characteristics of both parents? He discovered that all the plants were tall. They were like the plant from which he had taken the pollen.

Next he wanted to find out if it made any difference which plant he used for pollen and which he used to produce the seed. So he used a short plant for pollen and a tall one for seed production. Mendel found that the results were the same—all the offspring were tall.

Mendel then experimented with other characteristics. He studied only one trait at a time. For example, he crossed plants with just one contrasting trait, such as seed color (yellow seeds and green seeds). He found that all seeds resulting from this cross were yellow. He also found that when he crossed a round-seed pea with a wrinkled-seed pea, all the seeds produced were round. He repeated these crosses until he had tested the seven different traits.

It seemed to Mendel that in all seven crosses one of the traits present in a parent plant seemed to be lost in the next generation. What would happen if he permitted the offspring of the tall and short cross to self-pollinate? This step in his experiment was destined to make history.

Mendel called the *parent plants* used in the first cross P_1. He called the generation that resulted from this cross the *first filial*, or F_1, generation.

He allowed the F_1 generation to self-pollinate. This produced a *second filial*, or F_2, generation. The results of this self-pollination were quite striking. Three-fourths of the plants were tall, while one-fourth were short. None were in between.

The reappearance of short plants in this F_2 generation was very important. It meant that the F_1 generation had possessed a characteristic for shortness without showing it. This discovery led Mendel to three hypotheses.

Mendel's First Hypothesis Mendel reasoned that something within the plant controlled the trait of height. He called these unknown controls *factors*. Today they are

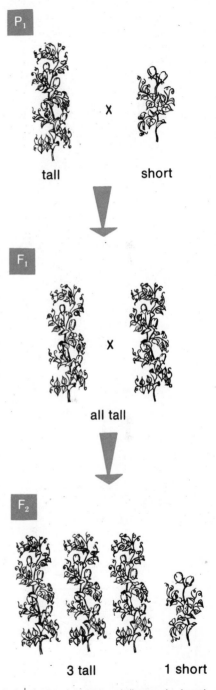

9-3 | A cross between a tall pea plant and a short pea plant results in tall offspring. The short trait shows up in the next generation.

called *genes*. Since some pea plants were tall and some were short, a pair of factors must control the height of pea plants. This led to Mendel's first hypothesis: **Inherited characteristics are controlled by factors that occur in pairs.**

Figure 9-4 is a modern interpretation of Mendel's crosses of tall and short plants. The gene, or factor, for tallness is shown as T, and the gene for shortness is shown as t. Since genes occur in pairs, Mendel's pure tall plant would contain the genes TT (one T from one parent and the other T from the other parent). His short plant would contain the genes tt (one t from each parent).

Mendel's Second Hypothesis Mendel reasoned further that the tall plants of the F_1 generation were not pure tall parent plants. The F_1 pea plants were carrying a hidden factor for shortness. This hidden factor would reappear in the F_2 generation. This reasoning led to his second hypothesis, the *principle of dominance and recessiveness.*

According to the principle of dominance and recessiveness, one factor (gene) in a pair may mask the other, or prevent it from having an effect. This hypothesis explains why factors for shortness seemed to be lost in the F_1. Mendel reasoned that the short trait was lost in the F_1 because the tall trait dominated over the short trait. The tall trait prevented the short trait from having an effect. Tallness is the dominant trait. Shortness is the recessive trait because its effect is masked.

Mendel also knew that the recessive trait (shortness) was not changed by the presence of the dominant trait (tallness). The recessive trait somehow stayed in the body of the F_1 plant but was not expressed.

Figure 9-4 shows what happened to the missing gene for shortness (t) in the F_1. The tall plant (TT) produces sperm nuclei that carry the gene for tallness (T). The short plant (tt) produces an egg carrying a gene for shortness (t). Fertilization occurs, and the resulting offspring plant has the genes Tt. This plant is tall because it has a dominant T gene; but it is carrying a recessive, or unexpressed, t gene. It is a *hybrid,* or an offspring of parents that differ in one or more traits. A hybrid expressed the dominant trait.

Mendel's Third Hypothesis Mendel's third hypothesis is now called Mendel's first law, or the *law of segregation.* It states that **a pair of factors (genes) are segregated, or separated, during the formation of gametes.**

With modern knowledge of chromosomes, the law of segregation can be explained. During meiosis a chromosome from one parent will go into one of the daughter cells,

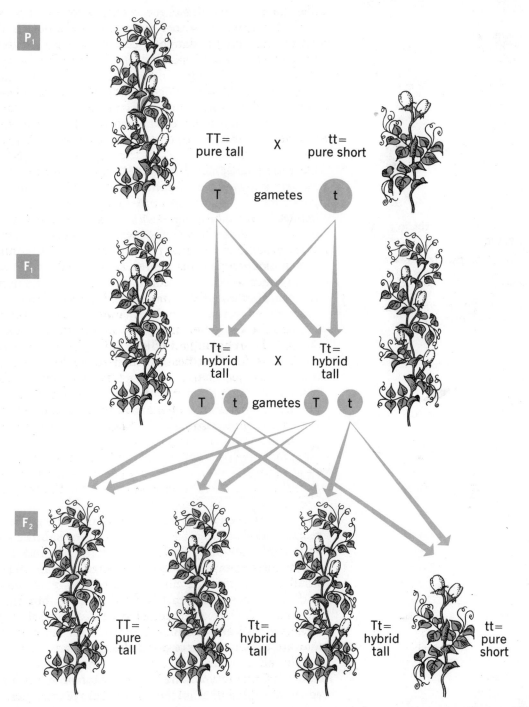

9–4 | Mendel's law of segregation. The F₁ generation consists only of tall plants, while the recessive gene for shortness is again expressed in the F₂ generation. What kinds of plants would result from a cross between the two F₂ plants, shown at the bottom left?

if chromosomes
pair this way

if chromosomes
pair this way

these gametes
result

these gametes
result

9-5 | Law of independent assortment show-
ing segregation of two gene pairs. The types
of gametes produced depend on how the
chromosomes are paired for the first division of
meiosis. Replication and the second division
are omitted here for simplicity.

and the corresponding chromosome (the homologous chromosome) from the other parent will go into the other
daughter cell. Each daughter cell then divides again, and a
total of four gametes results.

In the first division of meiosis the chromosome carrying
the gene for tallness (T) goes into one daughter cell. The
homologous chromosome carrying the gene for shortness
(t) goes into the other daughter cell. The second division
results in four gametes of two different types (T and t).

Law of Independent Assortment

Modern knowledge of chromosomes has made it possible to
put a fourth hypothesis into more exact terms. Mendel
believed that factors (genes) separated and were distributed to gametes in a way that was completely independent
of the other factor pairs. Today this hypothesis is called the
law of independent assortment. It means that yellow seeds,
for instance, do not have any connection with the height of
the pea plant. Many traits are completely independent of
many other traits.

Refer to figure 9-5. The genes that control the height of
the plant are on a different pair of chromosomes from the
genes for seed color. When the chromosome pairs separate
during meiosis, the seed-color pair of chromosomes separates independently of the height pair of chromosomes. The
kinds of gametes that result from meiosis depend on how
the paired chromosomes are lined up next to each other.

Some Modern Uses of Mendel's Work

As you have seen in the preceding section, the genes can be
represented by letters: T for tallness, t for shortness, Y for
yellow, y for green. In dealing with dominant and recessive
genes, the capital letter shows the trait is dominant; the
small letter shows the contrasting trait is recessive.

Since genes occur in pairs, various combinations are
possible: TT, Tt, tt. Such paired symbols show the **genotype**
(gene type) of an organism. That is, they show the genes
that are present in an organism's cells.

The effect caused in the organism by these genes is
called its **phenotype.** The word *phenotype* refers to what
you can see. For example, the genotypes for two plants, TT
and Tt, are different. But the phenotype is the same. They
are both tall.

The paired genes for a trait may be identical, as with TT
or tt. If both genes are the same, the organism is ***homozygous*** (home-o-ZY-gus), or pure, for that trait. If the paired

genos = race, king

phen = to show

homo = same
hetero = different

genes are not identical (Tt, for example), the organism is
heterozygous (HET-uh-roe-ZY-gus).

The genes that have contrasting effects on a trait are
called *alleles* (uh-LEELZ). With regard to the height of a
pea plant, for instance, T is an allele of t, and t is an allele of
T. In the heterozygous gene pair controlling seed color (Yy),
Y is an allele of y, and y is an allele of Y. Having an *allele*
means that the gene has a contrasting gene at the same
location on the homologous chromosome. Some genes have
three or more alleles. But usually only two genes for a
specific trait occurs in any one organism. One gene comes
from each parent.

Punnett Squares and Probability

In the study of genetics, special charts resembling checker-
boards are used to find the possible results of various
crosses. This grid system is called a **Punnett square.** It is
named after R. C. Punnett, its inventor.

The Punnett squares in figure 9-6 show the possible
gene pairings that can result in different pea plants. The
alleles are T and t, or tall and short.

Punnett square A shows the results of pollinating an egg
of a homozygous tall pea plant. Every one of the resulting
pea plants will be heterozygous tall. The same process of
finding the possible results of other crosses can be followed
on Punnett squares B, C and D.

Punnett squares also show the probability of each
resulting genotype. For instance, grid B shows that the
probability of producing tall plants from a cross between
heterozygous tall plants is three out of four. This means
there is one chance in four of producing a short plant from
such a cross.

Crosses That Involve One Trait When a pair of contrasting traits is considered in a cross, it is described as a ***monohybrid cross.***

Consider a cross between a homozygous black guinea
pig and a homozygous white one. All of the F_1 offspring are
heterozygous black. What happens if two of these hybrid
animals are crossed? The probability ratio for genotypes is
one fourth BB, one half Bb, and one fourth bb. The ratio for
phenotypes is three black to one white. These expected
results exactly match those in Mendel's crosses of pea
plants. The larger the sample of crosses involved, the
greater the probability will be that the results will match
the Punnett square ratios.

Crosses That Involve Two Traits When two pairs of
contrasting traits are considered in a cross, it is described

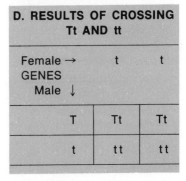

A. RESULTS OF CROSSING TT AND tt

Female → GENES Male ↓	t	t
T	Tt	Tt
T	Tt	Tt

B. RESULTS OF CROSSING Tt AND Tt

Female → GENES Male ↓	T	t
T	TT	Tt
t	Tt	tt

C. RESULTS OF CROSSING TT AND Tt

Female → GENES Male ↓	T	t
T	TT	Tt
T	TT	Tt

D. RESULTS OF CROSSING Tt AND tt

Female → GENES Male ↓	t	t
T	Tt	Tt
t	tt	tt

9–6 | The Punnett square is used to find the
probable results of crossing the traits of one
organism with another.

P₁ Cross	F₁ Generation	F₂ Generation	Actual Ratio	Probability Ratio
round X wrinkled	round	5,474 round 1,850 wrinkled	2.96:1	3:1
yellow X green	yellow	6,022 yellow 2,001 green	3.01:1	3:1
colored X white	colored	705 colored 224 white	3.15:1	3:1
inflated X constricted	inflated	882 inflated 229 constricted	2.95:1	3:1
green X yellow	green	428 green 152 yellow	2.82:1	3:1
axial X terminal	axial	651 axial 207 terminal	3.14:1	3:1
long stem X short stem	long stem	787 long 277 short	2.84:1	3:1

9-7 | Results of Mendel's monohybrid crosses.

as a *dihybrid cross.* The same principles apply to such a cross as apply to a monohybrid cross. However, the dihybrid cross is more complex because there are more possible combinations of genes.

Figure 9-8 illustrates a dihybrid cross. For shape, the dominant trait is round (R) and the recessive trait is wrinkled (r). The dominant seed color is yellow (Y), and the recessive color trait is green (y). One parent is pure for round, green seeds (RRyy). All gametes formed by this plant contain the genes Ry. The other parent is pure for wrinkled, yellow seeds (rrYY).

Each RrYy dihybrid can produce four different kinds of gametes: RY, Ry, rY, and ry. The chromosome with R on it goes into one gamete, and the chromosome with the r on it goes into the other gamete. The same is true for Yy. The way the chromosome pairs happen to line up during meiosis determines what kind of gametes are produced.

Look at figure 9-8. The gametes produced by the female dihybrid RrYy are shown across the top of the Punnett square. The gametes produced by the male dihybrid RrYy are shown down the left side of the Punnett square. What will the F^2 offspring produced from these gametes be like? A Punnett square gives the possible results. If you study the square, you will find that there are nine different genotypes (gene combinations) possible. And there are these four kinds of phenotypes:

9/16 of the seeds are round and yellow.

3/16 of the seeds are round and green.

3/16 of the seeds are wrinkled and yellow.

1/16 of the seeds are wrinkled and green.

9-8 | A cross involving two traits. A pea plant that produces round (R), green (y) seeds is crossed with a pea plant that produces wrinkled (r), yellow (Y) seeds.

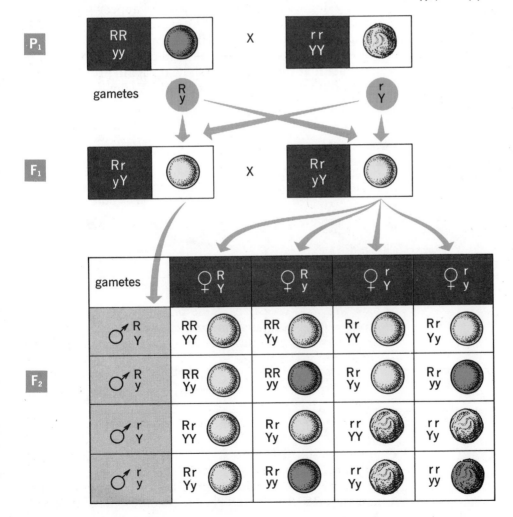

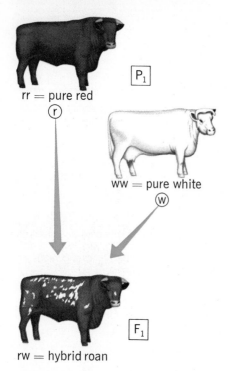

rr = pure red
(r)

ww = pure white
(w)

rw = hybrid roan

9-9 | Incomplete dominance in shorthorn cattle.

Thus the ratio of the four possible F_1 phenotypes is 9:3:3:1. Note that some seeds are pure round, while others are hybrid round. Some are pure yellow, while others are hybrid yellow. How many seeds are pure dominant for both traits? How many are pure recessive for both traits?

Crosses that Involve Incomplete Dominance

Genes are not always dominant or recessive. In some cases both alleles of a pair can affect a trait. Such genes show *incomplete dominance.*

Since both genes for the same trait exert an influence, new symbols can be used. Figure 9-10 illustrates the use of the symbols. Here *r* is used for red in flowers, and *w* is used for white flowers.

One case of incomplete dominance appears in the flowers known as four-o'clocks. In a cross between pure red (rr) and pure white (ww) four-o'clocks, neither color is completely dominant. Thus the F_1 flowers appear pink (rw). If these heterozygous pink flowers are crossed, the possible F_2 offspring will be as shown in figure 9-10. One fourth are pure red, one half hybrid pink, and one fourth pure white. The fact that the pure traits show up again proves that the genes did not somehow "mix" in the F_1 flowers.

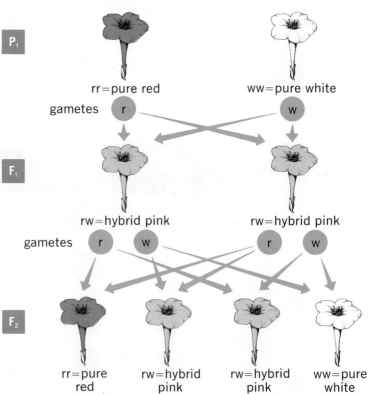

P_1

rr=pure red   ww=pure white

gametes (r)   (w)

F_1

rw=hybrid pink   rw=hybrid pink

gametes (r) (w)   (r) (w)

F_2

rr=pure   rw=hybrid   rw=hybrid   ww=pure
red   pink   pink   white

9-10 | Incomplete dominance in four-o'clocks.

fact that the pure traits show up again proves that the genes did not somehow "mix" in the F_1 flowers.

Another case of incomplete dominance involves a certain kind of cattle. A homozygous red animal mated with a homozygous white one produces a blend of red and white, called *roan*. This is illustrated in figure 9-9. If two roan animals are mated, the probability ratio for offspring is one fourth red, one half roan, and one fourth white. In incomplete dominance, you can tell the genotypes by looking at the phenotypes.

Summary

Your environment—the people, things, and influences around you—helps to make you the kind of person you are. But the kind of parents you had also makes you the kind of person you are. The characteristic traits handed down to you by your parents is your *heredity*. *Genetics*, the modern scientific study of heredity, was pioneered by Gregor Mendel.

Mendel reached a number of conclusions that are still the basis for our knowledge of heredity. Mendel's first hypothesis was that inherited characteristics are controlled by factors (now called *genes*), which occur in pairs. Mendel's second hypothesis was that one factor (gene) in a pair may mask the other, or prevent it from having an effect. Mendel's third hypothesis stated that a pair of factors (genes) are segregated, or separated, during the formation of gametes.

Biologically Speaking

heredity
environment
genetics
principle of dominance and
   recessiveness
hybrid
law of segregation
law of independent
   assortment

genotype
phenotype
homozygous
heterozygous
allele
Punnett square
monohybrid cross
dihybrid cross
incomplete dominance

Questions for Review

1. Distinguish between genotype and phenotype.
2. Explain how two organisms can have different genotypes but the same phenotype.
3. What observation led Mendel to his hypothesis that hereditary traits were controlled by pairs of genes?

4. State Mendel's principles of dominance.
5. Describe how different types of gametes are produced according to the law of independent assortment.
6. When two parents, each of which is heterozygous for a certain trait, are crossed, what ratios of genotype and phenotype can be expected?
7. What is meant by incomplete dominance?
8. Why may a theoretical phenotype ratio differ from the results of an actual breeding experiment in which several offspring result?

Applying Concepts

1. Outline a possible cross to determine whether a black guinea pig is homozygous or heterozygous for the color trait.
2. In guinea pigs black coat color is due to a dominant gene (B), and white is due to its recessive allele (b); short hair to a dominant gene (S) and long hair to its recessive allele (s). The gene for rough coat (R) is dominant over that for smooth (r). Show a cross between a homozygous black, short-haired, rough guinea pig with a white, long-haired, smooth guinea pig using Punnett square method. What are the phenotypes and genotypes of the F_1 generation? List the gametes that can be produced by one member of the F_1.
3. Why would a horse breeder pay a large amount of money to cross a mare with a winning stallion race horse?
4. In four-o'clocks, the gene for red flowers (r) is incompletely dominant to the gene for white flowers (w). The heterozygous condition results in pink flowers. A pink and a red four-o'clock are crossed. What are the expected genotypic and phenotypic ratios?
5. The phenotypic ratio of a certain cross is 3 black to 1 white. What are the possible genotypes of the parents? Use the Punnett squares to support your answer.

6. The results of a cross in cattle show 1 roan to 1 white. What must be the genotypes of the parents?
7. A black rabbit is crossed with a white rabbit, and one of seven offspring is white. What is the genotype of the black rabbit?
8. A pink flower is crossed with a white flower. What is the probability of getting a white flower as an offspring? What is the probability of getting a red flower?

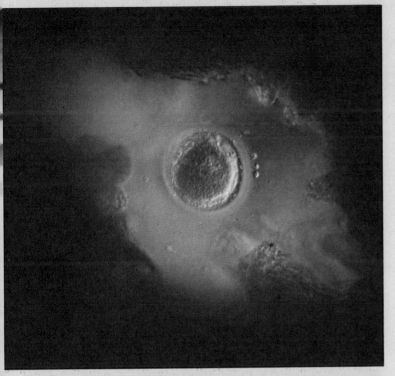

10–1 | The human egg *(© Lennart Nilsson, Behold Man, Little, Brown & Company, Boston)*

The Genetic Material

A **DESCRIBE** how Mendel's theories apply to the behavior of chromosomes and genes.

B **EXPLAIN** why **Drosophila** are used in genetic studies.

C **EXPLAIN** sex determination and sex-linked traits.

D **DESCRIBE** crossing over and discuss its importance.

E **DEFINE** a gene in terms of DNA.

F **DESCRIBE** the origins of mutation.

G **EXPLAIN** how gene and chromosome mutations can affect offspring.

Building on Mendel's work: The Search for the Source of Heredity

In his paper published in 1865, Gregor Mendel brilliantly described what happened in genetic crosses. He knew nothing of the structure or location of the hereditary code within a cell, or how that code worked. Yet his conclusions were correct. In their effort to understand heredity, scientists have been building on his work ever since.

Nineteenth-century biologists knew that in sexual reproduction the egg and sperm unite to form a new individual. They knew also that egg and sperm contain characteristics that they pass on to the next generation. They concluded that egg and sperm seemed to have equal influence on their offspring.

Every bit of knowledge raised new questions. Since the egg was larger than the sperm, why didn't it have a greater influence on the new individual? If both sperm and egg carried hereditary traits, why didn't each offspring have *all* of both parents' traits?

It is now known that the egg and sperm both contribute half their characteristics to offspring. As discussed in Chapter 8, the process of meiosis reduces the usual number of chromosomes in the sperm or egg to half the number. This reduction process was observed and described for the first time in the 1880s. But at that time no one connected this reduction of chromosomes with hereditary characteristics.

For years Mendel's paper containing his law of segregation of characteristics lay forgotten in the library in Brünn. Finally, in 1900 Mendel's paper was found. By this time biologists were familiar with chromosomes and thought that they might be the carriers of heredity. Mendel's paper showed how heredity worked in plants. Information about chromosomes and Mendel's papers could now be connected. A landslide of investigation and discovery in genetics followed.

Chromosome Theory

In 1902 Walter Sutton, a graduate student at Columbia University in New York, and Theodor Boveri, a German scientist, published papers independently. These papers suggested for the first time that Mendel's "factors" were heredity particles located on chromosomes. Later these hereditary particles were called *genes*. How did Sutton and Boveri connect what they knew about chromosomes with Mendel's factors?

First, they had studied Mendel's work on garden peas. They understood Mendel's law of segregation, which states that traits segregate when gametes are formed. They were familiar with the segregation of chromosomes during meiosis. This chromosome behavior matched Mendel's segregation of traits very well. They concluded that **chromosomes must carry the material of hereditary traits.**

Second, they knew from Mendel's experiments that it didn't matter whether a trait was supplied by the sperm nuclei or egg of the plant.

Sutton and Boveri knew that egg and sperm are not alike in size or structure. The one way in which sperm and egg are alike is that their chromosomes seemed to be the same. The chromosomes must be the part of sperm or egg that can pass hereditary characteristics to the offspring.

Third, Sutton and Boveri noted that **during meiosis each pair of chromosomes lined up independently of other chromosome pairs.** Thus segregation, the separation of each chromosome from its matching chromosome, happened independently.

Fourth, Sutton and Boveri knew that chromosomes replicate in ordinary body-cell division (mitosis). Each daughter cell contains all the chromosomes of the parent cell. The daughter cells also have the same traits as the parent cell. **It must be the chromosomes in each cell that carry the traits.**

Thus, Sutton and Boveri had strong evidence that the chromosomes were the carriers of heredity.

Sutton and Boveri reasoned that **different genes are distributed on different chromosomes.** When each chromosome separates from its matching chromosome, it carries a particular gene to one gamete or the other. This is done independently of genes on other chromosomes.

How Many Genes on a Chromosome?

An organism might have only ten pairs of chromosomes. But it could have hundreds or even thousands of inherited traits. Each trait is determined by at least one gene. Sutton reasoned that each chromosome must contain many different genes. Did all of these genes segregate independently during meiosis? Probably not. Genes evidently move with the chromosome to which they are linked. Sutton could not prove this, but today it is known that he was right.

Discovery of Sex Chromosomes

Soon after Sutton established the fact that genes and chromosomes are the materials of heredity, another important discovery was made. Thomas Hunt Morgan, who was later awarded the Nobel prize for his work in genetics, made a discovery in one tiny fruit fly. This discovery was destined to make genetic history.

Dr. Morgan and his associates at Columbia University were growing large numbers of fruit flies. Biologists refer to the fruit fly as *Drosophila melanogaster* (droe-SOFF-uh-luh MELL-an-noe-gass-ter). This small fly is common around overripe fruit. You probably think of *Drosophila* as a pest. But these flies are ideal for use in research. They are easy to raise in jars and can be fed simple foods such as mashed bananas. Its life cycle is only 10 to 15 days, so many generations can be studied in a short time. Also, it is easy to tell the difference between sexes in *Drosophila*.

One day Dr. Morgan and his associates were examining a large number of *Drosophila*. To their surprise, they found one fly that had white eyes instead of the normal red eyes.

The white-eyed fly was a male. Morgan mated this unusual fly with a normal red-eyed female. All of the F_1 generation resulting from this mating had normal red eyes. Morgan and his fellow workers concluded that red eyes are dominant over white eyes in *Drosophila*.

Next, members of the F_1 generation were mated to produce an F_2 generation. About three fourths of the F_2 flies had red eyes, while the other fourth had white eyes. Again,

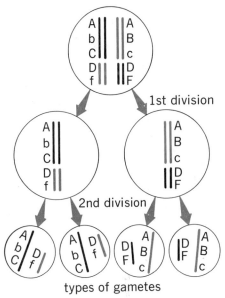

types of gametes

10-2 | Meiosis showing gene location on two pairs of chromosomes. Genes on different chromosomes of the same pair are segregated from one another. Chromosome pairs line up independently of one another.

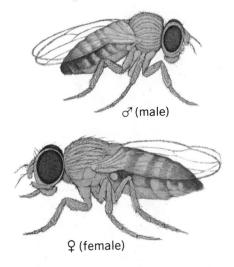

♂ (male)

♀ (female)

10-3 | The common fruit fly, *Drosophila melanogaster*. Note that the male (above) is smaller than the female. The posterior end of the male is darker and blunter than that of the female.

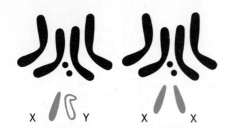

X   Y   X   X

10–4 | The sex chromosomes of *Drosophila* are shown in color. The male has one X chromosome and one hook-shaped Y chromosome (left), whereas the female has two X chromosomes.

Facts & Figures

Every human cell contains about 90 centimeters (3 feet) of DNA strands.

auto = by oneself
soma = body

SEX DETERMINATION		
Female **CHROMOSOMES** Male	X	X
X	XX	XX
Y	XY	XY

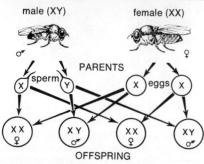

male (XY)   female (XX)

PARENTS

X | sperm | Y   X | eggs | X

XX ♀   XY ♂   XX ♀   XY ♂

OFFSPRING

10–5 | The inheritance of sex in *Drosophila*.

this matched Mendel's results with garden peas. But now came the surprise: All of the white-eyed flies were males!

Morgan had discovered a trait that is sex-linked in *Drosophila*. Two questions now arose. (1) How is sex determined in *Drosophila?* (2) How is the gene for white eyes related to sex? (The subject, sex-linkage, will be discussed in Chapter 11.)

Sex Determination Remember each chromosome consists of many genes that are somehow linked together. Genes on the same chromosome do not segregate independently of one another. If two genes are on the same chromosome, their corresponding traits will appear together in a single offspring.

Does this mean, then, that maleness and white eyes are two traits that are on the same chromosome in *Drosophila?* The answer came with further experimentation.

Morgan and his associates found that the nuclei of body cells in *Drosophila* had four pairs of chromosomes. Three of those four pairs were perfectly matched and were exactly alike in both sexes. But in the males the fourth pair did not match at all. One chromosome in males was rod shaped, and the other was bent like a hook.

Morgan and his group had found the *sex chromosomes* of *Drosophila*. They are the rod-shaped chromosomes called the X chromosomes and the hook-shaped chromosomes called the Y chromosomes. The remaining three pairs of chromosomes in *Drosophila* are called **autosomes,** or body chromosomes. They have nothing to do with sex determination.

Finding the sex chromosomes solved the problem of sex determination in *Drosophila*. The discovery led to the conclusion that **two rod-shaped X chromosomes (XX) produce a female. An X chromosome paired with a Y chromosome (XY) produces a male.** Later work has shown that the same thing happens in most animals, including humans, and in many plants that have sex differences.

In Chapter 9 Mendel's crosses were charted on Punnett squares. Sex determination can be charted in the same way. When eggs are formed, the XX chromosome pair segregates. Each contains a single X chromosome. When sperms are formed, the chromosome pair XY segregates to X and Y. So half of the sperms contain the X chromosome, and half contain the Y chromosome. The sex of the offspring is a matter of chance. If a sperm with an X chromosome fertilizes the egg, the offspring is female. If a sperm with a Y chromosome fertilizes the egg, the offspring is male. Notice that it is the male that determines the sex of the offspring. Each time fertilization occurs, there is a 50/50 chance that the offspring will be male (or female). In addition to genes for sex determination, the sex chromosomes have genes for other traits. These will be discussed in Chapter 11.

Genes and How They Act

In Chapter 7, you learned about DNA and how it transfers its genetic code to messenger RNA. RNA then passes this genetic code on to produce various protein substances that make up an organism. The effects of these proteins are expressed as traits. For example, genes enable a plant to make chlorophyll. Chlorophyll is essential in plant photosynthesis. Remember that this genetic code is in the form of a series of genes lined up along the DNA molecule. Some genes are a code for a sequence of amino acids as in figure 10-6. These are the *structural genes*. *Regulatory genes* control the activities of structural genes. All the genes together act to make the organism what it is.

In this chapter, genes have been described as being present or absent on a particular chromosome. Chromosome action has been the concern. Let us now turn to a discussion of a gene's activity in relation to chromosomes.

Gene Linkage and Crossing Over

Keep in mind that it is chromosomes, not individual genes, that segregate during meiosis. A single chromosome contains *many* genes linked together. If one chromosome in a pair has 50 genes, so will the other chromosome in the pair. And the sequences and positions of genes on each chromosome match each other exactly.

But this linkage is not perfect. **Under certain conditions part of a chromosome, holding many genes, may switch places with part of the homologous chromosome. This is called** *crossing over.* When do you think crossing over would be most likely to happen? When are the chromosomes in a pair closest together?

In Chapter 8, the stages in meiosis were discussed. At one point in the first stage of meiosis, the genes have replicated, and each chromosome has formed two joined chromatids. Remember that homologous chromosomes then come together in *synapsis*. The joined chromatids of a homologous pair lie close together and twist around one another. Such a group of four chromatids is called a *tetrad*. At this stage parts of two chromosomes may switch places. This explains how crossing over may occur.

Let's look at the results of crossing over. Refer to figure 10-7 as you read the following description. The letters A, B, and C stand for three of the many genes on a chromatid. The corresponding genes on a chromatid of the homologous chromosome are a, b, and c. Now, suppose that one section

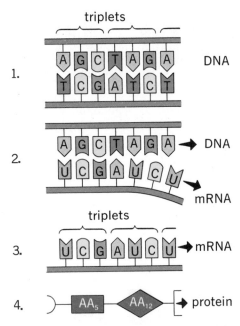

10–6 | A gene determines what kind of protein will be made. (1) DNA triplets located on a chromosome. (2) An active strand of DNA sends a messenger RNA to the cytoplasm. (3) The triplets on the messenger code for amino acids UCG (AA-5), AUC (AA-12). (4) A portion of a protein, a long chain of amino acids.

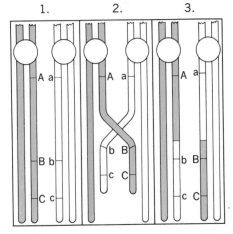

10–7 | Crossing over. Following the tetrad formation (1), crossing over occurs between adjacent chromatids (2). The final result shows a new grouping of genes on the chromosomes (3).

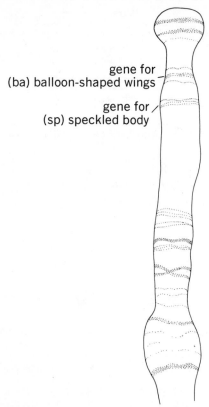

gene for
(ba) balloon-shaped wings

gene for
(sp) speckled body

10–8 | The dark and light bands and the "puffs" or enlargements on a *Drosophilo* chromosome help biologists to map the location of various genes.

mutare = to change

of a chromatid separates between genes A and B. A section of a chromatid on the other chromosome separates between genes a and b. The separated parts then switch places. Each of the two chromatids involved now has a new gene linkage. The new linkages are a, B, C and A, b, c. Neither of these linkages was present in either parent. But they will be passed on to the offspring after the chromatids separate in the second stage of meiosis. The gametes that result from the separation will be ABC, Abc, aBC, and abc.

Notice in figure 10-7 that without crossover only two gamete types are possible, ABC and abc. Crossover adds to the varieties of genetic makeup in gametes. During the formation of gametes, the genes on a chromosome that came from one parent could be exchanged with the genes on a chromosome that came from the other parent. **A single chromosome, then, can change as it passes from generation to generation.**

The genes shown on the chromosome diagrams in figure 10-7 are widely separated. Biologists have reasoned that genes that are close together rarely cross over. Genes that are farther apart will cross over more often. In figure 10-7, for instance, A is quite far from B. So the crossing over occurs between A and B. B is quite close to C, so crossing over occurs much less frequently between B and C.

Through crossover studies, scientists have been able to determine how often separations occur between certain genes on a chromosome. If there is frequent crossing over between two genes, then those two genes must be quite far apart on the chromosome. Determining how far apart genes are on a chromosome is one of the ways in which geneticists have been able to construct *chromosome maps*. **Chromosome maps show where the genes are located on a chromosome.**

Mutation

Genes replicate and chromsomes segregate during meiosis in a very regular way. They may do so millions of times without an error.

Still, from time to time, there is an error. An organism appears with a trait totally unlike any trait in either parent. A sudden genetic change like this is called a **mutation.** The organism in which it appears is called a *mutant.*

Mutants add diversity to a species. Diversity may help a species survive. This is true for the species as a whole. But usually the mutations that occur are harmful to the individual organism.

There are two types of mutation. These are gene mutations and chromosome mutations.

Gene Mutations

Gene mutations are by far the most common type of mutation. These mutations arise when the code of a DNA molecule is changed in some way. Since the code of the DNA is made of a series of genes, such a change is a change in a single gene. Gene mutations are also called *point mutations*.

Recall that genes direct the cell to make a certain protein. If there is any change in the code of the gene, the change will affect the protein. Usually, a gene mutation results in just one amino acid being out of place or missing. Therefore the proper protein cannot be formed. The result shows up as an abnormality, or mutation, in the organism.

The DNA molecule is made of a long string of base triplets as shown in figure 10-6. You might think of the DNA molecule as a sentence made of three letter words, such as "The fat cat ate the rat." The sentence makes sense as long as it is written correctly. But what if it was written "The fat cot ate the rat"? The substitution of *o* for *a* in the one word *cat* makes nonsense of the sentence.

Similar nonsense results if you leave a letter out of the sentence. Remember that the sentence (the DNA molecule) must be made of three-letter units. If the sentence is written, "The ftc ata tet her at," it makes no sense. But all that has happened is that one letter has been omitted—the *a* in *fat*. This disturbs the letter sequence of the sentence.

In the same way, a change in one base triplet within a DNA molecule can make nonsense of the code that the DNA sends out for the production of proteins.

For example, one easily observable gene mutation is albinism in animals. Albino animals lack the ability to make a pigment called melanin. Therefore, albinos lack normal pigment in the skin, eyes, and hair. As a result the hair of an albino is white. The skin and eyes appear pinkish because of the color of the blood in the surface blood vessels.

This mutation is caused by a change of one base in a base triplet of the gene. This change results in the wrong amino acid being placed in the protein chain. The protein in this case is an enzyme that is used to make melanin. Because of the amino acid "mistake," the protein cannot function, and the pigment is not formed. Albinism results.

The mutations that are observed in plants and animals are only a small portion of those that occur. Some muta-

Facts & Figures

Albinos occur in almost every species of plant and animal. In plants it is usually a lethal mutation, because a plant without the pigment chlorophyll cannot make food.

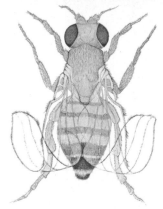

10–9 | The albino deer and the curly-winged fruit fly are examples of point mutations. The primary cause of such mutations is radiation. *(top: Leonard Lee Rue III, Animals Animals)*

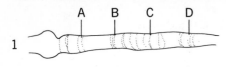

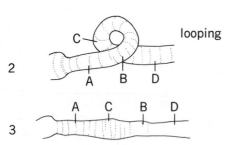

10-10 | A chromosome mutation. The gene sequence has been reversed.

tions, called *lethal mutations*, cause death. Other mutations have too small an effect to be noticed. Still others may have no observable effect at all. There are probably other mutations that are not noticed simply because the organism's structure or chemistry is not known.

Chromosome Mutations

Chromosome mutations are even more drastic in their effect on an organism than are gene mutations. This is because chromosome mutations involve many genes.

Often during meiosis or mitosis individual chromosomes are fragmented. Parts are broken off and lost. Sometimes the fragments recombine but in the wrong order, so that the genes are reversed. Sometimes the result is a chromosome with additional genes from another chromosome attached to it. Usually, these drastic changes result in death or serious deformities. Such mutations are not usually passed on to future generations.

Another type of chromosome mutation results in an increase in the number of chromosomes in a cell. In this type of mutation there is an unequal distribution of chromosomes during meiosis. One daughter cell receives more chromosomes than the other. As you will study in Chapter 11 (Genes in Populations) the results are usually harmful. A variety of abnormalities occurs, and many result in death.

In plants an unequal distribution of chromosomes is not harmful. It can happen when an egg receives all of the chromosomes during meiosis. So if a 2n egg instead of the normal (n) egg is fertilized by an n sperm, a 3n zygote is produced. Or if a 2n egg is fertilized by a 2n sperm, a 4n zygote is produced. Such plants with 3n, 4n, 6n, or more, chromosomes are examples of **polyploidy** (PAHL-ee-PLOID-ee). Polyploid plants are often bigger and more vigorous than ordinary plants. Many vegetables are polyploid. Polyploidy in animal cells is very rare.

Somatic Mutations and Reproductive-Cell Mutations

The type of cell in which mutation occurs is of great significance in genetics. A mutation that occurs in a body cell of a plant or animal is called a **somatic mutation.** The new trait appears in all cells that descend from the mutant cell. But the trait is not passed on to offspring, since reproductive cells are not involved.

Mutations that occur in reproductive cells may be passed on to offspring. These are called *germ mutations*. They have great genetic importance because these mutant genes are passed on to future generations.

Causes of Mutation

Mutations can occur when radiation or other *mutagenic agents,* also called **mutagens,** disrupt a cell's normal activity.

genic = producing

Body cells are subject to a wide range of mutagens. These include radiation, certain viruses, certain industrial chemicals and substances, tar, smoke, smog, and other environmental agents. Some food additives have been found to be mutagenic. Mutagens have always been present in the natural environment, but industrialization has caused the number and variety of agents to increase greatly.

Exposure to mutagens increases the chances that an organism's cells will mutate. If you smoke, the mutagens in smoke will increase your chances of having cells mutate. One form of mutant cells is cancer cells.

Although Gregor Mendel laid the foundations for modern genetics, scientists have made many discoveries since his time that have helped explain heredity principles. *Chromosomes* were found to be the carriers of the hereditary factors that were eventually called *genes*. The particular chromosomes that determine the sex of an organism were found. In females these *sex chromosomes* are a pair of matching chromosomes. In the male the sex chromosomes are a nonmatching pair. *Sex-linked traits* have been explained, as well as the abnormal traits caused by abnormal segregation of chromosomes during the process of *meiosis*.

Mutations, sudden changes in the genetic code, have been found to be the cause of the sudden appearance of entirely new traits in an offspring. Some of the causes of mutations are still being studied.

Summary

sex chromosome
autosome
crossing over
mutation

polyploidy
somatic mutation
germ mutation
mutagen

Biologically Speaking

Questions for Review

1. List three parallels that Sutton found between Mendel's hereditary factors and the behavior of chromosomes and genes.
2. Why are *Drosophila* used for genetic studies?
3. Give an example of a sex-linked gene and explain how its inheritance differs from other genes.

4. How does crossing over alter gene linkage?
5. List several natural causes of mutation.
6. Why are mutations that occur in body cells not important to the entire species?
7. Explain how a point mutation could cause a change in a trait.
8. What is the difference between a gene, or point, mutation and a chromosome mutation?
9. How is a gene related to DNA?

Applying Concepts

1. Discuss the significance of the gene hypothesis proposed by Sutton.
2. Give examples of how diversity within a group of organisms might aid in the survival of the species.
3. Discuss what measures can be taken to decrease the mutagens in the environment.

11

Genes in Human Populations

11–1 | Parent and child resemblance. *(Paul Fusco, Magnum)*

The Nature of Human Heredity

Most of the knowledge about genetics has come from experiments with organisms such as plants, fruit flies, and bacteria. From these experiments basic structures and characteristics common to many living things have been discovered. These include DNA, genes, segregation of chromosomes, mitosis, and crossover.

Humans are a part of nature. They are subject to the same mechanisms as other forms of life. The same factors that operate in fruit flies and pea plants also operate in humans. Mitosis in pea plants can be discussed as well as in humans. Sex-linked genes can be discussed in humans as well as in fruit flies.

There are several reasons why humans have not been used in genetic studies. **The most obvious problem is that they cannot be controlled by the investigators, as other organisms can. Another problem is the length of human life.** Many generations of *Drosophila* can be studied in a few months, or many generations of bacteria in a day.

Another problem involves the number of offspring humans produce. In many plants and animals, a single

ONE fertilized egg
divides into two cells

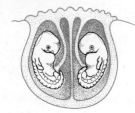

that separate and
develop as two genetically
identical individuals usually
sharing the same placenta
and fetal sac

TWO eggs fertilized
by different sperms
divide into cells

that form separate
masses of cells
and have separate
placentas and fetal sacs
and develop separately

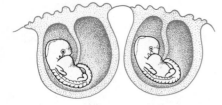

11-2 | (top) Since identical twins develop from a single egg and sperm, they have the same genetic makeup. (bottom) Fraternal twins, developing from different eggs and sperms, are no more alike than other brothers and sisters.

frater = brother

cross may produce hundreds or even thousands of off-spring. **Most human parents produce only a few offspring in a lifetime.** Thus, there is a very small sample of genetic results to study in a given family. If *geneticists*, scientists who study heredity, wish to study the probability of a certain trait showing up in future generations, they need to have large numbers of offspring to get an accurate predic-tion of how often the trait will appear. **Probability ratios will not work with a small number of offspring.**

Finally, the influence of the environment can cause problems in studying human genetics. Certain factors can affect humans in a way they do not affect other organisms. Some traits, like blood type or eye color, are relatively unaffected by the environment. Other traits, such as body size, are affected by environment.

Population Studies

Because studying humans is more complicated than study-ing *Drosophila*, geneticists have developed a number of special ways to learn about human heredity. These meth-ods include studying twins, taking samplings from the whole population, and observing and keeping careful records of the frequency of certain traits in a total popula-tion. A population is any group of like organisms, such as a number of rose bushes, squirrels, or humans.

Twins

Since genes and environment work together to produce a certain trait, heredity and environment cannot easily be considered separately. But one question that can be an-swered is: How might heredity be expressed in different environments? The natural occurrence of twins has given geneticists an ideal situation for studying this question.

There are two types of twins. The more common type of twins is *fraternal twins.* They develop from two different eggs, each fertilized by a different sperm. This occurs when the mother happens to produce two eggs at the same time, and both are fertilized. The two zygotes develop separately inside the mother. Fraternal twins are genetically different people. Their genes are no more alike than those of other brothers and sisters.

Identical twins, however, are of greater interest to geneticists. These are twins who have exactly the same genes. Identical twins are always the same sex. They de-velop from a single fertilized egg. At some point early in development, the zygote splits, and separates into two masses. Instead of developing into a single embryo, these cell masses develop into two genetically identical embryos. Since they develop from the same fertilized egg, identical twins have the same genetic makeup. The similarities between them are due to traits controlled by the same genes. The differences between them are due to environmental factors. Identical twins who are raised in separate environments give geneticists the opportunity to study heredity separately from environment.

One such example was the study of twins named Gladys and Helen. Gladys had no opportunity for schooling beyond the third grade. She grew up in isolated parts of the Canadian Rockies and eventually worked in a knitting mill and as a salesgirl in various stores. When she was given an intelligence test at the age of 28, she scored 92 (low normal).

Helen, on the other hand, went through college and became a teacher. She scored 116 (high normal) on the same intelligence test. This score is 24 points higher than the score of Gladys, who had exactly the same innate traits and potential.

Population Sampling

Population sampling is another way of studying human heredity. Opinion polls are one example of population sampling. Such polls can be very accurate. On a major election night, for example, television networks make early predictions of winners and losers. These predictions may be based on only two or three percent of the total vote, but they are seldom wrong.

The frequency with which a certain trait will appear in a population can be predicted by using the same sort of population sampling. Let's look at an actual case of population sampling for a genetic trait. The trait involves the ability to taste a certain substance called PTC or phenylthiocarbamide (fen'l-thy-oh-KAHR-buh-mide). To some people, called tasters, PTC tastes very bitter. To other people, called nontasters, PTC has no taste.

By population sampling the ratio of tasters to nontasters has been found for the population of the United States. This ratio is about 65 percent tasters to 35 percent nontasters. When two nontasters have children, they are always nontasters. With this information you can suspect that a single pair of alleles, T and t, control this trait. The tasters have a genotype of Tt or TT, and the nontasters would be tt.

Gene Pool

If it is known what traits are present in a certain population, that knowledge can be used to predict how often those traits will show up in the offspring. Thus it is very impor-

11-3 | What type of twins are these? *(Alpha)*

Facts & Figures

About 1 in every 25 births is twins. About 1 in every 5,000 births is triplets.

Facts & Figures

The probability ratio for being a twin is 1:95. The probability ratio for being one of triplets is 1:10,000.

11–4 | All of the ponderosa pine in a particular mountain range could be considered a gene pool. *(Courtesy of Western Wood Products Association)*

tant for geneticists to know the traits of a population. All of the genes in any particular population are known as a *gene pool.*

The gene pool maintains the continuity of traits as generations of organisms pass through time. Populations of people may gain in average height, or their average intelligence may rise or fall, but they will still be recognizable as people. Some gene pools appear to have remained relatively unchanged for probably long periods of time. For example, present-day clams appear very much like fossil clams over 350 million years old.

Gene pools can be affected by many environmental factors. Immigration can drastically alter a gene pool. Think of the history of this country. The people who have come to this country from Ireland, Africa, Poland, and so on during the past 200 years have all brought their own genetic traits. Their traits were added to the existing gene pool (the earlier settlers from England, Holland, France, Spain). The gene pool changed. It became more diverse. In this country there is a rich gene pool with a wide variety of genotypes.

Blood-Type Heredity   Some traits present in human gene pools have been studied in detail. A great deal about how traits are inherited has been learned through such studies. One such study of inherited traits involved *blood types.*

In 1900 Dr. Karl Landsteiner, a scientist in Vienna, was investigating blood *transfusions.* He had observed that when blood from two people was mixed together, one of

trans = across, over

two events occurred; the red blood cells from both people would freely intermingle with no apparent reaction, or they would stick together in clumps. This clumping was extremely dangerous if a person had received blood from another person in transfusion. The clumps would clog small blood vessels. Tissues would not receive oxygen and nutrients and wastes could not be carried away. This could cause death.

Dr. Landsteiner found that the clumping reaction was due to proteins on the surfaces of red blood cells. He also found that people could be grouped according to what kind of protein was present on their red blood cells. He called these four groups A, B, AB, and O. People in group A have protein A on the surface of their red blood cells. People in group B have protein B on their red blood cells. People in group AB have both proteins A and B on their red blood cells. The remaining group of people, type O, have neither protein A nor protein B on the surface of their red blood cells.

The A and B proteins on the surface of the red blood cells determine what type of blood a person can receive in a transfusion. That is, if you have type A blood, you can receive a blood transfusion from a person with type A blood. No clumping will occur. But if you have type A blood and receive a transfusion of type B blood, clumping will occur. Likewise, if you have type B blood, you can receive blood from a type B person, but not from a type A person. If you have type AB blood, you may be able to receive blood from anyone. Since your blood cells contain type A proteins, your blood will not form clumps with type A. And since you have type B proteins on your red blood cells, your blood will not form clumps with type B proteins. If you receive blood from a type O person, that blood has neither A nor B proteins with which your blood could form clumps. Thus type AB blood is a *universal recipient*.

If you have type O blood, you may be able to give blood to anyone. Type O blood is called the *universal donor* because it does not have the A or B proteins on cells that would cause type B or type A or type AB blood to clump. However, since people with type O blood have no A or B proteins on the red blood cells, they cannot receive type A or B blood. So type O blood can *receive* blood from only type O.

How is blood type inherited? In Mendel's garden peas and in other cases that have been discussed, each trait was determined by a pair of genes. These pairs of *alleles* were responsible for contrasting traits. But in the case of blood type, three genes are involved. These genes can be called A, B, and O. They are **multiple alleles,** since more than a single

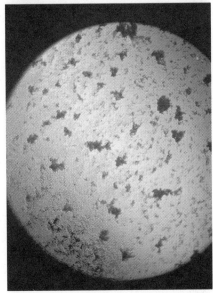

11-5 | (top) Normal red blood cells. (bottom) Mixing of different blood types could cause clumping of the red blood cells. (40X) *(Lester V. Bergman and Associates)*

results of crossing I^Ai and I^Bi		
female ⟶	I^B	i
GAMETES		
male ↓		
I^A	I^AI^B	I^Ai
i	I^Bi	i i

11-6 | A heterozygous type A blood male is crossed with a heterozygous type B blood female. What blood types can result from this cross?

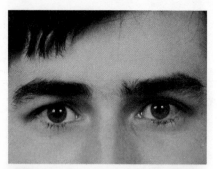
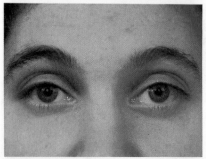
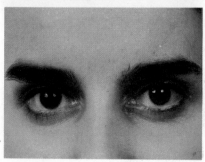

11-7 | The color of your eyes is coded by multiple alleles. *(HRW photos by Russell Dian)*

Table 11-1 BLOOD TYPE PERCENTAGES IN VARIOUS REGIONS OF THE WORLD

BLOOD TYPE	A	B	AB	O
U.S.A.—white	41.0%	10.0%	4.0%	45.0%
U.S.A.—black	26.0%	21.0%	3.7%	49.3%
Swedish	46.7%	10.3%	5.1%	37.9%
Japanese	38.4%	21.8%	8.6%	31.2%
Hawaiian	60.8%	2.2%	0.5%	36.5%
Chinese	25.0%	35.0%	10.0%	30.0%
Australian aborigine	44.7%	2.1%	0.0%	53.1%
North American Indian	7.7%	1.0%	0.0%	91.3%

pair of genes is involved in determining the characteristic. But each individual can inherit only two blood-type genes, one from the mother and one from the father. So only two of the genes are present in any single person. The type of blood a person has depends on which two of these three genes he or she has.

The symbols I^A, I^B, and i are used to represent these blood genotypes. The letter *I* means that the gene A or B associated with it is expressed. I^A, then, would code for, or produce, protein A. The letter *i* represents a recessive gene that does not produce a protein on red blood cells.

A person with type A blood may have a homozygous genotype of I^AI^A or a heterozygous genotype of I^Ai. A person with type B blood has the genotypes of I^BI^B or I^Bi. A person with type AB blood has only the heterozygous genotype of I^AI^B. In this case both proteins are produced. The AB blood type is a case of *incomplete dominance,* or blending inheritance.

A person of type O blood has only the homozygous genotype of ii. In this case neither protein is produced.

Consider a couple in which the male is a heterozygous type A (I^Ai) and the female is a heterozygous type B (I^Bi). What are the possible blood types of the children?

Look at figure 11-6. Remember that each parent can contribute only one blood-type gene to its child through its gamete, either sperm or egg. Each sperm of the male will contain either I^A or i. Each ovum of the female will contain either I^B or i. Possible combinations of these genotypes will determine the genotypes of the children.

Any single offspring of this particular example will have blood type A (I^Ai), B (I^Bi), AB (I^AI^B), or O (ii). Any blood type is a possibility in this case.

Eye and Skin Color The color of eyes and the color of the skin are other examples of traits controlled by multiple

11–8 | It is believed that from four to six pairs of genes determine skin color. Gene A produces more pigment than gene A', B more than B', and so on. The expression of the trait is the sum of the effects of all the genes. *(a: Monkmeyer Press Photo; B, D: HRW photos by Russell Dian; C: Rona Weissler-Tucillo)*

alleles. Eyes are not just either blue or brown. They are many different shades of blue or brown, depending on how many genes for blue or brown eyes are present.

Skin color is thought to be determined by four, five, or six pairs of genes. Some skin-color genes code for more pigment than others. This can be seen in figure 11-8. Here, four pairs of genes are shown to govern skin color.

Sex-Linked Traits in Humans

Do you know anyone who can't distinguish the color red from the color green? People with this red-green **color blindness** see the colors red and green as shades of gray. While it is rare in women, this trait appears in about eight percent of the male population. The fact that this trait appears more often in males than in females indicates that it is **sex-linked.**

The genes for red-green color vision are on the X chromosomes. The gene for normal color vision (C) is dominant over the recessive gene for color blindness (c). Thus, the possible combinations of these genes are as follows:

■ X^CX^C, a normal female, homozygous for normal color vision.

11-9 | If you cannot see the number 75, you have red-green color blindness.

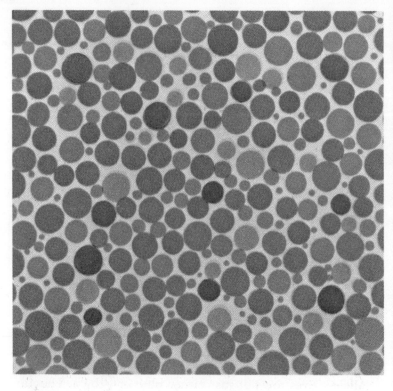

INHERITANCE OF COLOR BLINDNESS

Female	X^C	X^c
SEX CHROMOSOMES Male		
X^C	$X^C X^C$	$X^C X^c$
Y	$X^C Y$	$X^c Y$

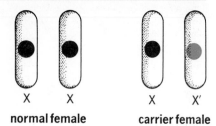

X   X
normal female

X   X'
carrier female

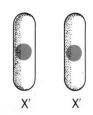

X'   X'
color-blind female

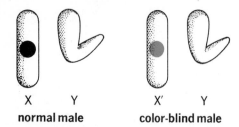

X   Y
normal male

X'   Y
color-blind male

11-10 | The gene for color blindness is indicated in color. The chromosome that carries it is designated as X'. Two such chromosomes are necessary for a color-blind female while only one is necessary for a color-blind male.

- $X^C X^c$, a carrier female, heterozygous for normal color vision. This person has normal color vision but is a carrier of the recessive gene.
- $X^c X^c$, a color-blind female, homozygous for color blindness.
- $X^C Y$, a normal male with a single gene for normal color vision.
- $X^c Y$, a color-blind male with a single gene for color blindness.

Look at a cross between a carrier female ($X^C X^c$) and a normal male ($X^C Y$) in figure 11-10. In such a cross, the male offspring have a 50/50 chance of being color blind. All of the female offspring will have normal color vision. However, there is a 50/50 chance that a female offspring will be a carrier of the color-blind gene. Can you think of a combination of parent genotypes that might produce a color-blind female?

Hemophilia

Hemophilia (HEE-muh-FILL-ee-uh), or "bleeder's disease," is another sex-linked trait passed on in much the same way as color blindness. People with hemophilia lack *antihemo-*

philic globulin, a substance in the blood that is needed for the normal clotting of blood. This substance is not produced in people with hemophilia. This is because the gene that codes for it is defective. Because of the lack of this clotting substance, victims of hemophilia bleed severely and may even die from loss of blood as a result of wounds that would be of slight importance to a normal person. For example, pulling a tooth can cause a major problem for a person with hemophilia. Transfusions of blood containing the missing antihemophilic globulin will help hemophiliacs for a time. Extracts of the globulin prepared from blood plasma are also used to treat hemophiliacs.

anti = against

hemo = blood

philia = tendency toward

One of the reasons hemophilia has received a great deal of attention is because of its occurrence in European royalty. Queen Victoria must have been a carrier of hemophilia because among her large family were a son with hemophilia and two daughters who had hemophilic sons. From the two carrier daughters the trait found its way into the royal families of Russia and Spain.

How did Queen Victoria become a carrier of hemophilia? Because there is no clear record of "bleeders" in her ancestry, it probably started as a gene mutation in the sperm or ovum that combined to form the zygote from which she developed. Through mitotic cell division each of her cells contained the gene mutation. When gametes were formed there was a probability that half the gametes contained the trait.

Of course, Queen Victoria had no way of knowing that she was a carrier of hemophilia. Now a simple blood test can tell whether a female is a carrier or not. The male either has the disease or is completely free of it, since the gene containing the trait to produce the missing globulin is on the X chromosome.

Sex-Influenced Traits

Some traits might appear to be sex-linked but actually are not. Such traits are called *sex-influenced* **or sex-limited traits.** These traits are not attached to the X chromosome. The father (like the mother) can pass these traits on to both daughter and son.

Baldness, for example, is not sex-linked, but it is sex-influenced. Both males and females can be bald, but there are more bald males than bald females. The reason for this is that **male and female hormones influence the expression of this trait.**

The gene for baldness can be represented by B and the

gene for keeping hair by b. Baldness is dominant over keeping hair. Both males and females with the genotype BB are bald. If they have the genotype bb, both have normal hair. However, females with Bb have normal hair, but males with Bb become bald. The action of the male and female hormones somehow influences the expression of this trait. Temporary loss of hair can, of course, occur in both males and females.

A sex-limited trait is one that appears in one sex but not the other as in a trait that influences a sex organ.

Nondisjunction of Human Chromosomes

Nondisjunction is the failure of homologous chromosomes to segregate during meiosis. The same thing may occur during meiosis in other animals and plants. Nondisjunction may involve either somatic chromosomes or sex chromosomes. It may take place in either the first or second division in meiosis. **Nondisjunction produces one cell with an extra chromosome and one cell lacking a chromosome.**

tri = three

mono = one
soma = body

Suppose that a gamete has an extra chromosome. This chromosome may be passed on to a zygote at the time of fertilization. The zygote will then have three chromosomes in place of a normal pair. This condition is called **trisomy.** On the other hand, if a gamete lacks a chromosome, the fertilized zygote will have only one chromosome instead of the normal pair. This condition is known as **monosomy.** If either trisomy or monosomy occurs in the fertilized egg, it will also appear in every body cell of the organism. Let's look at some examples of nondisjunction in humans.

Down's Syndrome

Down's syndrome is usually caused by the presence of an extra twenty-first chromosome in all body cells. This extra chromosome results from nondisjunction during meiosis, probably in egg formation. Because three twenty-first chromosomes are present, Down's syndrome is also known as trisomy-21. All other chromosomes are present in normal numbers.

Down's syndrome may result in severe mental retardation. Abnormal physical features, such as an enlarged tongue and weak muscles, may also result. About one in 600 babies is born with Down's syndrome. However, this rate varies with the age of the mothers. With mothers under 35, fewer than one baby in 1,000 have the syndrome. With mothers over 45, about one baby in 60 has it.

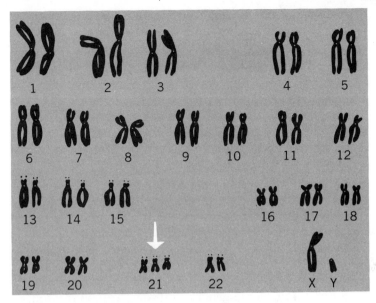

11-11 | Chromosomes of a person with Down's syndrome. The cause of this disease is the extra chromosome seen with pair 21.

Other Conditions Resulting from Nondisjunction

Several abnormal conditions result from nondisjunction in human sex chromosomes. Some of these conditions involve monosomy, and others involve trisomy. Abnormalities can occur in either male or female gametes.

- **Turner's syndrome,** or monosomy X, results from the absence of an X chromosome in an egg. When fertilized by a normal X sperm, the offspring has a genotype of XO. These females do not mature sexually. They are sterile, since their ovaries are underdeveloped. They are also abnormally short and often have a large neck.

- **Klinefelter's syndrome** can result from nondisjunction when an abnormal sperm, containing both X and Y, fer-

11-12 | (left) Chromosomes in Turner's syndrome (XO). *(Dr. Lillian Y. Hsu, New York University School of Medicine, N.Y.)*

11-13 | (right) Chromosomes in Klinefelter's syndrome (XXY). *(Dr. Lillian Y. Hsu, New York University School of Medicine, N.Y.)*

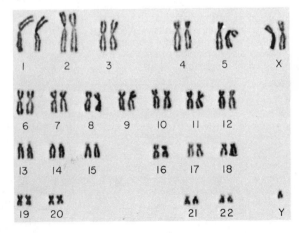

tilizes a normal X egg. The offspring has a genotype of XXY. These males have reduced fertility and are often mentally retarded. The fact that they are male shows that the Y chromosome has strong influence over the two X chromosomes.

Genetic Disorders

You may be familiar with diseases caused by such things as bacteria or viruses. **Some diseases, however, are caused by unfavorable genes. These are genetic diseases.** Due to advances in the field of genetics, it is often possible to find out what chance there is of your passing a genetic disease on to your children. This is helpful if a harmful trait may be suspected. Some people who have the possibility of passing on a lethal or harmful trait to their children choose to adopt children. Some genetic disorders can be treated.

PKU

One genetic disease that can be quite successfully treated is *PKU* or *phenylketonuria* (FEN-il-KET-uh-NYOOR-ee-ah). PKU is a disease that appears in infants. It can result in severe mental retardation. The disease is caused by a recessive mutant gene (p). A child with PKU is homozygous recessive, with a genotype of pp. Because of the double mutant gene (pp), the child lacks a certain enzyme. Most

Facts & Figures

Hereditary ailments account for 40 percent of infant deaths. Meanwhile, about 96 percent of all children are born free of any genetic disease.

Careers

Geneticists are concerned with the heredity of plants, animals, and microorganisms. Most geneticists are college teachers and genetic counselors and/or do research. A doctorate degree is required for advanced positions. Students interested in genetics should be good in mathematics and study a variety of science courses. A foreign language is also useful because professional papers are written in different languages.

11–14 | Genetic counselors can help couples make decisions about having children where there is a possibility of passing on lethal or dangerous traits. *(Courtesy of March of Dimes)*

parents of PKU children are of genotype Pp, and show no sign of the disease because they do not lack the enzyme. This enzyme would normally convert the amino acid *phenylalanine* (FE-nil-AL-a-NEEN) into another similar amino acid. Since the PKU child cannot break down phenylalanine properly, another acid, *phenylpyruvic* (FE-nil-pie-ROO-vick) acid, builds up in the body fluids. When this substance becomes highly concentrated in the body, it causes brain damage.

Brain damage can be prevented by early detection of the disease. Most hospitals detect early cases of PKU by testing the urine of infants. Treatment can then be given to prevent accumulation of phenylaline in the body and its conversion to phenylpyruvic acid. Treatment does not alter the genetic defect but its tragic effects can be prevented.

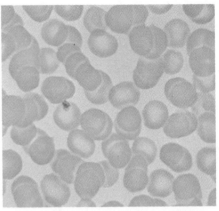

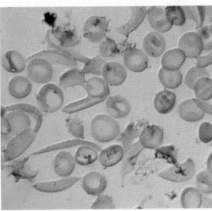

11–15 | (top) Normal red blood cells. (bottom) Sickle-shaped red blood cells from a patient with sickle-cell anemia. *(top: Manfred Kage, Peter Arnold; bottom: Phillip A. Harrington, Peter Arnold)*

Sickle-Cell Anemia

Sickle-cell anemia is a serious blood disease that is most common in Africa. In Western Africa as many as 40 percent of the population may carry the sickle-cell trait. The reason for a high percentage in this gene pool is that people with the sickle-cell trait are more resistant to malaria, a disease affecting the blood. This is a case where people who have a mild form of one disease are more resistant to a completely different disease.

This disease is called sickle-cell anemia because the red blood cells are sickle-shaped. Their sickle shape occurs because of a defect in the blood protein hemoglobin. The blood of a person with this condition cannot carry out the normal functions of blood, so there is a decreased oxygen supply to the tissues of the body. The defect can be traced to a gene, located on a DNA molecule in a chromosome. A single change in one of the DNA base pairs causes the wrong amino acid to be placed in a protein. This single misplaced amino acid, only one in a chain of 560 amino acids, is enough to cause the damage. Once this gene mutation occurs, it can be passed on to the offspring.

Detecting Genetic Disorders

Some genetic defects can be detected in a baby before it is born, through the process of *amniocentesis* (am-nee-oh-sen-TEE-suhs). A sample of fluid and loose cells is removed from the sac around the unborn baby. Neither the baby nor the mother is harmed by the process. By studying the chromosomes of these cells, a geneticist can identify genetic disorders. The sex of the unborn baby can also be determined by this method. Until the child is born, nothing can be done to treat any diseases detected by amniocentesis.

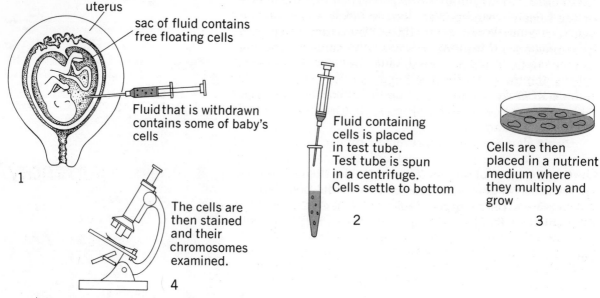

uterus

sac of fluid contains free floating cells

Fluid that is withdrawn contains some of baby's cells

1

Fluid containing cells is placed in test tube. Test tube is spun in a centrifuge. Cells settle to bottom

2

Cells are then placed in a nutrient medium where they multiply and grow

3

The cells are then stained and their chromosomes examined.

4

11–16 | Amniocentesis is a valuable method of detecting genetic diseases.

Genetics and Reproduction

A recent development in science is helpful in controlling genetic diseases. Usually in cases of severe disease, the family history is well known. In the case of a sex-linked disease, a female who is free of the disease often knows she is a carrier. For example, if a normal female's mother or father had a sex-linked disease, she must be a carrier. It would be best for such a carrier to have only female children. The carrier might pass on an abnormal X chromosome to her female offspring. But, if the father was free of the disease, he would pass a normal X chromosome to the female offspring. And so the female children would be free of the disease.

A newly-developed method available in some hospitals enables parents to improve their chances of having a child of the sex they prefer. Scientists can now take sperm donated by the father and separate about 80 percent of the male-determining sperm (Y) from the female-determining sperm (X). The technique makes use of the fact that the Y sperm swim faster than the heavier X sperm. Once separated, the desired sperm are placed in the female's reproductive system. Fertilization occurs and a normal pregnancy begins. This technique increases the chances that the baby will be the sex the parents have chosen.

Another scientific advance involves the ability to have children. About 10 to 15 percent of married couples cannot have children. This is because of defects in either the male's or the female's reproductive system. Now some women who were infertile can have children. The ovum, or egg, can be removed from the woman's ovary by surgery. The egg can then be fertilized in a test tube by the husband's sperm. After a few days the fertilized egg, now multicellular, is implanted in the uterus of the mother. She then can carry the child and give birth in the normal nine months.

Geneticists studying heredity as it appears in such organisms as fruit flies can raise many generations of fruit flies in a short time. They can deal with large numbers of flies, mating the males they choose to the females they choose. But when they are studying heredity in humans, scientists cannot use these same methods. They have developed other methods because only a few generations of humans can be studied at one time. These methods include studying twins, taking samplings from the whole population, and doing statistical studies of the frequency of certain traits in a *gene pool*.

Scientists now know a great deal about how certain traits are inherited. Blood type is one such trait. Certain *genetic diseases* are now well understood. Some of these diseases are PKU, hemophilia, and color blindness. Some genetic diseases can be quite successfully treated, others cannot.

Summary

Biologically Speaking

fraternal twins
identical twins
population sampling
gene pool
multiple alleles
color blindness
sex-linked trait
hemophilia
sex-influenced trait

trisomy
monosomy
Down's syndrome
Turner's syndrome
Klinefelter's syndrome
PKU
sickle-cell anemia
amniocentesis

Questions for Review

1. What factors can change gene frequencies? Give examples.
2. State the differences between fraternal and identical twins.
3. What is the meaning of the term *multiple allele?*
4. Why do more males than females have red-green color blindness?

5. Explain why males with a genotype of Bb are bald and females with a genotype of Bb have normal hair.
6. Explain how sickle-cell anemia is inherited.
7. List and describe some genetic diseases.
8. What chromosome abnormality is associated with Down's syndrome?
9. How might a population study for a certain trait reveal how that trait is inherited?

Applying Concepts

1. Albinism is the inability to make pigment. An albino has white hair and pink eyes. A person with normal pigmentation has a genotype of AA or Aa. An albino has a genotype of aa. Answer the questions about the following pedigree.
   a. What is the genotype of number 2?
   b. What are the genotypes of numbers 3, 4, 5 and 6?

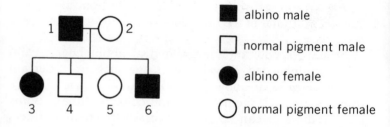

2. A child has a blood type of AB, and the mother has a blood type of A.
   a. What are the possible genotypes of the father?
   b. Could the father be type O? Explain.
3. A color-blind man marries a woman with normal vision. Five offspring result. One of the male children is color blind.
   a. What is the genotype of the mother? Explain how you know this.
   b. Is it possible for this couple to have a color-blind daughter? Explain.
4. A female carrier of hemophilia does not have the disease. Her genotype is $X^S X^s$. S is the gene for normal blood clotting, s for hemophilia. The carrier female mates with a normal male.
   a. What percent of the female offspring are normal, and what percent are carriers?
   b. What percent of the male offspring are normal, and what percent are hemophilic?

12-1 | Seedless oranges are a product of applied genetics. *(HRW Photo by Ken Karp)*

Applied Genetics

A **DISCUSS** how inbreeding, hybridization, and polyploidy are used to benefit people.

B **EXPLAIN** mass selection and how it was used before genetics became a science.

C **DESCRIBE** how applying the principles of heredity improves varieties and breeds of plants and animals.

Plant and Animal Breeding

If you walk down the aisle of any food store, you will see products of the increasing understanding of genetics. Juicy oranges without seeds, tangelos, which are a cross between tangerines and grapefruits, seedless grapes, and many other foods have been developed through the application of the principles of genetics.

Various animals have also resulted from applying the principles of genetics to animal breeding. Fancy-tailed guppies, Chihuahuas, Great Danes, and Arabian stallions are examples of breeding animals for specific traits.

Perhaps none of the examples mentioned so far are of great historic importance. People could survive without the Chihuahua. But consider the meaty turkey you see in modern supermarkets. It has been developed from the slender wild bird the Pilgrims in New England hunted. The average turkey today will supply food for many more people than an average wild turkey would have in the days of the Pilgrims. Applying genetic principles to food production is one way to produce more food for the growing world populations.

12-2 | The wild turkey is the ancestor of today's farm turkeys. *(New York Historical Society)*

151

Controlled Breeding

The main method of applying genetics is through *controlled breeding*. Gregor Mendel produced certain combinations of traits in garden peas by crossing certain parent plants. **In the same way, farmers have produced desired traits in plants and animals through controlled breeding.** Even before the time of Mendel, farmers knew that certain traits were passed from one generation of plants or animals to the next. They saved the seeds from their best plants for the next year's crops. They also bred the best farm stock—the fattest pigs, the cows that gave the most milk, the best egg-laying chickens.

Mass Selection

The process of selecting a few parent plants or parent animals from a large number of individuals is called *mass selection.* If the farmer had very few plants or animals from which to select a breeding stock, there would be little choice. In the same way you would have very little choice if you tried to buy a shirt in a store that had only two or three shirts. To practice mass selection you need a mass from which to select. This is one reason that developing improved strains of plants or animals through mass selection was, until recently, a slow process. Most individual farmers didn't have enough land or plants or animals for many large breeding experiments. Now, large companies and organizations carry on such experiments.

Inbreeding

Luther Burbank, the American naturalist who developed many new varietites of plants, made an observation that helped him to develop a new, better potato when he was only 24. When Burbank selected the potatoes he wanted to reproduce, he needed only to cut out and plant potato pieces with two or three buds, or "eyes." The products of this asexual reproduction were exactly like the parent plant. Other methods of asexual reproduction, such as the grafting, cutting, and budding of fruit trees and roses, also produce plants exactly like the parent plant.

With seed plants, such as corn or wheat, the problem is more complex. Fertilized seeds such as those that Burbank found on his original potato plant result from the joining of two different gametes in sexual reproduction. Thus, the offspring may have gene combinations quite different from those found in the parents. This is especially true of crop plants. Such plants have been crossed by human beings for centuries. They may carry genes from many different strains.

Facts & Figures

In the early 19th century there were 250 varieties of roses known in Europe. Since then growers have developed over 8,000 hybrid varieties.

12-3 | Potatoes are reproduced by asexual means. The buds or "eyes" are planted and a new potato plant results. *(HRW photo by Russell Dian)*

12–4 | The Dachshund was developed to drive wild animals out of their burrows. The dog's front legs are free to move forward in tight underground burrows. Dachshunds are now largely housepets.

To be sure of always getting the same good crop, farmers have performed control breeding on many generations of plants by the process called *inbreeding.* Inbreeding in plants involves self-pollination of a single parent, so that no new genes are introduced from a different plant. Inbreeding in animals is carried out by mating close relatives like brother and sister to produce offspring with similar traits. **After many generations of inbreeding, the offspring are largely homozygous for the desired trait.**

Inbreeding has some drawbacks. Offspring of the same parents tend to have the same recessive genes. When these offspring are bred with each other, any recessive genes have more chance of being expressed. **If the recessive traits are undesirable, the inbreeding cannot be considered a success.**

Facts & Figures

A modern hybrid corn cob has a yield of from 500 to 1,000 kernels. The first cultivated corn had a yield of only 48 kernels.

Hybridization

Today, farmers know that the corn they grow will have large, yellow, juicy kernels. The kernels will be of uniform size. The corn grower can even tell fairly well how much a given acreage will produce, provided the weather is good. Growers know all this because they use very standardized seed produced through another kind of controlled breeding called **hybridization**.

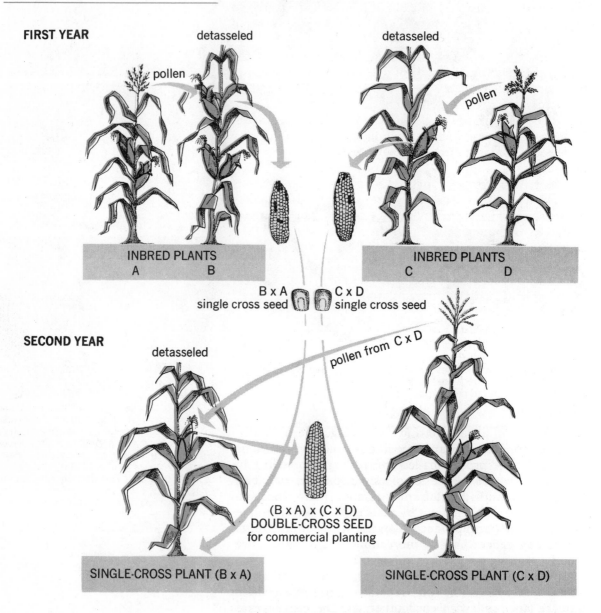

12–5 | Traits A, B, C, and D are desirable traits in the hybrid corn seed. Pure strain A is crossed with pure strain B and C is crossed with D. The resulting hybrid seeds AB and DC is grown. Plant AB is crossed with CD and the corn with traits ABCD is used as food.

Hybridization is the opposite of inbreeding. It is the crossing of two different but closely related strains of plants or animals. A new *hybrid* strain results. You can see hybrid corn seed advertised along the roads in corn-growing states such as Iowa and Illinois. The hybrid strain combines the traits of different parent strains. Each parent has been selected because it expresses a particular desired trait. Crossing the selected parent strains produces offspring with the desired traits of both parents. Thus hybrid corn can combine the trait of high yield with the trait of disease resistance.

Another example of successful hybridization is the mule, which is the offspring of a cross between a female horse and a male donkey. From the horse the mule gets its size and great strength. From the donkey it inherits sureness of foot, endurance, and ability to live on rough grasses. Mules are *sterile* and therefore cannot reproduce. Each new mule must come from the crossing of a female horse and male donkey.

The mule's sterility illustrates one of the difficulties of hybridization. When different strains of animals or plants are crossed, there are many new gene combinations aside from the few that interest the grower. Often these new gene combinations bring out traits not shown in either parent. Sometimes the hybrids have increased size, develop faster, and have other advantages. Such desirable qualities are called **hybrid vigor.** Sometimes, however, the unexpected traits are undesirable. There is always an element of chance in hybridization. One example is crossing a cabbage with a radish in an attempt to get a radish root with a cabbage head. The results, however, produce a cabbage root and "head" of a radish, which is a totally useless plant.

Genetic Manipulation

So far in this chapter natural methods of controlled breeding to produce desired strains of plants and animals have been discussed. In recent years new techniques have been found to artificially produce the desired genetic changes in various plants and animals. Most of these new techniques are still in the experimental stage. These experimental efforts will be mentioned briefly.

Polyploidy

At the grocery market, you may have noticed blueberries that are twice as large as ordinary ones. These blueberries have four sets of chromosomes. This condition, in which more than the usual diploid number of chromosomes are present, is called **polyploidy** (PAHL-ee-ploy-dee). Several

12–6 | Hybridization. (top) The mountain laurel has decorative pink flowers. But it grows too tall to be acceptable for some planting sites. (center) In contrast, the sandhill, or hairy laurel grows smaller, but has somewhat less attractive, white flowers. (bottom) Some of the hybrid offspring of a cross between the two above plants combine the desirable traits of both. *(Connecticut Agricultural Experiment Station)*

poly = many

tri = three

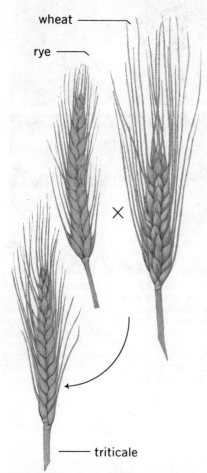

wheat

rye

×

triticale

12-7 | Wheat, genus *Triticum,* can be crossed with rye, genus *Secale* to produce Triticale, a new grain. There are many different varieties of grains produced with widely different characteristics.

other strains of fruit are examples of polyploidy. These include certain plums, grapes, cherries, strawberries, and cranberries.

Polyploidy sometimes occurs in nature, during the formation of gametes. Polyploidy can produce *triploid* (3n) rather than diploid (2n) number. Polyploidy can also produce organisms with four, five, six, or more complete sets of chromosomes.

Polyploidy is rare in animals but common in some plants where it often causes greater hardiness and greater size.

Polyploidy can be caused by artificial means through use of the drug *colchicine* (KAHL-chuh-seen). If plant shoots are put in weak solutions of colchicine, polyploidy occurs. Colchicine has been used to develop new strains of blueberries, lilies, cabbage, and other plants.

Polyploidy induced by the use of colchicine plays a vital part in growing a new hybrid grain that may increase yields of high-protein cereals. The hybrid grain, called *Triticale*, has been developed artifically by crossing wheat (genus *Triticum*) with rye (genus *Secales*). The process of crossing these two different plants is artificial because it involves doubling the normal number of chromosome sets. This occurs because the chromosomes contributed by the two different kinds of plants do not have homologous pairs. In order for the Triticale to have homologous pairs of chromosomes, the wheat gamete and the rye gamete must each contribute not just one chromosome to each pair of chromosomes in the zygote. It must contribute *both* chromosomes to make each homologous pair.

Other Hopes for Genetic Manipulations

In some instances, geneticists have been able to introduce new genes into an organism. The organism can then pass these genes on to its offspring. This work is still in the experimental stage. The new DNA, and the new genetic code that results, is called *recombinant DNA*. There is hope that safe methods of this kind of genetic manipulation will be useful for developing better strains of plants and animals and perhaps even curing some genetic diseases.

Another new development, still only in the experimental stage, is **cloning.** This is the development of an entire organism from a single body cell. At present cloning is used to reestablish forests in many areas. Complete trees can be grown from a single cell of a parent tree. Perhaps at some time in the future cloning will be a way of propagating a variety of useful animal and plant species.

Luther Burbank, the American naturalist who developed many new varieties of plants, used the methods of *controlled breeding* to produce the new, improved varieties. One form of controlled breeding is to select the desired parent plants from a large number of individuals. This is called *mass selection*. Another methods is *inbreeding*. This is self-pollination in plants or, in animals, the mating of close relatives.

Parent plants or animals with quite different traits are sometimes crossed to produce the combination of traits that the developer wants. This method of controlled breeding is called *hybridization*.

In addition to controlling the breeding of plants and animals, geneticists have developed ways of artificially changing the genetic traits of organisms. One method is *polyploidy*, which is the doubling of the normal number of chromosome sets.

mass selection	hybrid vigor
inbreeding	polyploidy
hybridization	cloning

1. Describe one contribution of Luther Burbank to genetics.
2. Describe the relation of mass selection to plant breeding.
3. What is hybridization?
4. Why is inbreeding practiced in plant and animal breeding?
5. In what way is the mule a true hybrid animal?

1. If inbreeding is practiced too long, offspring may become weak or sickly. What might cause this, and how can it be remedied?
2. Why is it important to have a wide variety of hybrid corn or wheat rather than just two or three good varieties?
3. A variety of wild corn has been found growing in relatively dry areas of Mexico. Why might this be an exciting and valuable discovery?

Summary

Biologically Speaking

Questions for Review

Applying Concepts

13

Organic Variation

A **DESCRIBE** Oparin's hypothesis.

B **LIST** some evidence of common ancestry.

C **DESCRIBE** Lamarck's theory of evolution.

D **DESCRIBE** Darwin's theory of natural selection.

E **DESCRIBE** how mutations relate to organic variation.

F **EXPLAIN** migration and isolation as factors in evolution.

G **DESCRIBE** the Hardy-Weinberg principle.

H **GIVE EXAMPLES** of adaptive radiation and convergent evolution.

years ago		
Today		
50 thousand		modern humans (*Homo sapiens*)
25 million		primates
180 million		mammals, birds, flowers
75-225 million		dinosaurs
400 million		first amphibians, insects, ferns
500 million		first fish, organisms on land
3 billion		simple organisms
2.5 billion		primeval seas
4.6 billion		Earth forms

13-1 | Theoretical development of life on earth.

The Changing Earth

Many scientists estimate that the earth is more than 4.5 billion years old. Try to imagine so much time. It's difficult, isn't it? Most people think of a few months or a few years as a long time. The time span of *billions* of years is such a great amount of time that it loses meaning.

Since its beginning, the earth has been changing constantly. Land masses have risen, then sunk below the sea. Mountains have been thrust up, only to be worn away by wind and rain. Rivers have cut deep channels in soil and rock. Long warm periods have been followed by ice ages. Deserts have spread, then disappeared as centuries of drought gave way to centuries of heavy rain.

Changes like these are still going on. But they take place so slowly that people are not aware of them.

Life on Earth

It is believed that life in the form of living cells first appeared on earth more than three billion years ago. But how did life begin? It is not certain. Several hypotheses have been offered, but none proven. One hypothesis was put forth by the Russian scientist A. I. Oparin in 1936.

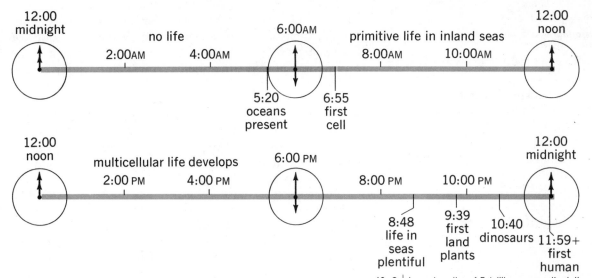

13-2 | Imagine the 4.5 billion years that the world has existed as if it were a 24 hour day. Starting at midnight, major events would occur in the time frame indicated.

Oparin suggested that the atmosphere of primitive earth was mainly made of gases such as ammonia (NH_3), methane (CH_4), hydrogen (H_2), and water vapor (H_2O). Such an atmosphere would have allowed far more of the sun's radiant energy to reach the earth than reaches it now. According to Oparin's hypothesis, energy from lightning, ultraviolet light from the sun, or gamma radiation split some of these gas molecules. Splitting of the gas molecules resulted in the bonding of carbon, hydrogen, oxygen, and nitrogen in new ways to form new molecules. The new organic molecules collected in shallow pools forming a sort of "organic soup." A warm rain continually added more molecules. Through millions of years the soup became more concentrated. Simple molecules reacted together to form more complex molecules. Oparin believed that the first cells could have formed in such a soup.

The idea that an organic soup could originate from a primitive atmosphere was tested in the laboratory by Stanley Miller in 1953. Charges of electricity were used to represent lightning on primitive earth. Electric sparks were passed through a mixture of gases like those thought to have been in the primitive atmosphere. These experiments produced organic molecules, including the amino acids glycine and alanine. This demonstrated that complex organic molecules could have been produced from inorganic ones.

If a DNA-like molecule formed in the organic soup, it might use the simpler molecules around it to replicate itself over and over again. But a replicating molecule is a long way from a cell.

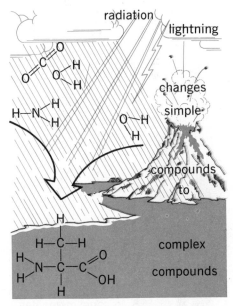

13-3 | The simple molecules of the primitive atmosphere might have been changed into complex organic molecules that eventually formed an organic soup.

hetero = other
trophic = one who feeds

an = without
aerobic = able to live and grow only where free oxygen is present

auto = by oneself or itself

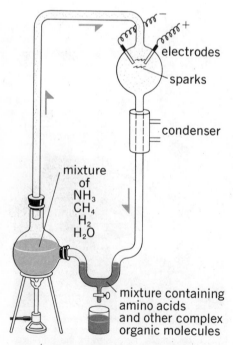

13-4 | Miller's experiment shows that under suitable conditions inorganic molecules can combine to form organic molecules.

mixture
of
NH_3
CH_4
H_2
H_2O

electrodes

sparks

condenser

mixture containing amino acids and other complex organic molecules

The First Cell: A Chance at Survival

The first cells are thought to have been heterotrophic. That is, they depend on the molecules in the organic soup for food and growth. Since there was little or no oxygen in the atmosphere at that time, their respiration must have been *anaerobic.*

These primitive cells could have flourished at first. They had plenty of food and could multiply freely. But with the passage of time and with increasing numbers of cells, the food supply would eventually be used up. If life was to survive, cells had to be set free of their dependence on the organic soup for food.

Photosynthesis gave cells the independence needed to survive. They could use the energy of the sun, carbon dioxide, and water to make their own food. They were *autotrophs.* Cells that could make their own food must have multiplied rapidly. The heterotrophic forms must have decreased in number.

With photosynthesis, oxygen was produced in great quantity. The atmosphere of the earth changed. An ozone (O_3) layer formed in the upper atmosphere and shielded the earth from much of the sun's ultraviolet radiation. Carbon dioxide was produced by plants in respiration and used in photosynthesis. Oxygen was used in respiration and produced in photosynthesis. With oxygen available in the environment, aerobic, animallike cells like protozoa could exist. The carbon dioxide they produced could also be used by plants.

Thus the plant and animal life was established. Autotrophs and heterotrophs formed a balanced relationship with the environment.

A Story Written in Rock

The kinds of changes that are believed to have occurred in the past are still going on today. Some changes such as earthquakes and volcanic explosions can still be observed. Other changes such as the wearing down of mountains, the formation of canyons or layers of sandstone, take thousands, sometimes millions, of years to occur. How is it known that these great changes occurred in the past? The earth holds the answer.

Geologists, scientists who study the earth, believe that *the present is the key to the past.* This means that **by studying what is happening now it may be possible to understand what has happened in the past.**

Deposits carried by wind or water are called *sediments.* As sediments accumulate on an area, the bottom layers are buried deeper. Great pressure helps to turn the lower layers of sediment to rock. Sedimentary rock is where the greatest

13-5 | An artist's conception of animals caught in the La Brea Tar Pits. *(American Museum of Natural History)*

number of fossils are found. Sedimentary rock is still being formed today.

Fossils   *Fossils* are traces of, or remains of, organisms that lived in the past. If remains of organisms are relatively unaltered, the fossilization process took place by a quick burial under conditions that prevented normal decay from occurring. Quicksand and tar pits make excellent traps for large animals. The La Brea tar pits of Los Angeles contain many skeletons of animals that lived during the ice age. Sometimes animals and plants buried in the acid mud of ancient bogs were preserved. The frozen earth in northern Canada has preserved mammoth elephants complete with skin, muscles, and organs.

Some of the most common fossils are the calcium carbonate skeletons of sea animals found in sedimentary rock. Corals in limestone and the shells of clams in limestone are typical examples. Other forms of fossils include the tracks of animals, the imprints of plants in coal, the hard parts of animals like teeth, bone, and scales.

Fossils also reveal what the earth and the climate were like in ancient times. Shark teeth in sedimentary rock in Colorado indicate that inland seas once covered that area. Fossils of corals and palm trees in Alaska show that that state once had a warm climate.

Scientists can measure the amount of radioactive elements such as carbon-14 in certain fossils to determine the age of those fossils. A similar process using other radioactive elements can be used to find the age of rocks. This dating of fossils and rocks can provide a good idea of how long ago certain animals may have existed on earth.

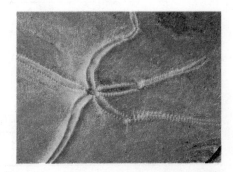

13-6 | A fossil brittle starfish from the Devonian period in a piece of slate. The body of the starfish was gradually replaced by the mineral *pyrite*. This type of fossil is known as a **cast**. *(Courtesy of Ward's)*

Time Scale of Life Based On Fossil Records

GEOLOGIC TIME TABLE

Era	Period	Epochs	Millions of years ago	Millions of years duration	Record of life change
Cenozoic age of mammals	Quaternary	Recent	—	(15,000 yrs)	Humans dominate life; many changes in natural environment.
		Pleistocene	1	1	Modern humans present. Glacial activity dominates. Climate becomes colder, many animals and plants become extinct.
	Tertiary	Pliocene	12	11	Large flesh-eating animals present. Evidence of ancient humans.
		Miocene	25	13	Herds of grazing animals. Monkeys present.
		Oligocene	35	10	Elephants and camels. Grassland and forest were present. Cooler climate.
		Eocene	60	25	Small horse present. Many rodents, monkey-like mammals and many small mammals present. Warm climate.
		Paleocene	70	10	
Mesozoic age of dinosaurs	Cretaceous		135	65	Rocky Mountains rise. Hardwood trees & flowers present. Dinosaurs begin to die out. Small mammals abundant.
	Jurassic		180	45	Many dinosaurs present. First feathered birds appear. First mammals appear.
	Triassic		225	45	Reptiles, turtles abundant. Many cone-bearing trees present. USA has present shape.
Paleozoic	Age of Amphibians	Permian	270	45	Appalachian Mountains rise. Reptiles plentiful. Desert climate.
		Pennsylvanian (late carboniferous)	330	60	Ferns are dominant type. Many amphibians, first reptiles. Swamps gave rise to present coal. Large insects present. Inland seas present.
		Mississippian (early carboniferous)	350	20	
	Age of fish	Devonian	400	50	Fish and sharks abundant. First amphibians and trees. Inland seas present.
		Silurian	440	60	First land plants. Giant scorpion present. Inland seas present.
	Age of invertebrates	Ordovician	500	40	First fish, (vertebrates). Inland seas present.
		Cambrian	600	100	Many fossils of invertebrates, snails, clams, coral, sponges, seaweed, trilobites plentiful.
(Pre-Cambrian) Proterozoic			1,700	1,100	Simple life was probably plentiful, but fossil evidence is scarce. Some shells and evidence of algae, fungi and worms present. Great volcanic activity. Formation of iron beds.
(Pre-Cambrian) Archeozoic			4,500+	2,800	Not much is known of life forms. Earliest fossils of algae date over 3 billion years. Much volcanic activity. Oceans formed, earth cooled.

13-7 | This geological time table shows the sequence and estimated length of the eras, periods, and epochs.

Geologic Time Geologists have divided the history of the earth into *eras* which are many millions of years long. Eras are divided into shorter time spans called *periods*. The geologic timetable shown in figure 13-7 is a summary of the eras and periods of the earth's history. The table indicates when certain mountain ranges formed and the occurrence of other important events. The information in the table is based on the study of primarily sedimentary layers like those in the Grand Canyon and the fossils contained within those layers.

What is Evolution?

Evolution means a slow, gradual development or change. If the fossils of the wooly mammoth of the ice age are compared with the elephants of today, the basic changes that have occurred can be seen. According to the *theory of evolution*, the hereditary traits, or characteristics, of a population of organisms gradually change over a period of time. The process of evolution occurs in a population of organisms as generations pass through time. During evolution, the **gene pool** of an entire population of organisms changes. You will recall from Chapter 11 that the gene pool contains all of the genes of a population. It represents all of their traits. When the genes change, the traits expressed by those genes change.

Facts & Figures

Mammoths (members of the elephant family) became extinct about 10,000 years ago, but parts of their bodies have been found fully preserved in ice.

13–8 | Homologous bones in the forelimbs of several vertebrate animals.

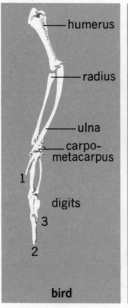

bird

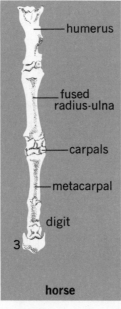

horse

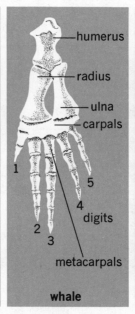

whale

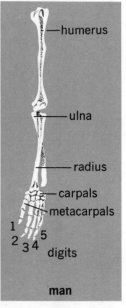

man

Evidence of Evolution

What evidence is there to show that evolution has taken place? Besides fossil evidence mentioned earlier in this chapter, there are the following:

- In both plants and animals, **homologous organs** are found. These organs are body parts that are similar in structure and seem to have developed in the same way, though they may have very different uses in different species. The bones of a bird's wing, a horse's front leg, a whale's paddle, and a human arm are homologous organs. These bones are so similar that, for the most part, they have the same names. The *differences* seen in these bones reflect adaptation to conditions in the environment. Their *likenesses* indicate a genetic relationship through a common ancestor.

homo = same
logo = proportion

- Most animals have certain structures that seem to have no use, though similar structures are quite useful in related species. Such structures are called **vestigial organs.** The human coccyx, (KAHK-siks) or tailbone, is a familiar example. This group of bones has no known function in humans. However, in certain mammals the bones of the coccyx are extended into a tail. It is believed by some scientists that the genes for the human coccyx were inherited from some ancestor in which it was useful.

- Likenesses between *embryos*, the developing organisms, also seem to indicate a common ancestor. For example, the embryos of different vertebrate animals, animals with backbones, are very similar during certain stages in early development. In these early stages it might be difficult for an untrained person to tell a fish embryo from that of a bird or mammal. It appears that all of these animals share some genes that control some stages of embryonic development. Later, other genes take over and cause the fish, bird, and mammal to develop in different ways.

- All organisms seem to be alike in some fundamental ways. For example, all organisms have DNA or RNA as a genetic material. As you read in Chapter 3, all organisms use ATP in energy transfer. In addition, aerobic forms of life possess many of the same enzymes used in cell respiration. The same is true for cells that carry on photosynthesis.

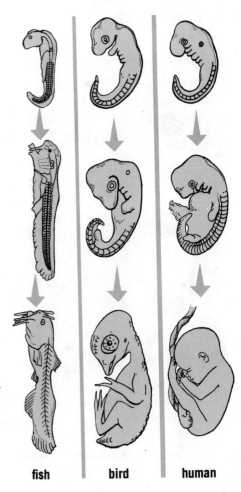

fish   bird   human

13–9 | Different stages in the development of three vertebrate animals. Note their similarities in the very early stages and their differences in the later stages.

Theories of Evolution

Two theories of evolution were presented in the nineteenth century. One theory was presented by Jean Lamarck. Later

Charles Darwin presented another theory that was in disagreement with Lamarck's.

Lamarck's Theory of Evolution

In 1801, the French biologist Jean Lamarck was one of the first scientists to theorize about evolution. Lamarck believed organisms change from generation to generation. He also believed that environment was a key factor in evolution. These ideas agree with currently accepted theory. But Lamarck's ideas about *how* organisms changed in response to the environment are in disagreement with current theory. Lamarck's theories are as follows:

- *The theory of need.* Lamarck thought that plants and animals change because of an inner need to change. For example, in the early evolution of monkeys tails could not be used for swinging from branch to branch. But for the monkeys to live in trees successfully, there was a need to develop such a tail. As a response to this need a tail capable of holding on to branches evolved.

- *The theory of use and disuse.* Organs remain active and strong when they are used. If they are not used, they weaken and disappear. According to this theory, your little toe and the muscles that move the ears are examples of structures that are disappearing because they are not used. The leg bones found in a snake such as the boa constrictor are another example.

- *The theory that acquired traits can be passed on to offspring.* Lamarck believed that a trait acquired by an individual during its life was passed on to its offspring. For example, Lamarck said that giraffes once had short necks and legs. Then the competition for food such as grass became too great. The giraffe began to stretch its neck and legs so that it could reach the leaves of trees. Later generations inherited the longer neck and stretched it even more. Finally the modern giraffe resulted.

13-10 | Lamarck's theory of the evolution of the giraffe's long neck. The competition for food caused the giraffe to stretch its neck to reach the leaves. Later generations inherited the longer neck.

Lamarck's theory at first seems to make sense. For example, a football player develops strong legs through use. If the football player breaks a leg, the muscles will become small and weak from disuse while in a cast. However there is *no* evidence that either of these acquired traits can be passed on by heredity.

Darwin's Theory of Natural Selection

In 1859, the English scientist Charles Darwin published his theory of **natural selection.** This theory of how different species develop in evolution is one of the most important in the history of science. The theory can be summarized in the following five steps:

- *All organisms produce more offspring than can actually survive.* This fact is very clear in some organisms. For example, a fern plant may produce 50 million spores in a year. If all spores survived, fern plants would cover North America within two fern generations. In the same way, an oyster may shed more than 100 million eggs in a single spawning. If all offspring survived, oysters would soon completely fill the ocean.

- *Every organism faces a constant struggle to survive.* All species overproduce, but only a fraction of the offspring survive. Each individual organism must struggle constantly to get enough food, water, space, and so on. This struggle is at its worst among members of the same species because they compete for the same things. Those who win the struggle survive. The others die.

- *The individuals of a given species vary.* Except for identical twins, every individual differs in some ways from all other members of the species. This is clearly seen in human beings and other complex organisms. But it is also true of even very simple organisms.

- *The individuals that are best adapted to the environment survive.* Individuals vary because they inherit different traits. Some of these traits are better suited to the environment than others. Individuals with these helpful traits tend to survive. Individuals without them tend to die. A good example of individuals with helpful traits surviving occurs when disease strikes a plant crop. A few plants may have traits that allow them to resist the disease. These plants will survive, while the others will die. Darwin called this part of his theory the **survival of the fittest.**

- *The organisms that survive pass their traits on to offspring.* In general, offspring resemble their parents. Parents that survive because of some helpful trait pass the genes for that trait on to their offspring. Offspring in which the trait appears will also tend to survive. The same will be true in each generation, so long as the same forces are at work in the environment. At some time, all members of a species may have the helpful trait.

13-11 | Darwin's theory of the evolution of the giraffe's long neck. Giraffes had different size necks. Those with the longer necks survived while the giraffes with shorter necks died.

You can see how Darwin's theory differs from that of Lamarck. Lamarck was right about the importance of the environment. But his ideas about how evolution takes place were backwards. Organisms do not change in order to survive in their environment. Rather, it is the environment that determines which organisms, through natural selection, have a chance to survive.

Facts & Figures

All 1,250 copies of the first edition of Darwin's *Origin of Species* were sold in one day.

In other words, organic variation has nothing to do with need. **Organisms vary whether they need to or not. Whether a variation is helpful or harmful depends on the environment.** Darwin recognized these facts. However, Darwin worked in an age in which little was known of genetics. Thus, while he knew that organisms do vary, he had no idea of why they vary. Years later the Dutch botanist Hugo De Vries pointed out a main cause of organic variation.

Mutation Theory of Evolution

In 1901, De Vries presented his mutation theory of evolution. He based this theory on many years of work with primrose plants. Of some 50,000 plants, at least 800 showed striking new traits not present in the parents. Yet these traits were passed on to offspring of the mutant plants. **De Vries concluded that mutations must occur often in other organisms as well. This change by mutation, he believed, was the basis for evolution.** These conclusions supported Darwin's theories of variation and survival of the fittest.

Today, scientists have a better understanding of the theory first offered by De Vries. Modern methods and discoveries have made it possible to look closer at mutations and how they occur.

Mechanisms of Evolution

Mutation

Genes tend to be stable. The DNA of which they are made replicates time after time without change. Yet *gene mutations* changes within the DNA molecule are the main way new genes are introduced into a population. The changed genes may produce traits completely new to the population. Mutations have been found in every kind of plant or animal studied by geneticists.

Many gene mutations have such slight effects that they are hard to detect. Mutant genes are also almost always recessive. For this reason, the mutant trait often will not immediately appear in the offspring.

Chromosome mutations, changes involving complete chromosomes, occur less frequently than gene mutations. Because so many genes are affected by chromosome mutation, the effects are often harmful for the organism. In fact, the result is often death. However, one type of chromosome mutation in plants called *polyploidy*, explained in Chapter 12, sometimes results in larger, better adapted plants.

Gene Mutation and Natural Selection

Where environment changes, a certain gene mutation can be favored by natural selection. The following case is an especially clear example. It involves the peppered moth population in the region of Manchester, a British industrial city.

Before 1845, the peppered moth was light-colored with a pattern of dark specks. It could hardly be seen when it rested on the light gray bark of trees. Then, in 1845, an almost completely black peppered moth was found in Manchester. A gene for color had mutated.

Normally this mutation would be harmful. A black moth on light bark would be easy prey for birds. But something else was happening in Manchester. The city was becoming an industrial center. Coal smoke pouring from factory chimneys was turning gray tree bark nearly black all over the area. In the changed environment a mutation for dark color was very helpful, since birds couldn't see the dark moths as well on dark trees.

The results of these changes are a good example of the theory of evolution in action. Between 1845 and 1895, the black moth population increased from a few individuals to *99 percent of the population.* Because of natural selection in a new environment, the peppered moth completely changed color in only 50 years!

Now, the city of Manchester has anti-pollution laws that forbid the release of coal smoke into the air. It will be interesting to see if the peppered moth will undergo reverse evolution and become again light-colored.

13–12 | The principle of industrial melanism. In each situation, which peppered moth is likely to survive the longest? *(© M. W. F. Tweedie, Photo Researchers, Inc.)*

Isolation

Two squirrel populations in the Grand Canyon area clearly show the effects of *isolation* on evolution. On the north rim of the canyon, the Kaibab squirrel is found. This animal has long ears, a white tail, and dark underparts. On the south rim, the Abert is found. The Abert has long ears, but its tail is gray and its underparts are light. The Kaibab and Abert are two different species, but they are thought to have developed from the same ancestor species. Why did they develop different traits in almost the same environment?

The answer is that the Kaibab and Abert were isolated from each other by the canyon. Thus, they could not share their gene pools by breeding with each other. As mutations occurred over thousands of years, the gene pools of the two populations became quite different. This resulted in the different species seen today.

In this case, the canyon and the river running through it acted as a physical *barrier* between the squirrel populations. Other such barriers include deserts, mountains, and oceans. The ocean is an especially strong barrier to breeding between populations. Thus, the plant and animal populations of islands are often striking examples of the effects of isolation.

13–13 | (top) The Kaibab squirrel lives on the north side of the Grand Canyon. (bottom) The Abert squirrel lives around the south side. The canyon, which serves as a barrier, has isolated these two species. *(top: Sonja Bullaty, Audobon Society; bottom: Al Lowry, Photo Researchers)*

13–14 | Camel ancestry; dromedary or Arabian camel; Bactrian or Asian camel; a South American Llama. *(American Museum of Natural History; Rue, National Audubon Society; Jerry Frank; George Holton, Photo Researchers)*

Migration

Migration is the movement of animals from one environment to another. Migration opens the door to change in two different ways. To see how this works, assume that several members of an animal population have migrated to a new area.

First, these animals all carry certain gene combinations found only in the population from which they came. Suppose these animals breed with the native animals in the new area. The native animals also have certain gene combinations found nowhere else. When these two different gene pools are mixed, new traits will result from the new gene combinations.

Migration has taken the animals into a new environment. New traits caused by mutations and new gene combinations may make offspring more likely to survive in this environment. All members of the population may have these traits. Thus, migration also opens the door to further change by natural selection.

A good example of the change that can result from migration is seen in camels. It is thought that the first camels developed in North America. Some of these early camels migrated to Asia across a land bridge believed to have existed at that time. Others migrated to South America. Migration continued until the camels' ancestors were spread around a large part of the world.

Then came a great ice age. The camel populations in most areas died. Camels survived only in a few widely scattered areas. In one area, they developed into the African camel, a species with one hump. In another area, evolution produced a different species, the Asian camel, with two humps. Though these modern animals look somewhat different, both are suited to life in a dry environment.

Early camels also survived in the mountains of South America. There they developed into the llama, an animal quite different from the two modern camels. The llama has no hump but is surefooted and has a thick coat of hair. These traits are most helpful in the cold, rocky mountains where the llama lives. You can imagine how such traits must have developed over the ages. In each generation, animals with slightly thicker coats were more likely to survive the cold winter. Sure-footed animals with shorter legs were better able to escape enemies on the rugged mountain slopes. Animals with these traits tended to survive and reproduce. Those without them tended to die.

Speciation

In this unit on heredity, you have learned about different species. **A *species* is a group of organisms that are similar** in structure and that can mate and produce fertile off-spring. All members of a species have the same number of chromosomes, and the genes on these chromosomes are arranged in the same way.

The development of a species is called *speciation.* Since life began, species have been disappearing and developing. This process is still going on today. You already have studied the forces involved in speciation: migration, change in environment, mutation, natural selection and isolation.

The examples of squirrels and camels illustrate how a new species might evolve. Isolation is important to speciation because it allows the gene pool of the isolated group to evolve separately from the original population. When the genes within the isolated group change to such an extent that interbreeding with the original population can no longer occur, a new species has evolved.

Nonevolving Populations and Hardy-Weinberg Principle

Hemophilia is a genetic disease that prevents normal blood clotting in humans. In any population of humans, some of the genes that produce normal clotting *mutate,* or change, to genes that produce hemophilia. The number of people with hemophilia depends on the number of genes for hemophilia present in that human gene pool. **The *gene frequency* is how often that gene occurs in the population.**

Gene frequencies can be determined for many different traits. Once known, they can be used to determine how many organisms of a certain population have certain traits. They also can be used to predict changes in future populations.

The increase or decrease of a certain trait in succeeding generations of a population, simply because of chance, is called *genetic drift.* For example, if you have a small population of white guinea pigs and black guinea pigs, an unusual pattern of mating might occur to alter the gene pool. Mating is random, but consider what would happen if all of the white guinea pigs mated with white guinea pigs. The result would be an abnormally large number of white offspring. The gene pool would be changed. The population would have undergone genetic drift.

In 1908, two men, a British mathematician named G. H. Hardy and a German named W. Weinberg, came to the following conclusion about gene frequency: If mating is random, and there are no mutations, and natural selection is not operating, then the frequency of a gene will not change. This idea is called the ***Hardy-Weinberg principle.*** It describes how a gene will appear unchanged in succes-

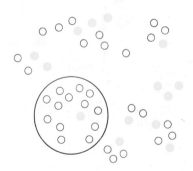

13-15 | Genetic drift in a population. The colored dots represent plants that carry a certain trait. Yellow colored petals, for example. The clear dots represent plants that carry a trait for white colored petals. What will happen to the frequency for the gene that carries the yellow trait if only those plants in the large colored circle live and reproduce?

13–16 | Adaptive radiation. Genetic variation produced adaptions for different environments and changes in body structure in each species: (top) mule deer, (center) elk, and (bottom) moose. *(Leonard Rue IV, Monkmeyer Press)*

con = together
vergere = to turn

ana = again

sive generations. So, a change in the Hardy-Weinberg principle describes a changing gene pool.

In real life, populations are thought to be changing. Some species, like the shark and turtle, change very slowly. Others, like certain insects, may change within a few generations. If you try to picture the conditions necessary to keep a population from changing, you can see why populations might evolve.

Genetic equilibrium, a nonevolving gene pool, requires special conditions which most scientists believe are never entirely met in the real world. Evolution is thought to be the usual condition of life. It occurs through mutation, environmental change, and natural selection.

Patterns of Evolution

Adaptive Radiation

The pattern in which different species develop from a common ancestor is called *adaptive radiation.*

It is possible to imagine some ancient population of animals invading a new land. Many small groups might separate from the original population and in isolation adapt to new environments. One example of adaptive radiation is the camel. The results of this kind of evolution can also be seen in the different members of the deer family in North America.

It is believed that the mule deer, elk, and moose all originated from the same ancestors. All these species have adapted in different ways but are still similar in many respects. Both the mule deer and elk live in mountain forests in the summer and move to sheltered valleys in the winter. The moose, the largest of the deer family, lives in northern swamp and lake areas in the summer. It winters on higher ground in nearby forests.

Convergent Evolution

In some ways, *convergent evolution* has effects opposite those of adaptive radiation. *Convergent* means "moving closer together." In convergent evolution, organisms with very different ancestors become more alike because they share the same environment.

The bat and a bird are not closely related. But they both have adapted to life in the air; they both have wings. The wings of bats and birds are called *analogous structures.* Analogous structures are similar in function and appearance but not in origin. Analogous structures are the result of convergent evolution. The flippers of a seal and the fins of a fish are other examples of analogous structures resulting from convergent evolution.

Sometimes convergent evolution has some strange effects. What is similar about a Himalyan rabbit, a panda bear, and a Siamese cat? All are light in color with dark patches. The dark patches develop on the colder parts of the body. If you shave the white fur from the back of a Himalayan rabbit and place an ice pack on it, the fur will grow back black. In all three animals the areas that are subjected to colder temperatures are dark, such as the feet and tail of the Siamese cat. In the case of these three animals species, natural selection favored genes for the same trait in entirely different organisms. The black color absorbs heat from the environment. These traits represent adaptations to very similar environments.

13–17 | How are these very different animals examples of convergent evolution? *(left: Delaware Photo Library Inc.; center: L. Alex Langley, DPI; right: Rob Chabot, DPI)*

Since its beginning, the earth has been constantly changing. Land masses have risen and sunk below seas, and mountains have thrust up and been worn away by wind and water. Ice ages have come and gone. Changes like these are still going on.

These changes in environment are thought to have brought about the many changes in life forms. New climates have favored certain traits. So the animals or plants with those favored traits survive and pass those traits on to offspring. The organisms with unsuitable traits die. With the passage of time, organisms may be quite different from their ancestors. New species are thought to have evolved over the ages in this way.

Some of the mechanisms of change, or evolution, are mutations that introduce new traits into the gene pool, migration of populations to different environments, and isolation of a population with resulting inbreeding.

Summary

Biologically Speaking

fossils	migration
evolution	species
gene pool	speciation
homologous organs	gene frequency
vestigial organs	genetic drift
natural selection	Hardy-Weinberg principle
survival of the fittest	genetic equilibrium
gene mutations	adaptive radiation
chromosome mutations	analogous structures
isolation	

Questions for Review

1. How does natural selection enter into the process of evolution?
2. What role does mutation play in the origin of species?
3. Describe Lamarck's idea of evolution.
4. How can migration lead to the origin of a new species?
5. Compare adaptive radiation to convergent evolution. Give examples of each.
6. Give an example of how isolation can act as a factor in evolution.
7. Explain the impact of environmental change on the evolution of the peppered moth.
8. How did Stanley Miller's experiment support Oparin's theory of how the first cell originated?
9. How do homologous structures indicate a relationship or a common ancestral oganism?
10. What factors would have to be met if a population did not evolve?

Applying Concepts

1. Discuss the importance of structural, physiological, and biochemical similarities in attempting to determine the paths of evolution.
2. Explain the development of the long neck of the giraffe according to Lamarck, and according to Darwin.
3. Discuss the genetic and social significance of the results of studies of the peppered moth in Manchester, England.
4. Discuss how future populations of organisms might be affected by the rapidly changing environment.

14-1 | The diversity of living organisms.

Diversity of Life

A **EXPLAIN** why there is a need to classify organisms.

B **DESCRIBE** some contributions of Carolus Linnaeus.

C **EXPLAIN** the binomial nomenclature method of scientific naming.

D **DESCRIBE** the bases of scientific classification.

E **NAME** the groupings in the system of classification.

F **WHAT** are some of the problems in classification systems?

The Science of Classification

You learned in Chapter 13 how organic variations developed over millions of years. You learned how the changing environment selects the forms of life that will survive. This selection process, at work for hundreds of millions of years, has led to many different species. Many species of life, such as insects, are very similar to each other. But each species has adapted differently. To study each species would be extremely difficult. There are over 800,000 species of insects alone! You can, however, pick a few examples to represent many organisms. Scientists have grouped various forms of life together. This enables one of each general type to be studied as an example of an entire group of organisms.

From earliest times people have had a need to classify life forms in order to better understand them. Some of the groups in their classification system would surely be meat-eating animals, plant-eating animals, and plants.

With the coming of civilization, humans learned more and more about the life around them. They recognized that the new knowledge gained about one animal or plant might

Facts & Figures

There are 500 different species of fleas alone.

175

apply to others of the same general type. Techniques for treating sick sheep, for instance, might be applied to cattle as well. There was a natural tendency to group similar organisms together. People based their groupings on the organization they saw in nature.

More than 2,000 years ago, the Greek philosopher Aristotle was one of the first to devise a formal classification system for studying plant and animal life. Aristotle divided plants into three groups: herbs, with soft stems; shrubs, with several woody stems; and trees, with a single woody trunk. Animals also were placed in three groups: land dwellers, water dwellers, and air dwellers.

If such a system seems overly simple today, it is because now more information is known. **The science of genetics has helped us to understand how changes occur. The study of evolution, in turn, has helped us to see the natural relationships that exist between living things. It is on these relationships that the modern science of classification, known as** *taxonomy,* **is based.**

taxis = arrangement

nomy = law

The Work of Linnaeus

Despite the importance of genetics and the theory of evolution, modern taxonomy owes a great deal to an eighteenth-century scientist who knew little of either. This scientist was Carolus Linnaeus, the great Swedish botanist. Linnaeus set up a classification system that is the basis for a system still used today.

The key to Linnaeus' system was *structural similarity.* He divided living organisms into two major groups, or **kingdoms.** He recognized only the plant kingdom and the animal kingdom. Each kingdom contained a number of smaller groups, and these in turn were divided into successively smaller groupings. The smaller the grouping, the more alike the members of the group were. **Linnaeus' system of classification recognized similarities and differences, which became the basis for his groupings of organisms.**

Another practice of Linnaeus was his use of scientific names made of Latin words. Latin words are still used in classification systems today. There were good reasons for him to use Latin. Latin was the language that scientists used in the eighteenth century. It was understood by scientists of all countries.

The scientific names given by Linnaeus usually described some trait of the organism. Each name was made of two or more parts. This system, still used today, is called

bi = two

nomen = name

binomial nomenclature, which means *two-word naming.* The first word names a larger group, the **genus,** to which the organism belongs, and the second word names a smaller group, the **species.** For example, both garden peas and field peas belong to the genus *Pisum.* The scientific names of both begin, therefore, with *Pisum.* Garden peas are *Pisum sativum,* and field peas are *Pisum arvense.* Notice that the genus name is capitalized, and the species name, which is an adjective, is not.

Modern Taxonomy

From the time of Linnaeus until recently, structural similarity has been the main basis for classifying living things. For example, the cow, bison, and deer are similar in structure. All three chew cuds, have large teeth for grinding plants, have two-toed hoofs, and so on.

In recent times, because of the development of the electron microscope and the increasing knowledge of biochemistry, other traits besides structure have become important in taxonomy. One such trait is *cellular organization.* For example, some types of cells are prokaryotic. They do not have membranous structures such as nuclei. Another factor that can be a reason for grouping organisms together is *biochemical similarity.* Cells of closely related organisms may form the same organic compounds, such as chlorophyll. Also, the more closely related organisms have similar proteins.

All of the above traits are coded by genes. The reason certain cells are prokaryotic is that they lack the genes that would code for making membrane-bound organelles. Thus the strongest evidence of relationship is *genetic similarity.* Suppose two animals have the same number of chromosomes. Also, suppose these chromosomes are identical or very similar in structure and arrangement of genes. It can then be assumed that these animals are closely related.

Groupings in the Classification System

More than a million different plants and animals are known to exist. Suppose you had a sample of each species. How would you begin to classify them? Probably you would first separate them into plants and animals, and then into smaller and smaller groups. This is exactly what biologists have done.

The largest groups are known as *kingdoms.* Each kingdom is broken down into smaller groups known as **phyla** (singular, phylum). Each phylum, in turn, is divided into

14-2 | These are two different species of the genus *Lilium.* (top: Manuel Rodriquez; bottom: T. E. Adams, © Peter Arnold)

14–3 | How would you classify these organisms? *(a: Tom Brakefield, Taurus Photos; b: Phil A. Dotson, DPI; c: Leonard Lee Rue III, DPI; d: © Animals Animals; e: M. E. Browning, DPI; f: © Animals Animals; g: © Dr. J. A. L. Cooke, Animals Animals; h: Grant Heilman)*

a

b

classes. A class contains many **orders.** A division of an order is a **family.** The family is made of *genera* (singular, genus). Finally, each genus is divided into *species.* Sometimes members of a species vary slightly, but not enough to be considered different species. Such slightly different organisms are called **varieties.** The variety name is added as a third part of the scientific name.

To see how this system of grouping organism works, let's say that you have a mule deer, a moose, a sheep, a white-tailed deer, a cat, a bird, a pine tree, and a clam that must be placed in smaller and smaller groups of greater and greater similarity.

First, the pine tree is set aside in the plant kingdom and all the other seven organisms are classified as belonging to the kingdom Animalia. Now which six animals are most alike? They are the mule deer, moose, sheep, the white-tailed deer, the cat, and the bird. All these belong to the phylum Chordata because, unlike the clam, they have backbones.

Next the bird is excluded because it has feathers. The mule deer, moose, sheep, white-tailed deer, and the cat are in the class Mammalia because they produce milk for their young. Next the cat is excluded because it has claws, and the group of the mule deer, moose, sheep and white-tailed deer are placed in the order Artiodactyla because they have even-toed hooves. The antlered animals, the mule deer,

c

d

e

f

g

h

Table 14-1 THE CLASSIFICATION OF SIX DIFFERENT ORGANISMS

	HUMAN	GRASS-HOPPER	DANDELION	WHITE PINE	AMEBA	TYPHOID BACTERIUM
KINGDOM	Animalia	Animalia	Plantae	Plantae	Protista	Protista
PHYLUM	Chordata	Arthropoda	Tracheophyta	Tracheophyta	Sarcodina	Schizomycophyta
CLASS	Mammalia	Insecta	Angiospermae	Gymnospermae	Rhizopoda	Schizomycetes
ORDER	Primates	Orthoptera	Campanulales	Coniferales	Amoebida	Eubacteriales
FAMILY	Hominidae	Acridiidae	Compositae	Pinaceae	Amoebidae	Bacteriaceae
GENUS	*Homo*	*Schistocerca*	*Taraxacum*	*Pinus*	*Amoeba*	*Eberthella*
SPECIES	*sapiens*	*americana*	*officinale*	*strobus*	*proteus*	*typhosa*

moose, and white-tailed deer, belong to the family Cervidae (the deer family). The sheep is excluded because it has horns, not antlers. Both the mule deer and the white-tailed deer belong to the same genus, *Odocoileus*. The mule deer belongs to the species *hemionus*. The white-tailed deer belongs to the species *virginianus* and is called *Odocoileus virginianus*.

Thus the mule deer has been classified as belonging to the species *hemionus* within the genus *Odocoileus* of the family Cervidae of the order Ungalata within the class Mammalia in the phylum Chordata of the Kingdom Animalia.

Scientific Names

Members of a *species* are similar in structure and can mate and produce fertile offspring. For example, all domestic cats are of one species, though they differ in size, color, and other traits.

The binomial system avoids the confusion of using common names. The mountain lion, for example, is also called the puma, cougar, panther, and perhaps a dozen other common names. All scientists, however, can identify this animal as *Felis concolor*. Other cats belong to the same genus, but not the same species. For example *Felis onca* is the jaguar. Lions, tigers, and leopards belong to a different genus, *Panthera*.

Some common names are actually misleading. For example, clams and oysters are called shellfish, but are not true fish at all. Neither is the crayfish, jellyfish, or starfish. The silverfish is an insect. In your study of biology, some of these common names will be used because they are familiar. But when you need to be really accurate, you can avoid problems by using scientific names.

calator = caller

chorda = cord

mammae = breast

artio = even-numbered

dactylo = digit, foot

cervi = antlers

odonto = tooth

coelo = hollow

hemi = half

onus = weight

Table 14-2 A MODERN CLASSIFICATION OF ORGANISMS

Kingdom—Monera

Organisms with prokaryotic cells (cells without an organized nucleus). They also lack chloroplasts and mitochondria. They are unicellular or colonial.

PHYLUM	ORGANISMS
Schizophyta	bacteria
Cyanophyta	blue-green algae

Kingdom—Protista

Organisms having a simple structure; many unicellular, others colonial or multicellular but lacking in specialized tissue; both heterotrophic and autotrophic; neither distinctly plant nor distinctly animal.

	PHYLUM	ORGANISMS
Algal Protists	Chlorophyta	green algae
	Chrysophyta	golden-brown algae, or diatoms
	Pyrrophyta	dinoflagellates and cryptomonads
	Phaeophyta	brown algae
	Rhodophyta	red algae
Fungal Protists	Eumycophyta	fungi
	Myxomycophyta	slime fungi
Protozoan Protists	Sarcodina	amoeboid organisms
	Mastigophora	flagellates
	Ciliophora	ciliates
	Sporozoa	*Plasmodium*

Kingdom—Plantae

Multicellular plants having tissues and organs; cell walls containing cellulose; chlorophyll *a* and *b* present and localized in chloroplasts; food stored as starch; sex organs multicellular; autotrophic.

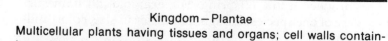

DIVISION	SUBDIVISION	CLASS	ORGANISMS
Bryophyta			liverworts, hornworts, and mosses
Tracheophyta	Psilopsida		"whiskferns"
	Lycopsida		club mosses
	Sphenopsida		horsetails (*Equisetum*) and calamites
	Pteropsida	Filicineae	ferns
		Gymnospermae	seed ferns, cycads, *Ginkgo*, and conifers
		Angiospermae	flowering plants

Kingdom—Animalia

Multicellular animals having tissues and, in many cases, organs and organ systems; pass through embryonic or larval stages in development; heterotrophic. (Only the major phyla are listed.)

PHYLUM	SUBPHYLUM	ORGANISMS
Porifera		sponges
Coelenterata		jellyfish, sea anemones, corals
Platyhelminthes		flatworms
Nematoda		roundworms
Trochelminthes		rotifers
Bryozoa		bryozoans, sea mosses
Brachiopoda		brachiopods, or lampshells
Mollusca		clams, snails, squids, octopi
Annelida		segmented worms (earthworm)
Arthropoda		insects, spiders, crustaceans
Echinodermata		starfishes, sea urchins
Chordata	Hemichordata	tongue worms, acorn worms
	Tunicata	tunicates
	Cephalochordata	lancelets
	Vertebrata	vertebrates

Problems in Classification

Any classification system is only a useful tool developed by taxonomists to describe organisms. If you are told that a certain animal belongs to the order Ungalata, you immediately know a great deal about that animal. It has hoofs, it's a grazing animal, it is a mammal, it has a backbone, and so on.

In the same way, if a tree belongs to the genus *Pinus*, you know it has all of the characteristics of a pine tree. It has cones, needlelike leaves, and water-conducting tissue. **A classification system presents a great deal of information in an orderly way.**

However, systems of classification also present problems. How should a single-celled organism with cholorophyll be classified? As a plant? But what if this organism swims around like an animal? It seems to be neither animal nor plant. The first system of classification recognized only plant and animal kingdoms. This system had no place for such "inbetween" organisms.

Problems like this have resulted in the creation of several different systems of classification. The system of classification used throughout this book is seen in Table 14-2. In this system two new kingdoms have been added to the original animal and plant kingdoms.

One of the new kingdoms is the *Kingdom Monera* (mo-NEER-uh). This group is made of *prokaryotic cells*, cells without nuclei. These include bacteria and blue-green algae.

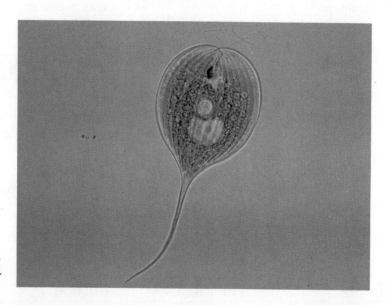

14–4 | Why is this organism, a *Phacus,* so difficult to classify? *(T. E. Adams, Peter Arnold, Inc.)*

The other new kingdom is the kingdom *Protista*. The organisms in this kingdom have cells with nuclei, but they are neither distinctly plant nor animal. They lack specialized tissues. Some make their own food, and so are plantlike, and others do not. This kingdom includes the algae other than blue-green, fungi, and protozoa.

In the Kingdom Plantae, *divisions* rather than *phyla* are used. In the system that is used in this book, *Tracheophyta* identifies plants with water- and food-conducting tissue, separating them from other plants that lack this tissue. Other systems base their classifications of plants on features like embryology (see Appendix).

A Job That Has Only Begun

Some 1.5 million animals, plants, and protists have been named and classified. But some biologists estimate that there may be as many as five million different kinds of organisms in the world population. If so, millions of organisms remain to be found. Many of these may be hidden deep in the seas or in remote regions of the earth. Some may be in the school yard or in a dusty corner.

If the number of living species seems large, remember that many times more have become extinct. They are no longer in existence. These extinct species, too, have their place in any system that attempts to classify life of all ages.

Also, what if life is found on another planet? Strange forms that require new categories in the classification of life may eventually be discovered. The work of classification is far from over. In fact, it has only begun.

Summary

The great Swedish botanist, Carolus Linnaeus, set up a classification system based on structural similarities between organisms. This system has until recently remained the basis of *taxonomy*. His system of two-part scientific names based on *genus* and *species* is still in use.

With the development of the electron microscope and the increasing knowledge of biochemistry, other traits besides structure can be considered in classification systems. The strongest evidence of relationships between organisms is *genetic similarity*. Two animals with similar chromosomes are probably closely related.

Some 1.5 million animals and plants have been named and classified, but millions of species remain to be identified. There are several different systems of classification, each with advantages and disadvantages. As more knowledge is gained, the relationships between different organisms may become more clear.

Biologically Speaking

taxonomy | phylum
kingdom | class
binomial nomenclature | order
genus | family
species | variety

Questions for Review

1. What animal or plant characteristics was the Linnaeus system of classification based on?
2. What is binomial nomenclature?
3. Why is Latin used as the language for biological classification?
4. Discuss ways in which common names can be confusing and misleading.
5. What characteristics of an organism are used as the basis of its classification?
6. Why is there a need for a system of classification?
7. List the classification groups from the largest to the smallest.
8. What are some of the problems biologists have in classifying organisms into kingdoms?

Applying Concepts

1. What are some of the reasons scientists can't agree on one scheme of classification?
2. In what ways might a system of classification present a distorted or wrong picture of nature?
3. The fox, wolf, and coyote are different species of the dog family. On the other hand, the collie, poodle, and terrier are breeds of domestic dog. Distinguish between a species and a breed or variety.

Activities

1. Look up the formula for the volume and surface area of a sphere. Substitute the values 1, 2, 3, 4, and 5 for the radius. See if the volume increase exceeds the area increase. Apply this to your knowledge of cell size.

2. Use two coins to demonstrate how the probability of flipping two heads, head-tails, or two tails is related to the 1:2:1 genotypic ratio seen in some crosses.

3. Use magazines and newspaper articles as the basis for a report on one recent event or discovery in genetics that might influence your life.

4. Use PTC paper to conduct a survey in the class to find out how many students are tasters and how many are nontasters. What is the the ratio of tasters to nontasters? How do these results compare with the gene pool of the United States?

5. Use your pet store and library as a source for a report on one of the following topics: (a) The tropical fish market: how new varieties are obtained and sold to the public; (b) How to breed and sell registered dogs and cats.

6. Observe a group of different birds feeding. Write a brief report on your observations and how they relate to evolution. Observe and describe feeding behavior, aggressive behavior, structures (such as beak types), and how they are used to advantage. List and discuss advantages and disadvantages of certain structures and behavior patterns.

7. Study the "life style" of a group of wild or free animals in your neighborhood. List the environmental factors that influence their survival. Discuss these factors and explain how a change in environment would influence natural selection. Write a paper on their struggle for survival.

8. Try to determine the genus and species of any three birds, flowers, or trees in your neighborhood. Use the library as a resource.

9. Make a list of the books available in your library for classifying plants and animals. Try using any one of the books and write a brief report on your successes or difficulties.

Related Readings

Books

Asimov, Isaac, *The Genetic Code*. New American Library, Inc., New York, 1962 (paperback available). Tells how the arrangement of the bases in the DNA molecule controls traits of living organisms.

Beadle, George and Muriel, *The Language of Life: An Introduction to the Science of Genetics*. Doubleday and Co., Inc., Garden City, NY, 1961. A presentation of some of the many scientific studies in genetics.

Eiseley, L., *Darwin's Century: Evolution and the Man Who Discovered It*. Doubleday and Co., Inc., New York, 1958. (Avon paperback, 1961). A remarkable story of how the theory of evolution was developed.

Folsome, C. E., *The Origin of Life: Readings from Scientific American*. Freeman, San Francisco, 1968 (paperback available). A very current summary of research into the origin of life.

Grzimek, Bernhard, *Encyclopedia of Evolution*. Van Nostrand, Reinhold, New York, 1976. A generous supply of color pictures shows the evolution of various animal groups. There is also a general discussion of evolutionary principles.

Jenkins, J. B., *Genetics*. Houghton Mifflin, Boston, 1979. An up-to-date general textbook in genetics. Well balanced between molecular and classical genetics.

Simon, E. H. and J. Grossfield, *The Challenge of Genetics*. Addison-Wesley, Reading, PA, 1971 (paperback available). A collection of problems and ways to solve them.

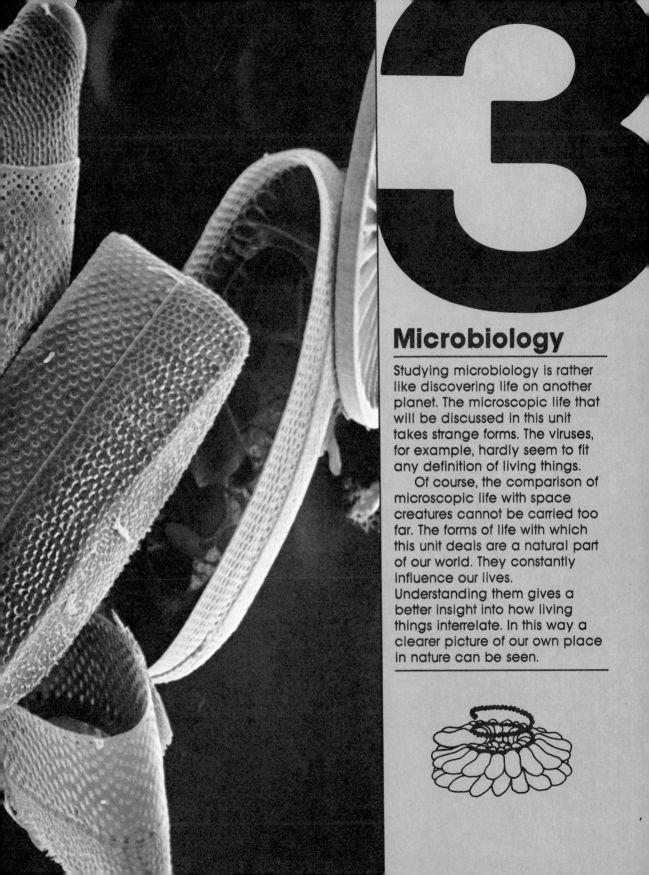

3

Microbiology

Studying microbiology is rather like discovering life on another planet. The microscopic life that will be discussed in this unit takes strange forms. The viruses, for example, hardly seem to fit any definition of living things.

Of course, the comparison of microscopic life with space creatures cannot be carried too far. The forms of life with which this unit deals are a natural part of our world. They constantly influence our lives. Understanding them gives a better insight into how living things interrelate. In this way a clearer picture of our own place in nature can be seen.

15

The Viruses

A **EXPLAIN** why viruses could be considered living or nonliving.

B **DESCRIBE** some early discoveries about viruses.

C **DESCRIBE** the structure of a phage virus.

D **DESCRIBE** how viruses are different from cells.

E **DESCRIBE** the lytic cycle of a virulent phage virus.

F **EXPLAIN** what a temperate phage is and how it involves a cell.

G **LIST** some viral diseases.

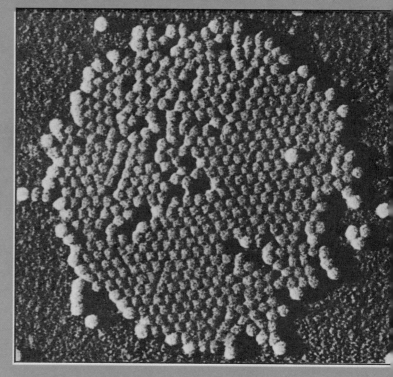

15–1 | Polio virus particles (180,000X). *(Dr. Robley C. Williams, Courtesy March of Dimes)*

The Discovery of Viruses

patho = disease
genic = causing

You probably have heard someone say, "I had a twenty-four hour virus. I felt awful." Some viruses cause disease. They are said to be ***pathogenic.*** These were the first viruses studied. However, many viruses apparently are harmless.

Scientists worked with viral diseases long before the existence of viruses was known. Dr. Edward Jenner performed the first vaccination against smallpox virus in 1796. He transferred a virus-containing fluid from a cowpox sore on the hand of a dairy maid to a scratch on the arm of an eight-year-old boy. About a century later, Louis Pasteur discovered that the virus that caused a rabies infection centered in the brain and spinal cord. He successfully transmitted the disease to a laboratory animal by injecting the animal with substances from a brain and spinal cord of an infected animal. Neither of these men realized that the agent of infection with which they were dealing was a virus. Even into the 1930s, viruses remained undiscovered. Until that time many scientists had been studying diseases that were found later to be caused by viruses.

Tobacco Mosaic Virus

In 1892 a Russian biologist, Dimitri Iwanowski, was studying a disease of tobacco plants known as tobacco mosaic. The word *mosaic* refers to a pattern of light green and yellow areas that appear on the diseased tobacco leaves. Iwanowski first squeezed fluid from diseased leaves, then rubbed this fluid onto healthy plants. The healthy leaves soon showed the mosaic pattern of the disease.

Iwanowski varied the experiment. He passed the fluid from the diseased leaves through a filter with pores small enough to remove all bacteria. The microscope revealed no bacteria or other bodies that might cause disease in this fluid. But when the fluid was rubbed on healthy plants, it still caused the disease.

The results on healthy plants puzzled Iwanowski. In his day bacteria were thought to be the smallest possible agents of disease. The organism that caused the tobacco mosaic was far too small to be seen through his light microscope. He could only assume that some invisible poison, given off by the bacteria, had passed through the filter.

Six years later the Dutch botanist, Martinus Beijerinck, repeated Iwanowski's work. He reached a different conclusion. He believed that the fluid must contain some invisible agent smaller than the smallest bacteria. He named this unknown agent **virus,** a Latin word meaning "poison."

It was not until 1935 that the virus was found. The discoverer was Dr. Wendell Stanley. Stanley ground and removed the fluid from more than a ton of diseased tobacco leaves. From this fluid he obtained about a teaspoonful of needlelike crystals. Stored in a bottle, these crystals seemed to have no life. Yet when they were put in water and rubbed on tobacco leaves, they produced the mosaic disease. Stanley had isolated the tobacco mosaic virus. For this work he received the Nobel prize in chemistry in 1946.

Stanley was not able to see an individual virus. One of the most important developments in the study of viruses was the invention of the electron microscope. Electron microscopes became available in 1944, and for the first time a magnification high enough to see a virus was available to scientists.

Nature of Viruses

Two things are striking about the Stanley experiments. One is that the viruses he isolated were in the form of crystals. In the crystal form, viruses are as nonliving as crystals

15–2 | Tobacco mosaic virus: (bottom) infected leaf showing mottling and (top) healthy tobacco leaf. *(Marvin Williams, North Carolina State University; Courtesy North Carolina State University)*

of sugar or salt. Yet when placed in living cells, these same viruses are able to be reproduced.

The other significant thing about the Stanley study is the small amount (about a teaspoonful) of crystals Stanley got from a ton of tobacco leaves. This is because viruses are extremely small.

Size of Viruses

The tobacco mosaic virus is about 300 nanometers (nm) long. One nanometer is one millionth of a millimeter (1 nm = 4×10^{-8} inches). Other viruses range in size from 25 nanometers to over 250 nanometers. It would take about 4,000 large viruses to stretch across the inside of the letter *o*. One of the smaller sphere-shaped bacteria, which appears as a speck under the light microscope, is about 750 nanometers in diameter.

Viruses are much larger than a molecule, but much smaller than the smallest cell. Viruses are called **filterable viruses** because they pass through the pores of filters through which bacteria could not pass.

Magnified 60,000 times by an electron microscope, the tobacco mosaic virus is seen as a rod-shaped body. Figure 15-4 is a good example of how some viruses are constructed.

Composition of Viruses

The outermost part of the virus consists of a thick protein coat. The protein coat covers a central strand of RNA (ribonucleic acid). RNA is the molecule that carries the genetic code of the virus and controls the making of its protein. A spiral strand of RNA runs the length of the rod-shaped virus. The tobacco mosaic virus looks somewhat like a chromosome found in a cell nucleus. The protein coat makes up about 95 percent of the virus. The other five percent of the virus is its RNA core.

Many different kinds of viruses have been seen with the electron microscope. They have a wide variety of shapes. Some are oval-shaped with tiny necks; some are shaped like spheres, cubes, or needles. Viruses have an outer coat made mostly of protein, and they all contain either DNA or RNA as their genetic material.

Some viruses seen with the electron microscope are extremely beautiful in design and look very complex. They are all *subcellular*. That is, they lack the organization of cells. They have no nucleus or cytoplasm. They do not contain any of the structures of a cell that are used for making protein or high-energy molecules.

How, then, does a virus work? How does it reproduce? How can it be considered living?

cowpox, smallpox
(275 nm)

flu, mumps
(115 nm)

bacteriophage
(100 nm)

human
red blood
cell
7500 nm

tobacco mosaic
(300 × 15 nm)

polio
(25 nm)

15-3 | Some viruses drawn for comparison over a portion of a human red blood cell.

How a Virus Lives

All viruses have similar life cycles. When it is outside a cell, a virus shows no sign of life. It does not grow or carry on respiration. It does not carry on any of the constant chemical activities associated with life. **To become active, a virus requires a** *host cell.*

A host cell is any cell that is attacked by a virus. Once viral genetic material enters the host cell, the virus genes take control of the chemical energy and structures within the cell. They then cause the cell to replicate nucleic acid and synthesize protein. Virus structures are assembled instead of structures of the original cell.

The Virulence of Viruses

A virus's ability to cause disease is called its **virulence.** The virulence of viruses varies. For example, colds are caused by many different viruses. Some viruses cause mild colds, others cause colds that are more severe.

Not only do viruses differ in their virulence, but different strains of the same virus may have different virulence. Each year humans seem to be threatened by a new strain of influenza, or "flu." The reason is that viruses vary due to mutation. When a particular type of virus has a change in its genetic makeup, it may gain in virulence and sweep through a population. An infection that affects many individuals at the same time is called an *epidemic.* In one month in 1918, 400,000 Americans died of flu or from complications caused by flu. The Asian flu of 1958 was equally virulent, but by that time a treatment had been developed, and many lives were saved.

Classification of Viruses

Viruses in general invade only specific kinds of cells. For this reason, viruses are classified according to their host organisms. This system of classification is as follows:

- *Bacterial viruses,* which invade the cells of bacteria.
- *Plant viruses,* which invade the cells of plants.
- *Animal viruses,* which invade animal cells.

Actually, the relationship between virus and host is more specific than these large groups. A bacterial virus can invade only a specific plant and only specific cells within the plant, such as leaf cells. The tobacco mosaic virus is an example of a specific plant virus. An animal virus may become active only in certain tissue cells, such as skin cells, in a specific animal. Some viruses are even more specific. Polio viruses are human viruses that attack only *one kind* of nerve cell in the brain and spinal cord.

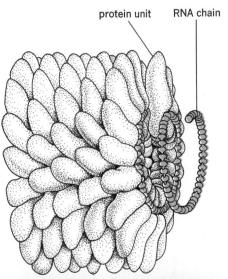

protein unit   RNA chain

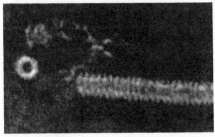

15-4 | Tobacco mosaic virus. Compare the schematic drawing with the electron micrograph (300,000X). *(Courtesy R. W. Horne)*

Facts & Figures

Influenza killed approximately 20 million people in 1918 and 1919.

Bacteriophages

Much of what is known about viruses has come from the study of viruses that attack bacteria. **Viruses that attack bacteria are called** *bacteriophages* (bacteria eaters), or simply *phages*. They were first discovered in England in 1915. Scientists noticed that something strange happened when growing certain bacteria. Small circles, or *plaques*, spread around a whole colony of bacteria until it was destroyed. The agent that destroyed the bacteria could be transferred to other colonies.

Structure of Bacteriophages

The electron microscope made it possible to search for the "bacteria eater." Scientists found the strange, almost mechanical-looking structure seen in figure 15-6. This was the agent that killed the bacteria. The structure contained protein. Its bulb, or head, appeared to have a narrow tail, resembling a table lamp.

A way was found to break open the bulblike head. The head was then found to contain a single long strand. The strand proved to be DNA (deoxyribonucleic acid), the genetic material of this particular phage. These observations were important in determining the physical and chemical structure of the phage.

The Lytic Cycle of a Virulent Phage

With the use of an electron microscope, phages have been photographed at every step of their attack on bacteria.

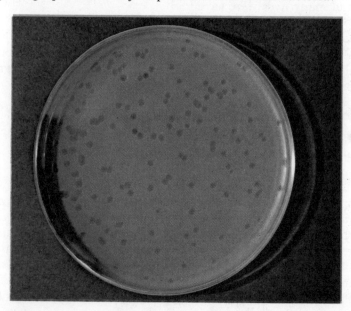

15-5 | A bacteria culture spotted with *plaques. (Lewis Koster)*

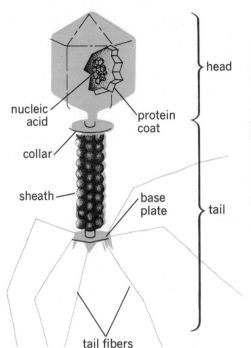

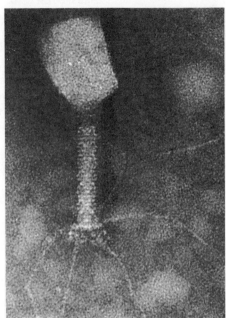

15–6 | A bacterial virus, or phage. Compare the schematic drawing (left) with the electron micrograph. *(Courtesy T. F. Anderson)*

15–7 | An "exploded" T_2 bacteriophage. Its central core of DNA is seen to be a single strand. *(Courtesy A. K. Kleinschmidt and* Biochimica et Biophysica Acta*)*

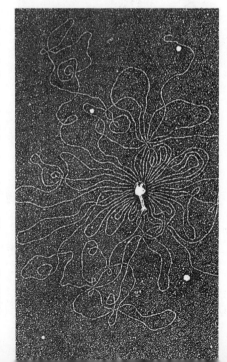

The destruction of a bacterial cell by a phage is called **lysis** (LICE-is). A phage that produces such a **lytic cycle** of destruction is called a *virulent phage*. The lytic cycle can be broken down into five steps (see figure 15-8).

1. The cycle begins when a phage attaches, tail down, to the cell wall of the bacterium. The tail attaches at a specific *receptor site* on the cell wall.
2. The tail is used like a hypodermic needle. The sheath on the tail penetrates the cell wall and the cell membrane. The phage's DNA is then injected into the bacterium. The empty protein coat remains outside and plays no further role in the cycle.
3. Within minutes after entering a cell, the phage DNA serves as a new genetic code for the cell. The viral DNA takes complete control of cell activity and codes for more phage DNA and protein. The cell becomes a factory for making more viruses.
4. Soon the bacterium may contain 300 or more virus particles.
5. The cell wall breaks open. The phages are released and can now attack other bacteria.

Biologists often use a story to explain this process more clearly: A tank rolls up to an automobile factory and breaks a hole through the factory wall. The tank crew enters and

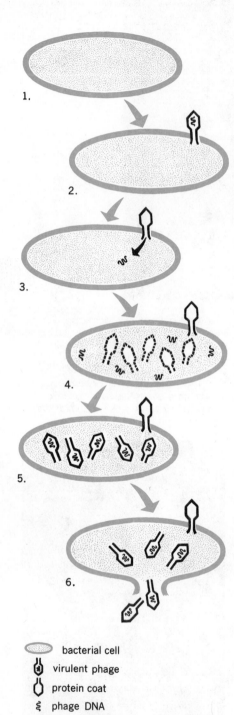

takes control of the factory. Machines are reset, and the materials once used to make cars are now used to build more tanks. Soon hundreds of tanks are rumbling through the factory. A wall is broken down, and the tanks spread out into the countryside to attack other factories.

Notice in this story that the tank crew needs the factory machinery in order to build more tanks. The crew cannot produce more tanks on its own. In the same way, a phage cannot reproduce itself. It needs the machinery of the host cell.

Temperate Phages

Sometimes a phage injects its DNA into a bacterium without causing new phages to be produced. Such a phage is called a *temperate phage.* It is thought that some chemical property of the bacterial cell keeps the phage from becoming virulent.

However, the DNA of a temperate phage does not simply disappear. Biologist believe that it attaches to the bacterial chromosome. There it remains, like an extra gene. In this condition it is called a **prophage.** When the bacterial chromosome replicates at the start of cell division, the phage DNA also replicates. Thus, when the bacterium splits in half, each new cell receives the normal bacterial DNA and the phage DNA genetic code. In this way the phage DNA may be multiplied generation after generation with no damage.

Even though there are no immediate effects from a temperate phage, the phage DNA remains dangerous. In a way it is like a bomb that needs some slight jolt to set it off. At some time, the prophage may mutate and become *virulent.* Or the cell itself may lose the trait that resists the phage. It is thought that some cancers might be caused by certain prophage-like viruses. An internal change in a human cell damaged by radiation might cause the phage genes to become active inside the cell. This kind of damage also may be caused by cigarette smoke.

Defenses Against Viruses

Many familiar diseases of human beings and animals are caused by viruses. Several diseases that affect humans have already been mentioned. To this list viral pneumonia, viral hepatitis, warts, chicken pox, yellow fever, cold sores, and many other diseases can be added. The symptoms of muscle ache, headache, sore joints, and stomach upset are typical of the more common viral infections.

If viruses are so effective, how can organisms defend themselves? What stops a virus from multiplying and destroying enough cells to cause death?

1.
2.
3.
4.
5.
6.

bacterial cell
virulent phage
protein coat
phage DNA

15-8 | The lytic cycle of destruction caused by a virulent phage.

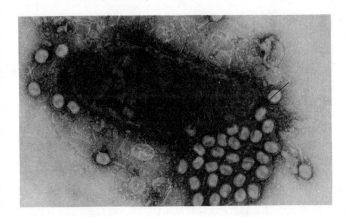

15-9 | An electron micrograph of a T$_4$ bacteriophate destroying a cell of *E. coli* (45,000X). *(Drs. D. T. Brown and T. F. Anderson, Institute for Cancer Research, Philadelphia)*

The best defense against viral disease is *immunity.* As soon as a virus invades your body, certain cells react to the foreign protein of the virus. The cells produce chemical compounds called *antibodies.* The antibodies react with the virus protein, changing its chemistry and making it harmless.

The weakened polio virus vaccine given today is harmless, but it stimulates your cells to produce antibodies. If a virulent form of polio virus should later enter your body, these antibodies attach to the surface of the virus and prevent it from infecting your cells. This is how you become immune to polio.

The antibodies against polio will not work against measles virus or bacteria. Each antibody is specific for a certain protein. Antibodies should not be confused with *antibiotics* such as penicillin, which will be mentioned in Chapter 17.

Transduction

Viruses do not always kill the host cell. Under certain conditions viruses can transfer host genes from one cell to another. This is called *transduction.*

In transduction, the virus usually transfers one or more of the genes from its host bacterium to a bacterium of a different strain. In this way the newly infected strain acquires new characteristics. These new traits might include making a new substance, like alcohol, or producing a certain amino acid.

Interferon: Hope for the Future

Vaccines for many viral diseases have been developed. Some have been mentioned in this chapter. But, once you get a viral disease, such as a cold, your body's own defenses are the best cure. Perhaps before too long, medical doctors may have a new defense to offer patients. This new defense

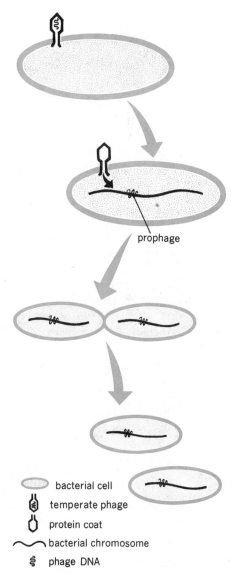

prophage

bacterial cell
temperate phage
protein coat
bacterial chromosome
phage DNA

15-10 | The invasion of a bacterial cell by a temperate phage.

against viruses, which is still in the experimental stage of development, is ***interferon.***

Interferon is a protein produced by animal cells when they are attacked by viruses. It was discovered in 1957 and named *interferon* because it interfered with the action of viruses. **Interferon is a natural part of an organism's defense against disease, and seems to be effective against many different viruses.**

When interferon is released by the host cell, it attaches to the cell membranes of noninfected cells. The interferon then causes the cells to produce a certain enzyme that prevents the host cell from making viral protein. It does this by interfering with the virus's chemistry. Although the virus can enter healthy cells, the interferon keeps it from reproducing. The infection is then halted.

Scientists would like to learn how to use interferon to fight disease, but interferon is difficult to obtain for medical use. It is *species specific.* That means that the interferon produced by a chicken, for example, will work only for chickens. Chicken interferon will not work on ducks. Interferon used in treating humans has to be produced from human cells. The process of obtaining interferon from human cells grown in the laboratory is slow, difficult, and expensive. Only small amounts are available, so medical use is still experimental and limited.

15–11 | Transduction.

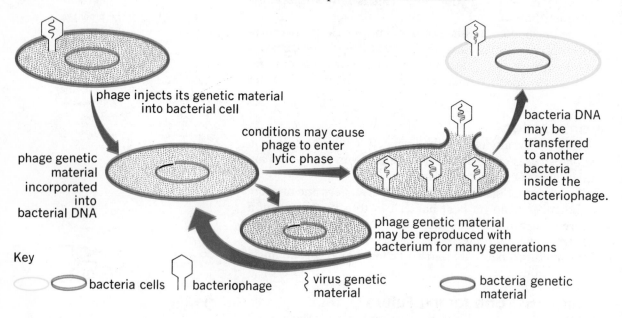

phage injects its genetic material into bacterial cell

conditions may cause phage to enter lytic phase

bacteria DNA may be transferred to another bacteria inside the bacteriophage.

phage genetic material incorporated into bacterial DNA

phage genetic material may be reproduced with bacterium for many generations

Key

bacteria cells | bacteriophage | virus genetic material | bacteria genetic material

Viruses are so small that they can be seen only with the electron microscope. They are nonliving in the crystal form. Yet when placed in living cells, viruses control the chemical energy and structure within the host cell.

Scientists have classified viruses according to the kinds of organisms they attack: bacteria, plants, or animals. Much of what is known about viruses has come from the study of *bacteriophages*, the viruses that attack bacteria.

Vaccines, such as smallpox vaccine, have been developed. Increased knowledge of *interferon*, a natural protein that combats viral infection, holds some promise in the battle against viral disease.

pathogenic	bacteriophages	immunity
virus	lysis	antibodies
filterable virus	lytic cycle	transduction
host cell	temperate phage	interferon
virulence	prophage	

1. What are viruses, and how do they differ from cells?

2. How does the term "filterable viruses" describe virus size?

3. How were viruses discovered?

4. Why are bacteriophages easier to work with than other viruses?

5. Classify the viruses into three groups on the basis of the host organism.

6. What is the relationship between a host cell and a virus?

7. Describe the lytic cycle of the virulent phage.

8. In what way is a temperate phage a potential "seed of destruction?"

9. List some better-known human diseases caused by viruses.

1. Explain various factors that may alter the virulence of a virus.

2. Discuss several biological principles shown by the lytic cycle of a virulent phage.

3. Discuss how genetic engineering might be useful in combating viral disease.

4. Are viruses alike? Explain why or why not.

16

Bacteria

A **DESCRIBE** the contributions of Louis Pasteur to microbiology.

B **NAME** and **DESCRIBE** three general types of bacteria.

C **DISTINGUISH** a heterotroph from an autotroph.

D **DESCRIBE** the various types of bacterial respiration.

E **DESCRIBE** three ways bacteria gain new genes.

F **DESCRIBE** the structure and size of bacteria.

G **LIST** some benefits derived from bacteria.

H **LIST** three ways to limit bacterial growth.

I **DESCRIBE** some experiments in genetic engineering.

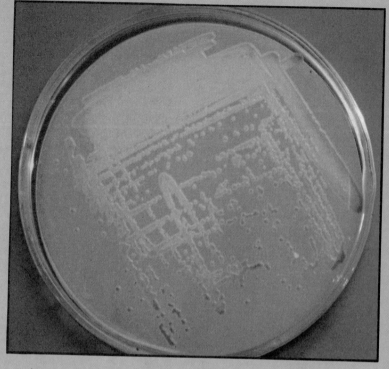

16-1 | Colonies of bacteria on an agar plate. (© L. V. Bergman Inc.)

16-2 | This electron micrograph shows a fossil bacterium in rock that is over three billion years old. The rod-shaped bacterium is about 0.5 micrometers long. The space below is an imprint of a dislodged bacterium. (Courtesy of Prof. Elso S. Barghoorn, Harvard University)

Bacteria: The Oldest Form of Life?

It is now believed that bacteria may have existed over three billion years ago. Most scientists believe bacteria were the first living cells on earth. Until recently there was very little evidence to support this. Bacteria are very small, and their bodies are soft. They leave very little evidence behind after they die. No one believed that fossil remains of bacteria could be found. But scientists studying ancient rocks with electron microscopes have found fossil bacteria. The fossils are more than two and a half billion years old.

It is believed that these ancient forms of life must have lived without oxygen. They may have obtained energy through chemical reactions with iron, sulfur, or nitrogen. Some bacteria today do this very thing. The world's great deposits of iron ore may be a result of bacterial action.

When algae and green plants became plentiful, great amounts of oxygen were thought to have been produced. The bacteria adjusted well to this change. Today bacteria are found everywhere life can exist. Bacteria are found in air, water, soil, your food, your bodies, and in the bodies of all living organisms.

Although bacteria are probably the oldest living forms of life, they are considered the simplest of cells. They are called *prokaryotes*. This means they do not have an organized nucleus. For this reason, bacteria and blue-green algae are often classified in the kingdom Prokaryotae.

Louis Pasteur and the Birth of Bacteriology

In any science, a few names stand out above all others. In biology, one such name is Louis Pasteur. Among other things, Pasteur developed a vaccine for rabies and defeated the theory of spontaneous generation. Even if he had done nothing else, he would still be remembered for these achievements. However, they represent only a small part of his work.

Pasteur actually began his scientific career as a chemist. In 1854 he was appointed professor of chemistry and dean at the University of Lille. This location was quite important. The city of Lille was a center for making alcohol by fermenting the juice of sugar beets.

A serious problem arose with the juice in several vats. It began to turn sour instead of changing to alcohol. Pasteur was called in to find out what was wrong.

Pasteur studied the juice that was fermenting normally. Through his microscope he saw many yeast cells spread through the liquid. Over several hours, more yeast cells grew. As they grew, the alcohol content of the juice rose.

16-3 | The laboratory of Louis Pasteur 1885. Pasteur could be considered the first bacteriologist. *(The Bettmann Archive, Inc.)*

Were the yeasts producing the alcohol? In trying to learn the answer, Pasteur next examined the sour juice. This juice contained lactic acid, not alcohol. Microscopic observation showed the fermented juice contained smaller, rod-shaped bodies instead of the usual yeasts. These bodies moved and seemed to be alive; they increased in number just as the yeasts had done before. But as these rod-shaped bodies increased, the lactic acid content of the juice also increased.

These discoveries led Pasteur to begin a much more complete study of fermentation. After three years he set up a small laboratory in Paris. There he finally proved his theory. **Fermentation results from the action of microorganisms, and the products formed depend on the organisms involved. Yeasts produce alcohol. Lactic acid is formed by bacteria.**

This was only one of many discoveries by Pasteur. He lived and worked in a time of ignorance and fear of science. His discovery of a vaccine against *anthrax*, a disease that killed cattle and sheep, created a great deal of interest. Other scientists felt encouraged to investigate disease and immunity. Pasteur's work helped change people's attitude toward science. His influence affects you in many ways today. The milk you drink, for example, is pasteurized. This process of heating milk to prevent the growth of bacteria was developed by Pasteur.

Helpful Activities of Bacteria

Many people think of bacteria only as disease-causing organisms. But most bacteria are not harmful. Bacteria are necessary in production of certain foods and in the decay of dead organisms. Some bacteria are beneficial and necessary for proper function of our bodies. *Escherichia coli* (ESH-uh-RICK-ee-uh KOE-lee), or *E. coli*, is a bacterium that lives in our intestines, especially the large intestine. They seem to be essential to proper digestion and elimination of waste. At some time or another, you have probably been given an *antibiotic* by a doctor when you were sick. This is a germ-killing substance. Antibiotics also kill *E. coli*. If these essential bacteria are destroyed by antibiotics, a special diet may be needed to restore these organisms to the intestine.

Some bacteria are necessary for the production of foods, especially dairy products. Buttermilk, cottage cheese, yogurt, and cream cheese production all utilize bacteria that produce lactic acid. Production of hard cheeses like cheddar may involve the use of more than one type of bacterium. Some cheeses like Roquefort are produced using the action of bacteria and molds. Vinegar is another product in which bacteria are used.

Organisms are decomposed after death and their materials are returned to the earth and atmosphere. Did you know that bacteria are largely responsible for decomposition? **During decay, bacteria break down complex molecules in dead plant and animal matter and form simpler chemical compounds.** Bacteria do this in order to get food and energy. The matter that once composed a living organism is broken down by bacteria into substances that can then be used by other living things. The materials, therefore, can be used over and over again.

This process of recycling matter is essential to life. If matter were "locked up" as complex molecules in dead organisms, soon there would not be enough raw material to support life. Bacteria are essential in this recycling process.

Bacteria and How They are Identified

About 2,000 different species of bacteria have been identified. There are many more that are not classified. Identification of bacteria can be very important. If, for example, there is an outbreak of a deadly type of food poisoning, the source of that disease must be found to prevent further spread of disease.

Usually the first step in finding and identifying bacteria is to put a small particle of the suspected food into a nutrient medium. If present, the bacteria will grow in nutrient medium. The nutrient medium provides all the food that the bacteria need. It may be a soup or broth. Sometimes *agar*, a thick jellylike substance, is mixed with nutrients. This forms a solid substance that is an ideal medium on which to grow bacteria. A growth of bacteria in or on a nutrient medium is called a bacterial *culture*. Once a culture of an unknown type of bacteria is grown, certain identifying traits can be noted.

The most important traits are the shape of the bacteria cells and the kinds of colonies of cells they form.

The basic shapes of bacteria and the forms they assume in colonies are as follows:

- *Coccus* (plural, *cocci*): sphere-shaped cells
  diplococcus: cells often joined in pairs or short filaments.

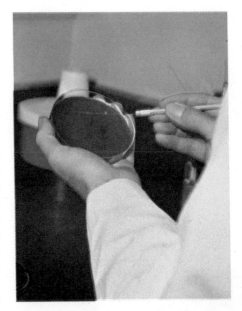

16-4 | How bacteria are grown in a lab—inoculating an agar plate. (above) Smear is made on a nutrient medium. Then colonies of bacteria grow on the nutrient medium. Later they can be used as a source of bacteria for new innoculations if necessary. (© Lester Bergman and Associates, Inc.)

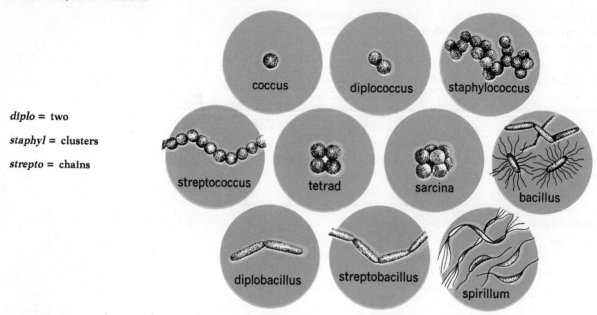

diplo = two

staphyl = clusters

strepto = chains

16-5 | Some examples of the three basic forms of bacteria—coccus, bacillus, spirillum.

staphylococcus: clusters of cells
streptococcus: chains of cells
tetrad: four cells arranged in a square
- **Bacillus** (plural, *bacilli*): rod-shaped cells
diplobacillus: cells in pairs
streptobacillus: cells joined end to end, forming a filament
- **Spirillum** (plural, *spirilla*): cells shaped like bent rods or corkscrews

Size of Bacteria

Compared to a virus, a bacterium is large. A single bacterium can contain 300 phage viruses. Bacteria are measured in micrometers, sometimes referred to as microns. One micrometer (μm) equals one thousandth of a millimeter ($1 \mu m = 4 \times 10^{-5}$ inches). A typical sphere-shaped bacterium is one micrometer in diameter. It would take well over one thousand of them to stretch across the inside of the letter *o*.

The smallest bacteria are rickettsia (ri-KET-see-ah). They cause a variety of infections. They are transmitted by arthropods (insects, spiders, and so on.) These are disease-causing bacteria that are from .3 to .5 micrometers in diameter. They can barely be seen with the light microscope.

The general shape of bacteria can usually be seen under the light microscope, but little of their structure can be identified. Bacteria are stained with special dyes in order to see some of their structures more clearly. Special lenses, such as the oil-immersion lens, can be used to increase magnification to 1,000X. With this lens more details of a bacterium can be seen.

Structure and Function of a Bacterial Cell

Have you ever wondered why some infections, such as bacterial pneumonia, are so hard to fight? The reason is that **bacteria have a covering around them that protects them against attack by the body's defense mechanisms.** The protection is in the form of slime called the *slime layer.* Some bacteria have a layer that is a gummy substance, which forms a *capsule.*

Inside the protective covering most bacteria have an outer cell wall. There is one small, primitive group of bacteria that do not have cell walls. These are the *mycoplasmas.* These strange organisms change shape continually and are found only in living organisms. They are thought to be a link between viruses and cells. Except for these mycoplasmas, bacteria have a nonliving wall that maintains the shape of the cell and serves as added protection.

Pressing against the inner surface of the bacteria's cell wall is the cell membrane. The membrane is semipermeable. Only certain substances can pass through the membrane to enter or leave the cell.

Inside the membrane is the cytoplasm, which is highly organized. It contains the structures necessary to make protein and the genetic material.

The genetic material in bacteria consists of a single long, thin chromosome. The chromosome appears like a tangled bundle in the cytoplasm. The genetic material is in constant contact with the cytoplasm because there is no nuclear membrane. In some bacteria, additional separate, small elements of genetic material called *plasmids* also occur in the cytoplasm. Some bacteria have *flagella,* or tails. The flagella are too small to be seen without special stains. These long, whiplike strands are used for moving.

Some species of bacteria have a single flagellum. Some have a group of flagella at each end. Others have flagella scattered all over their surfaces. Bacteria capable of motion are said to be *motile.*

When bacteria are actually moving, they move rapidly and in fairly straight lines. Their movement is a quivering, twisting motion.

Nutrition in Bacteria

One reason bacteria are present almost everywhere is that they get their energy in many different ways. Let's look first at the **autotrophic** bacteria, those few bacteria that can make their own food. *Autotrophic* bacteria make their own

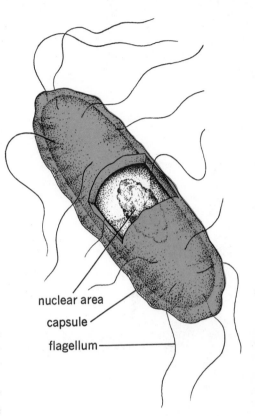

nuclear area
capsule
flagellum

16–6 | The general structure of a bacterial cell. Which characteristics are plantlike? Which are animallike?

myco = fungus

short for frog

auto = self
troph = food

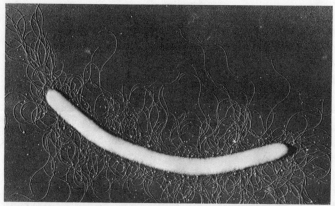

16–7 | The flagella of *Proteus vulgaris* show clearly in this electron micrograph. *(Courtesy Houwink, Van Iterson and* Biochimica et Biophysica Acta)

food from inorganic substances. Some bacteria contain molecules similar to the chlorophyll found in green plants. These bacteria use light energy and make food by the process of photosynthesis.

Other autotrophic bacteria use inorganic substances as a food source through **chemosynthesis.** In chemosynthesis bacteria use inorganic molecules, rather than light, as a source of energy for making food. For example, one type of soil bacterium uses inorganic nitrogen gas from the atmosphere. This process, called *nitrogen fixation*, converts nitrogen gas into nitrates. The nitrates can be absorbed and used by plants to make proteins. **Heterotrophic** bacteria feed on organic molecules made by other organisms. The type of food that bacteria can digest depends on the kinds of enzymes the bacteria can make. Each enzyme acts on only one kind of food. Some heterotrophic bacteria compete with people for food. They tend to ruin some of the foods humans eat. Sour milk and rotting fruit are examples of foods that are being digested by heterotrophic bacteria.

Heterotrophic bacteria digest their food outside the bacterial cell. Enzymes secreted by the bacteria pass out of the bacterial cell membrane and break down the food molecules. Digested foods then pass into the bacterial cell.

Some heterotrophic bacteria are **saprophytes** (SAP-row-FITES). This means that they get their food from organisms that have died or from the products that these organisms produced when alive. These are the decay bacteria. Other heterotrophic bacteria are **parasites.** They get their food from living cells. **Parasitic bacteria, called *pathogens,* are the disease-causing bacteria of living organisms. Their digestive enzymes and poisons destroy living cells or disrupt normal cell activity.**

hetero = other

sapro = putrid
phyte = plant

Respiration in Bacteria

Atmospheric oxygen is an important factor in the growth of bacteria. Some forms require oxygen for life, while oth-

ers cannot live in its presence. **Still other bacteria can live either in the presence or absence of oxygen.** *Aerobic respiration* is the process that requires free oxygen to *metabolize* organic substances within the cell. The energy resulting from metabolism is used to carry on life functions. Bacteria that require oxygen and cannot survive without it are called **obligate aerobes** (AIR-obes). The obligate aerobes are found in airy environments such as well-aerated water and soil and on the surfaces of objects. Diphtheria, a disease of the throat, and tuberculosis, a disease of the lungs, are caused by bacteria that are obligate aerobes. The throat and lung tissues are close to a good oxygen supply.

aero = air

Anaerobic respiration involves energy production *without* the presence of oxygen. The bacteria that cannot grow in the presence of oxygen are called **obligate anaerobes** (AN-uhr-obes). If they are exposed to the atmosphere for any length of time, they die. One of the best-known obligate anaerobic bacteria causes tetanus (lockjaw). Puncture wounds that introduce bacteria deep into the muscle tissue of the body where there is very little free oxygen are dangerous. Among the bacteria carried into the wound might be the spores of tetanus bacteria, which multiply in a low-oxygen environment.

an = without

Other anaerobic bacteria are associated with unaerated water in bogs, swamps, and ponds, where they rot organic matter and produce methane gas. Methane is sometimes called *marsh gas*. Though it is produced in some unpolluted swamps and bogs, the anaerobic conditions that produce it are often associated with pollution. Bubbles of methane can sometimes be seen rising from the black, oily mud of polluted lakes and ponds. Methane makes up the major portion of natural gas. The use of anaerobic bacteria to produce it may eventually be a major source of alternative energy for humans.

A third type of bacteria, the **facultative bacteria,** can live in either anaerobic or aerobic conditions. Their growth is generally more rapid in the presence of oxygen. One facultative bacterium is the *E. coli* that lives in your intestine.

Factors That Affect the Growth of Bacteria

Throughout history, even before they knew of the existence of bacteria, people have had to fight the spoilage of food. They learned to prevent many of the conditions that favored the growth of bacteria. Some of the factors that influence the growth of bacteria are temperature, moisture, radiation, and chemicals.

Bacteria, like all organisms, can live only within a certain temperature range. Most bacteria that compete for food are active at fairly warm temperatures, about 26°C to 38°C (79°F to 100°F). So refrigeration slows bacterial growth. Freezing stops bacterial growth. In the canning process food is first heated to kill all bacteria. Then the food is sealed tightly.

Certain disease bacteria multiply best at normal human body temperature. A fever is one of the body's defenses against infection. A higher body temperature slows the growth of these bacteria.

Bacteria are about 90 percent water. In dry surroundings bacteria become inactive. Dryness over a long period of time will prevent growth of bacteria. That is one reason dried cereal and flour keep so well. Dehydrated foods do not decay because all or most of their water is removed. Salt and alcohol destroy many of the bacteria by removing their water.

When bacteria are exposed to direct sunlight, their growth slows and may even stop. The drying action and heat of the sun kill some bacteria. Most bacteria, however, are killed by the sun's ultraviolet light. Bacteria have little defense against these short wavelengths. The bacteria's DNA absorbs the short wavelengths, and the ultraviolet light interferes with the replication of DNA. The mutations often cause death of bacteria.

Ultraviolet light, then, is another tool for destroying bacteria. Ultraviolet lamps are used in food preparation, in treating skin disease, in hospital operating rooms, and in many other places where bacterial growth is a problem.

Like all living organisms, bacteria can be killed by various chemicals. Chemicals can destroy their cell membranes, react with molecules within the bacteria, or in some other way destroy the chemical balance that the bacteria require for life.

People have developed many chemical means of preventing bacterial growth. One of the most familiar is chlorine, which even in small amounts is a deadly poison to bacteria. The use of chlorine in the water supply has prevented outbreaks of many bacterial diseases.

Many edible chemicals are used in preserving foods. Some are natural preservatives that have been used for centuries. Most bacteria, for example, will not grow in a strong acid solution, so vinegar has been used to preserve some foods. A concentrated sugar solution draws the moisture from bacterial cells, so under the right conditions sugar solutions can prevent bacterial growth. For this reason sugar has been used in making sweet jellies and jams.

Recently many artificial preservatives, such as sodium nitrite, have been added to foods to prevent bacterial

a. Dehydration
Water is removed from food to the point that bacteria cannot grow. Freeze-drying is a method of dehydration widely used today.

d. Temperature

Sterilization: heating under pressure (15-20 minutes)

126°C

120°C

b. Preservatives
Raising the acidity by adding acid, reduces the growth of bacteria. Salting of food also destroys bacteria. Chemical preservatives may also be used. However, their use has declined in recent years, due to possible harmful side effects.

Pasteurization: heat at 71°C for 15 seconds or at 62°C for 30 minutes

71°C

62°C

Refrigeration: for several days to several weeks

15°C

10°C

c. Radiation
Foods could be packaged and sealed, then exposed to radiation to destroy all bacteria. The Food and Drug Administration allows only certain foods to be irradiated.

Freezing: for several weeks to several months

−10°C

−18°C

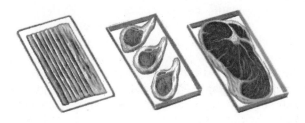

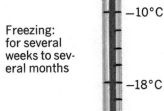

16-8 | The prevention of food spoilage.

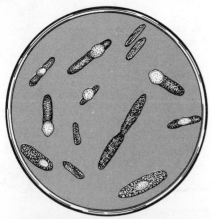

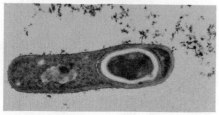

16-9 | (top) Various types of bacterial endospores. (bottom) An electron micrograph of an endospore (43,000X). *(Courtesy of Dr. George Chapman, Georgetown University)*

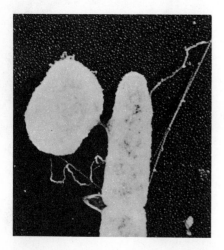

16-10 | A photomicrograph of conjugation in bacteria. Note the cytoplasmic bridge joining the two cells (26,000X). *(T. F. Anderson, E. L. Wollman, F. Jacob)*

decay. However, there is some concern over side effects that preservatives, especially artificial preservatives, cause in humans.

Bacterial Reproduction

Bacteria have a very simple way of reproducing. They simply pinch in half in the process called *binary fission.* In this process the genetic material is replicated (duplicated). Then the bacterium splits into two with each new cell receiving the same genes.

As bacteria multiply, their waste products accumulate. This slows the bacteria's growth. For example, a certain species of bacterium might grow well in a slightly acid environment, and the accumulation of waste might make the environment either more acid or less acid. Then the environment is less favorable for the bacteria. Other factors that limit growth are lack of food, water, and space. In addition, bacteria in an organism are attacked by that organism's defense system. For example, *antibodies* that your body makes to combat foreign protein attach to bacterial cell walls or membranes and cause the bacteria to clump together. Sometimes the antibodies cause the bacteria to burst.

Spore Formation

Many bacteria die when their food supply is used up or other conditions are unfavorable. However, some rod-shaped bacteria have an unusual way of surviving poor conditions. They form structures called **endospores.** A single bacterium will form a small sphere-shaped or oval-shaped spore within its cytoplasm. This endospore is protected by a tough outer covering. When the bacterium dies, the endospore survives. Endospores can sometimes resist severe drought, radiation, heat, and various chemicals. Some scientists claim endospores can remain dormant, or inactive, for over 50 years. When favorable conditions exist, the spores develop into bacteria cells.

Endospores are not a means of reproduction. They are a method of surviving unfavorable conditions. Endospores are carried by wind and water. They are especially dangerous in improperly canned food. If you ever open a can of food other than those that are vacuum sealed and hear a hissing sound, the food should be thrown away. The gas may be the product of bacterial action. Any treatment or method designed to destroy bacteria must be strong enough to destroy endospores.

Transfer of DNA in Bacteria

Certain natural processes in which genes (portions of DNA) are transferred from one bacterium to another have been discovered. These processes give rise to bacteria with new gene combinations. These new gene combinations are expressed as a variety in a particular trait.

The three processes by which DNA is transferred from one bacterium to another are transduction, conjugation and transformation.

Transduction During *transduction* a virus (a bacterio-phage) picks up part of the genetic material of the host bacterium. Usually only one gene is involved. The host cell is destroyed, and the virus carrying bacterial genes infects another bacterium. This new host bacterium receives the new gene. If the bacteria is immune to the virus, the gene will then be passed on to other bacteria by cell division.

Conjugation During *conjugation,* the donor bacterium contains, in addition to its regular genetic material, an extra piece of genetic material, or *plasmid*. This genetic material is called an *F*, or *fertility*, factor. The bacterium that contains the F factor is called plus (+). The bacterium without the factor is minus (−).

Transfer of the F factor occurs when the plus and minus bacteria come in contact. The sexual union of the two bacteria is called *conjugation*. A tube grows from the side of the plus and attaches to the minus. The F factor moves from the plus through the tube to the minus. The two bacterium separate. The minus receiver cell is now a plus because it contains the plasmid. Sometimes an additional gene from the plus's DNA is transferred with the F factor. Traits such as antibiotic resistance are transferred from bacterium to bacterium in this manner.

Transformation In *transformation* part of the DNA from a dead bacterium is taken in by a live bacterium. The live bacterium then has the traits of the dead bacterium in addition to its own genetic characteristics.

Though transformation can occur in nature, one of the best illustrations of this process is the following experiment that was carried out in a laboratory: Deadly pneumonia-causing bacteria were killed. Their membranes were broken, and their DNA was released in solution. These dead bacteria were then mixed with harmless bacteria of the same strain. The harmless bacteria became deadly. The genes for the deadly trait had passed through the membrane of the living bacteria. Once the harmless bacteria acquired the deadly genes, they acquired the deadly trait. The bacteria then multiplied in number and the trait was passed on to the offspring. If injected into animals, the once harmless bacteria could cause pneumonia.

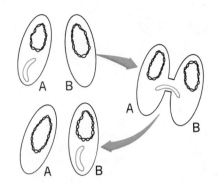

16–11 | Conjugation. The F, or fertility factor, genes (DNA) are transferred from the donor A to the receiver B.

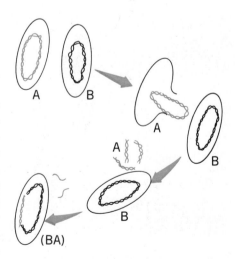

16–12 | Transformation. A fragment of DNA (a gene) from bacteria A has been taken into bacteria B.

Careers

Microbiologists are employed in a wide variety of fields. Microbiologists are employed by hospitals, drug companies, and private laboratories. For example, they continually check city water supplies for bacteria content. A bachelor's degree will qualify you for some positions. A technician's license will qualify you for other positions. A doctoral degree is required for most independent research.

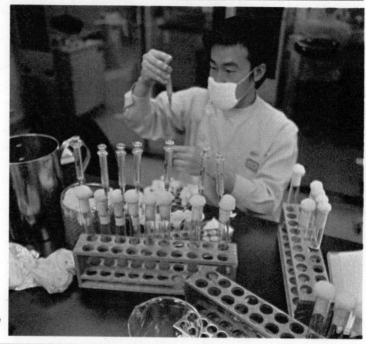

16-13 | Modern bacteriology laboratories are well-equipped. *(Courtesy of Pfizer, Inc.)*

Genetic Engineering

Genetic engineering is a term used to describe methods of introducing new genes into an organism. The organism can then pass these genes (and traits) on to its offspring. The new DNA that results from genetic engineering is called *recombinant DNA.*

Scientists learned from studying what happens in nature how genes could be transferred from one strain of bacterium to another strain of the same kind. This knowledge helped scientists to develop methods of transferring genes from one *species* of bacterium to an entirely different species of bacterium.

For example, an experiment can be set up to illustrate the effect of transferring genes. Certain bacteria of the species *E. coli,* the intestinal bacteria, are killed by penicillin. Certain bacteria of another species, called *Staphylococcus aureus, (S. aureus),* are resistant to penicillin. *E. coli* becomes resistant to penicillin when the genes of *S. aureus* are transferred to it. Furthermore, the genes, and so the trait, are passed on to future generations of *E. coli.*

If genes could be transferred between different species of bacteria, could bacteria be given desired traits? Scientists have been able to get bacteria to make a human protein, insulin. Insulin is used by the body to control the body's use of sugar. People whose bodies do not produce their own insulin are *diabetics*, and they must take insulin in the form of pills or injections. This insulin is expensive. If bacteria could be "programmed" to produce insulin, the cost of insulin might be reduced.

Artificial genes were synthesized to produce protein chains for making insulin. The genes were then attached to bacterial plasmids. The plasmids were then taken into the bacteria. The bacteria proceeded to make two different kinds of proteins. These proteins were later extracted from the bacteria and united chemically to form insulin. Thus, though genetic engineering, bacteria had been made to produce the components of insulin. The final step, the chemical uniting of the components, was done outside the bacteria.

Genetic engineering is a new science. It has grown because of increased knowledge of viruses and bacteria. As you can see from experiments with insulin, it does hold a promise for improving people's lives.

As you might guess from the experiments that produced penicillin-resistant bacteria, genetic engineering could also be used to create harmful forms of life. So far, most of the work in genetic engineering has been done with bacteria. This is because of their rapid growth rate and also because bacterial chromosomes have been mapped. Some scientists fear that research in recombinant DNA will create problems such as antibiotic resistance. The National Institutes of Health, a federal organization, has proposed rules for scientists to follow when working with recombinant DNA.

The Spirochetes

The *spirochetes* (SPY-row-KEETS) seem to lie between the bacteria and the more specialized protists called protozoans. Many of the spirochetes are in the size range of bacteria. Some, however, may be as long as 500 microns. The cells of spirochetes are long cylinders. Some have a spiral shape, while others are tight corkscrews.

So far, no spirochete is known to have an organized nucleus. Reproduction is by fission. Endospores are not produced. Spirochetes can move through fluids by a quivering action. Some have been found that have structures that look like flagella, but these are not true flagella.

The most familiar spirochetes are the ones that cause human diseases. Among these is the syphilis organism, *Treponema pallidum*. This spirochete lives in the blood and may invade the nervous system.

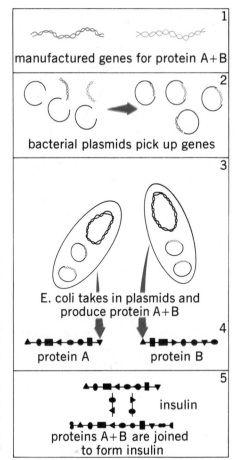

1 manufactured genes for protein A+B

2 bacterial plasmids pick up genes

3 E. coli takes in plasmids and produce protein A+B

4 protein A   protein B

5 insulin
proteins A+B are joined to form insulin

16–14 | Plasmids are DNA in a ring found in *E. coli.* They unite with the "artificial" genes and are taken into *E. coli* bacteria. There they produce two proteins, A and B. The proteins are extracted and combined to form insulin.

Summary

Bacteria are believed by some scientists to be the oldest forms of life. They may have existed over three billion years ago. Bacteria and blue-green algae are *prokaryotes*.

Some bacteria are *autotrophic*. They make their own food through a kind of photosynthesis or through *chemosynthesis*. Other bacteria are *heterotrophic*.

Bacteria vary also in their respiration. *Aerobes* require the presence of atmospheric oxygen for their respiration. *Anaerobes* require an oxygen-free environment. *Facultative* bacteria can live under either aerobic or anaerobic conditions.

Bacterial growth can be controlled by regulating temperature, moisture, radiation, and the chemical environment of the bacteria. As more is learned about the ways genes are transferred from one bacterium to another, harmful effects of bacteria may be overcome.

Biologically Speaking

coccus	autotrophic	facultative bacteria
bacillus	chemosynthesis	binary fission
spirillum	heterotrophic	endospore
slime layer	saprophyte	transduction
capsule	parasite	conjugation
plasmids	pathogen	transformation
flagella	obligate aerobe	genetic engineering
motile	obligate anaerobe	recombinant DNA

Questions for Review

1. Describe Pasteur's contributions to bacteriology.
2. Classify bacteria into three groups based on shape.
3. List the structural differences between a bacterium and a generalized plant cell.
4. List three factors that limit bacterial growth.
5. Describe how genetic engineering has been used to make insulin.
6. List several ways bacteria benefit humans.
7. Distinguish aerobic bacteria from anaerobic.
8. Distinguish heterotrophs from autotrophs.
9. Describe ways genes are transferred in bacteria.

Applying Concepts

1. Discuss how gene transfer is similar to but different from sexual reproduction.
2. Compare factors that limit growth rate of bacteria to those that limit growth rate of human populations.
3. Discuss the potential benefits and dangers in genetic engineering.

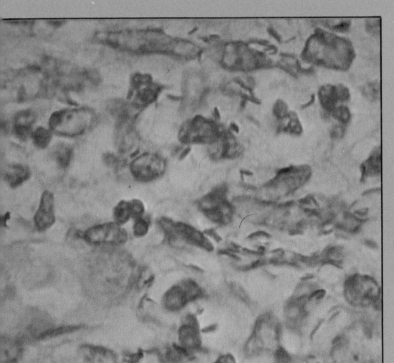

17-1 | Tuberculosis infection of the small intestine. *(C. E. Roberts)*

17

Infectious Disease

A LIST three ways infectious diseases can be transmitted.

B DESCRIBE how microorganisms cause disease.

C EXPLAIN the defenses the body has against disease.

D DESCRIBE the various types of immunity.

E DESCRIBE early contributions that led to cures for many diseases.

F EXPLAIN immune therapy and antibiotic therapy.

What Is Disease?

If you have a sore finger, is that a disease? When a person suffers a nervous breakdown and loses touch with reality, is that a disease? Is one pimple a disease? How about a hundred pimples? **Disease** is defined as a condition that impairs or interferes with the well-being of an organism. The meaning of the term *disease* therefore involves a certain amount of individual judgment. One might justify calling all of the conditions mentioned above *diseases*, but most people would not.

Some diseases, like a nervous disorder or kidney stones, are caused by some breakdown in the normal processes of the body. Others result from pathogenic agents. This chapter will deal primarily with *infectious diseases* that are passed from one organism to another. These diseases are caused by *pathogenic* or disease-causing agents such as viruses, bacteria, and parasites. Diseases can also be caused by industrial chemicals or other foreign substances that enter the body. Asbestos fibers and a great many different chemicals, for example, have been shown to cause cancer. Although this chapter deals with human disease, the ideas discussed generally apply to the diseases of other animals and some plants as well.

patho = disease

genic = suitable to

213

17-2 | One sneeze can spread great numbers of viruses and bacteria. *(Society of American Bacteriologists)*

17-3 | (top) Lice are arthropods that carry typhus fever and other diseases. (bottom) Fleas transmit a bacillus form of bacteria that cause plague, a dreaded disease throughout history. *(top: Oxford Scientific Films, © Animals Animals; bottom: William E. Ferguson)*

How Pathogenic Organisms Attack the Body

How do you come into contact with disease-causing organisms? For one thing, viruses or bacteria are said to be *infectious* when they can spread from person to person. **Airborne infections, waterborne infections, and contact infections describe the most common ways infection spreads from one person to another.**

When a person has a cold or a sore throat, a sneeze or cough may discharge thousands of tiny droplets into the air. These droplets contain the disease-causing viruses or bacteria. This particular type of air borne infection is called a **droplet infection.**

Waterborne infections usually spread most rapidly. This is especially true with viruses and bacteria associated with human body wastes. Many communities depend on underground water for their drinking water. If it becomes contaminated with sewage, groundwater can seep through the ground and spread disease, often many miles from the source of contamination.

Contact infections are slower in spreading disease. A person serving food in a restaurant can be a source of a contact infection. A contaminated fork is all that is needed to introduce pathogenic bacteria into the body. Sexual contact is another way viruses or bacteria can make contact with the body.

People sometimes carry disease organisms in their bodies and yet are immune to the disease. These *immune carriers* present a problem. They do not suffer from the disease, but they are infectious. They can transfer the disease-causing agents to other people. Also, a person who recovers from a disease may be an immune carrier for weeks, months, or even years without even realizing it. Because people in our society travel a lot, the disease can be spread over wide areas by immune carriers.

Arthropods, insects and their relatives, are associated with certain infectious diseases. Houseflies carry disease organisms found in body wastes that they pick up on their feet and bodies. The flies spread the disease organisms when they get on food. Lice, fleas, ticks, and mosquitoes introduce pathogenic organisms directly into the body by penetrating the skin when they "bite."

If you have contact with disease-causing agents, it does not necessarily mean that you will become ill. Most pathogenic agents must enter the tissues of the body to cause an effect. **The main way pathogenic organisms enter the body is through breaks or weaknesses in the mucous membranes** that line the **digestive and respiratory tracts.** Airborne bacteria and viruses can easily enter the respiratory tract through these weaknesses. Food and water may also contain bacteria and viruses as well as parasites that can enter the digestive tract. Punctures, cuts, or scratches in the skin can introduce bacteria directly into the tissue.

How Microorganisms Damage the Body

Many bacteria secrete poisonous compounds called *exotoxins.* **These poisons dissolve in the body fluid and eventually reach the blood stream.** They are then distributed throughout the body and affect tissues some distance from the site of infection. For example, the spores of tetanus bacteria may enter your body if you step on a rusty nail. The spores become active in the muscle tissue. The resulting bacteria multiply and produce an exotoxin. Exotoxins may reach quite distant areas of the body, including the jaw muscles. Here the poison causes muscle spasms and paralysis. Because of this effect tetanus is commonly called *lockjaw.*

In some cases, exotoxins are formed by bacteria in foods. These toxins formed outside the body produce food poisoning when the foods are eaten. The most deadly type of food poisoning is *botulism.* Like tetanus bacteria, botulism bacteria form spores. These spores may reach food before it is canned. If the food is not properly cooked and canned, the spores survive. When the food is sealed in an airtight can, the spores become active cells. These cells multiply and release exotoxins.

In this process of making exotoxins, a gas is produced by the bacteria. Often the gas causes the can to bulge, especially on the top. When the can is first opened, the gas sometimes makes a hissing sound as it escapes. Food from such cans should never be eaten. The poison is tasteless and odorless, but deadly.

Botulism symptoms usually appear within 12 to 36 hours after the spoiled food is eaten. These symptoms include double vision, weakness, and paralysis that creeps from the neck to other body areas. Botulism is fatal in about 65 percent of the cases.

Other organisms that form toxins in foods include certain *Salmonella* and *Staphylococcus* bacteria. These types of food poisoning are more common but less deadly than botulism.

Some bacteria form *endotoxins.* **These poisons remain part of the bacteria and are released only when the bacterial cells die and break down.** Endotoxins cause severe tissue reactions that may be fatal. Typhoid fever, tuberculosis, cholera, bubonic plague, and bacterial dysentery are endotoxin diseases.

Facts & Figures

The term "Typhoid Mary" originated from an immune carrier.

exo = outside

toxin = poison

endo = within

17–4 | Botulism bacteria produce gases that cause cans of spoiled food to bulge. If you are able to push in the top of the can, you know gas is present.

The Body's Defense Against Disease

In some ways your environment can be considered hostile. You come into continual contact with many different disease-causing agents. However, most of these agents never affect you. If you are relatively healthy, you can resist most of these agents. Your body has two main lines of defense.

The First Line of Defense

The first line of defense prevents bacteria from entering your body tissues. Skin offers an effective barrier against bacteria. The outer layer of skin consists of a dense layer of dead cells that effectively stops bacteria from entering the living tissue beneath. If the skin is scraped or cut, clots form in the blood to close the wound. A blood clot is usually an effective barrier against bacteria. Of course, the skin is not always effective in keeping bacteria out of the body. Puncture wounds, such as those caused by a metal nail, can introduce bacteria deep into the tissue. Sometimes bleeding can wash the bacteria out of such a wound, but punctures tend to close tightly so that little bleeding occurs.

Mucous membranes in your nasal passages and along your digestive tract also prevent bacteria from entering body tissues. The mucous membranes lining the nasal cavity consist of a very thin layer of dead cells covered by a thin layer of mucus. Airborne organisms, including those on dust particles, become trapped in the mucus. Mucus, together with the hairs in the nasal cavity, clean the air before it passes to the lungs.

The lining of the windpipe, or trachea, and of the small branches of the respiratory tract is composed of a single layer of living cells.

These cells are equipped with tiny hairs called *cilia*. Cilia all beat in unison and move a thin layer of mucus from the lungs up the windpipe to the throat. There the mucus is swallowed. As the air comes down the trachea, any bacteria or dust particles that contact the mucus stick to it. Bacteria are then carried back up the trachea with the mucus against the action of air moving down the trachea, as well as gravity. In this way bacteria are prevented from entering the lungs.

Cigarette smoke places a real burden on cilia and the lining of the air passages. Tars and particles in smoke eventually damage the mucus layer, the cilia, and the underlying cells. This makes the air passages more vulnerable to infection because more material passes into the lungs.

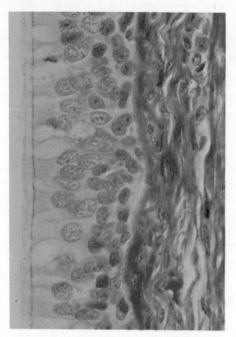

17–5 | Ciliated cells and mucous layer of the lining of the trachea. How does this help provide a defense against infection? *(Manfred Kage, © Peter Arnold, Inc.)*

Great numbers of bacteria are swallowed with food, mucus, and saliva. Acid secretions of the stomach are another first-line defense of the body. They destroy most bacteria that reach the stomach.

Some bacteria, however, survive and enter the intestines. When this happens, the mucous layer and the digestive enzymes of the intestine aid in preventing bacteria from entering the body tissues. The intestine normally contains populations of bacteria and fungi. These organisms seem to be beneficial. In fact, some species of bacteria produce vitamins such as B12 and K, which are absorbed and used by the body. The presence of these nonpathogenic bacteria in the intestine seems to prevent the growth of invading, pathogenic bacteria.

Tears are another part of the first line of defense. Tears secreted by tear glands continually flow over the eyes. They clean the eyes as well as lubricate the surface. Any bacteria coming in contact with the tears are washed away. Tear ducts carry the fluid into the nasal cavity. Bacteria enter the tear ducts, then pass into the nasal cavity. Both tears and mucus contain an enzyme called **lysozyme** (LIE-suh-ZIME). This enzyme protects against bacteria by dissolving their cell walls. Once the walls are weakened, the bacteria expand, their membranes break, and they die.

lyso = dissolving

zyme = broth

The first line of defense against bacteria is mostly mechanical. It places physical barriers such as skin and mucus between you and the bacteria in the environment.

The Second Line of Defense

The second line of defense deals with organisms that do manage to enter the tissues of the body. This line of defense includes cellular and chemical means of destroying bacteria.

Cells That Devour Bacteria Cells within the body that devour bacteria are called **phagocytes.** There are many different kinds of *phagocytes*. Some are certain types of white blood cells or **leucocytes.** These, along with the red blood cells, travel through your arteries, veins, and capillaries. Capillaries are the smallest blood vessels. Other phagocytes move continually through the body tissues. Others are relatively fixed in position and are associated with certain organs like the lymph nodes, liver, and spleen.

As soon as bacteria enter the tissues of the body, their presence is somehow detected by phagocytes. This is thought to be a chemical response. Upon detecting the presence of bacteria, phagocytes move toward the site of infection. Leucocytes leave the bloodstream to enter the tis-

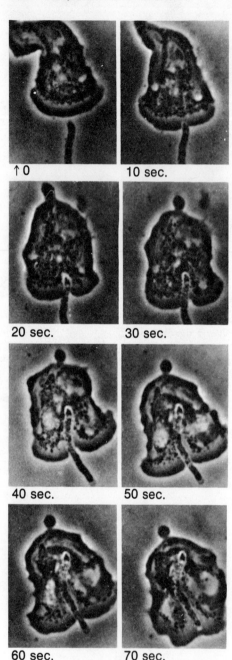

↑ 0   10 sec.

20 sec.   30 sec.

40 sec.   50 sec.

60 sec.   70 sec.

17–6 | Phagocytosis. This series of photographs, taken at ten-second intervals, shows a human white blood cell engulfing a chain of bacteria. *(Courtesy James G. Hirsch)*

anti = against

sues, pushing their way out between the cells of the capillaries. Leucocytes and other phagocytes move with an amoeboid flowing motion. When contact is made with bacteria, they flow around the bacteria and engulf them as in figure 17-6. Bacteria are then destroyed with digestive enzymes within the phagocyte.

If you have seen an infection you might have noticed that it is often red, swollen, and warm. The swelling is due to the increased blood flow into the area of infection. It is normal for fluid to seep from the capillaries and bathe the surrounding tissues. With increased blood flow, an increased amount of fluid seeps from the capillaries. This accounts for the swelling. If the infection continues, the buildup of fluid, dead phagocytes, dead bacteria, and dead tissue forms a substance known as **pus.**

The tissue fluid that bathes cells is collected in *lymph vessels.* These are part of the body's normal circulation system. Lymph vessels pass through many *lymph nodes.* These lymph nodes contain phagocytes that capture and destroy bacteria. Lymph nodes become enlarged during bacterial infections. You may have felt the lymph nodes in your neck or armpits when you have had an infection. The lymph fluid, cleansed of bacteria, then returns to the bloodstream. If some bacteria do get into the bloodstream and travel with it through the body, they can be destroyed by other phagocytes located in organs such as the liver and spleen.

Another reaction to infection may be fever, a rise in body temperature. This is an effective defense because higher temperatures slow the growth of many bacteria. Fever also sets off other body defenses and increases the general rate of chemical activity in the body. Fever is helpful unless it is too high or lasts too long. If this happens, the host's own cells may be damaged or destroyed.

Chemical Defenses Among the body's chemical defenses against bacteria is the production of **antibodies.** Antibodies are molecules that are produced in response to the presence of some foreign protein. These proteins are called **antigens.** An antigen may be part of a bacterial cell membrane, or it could be a poisonous protein produced by bacteria. It also could be part of the protein coat of a virus.

Antibodies are produced by a complex series of events involving certain types of white blood cells called *lymphocytes.* Once production starts, the concentration of antibodies in the body increases rapidly.

Antibodies combine with the antigens in antibody-antigen reactions. The reaction changes the chemistry of

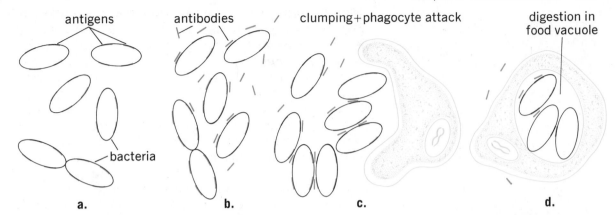

a. antigens — bacteria **b.** **c.** clumping+phagocyte attack **d.** digestion in food vacuole

17-7 | Antibodies produced by the host attach to the antigens on the bacteria. Antibodies, in this case, cause the bacteria to clump together. Phagocytes can then devour them more efficiently.

the antigens. If the antigen is a poison produced by bacteria, it is made harmless. If the antigen is part of the structure of a bacterium or virus, the structure is changed. As a result the bacterium or virus may die or become inactive. Antibodies have been observed to cause bacteria to clump together. This makes it easier for the phagocytes to devour them. Antibodies may also cause the cell membranes of bacteria to break down.

Antibody-antigen reactions are very specific. Each antigen causes the production of a specific antibody. An antibody produced to combat one species of bacteria will not affect a different species.

After all the bacteria are destroyed, some of the antibodies remain in the body fluids for a time. If the same type of bacteria invade the body again, the antibody-antigen reactions take place immediately and disease is prevented from occuring again. With time, the number of antibodies present decreases, but once the body has produced a specific antibody, it can do so again rapidly if reinfection occurs. Thus people get some diseases only once during their lifetimes.

In most cases, invading bacteria are destroyed rapidly by the combined devouring action of the phagocytes and the chemical action of antibodies. Thus infection is stopped.

Another chemical defense is the body's production of a compound called *inteferon*. It is discussed in Chapter 15.

Immunity If you are *immune* to a disease, that means that you are free from the threat of that disease. ***Immunity*** may be natural (present at birth), or you may acquire immunity during your life. Human beings have natural immunity to most diseases that affect other animals and plants. Conditions in the human body simply do not support the growth of organisms that cause these diseases. Our inher-

Facts & Figures

During the course of a lifetime the average person may be exposed to as many as 100,000 different antigens.

ited structures, chemical makeup, body temperature, and other traits give us this immunity. *Acquired immunity* may be active or passive.

Active immunity is the immunity your body acquires by making antibodies. Active immunity may be acquired *naturally* as an individual recovers from certain infections. During these infections the body takes an active part in producing specific antibodies against the pathogenic organisms or their products. In some cases the antibodies remain for some time after recovery. The capacity to produce antibodies continues to be present after recovery, giving long-lasting, sometimes permanent, immunity. Diphtheria, scarlet fever, measles, and mumps are some diseases that often result in this kind of immunity.

Active immunity may also be acquired *artificially* through the use of vaccines. Vaccines contain dead or weakened pathogenic organisms or their products. The vaccines, then, contain antigens. When introduced into the body, vaccines cause antibodies to be formed just as the actual live organism would. The difference is that the individual does not suffer the symptoms and dangers of the full-strength disease.

Although active immunity is long-lasting, the number of antibodies present for immediate use in the body decreases with time. "Booster shots" of antigens may be given to increase the level of antibodies present in the body.

Passive Immunity is acquired by introducing antibodies into the body. This kind of immunity may be acquired

17–8 | (top). Natural immunization. An infectious pathogen enters the body cells. The pathogen multiplies and attacks other cells. The body responds by producing antibodies to destroy the invader. (bottom) Artificial immunization. A dead or weakened pathogen is introduced into the body by vaccination. This pathogen does not infect the body cells. The body responds by producing antibodies to destroy the invader. These antibodies remain to destroy live pathogens, of the same type, that might enter the body later.

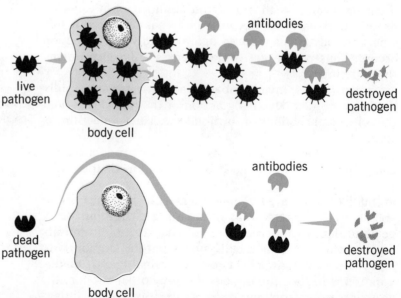

live pathogen

body cell

antibodies

destroyed pathogen

dead pathogen

body cell

antibodies

destroyed pathogen

Table 17-1 TYPES OF IMMUNITY

TYPE		HOW ESTABLISHED	DURATION
INBORN	species	through inherited anatomical, physiological, and chemical characteristics	permanent
ACQUIRED active	natural	by experiencing an infection during which contact with microorganisms or their products stimulates antibody production	usually lasting or permanent
	artificial	by injecting vaccines, toxoids, or other weakened bacterial products	usually from several years to permanent; booster shots may be necessary
passive	natural	by transfer of antibodies from mother to infant through the placenta prior to birth or in colostrum after birth	from 6 months to 1 year
	artificial	by injecting a serum containing antibodies	usually from 2 or 3 weeks to several months

naturally or artificially. In either case, it is only temporary.

Passive immunity is acquired naturally when an unborn infant receives antibodies from its mother's blood through the placenta. Antibodies also may be transferred to the infant in the first milk received from its mother. The immunity acquired by the baby usually lasts from six months to one year.

Artificial passive immunity is acquired when an individual receives antibodies produced in other animals. The part of the blood that contains antibodies is the **serum** (plural, *sera*), the liquid part of the blood. When serum containing antibodies is introduced into an individual, immediate immunity is acquired. In most cases, this immunity lasts from a few weeks to several months. For example, serum you receive in a tetanus shot came from a horse; your immunity to tetanus may last several years.

Medical Defenses Against Disease

Our knowledge of immunity and how to create it is an important part of medicine today. Yet this field of *immune therapy* had its beginning some two centuries ago in the work of an English country doctor, Edward Jenner.

The disease, smallpox, took its greatest toll in cities.

Facts & Figures

Before Jenner's vaccine, smallpox killed 30 percent of all English babies.

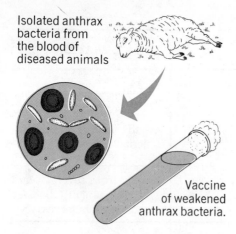

Isolated anthrax bacteria from the blood of diseased animals

Vaccine of weakened anthrax bacteria.

Two groups of animals were selected.

Experimental group   Control group

Injected the experimental group with the anthrax vaccine.

Twelve days later, the experimental group received a second injection.

After two more weeks, both groups of animals were injected with living anthrax bacteria.

Two days later . . . .

Experimental group   Control group

all animals healthy and alive.   all animals dead or dying

17–9   Pasteur's experiment with anthrax.

Jenner noticed that it seldom struck country people who worked around cattle. Further, most of these people had had cowpox, a minor disease whose main symptom was a small sore that left a scar. Had cowpox made its victims immune to smallpox? If so, why not deliberately infect people with cowpox to protect them from smallpox?

On May 14, 1796, Jenner had a chance to test his theory. Jenner made two small cuts on the arm of an eight-year-old child. Into these cuts he placed matter taken from a cowpox sore on another person. The child developed a cowpox sore which healed and left a scar.

Jenner wrote a paper explaining what he had done. He called his method **vaccination.** At first, other doctors refused to listen to Jenner. Many townspeople even joined in anti-vaccination campaigns. Slowly, however, doctors and their patients accepted vaccination. Today smallpox has virtually been eliminated throughout the world because of smallpox vaccination.

Pasteur's Experiments with Anthrax

About 80 years after Jenner's first vaccination, Louis Pasteur did a famous series of experiments on immunity. Pasteur made a vaccine from anthrax bacteria that were weakened after being isolated from the blood of diseased animals. He claimed that this vaccine would protect healthy animals against anthrax. Other scientists challenged him to prove this claim. Pasteur was ready for the challenge. He separated 48 healthy animals, mostly sheep, into an experimental group and a control group. He injected the animals in one group with the anthrax vaccine. Twelve days later, he gave them a second injection.

After two more weeks, Pasteur injected all 48 animals with living anthrax bacteria. Two days later the scientists met at the pens where the animals were kept. To their surprise, all of the animals that had received vaccine were alive and healthy. All of the others were dead or dying of anthrax. This famous experiment marked an important advance in the battle against disease.

Koch and Isolation of Pathogenic Organisms

Robert Koch, a German doctor, experimented with infectious diseases at the same time as Louis Pasteur. He was the first to isolate the bacteria that cause such major diseases as anthrax and tuberculosis. Just as important are the tools and methods he developed for the study of such organisms. Kock developed the following methods to show that a particular organism causes a given disease:

1. Isolate the organism suspected of causing the disease.

2. Grow the organism in laboratory cultures.

3. Inoculate a healthy animal with the cultured organisms. See if the animal contracts the disease.

4. If the animal contracts the disease, examine the animal and reisolate the organisms that caused the disease.

The Conquest of Diphtheria

In the nineteenth century diphtheria swept through crowded American cities and killed a great number of people. At the end of the nineteenth century a German scientist, Emil von Behring, isolated the diphtheria exotoxin. When he injected the exotoxin into animals, the animals developed the symptoms of diphtheria even without the diphtheria bacteria. They also developed an immunity against the toxin. If the animals were injected with the poison a second time, there was no effect. Von Behring then isolated the substance that produced the immunity and called it an **antitoxin.** He received the Nobel Prize in 1901 for his work with the diphtheria antitoxin.

This early work was used by Dr. William Hill and other workers in the United States to develop an effective method of preventing diphtheria. The DPT shots you receive give immunity against diphtheria, pertussis (whooping cough), and tetanus. The DPT shots consist of antigens of these three bacterial diseases.

A Vaccine Against Polio

One major modern breakthrough in immune therapy was the development of a vaccine to prevent poliomyelitis, a crippling disease that previously reached epidemic proportions. Jonas Salk, an American who is still involved in scientific research, isolated polio viruses and treated them so that they were not virulent. He then used them as antigens. Antibody production occured and this created immunity against polio. At about the same time, another American, Albert Sabin, developed another polio vaccine, using weakened polio viruses rather than completely nonvirulent ones.

Following mass immunization against polio, the incidence of the disease dropped dramatically. In 1952 there were 57,879 cases of polio in the United States. In 1978 there were only 20 cases of polio in the country.

Chemotherapy

Chemistry as well as biology plays a major role in modern medicine. In **chemotherapy,** specific chemical compounds are used to destroy pathogenic organisms without harming the host.

The early development of chemotherapy owes much to the brilliant German chemist, Paul Ehrlich. Ehrlich spent

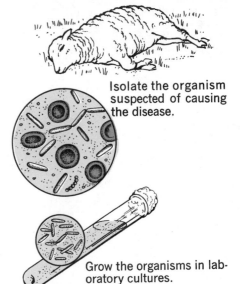
Isolate the organism suspected of causing the disease.

Grow the organisms in laboratory cultures.

Inoculate a healthy animal with the cultured organism and see if it contracts the disease.

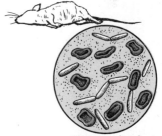
If the animal contracts the same disease, examine the diseased animal and reisolate the organism that caused the disease.

17–10 | Koch's procedure, used to show that anthrax was caused by bacteria.

many years trying to find a drug that would kill syphilis organisms in the blood without damaging the blood or other parts of the body. After 605 attempts had failed, he finally succeeded. On his next try the 606th drug, an arsenic compound called salvarsan, was developed. It was used in treating syphilis long before penicillin.

Another German scientist, Gerhard Domagk (DOE-mahk), discovered in 1932 that the red dye prontosil was effective in killing germs. He used this drug to save the life of his own daughter, who was dying of a streptococcus infection. Later it was learned that most of the power of prontosil lay in only one part, called *sulfanilamide* (SULL-fuh-NILL-uh-MIDE). This was the first of an important drug family known as the sulfa drugs. Though they are used in treating many diseases, sulfa drugs may be dangerous and should be taken only on the advice of a doctor.

Antibiotics

The chemicals called *antibiotics* are produced by living organisms, unlike the drugs used in chemotherapy. Antibiotics are used in treating many infectious diseases today.

Penicillin is the best known antibiotic, and it was also the first. It was discovered by accident in 1929 by Sir Alexander Fleming of Scotland. Fleming was working with cultures of staphylococcus bacteria. In some of the cultures, he noticed fluffy masses of mold growing. In the area around each mold colony, no bacteria would grow. It seemed that the mold gave off some substance that killed the bacteria.

17–11 | The antibiotic penicillin is obtained from this common mold, which can be seen below on a piece of bread. *(Matthew Stettler).*

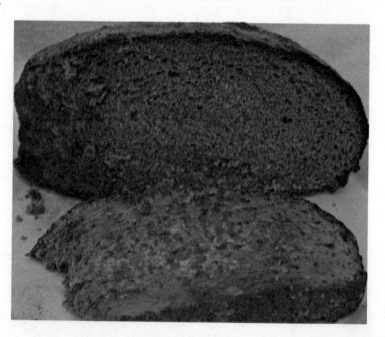

This probably was a helpful adaption, since the mold and the bacteria were competing for the same food supply.

The mold was later identified as *Penicillium notatum*, the common blue-green mold you see on bread or citrus fruit. The substance given off by it was named *penicillin*. However, penicillin was not used against infections until World War II. At that time a great search was on for substances that would help cure wound infections. Attention turned to Fleming's work and, with his help, penicillin was developed, tested, and put to use. Penicillin may be taken in several forms, including liquid, tablets, and ointment.

A large number of different antibiotics have now been developed. Many of them are of a type known as *tetracycline*. They destroy bacteria by interfering with their internal chemistry. The ideal antibiotic is one that works against a wide range of diseases without harming the host.

Dangers of Antibiotics **No antibiotic should be used unless prescribed by a doctor.** There are two basic reasons for this.

The first reason is that antibiotics may produce harmful side effects. For example, quite a few people have an allergic reaction to penicillin. In some cases, this reaction is strong enough to be fatal. Certain other antibiotics destroy the normal bacteria population of the intestines. Other bacteria may then grow in the intestines and cause diarrhea or other disturbances.

A second reason for caution in using antibiotics involves adaptation in bacteria. Like all organisms, bacteria vary. Some may have traits that allow them to resist the effects of an antibiotic. These bacteria will tend to survive repeated use of the antibiotic. In the end, a whole new strain may develop in which all members resist the antibiotic. For example, penicillin was very effective against staphylococcus bacteria for many years, but several new strains of these bacteria now resist penicillin.

Resistant strains of bacteria are becoming more of a problem. They are also a problem in countries where massive amounts of antibiotics are sold to people without a prescription or medical guidance.

Infectious Disease Today

Thanks to scientists such as Pasteur, Koch, Salk, and Sabin, many of the horrible infectious diseases of the past are preventable or curable. It is important to realize, however, that though a disease might not be visible in our population, the disease organisms may still be present. Cases of the Black Death, the bubonic plague that killed over half

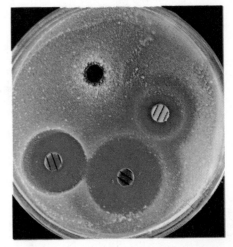

17-12 | Each of the four paper disks has been soaked in a different antibiotic and then placed in a bacterial culture. The size of the zone of no growth shows the effectiveness of each antibiotic. Note that the antibiotic on the black disk does not inhibit bacterial growth. What does this mean? *(Walter Dawn)*

the people of Europe in the fourteenth century still occur occasionally in this country. So does leprosy. Influenza and pneumonia kill a great many people, especially elderly people.

Two infectious diseases that are becoming more common in our society are gonorrhea and syphilis. Gonorrhea is the more common of the two and affects an estimated 2.5 to 3 million people in the United States. These diseases are completely and quickly cured with the proper antibiotics. If left untreated, these bacterial infections can damage internal organs, cause heart disease and blindness, and even infect unborn children.

Summary

All around us are viruses, bacteria, and parasites that can enter the body and cause disease. *Pathogenic* organisms can be encountered in the air, in water, and through direct contact with infection. Infections can cause damage in a number of ways.

The body has two main lines of defense against infections. One defense is largely mechanical. The other defense includes cellular and chemical means of destroying bacteria that do manage to enter the body tissues. Body cells called *phagocytes* devour bacteria. Other body cells produce *antibodies* that combat specific bacteria by combining chemically with the bacteria and thus changing them.

If you are *immune* to a certain disease, this means that you are free of the threat of that disease. People are born with some immunities. Others are acquired naturally by contacting and recovering from certain infections. One way of providing artificial immunity is to introduce dead or weakened pathogenic organisms into the body so that the body will produce antibodies. Another way is to introduce antibodies produced outside the body. Many bacterial diseases that once were common have been brought under control by this *immune therapy*.

Various chemicals have been found that destroy pathogenic organisms. Chemicals called *antibiotics*, produced by living organisms, are useful in fighting many diseases.

disease
airborne infection
waterborne infection
contact infection
droplet infection
exotoxins

endotoxin
lysozyme
phagocyte
leucocyte
pus
antibodies
antigen
immunity

active immunity
passive immunity
serum
vaccination
antitoxin
chemotherapy
antibiotic

Biologically Speaking

Questions for Review

1. List the four steps in Koch's investigation of anthrax disease.
2. Describe the various ways that infectious organisms are spread.
3. What is meant by *immune carrier*?
4. Distinguish between exotoxins and endotoxins.
5. How does food poisoning occur? Give one example.

6. List the body's principal structural defenses against disease.
7. Describe how leucocytes help to defend against disease.
8. In what way is fever an important body defense?
9. Distinguish between natural and artificial immunity.

10. Why was Dr. Jenner's experiment important?
11. What is the difference between an antibody and an antibiotic?

Applying Concepts

1. Explain how resistant forms of bacteria come into being.
2. Discuss the question: Why might an infection contracted in a hospital be more severe than one contracted at home or in school?
3. Give a possible reason for the fact that Eskimos never had colds until whalers came.
4. Venereal disease can be cured with proper treatment. Discuss why these diseases exist in such a large number of people. What is being done, and what can be done about it?
5. Why might immune therapy be better than antibiotic therapy?

18

The Protozoa

A **DESCRIBE** the identifying characteristics of protozoa.

B **IDENTIFY** the parts of the Ameba, *Euglena,* and Paramecia and discuss their functions.

C **DESCRIBE** various methods of locomotion in protozoa.

D **DESCRIBE** various methods of reproduction in protozoa.

E **NAME** and **DISCUSS** some disease-causing protozoa.

F **DESCRIBE** the economic importance of protozoa.

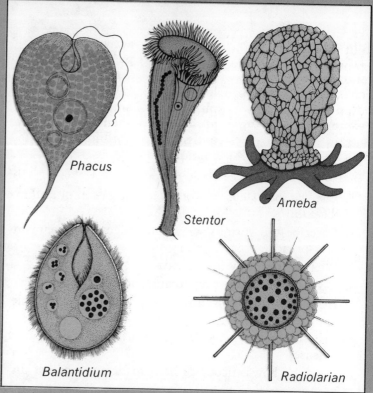

Phacus

Stentor

Ameba

Balantidium

Radiolarian

18-1 | Protozoans. What characteristics do they have in common?

What Are Protozoa?

proto = first
zoa = animal

Protozoa are microscopic, unicellular, animallike organisms. Some are barely visible, and appear as tiny specks to the naked eye. Protozoa are quite different from more familiar plants and animals. Many scientists have placed them in a separate kingdom, the *Protista.*

Although protozoa are considered among the simplest organisms, they are far from simple. **Protozoa perform all of the many functions of life that multicellular organisms perform, such as digestion, excretion, and respiration. However, in protozoa all of these functions take place within a single cell.**

Some protozoa form a group, or cluster, of cells called a *colony.* Each cell within a colony maintains its independence as a separate organism because each cell performs all life functions. Only the function of reproduction may be shared between individual cells of a colony.

There are about 30,000 species of protozoa. Each has its own life style and habitat. Protozoan habitats include ponds, oceans, mud, soil, and even on or in certain plants and animals. Some species live only in the body cavity and gut of certain worms, grasshoppers, humans, and other protozoa. Some cause diseases in humans such as amebic dysentery, malaria, and African sleeping sickness.

Not all protozoa are harmful to the animals with which they are associated. Some are beneficial. For example, certain flagellated protozoa live in the intestines of termites, where they secrete digestive enzymes. The enzymes break down the wood that the termites eat. The usable nutrients that result are absorbed by both the protozoa and the termites. The termites benefit by having their food digested; the protozoa benefit by having a source of food and a place to live.

Protozoa are classified in four phyla based on their method of movement. An example of a typical protozoan from each phylum will show you the characteristics common to each group.

Phylum Sarcodina: Ameba

The genus *Amoeba* includes several interesting protozoan species. At first glance, you might mistake an ameba for something nonliving—a microscopic bit of jelly, for example. Yet this tiny blob of grayish "jelly" is a complete living organism. It moves, reproduces, and performs all other life functions.

Through the microscope an ameba appears as a shapeless mass of cytoplasm surrounded by a thin plasma membrane. In an active ameba you will see that the cytoplasm has a constant flowing motion. This streaming cytoplasm presses against the plasma membrane and pushes out projections called **pseudopodia** (soo-doe-POE-dee-uh).

pseudo = **false**
pod = **foot**

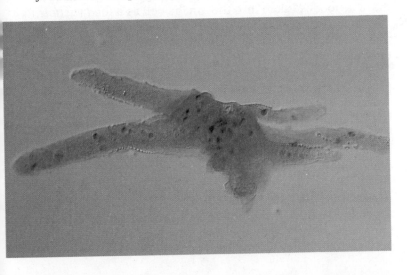

18-2 | An ameba is a common protozoan often studied in the laboratory. *(Manfred Kage, Peter Arnold)*

Pseudopodia (singular, *pseudopod*) means "false feet." The name is fitting, since amebas move by means of their pseudopodia. The motion is sort of flowing, with new pseudopodia reaching out and old ones disappearing back into the cytoplasm. **On the basis of this *ameboid movement*, amebas are placed in the protist phylum Sarcodina.**

A closer look at an ameba such as *Amoeba proteus* shows that amebas have two types of cytoplasm. A clear, watery ***ectoplasm*** is found just inside the cell membrane. Ectoplasm is outside the denser, grainier ***endoplasm,*** which looks like gray jelly with pepper sprinkled through it. The inner part of the endoplasm is more fluid than the outer part and flows more rapidly when the ameba moves. A disk-shaped nucleus, which changes position as the cytoplasm flows, is present.

Amebas live in water. They are found in slime at the bottom of streams and ponds, and on the leaves of water plants. The oxygen needed for life enters through the cell membrane by diffusion from the surrounding water. Carbon dioxide and soluble wastes such as ammonia pass out through the membrane in the same way.

Much useless water also enters the ameba cell, mainly by osmosis. If the ameba could not rid itself of this water, it would swell and burst like a balloon. This does not happen, of course. Instead, the extra water gathers in a *contractile vacuole.* When this vacuole reaches a certain size, it contracts sharply, and the water is squeezed out. A temporary break in the cell membrane occurs when this happens.

How Amebas Get Food

The food supply for amebas includes cells of algae and of certain other protists. When an ameba contacts such a cell, it simply engulfs the cell by surrounding it with pseudopodia. The food is taken into the ameba cell as a *food vacuole.* Part of the cell membrane of the ameba surrounds this vacuole. A new membrane quickly forms at the point where the food entered the ameba cell.

Digestion is carried on by enzymes formed in the cytoplasm. These enzymes pass into the food vacuole and act on the food. Digested food is absorbed by the cytoplasm. Then it is ready for use as an energy source or as raw material for building more protoplasm. Particles that are not digested remain in the vacuole and may pass out at any point on the cell membrane.

Response in the Ameba

Amebas respond to the conditions around them. Though they have no eyes, they are sensitive to light and seek dim or dark areas. They do not have nerve endings for a sense of

ecto = outside
endo = inside

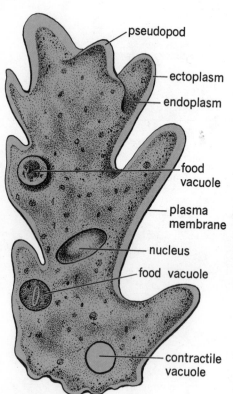

18-3 | The structure of an ameba. This protist changes its shape as it moves.

pseudopod

ectoplasm

endoplasm

food vacuole

plasma membrane

nucleus

food vacuole

contractile vacuole

touch. Yet they react to movement around them and move away from objects they touch.

Some species of ameba respond to conditions such as dryness, cold, or lack of food. Such amebas become inactive and withdraw into a round mass called a **cyst.** When conditions improve, the amebas become active again.

Reproduction of Amebas

Under good conditions, an ameba may double its volume in a day or two. When this occurs, it reproduces by simple cell division. The nucleus divides and the two daughter nuclei move to opposite ends of the cell. The cell then pinches in at the center, and the two halves pull apart. Each daughter cell has a nucleus and is capable of independent life and growth. The division itself takes about an hour.

Phylum Ciliophora: Paramecium

Amebas are fairly simple cells with few specialized structures. Members of the genus *Paramecium*, however, are a much more complex form of one-celled life. Species of this genus live mainly in quiet or stagnant ponds. Great numbers of paramecia are found in the scums that form on such ponds.

Oxygen gas (O_2) dissolved in the water diffuses through the cell membrane and enters the cytoplasm. It is used in the process of respiration. Carbon dioxide (CO_2), a waste product of respiration, diffuses out of the cell into the water.

The paramecium cell is shaped like a slipper. Although they are flexible enough to bend, paramecia do not change shape like amebas. Their definite shape results from a thick outer membrane, the **pellicle,** which surrounds the cell membrane.

Paramecia move by means of hairlike threads called *cilia.* These cilia are arranged in rows and beat back and forth like tiny oars. They cover the whole cell but are most easily seen at the edges. Cilia can beat either forward or backward, moving the cell in either direction and allowing it to turn. This kind of movement places paramecia in the protist phylum *Ciliophora.*

How Paramecia Get Food

A striking feature of the paramecium is the **oral groove** along one side of the cell. The cell also has a definite front end, or *anterior* part, which is rounded. The rear end, or *posterior* part, is more pointed. The oral groove runs from the anterior toward the posterior end.

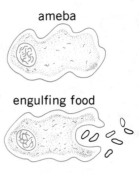

ameba

engulfing food

forming food vacuole

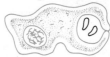

enzymes pass into the vacuole

enzymes digest the food

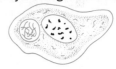

food not digested passes out the cell membrane

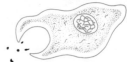

the search for food continues

18-4 | Feeding and digestion in the ameba.

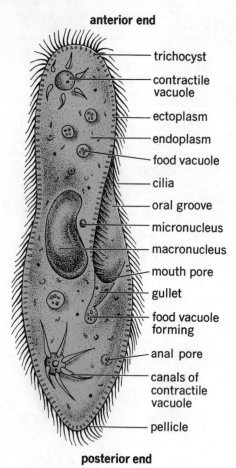

anterior end

- trichocyst
- contractile vacuole
- ectoplasm
- endoplasm
- food vacuole
- cilia
- oral groove
- micronucleus
- macronucleus
- mouth pore
- gullet
- food vacuole forming
- anal pore
- canals of contractile vacuole
- pellicle

posterior end

18-5 | The structure of the paramecium. In what ways are the paramecium and the ameba alike? In what ways are they different?

Cilia line the oral groove and cause the paramecium to spin around its long axis as it swims. More important, these cilia sweep food particles back toward the **mouth pore.** This pore, in turn, opens into a funnellike **gullet,** which reaches into the cytoplasm. Bacteria and other foods forced into the gullet are formed into a *food vacuole.*

When a food vacuole reaches a certain size, it breaks away from the gullet. The movement of the cytoplasm carries the vacuole around the cell. During this movement, foods are digested and absorbed, as in amebas. Undigested particles are passed out through the **anal pore.** This tiny opening in the pellicle is found near the posterior end. It is completely closed except when in use.

How Paramecia Remove Wastes

A contractile vacuole for removing extra water is found near each end of the cell. Around each vacuole are *canals* leading into the cytoplasm. These canals enlarge as they fill with water, which is then passed on to the central part of the vacuole. From there, the water is emptied through an opening in the cell surface. Biologists estimate that in just 30 minutes a paramecium pumps out a volume of water equal to the whole cell content. Most other waste products appear to diffuse out the cell membrane.

Response in Paramecia

Like amebas, paramecia have no specialized sense organs. Yet paramecia, too, respond to conditions around them. Except when feeding, the cells swim constantly. When they bump into something, they reverse, turn, and swim off in a new direction. This kind of trial-and-error response is called the *avoiding reaction.* They also avoid areas of extreme heat or cold, areas that lack dissolved oxygen, or areas that contain foreign chemicals. They also tend to stay in areas that have a good food supply.

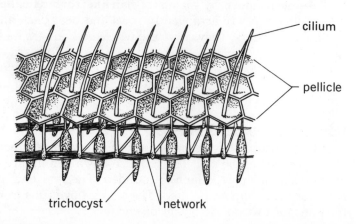

- cilium
- pellicle

trichocyst   network

18-6 | The network of fibers beneath the pellicle coordinates the beating cilia.

Paramecia also have a defense response. Just inside the pellicle are the ***trichocysts,*** which appear as tiny lines when seen through a microscope. When a larger protozoan approaches, the trichocysts shoot special threads of protoplasm out into the water. These threads are quite long and give the paramecium a bristly appearance. This response may be caused by chemicals given off by the larger organism. Adding acetic acid or iodine to water containing paramecia often causes their trichocysts to "fire."

Reproduction in Paramecia

Paramecia have two different kinds of nuclei, both found near the center of the cell. A large ***macronucleus*** controls normal cell activity. A much smaller ***micronucleus*** functions during reproduction. Some species have more than one micronucleus.

Paramecia reproduce by cell fission. The macronucleus and micronucleus divide during this process. Under good conditions, fission may occur two or three times a day.

From time to time, paramecia also reproduce by a type of sexual reproduction called *conjugation.* After a series of nuclear divisions and other steps, two paramecia exchange micronuclei, then continue to divide by fission. This causes mixing of genetic material and provides more variation. **Variation increases the chances for the species to survive.**

Phylum Mastigophora: Euglena

mastigo = whip

Several species of the genus *Euglena* live in ponds and streams. Under the microscope, euglenas have an oval or pear shape. The anterior end is rounded, while the posterior end usually is pointed.

18–7 | The avoiding reaction in the paramecium.

a. fission　　**b. conjugation**

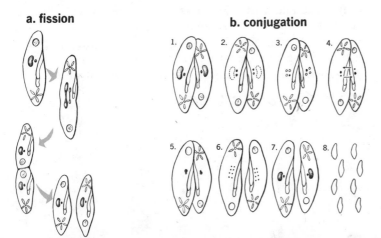

18–8 | The two types of reproduction characteristic of paramecia: (a) fission, and (b) conjugation.

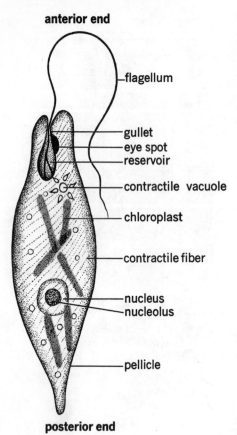

anterior end

— flagellum

— gullet
— eye spot
— reservoir

— contractile vacuole

— chloroplast

— contractile fiber

— nucleus
— nucleolus

— pellicle

posterior end

18–9 | The structure of euglena. Which way does this protist move?

Facts & Figures

The flagellum of an animal sperm has the same structure as the flagellum of a protozoan.

Euglenas were classed as plants in some systems and as animals in others because the cells have certain traits of both kingdoms. Today, they are often placed in the protist phylum Mastigophora (MAS-ti-GAH-fuh-ruh). **This classification is based on the fact that euglena swims by means of a flagellum.** This flagellum, at the anterior end of the cell, whirls in a way that pulls the cell through the water.

Unlike any other member of its phylum, the euglena has a second method of movement. This **euglenoid** (yoo-GLEE-NOID) **movement** involves a gradual change in the shape of the cell. The cell becomes rounded as the posterior part is drawn forward. Then the anterior part is stretched forward, resulting in wormlike movement. This contraction and stretching movement is caused by specialized **contractile fibers** in the cell.

A typical euglena is *Euglena gracilis*. This cell is surrounded by a thin, flexible pellicle. At the anterior end, a small gullet opening leads into a larger **reservoir.** However, euglenas have never been seen to take in food through their gullets. Thus, this structure may serve only as an attachment point for the flagellum. A contractile vacuole near the reservoir pumps out extra water.

A red **eyespot** is clearly seen near the gullet. This tiny bit of specialized protoplasm is highly sensitive to light. Unlike many other Protozoa, euglenas seek out bright areas where it thrives. Euglenas have many oval *chloroplasts* spread through the cell. Light is helpful to euglena because most of them carry on photosynthesis.

Besides forming foods by photosynthesis, euglenas can absorb organic materials through the cell membrane. In fact, some species lose their chlorophyll during long periods of darkness and survive only by absorbing needed substances.

A large nucleus containing a nucleolus is near the center of the euglena cell. Euglenas reproduce by cell fission. Under good conditions, they divide about once a day. Thus, a single euglena may give rise to millions of daughter cells in less than a month. Great numbers of euglenas in ponds and streams often make the water look bright green.

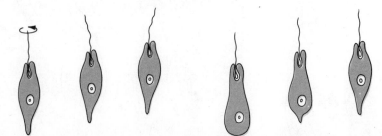

18–10 | The euglena can move forward by twirling its flagellum in a circular pattern, or it can move with a wormlike ameboid motion.

Phylum Sporozoa: Plasmodium

Protozoa in the protist phylum Sporozoa have no method of movement on their own. These protists are all parasites. They live by absorbing food from the cells or body fluids of a host organism. Many species live in two hosts during their life cycle.

Reproduction is by means of spores. The nucleus divides into many small nuclei. A small amount of cytoplasm surrounds each nucleus, forming a spore. The parent cell

sporo = spore

18–11 | The life cycle of *Plasmodium,* the parasitic protozoan that causes malaria in people.

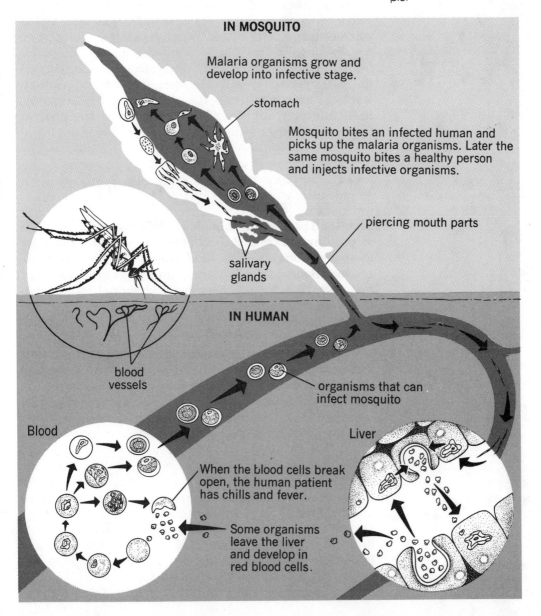

IN MOSQUITO

Malaria organisms grow and develop into infective stage.

stomach

Mosquito bites an infected human and picks up the malaria organisms. Later the same mosquito bites a healthy person and injects infective organisms.

piercing mouth parts

salivary glands

IN HUMAN

blood vessels

organisms that can infect mosquito

Blood

Liver

When the blood cells break open, the human patient has chills and fever.

Some organisms leave the liver and develop in red blood cells.

breaks apart and releases these spores, which can grow into mature cells. In some species, spores are protected by a thick coat. In others, there is only a plasma membrane.

A good example of the Sporozoa is *Plasmodium*. This is the organism that causes malaria in human beings and other warm-blooded animals. Malaria is transmitted by the female *Anopheles* mosquito. When this mosquito bites a person who has malaria, some of the *Plasmodium* cells are taken into the mosquito's stomach. They grow, reproduce, work their way into the insect's blood, and are carried to the salivary glands. See figure 18-11 for details.

After several cycles of forming spores, some of the parasites enter a sexual stage and form gametes. These gametes continue the cycle in the stomach of a mosquito.

When fighting malaria, it is important to isolate people from *Anopheles* mosquitoes. This interrupts the life cycle of the parasite and prevents its spread to other people. It would be even better to destroy the *Anopheles* population itself. However, this is difficult to do, especially in areas with many marshes where the mosquitos breed.

Other Pathogenic Protozoa

Almost all people and animals are infected with some type of protozoan during their lifetimes. The usual place for these infections is the intestine, where a great many protozoa may flourish. Some of these protists are harmless and may even be helpful. Others live on material in the intestine, robbing the host of food. Some enter the blood and may be carried to other parts of the host's body where they cause illness.

A type of ameba causes the disease known as *amebic dysentery*. The parasite is usually transmitted in food or water. Dysentery is most common in the tropics but can occur in other areas as well. The infection centers in the large intestine. The parasites feed on the intestine wall and blood cells, causing bleeding ulcers.

Cysts containing inactive ameba cells are excreted in the feces of infected people. Amebic dysentery is common where sewage disposal methods are crude or human waste is used as fertilizer. Human carriers may also transmit the disease. People may carry the parasite but may not have any symptoms of the disease. Drugs are effective against dysentery, but proper sanitary measures are far more important in eliminating this disease.

Two flagellated protozoa known as *trypanosomes* cause *African sleeping sickness*. These organisms are classed in the

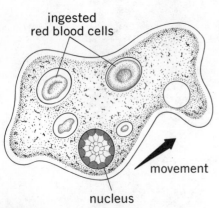

ingested red blood cells

movement

nucleus

18-12 | *Entamoeba histolytica,* the cause of amebic dysentery. Red blood cells are digested inside food vacuoles.

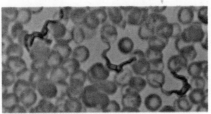

Trypanosoma gambiense

flagellum

nucleus

undulating membrane

18–13 | *Trypanosoma gambiense,* the cause of African sleeping sickness. They can be seen among human blood cells in the above photograph. *(Walter Dawn)*

same phylum as *Euglena.* Trypanosomes live in the blood of many African mammals and insects. They are transmitted to human beings by the bite of the *tsetse fly.* The cycle involved is much like the one by which malaria is transmitted.

The infection caused by the trypanosomes is serious and often fatal in human beings. In the blood, the organisms multiply for several weeks before the first symptoms appear. Early symptoms include headache, fever, and general fatigue. As more blood cells are destroyed, the victim becomes weak and anemic. Finally, the trypanosomes attack the central nervous system. This results in a long coma, followed by almost certain death.

As with malaria and the *Anopheles* mosquito, the best measure against sleeping sickness would be to wipe out the tsetse fly. However, the fly is found in such a vast area that this is almost impossible.

Economic Importance of Protozoa

The fishing industry is dependent on protozoa. Protozoa serve as a base of an aquatic food chain. Protozoa are eaten by small animals, which in turn are eaten by larger fish. Without protozoa the great populations of cod, herring, mackerel, and other fish would not exist.

Two orders of protozoa, *Foraminifera* and *Radiolaria,* have shell-like skeletons of lime (calcium carbonate). The skeletons of countless billions of these organisms laid down millions of years ago are the basic material for limestone deposits. The Egyptians used limestone to build the pyramids in Gizeh. Limestone is used today in building construction.

In the past, diseases have kept people from settling in certain areas. Even today, in Africa, the danger of sleeping sickness prevents the settlement of vast areas of land. Control of the tsetse fly would open up an area in Africa about the size of the United States to agriculture and cattle raising.

Summary

COMPARISON OF THREE PROTOZOA

	AMEBA	PARAMECIUM	EUGLENA
FORM	variable	slipper-shaped	pear-shaped or oval
LOCOMOTION	pseudopodia (ameboid movement)	cilia	flagellum or euglenoid movement
SPEED	slow	rapid	rapid or slow
FOOD-GETTING	pseudopodia surrounding food	cilia in oral groove, mouth cavity, and gullet	photosynthesis or absorption
DIGESTION	in food vacuole	in food vacuole	in cytoplasm
ABSORPTION	from food vacuole by diffusion and cyclosis	from food vacuole by diffusion and cyclosis	from cytoplasm by diffusion and cyclosis
RESPIRATION	diffusion of O_2 and CO_2 through plasma membrane	diffusion of O_2 and CO_2 through plasma membrane and pellicle	diffusion of O_2 and CO_2 through plasma membrane and pellicle
EXCRETION	through plasma membrane	through plasma membrane and pellicle	through plasma membrane and pellicle
SENSITIVITY	responds to heat, light, contact, chemicals	responds to heat, light, contact, chemicals	eyespot sensitive to light; responds also to heat, contact, chemicals
REPRODUCTION	fission	fission and conjugation	fission

Biologically Speaking

pseudopodia
ameboid movement
ectoplasm
endoplasm
cyst
pellicle
cilia
oral groove
mouth pore
gullet

anal pore
trichocyst
macronucleus
micronucleus
conjugation
euglenoid movement
contractile fiber
reservoir
eyespot

Questions for Review

1. Name four phyla of Protozoa and give an example of each.
2. Describe ameboid movement.
3. How does an ameba take in food?

4. Explain the vital function of a contractile vacuole.
5. Describe locomotion in the paramecium.
6. What types of reproduction are exhibited by paramecia?
7. How do trichocysts act as a means of defense?
8. Why do euglenas seek light while amebas and paramecia avoid it?
9. Describe the life cycle of *Plasmodium*.
10. Explain the relationship between amebic dysentery and unsanitary conditions.

Applying Concepts

1. Biologists frequently say that understanding the life processes of single-celled protozoa helps them to understand the life processes of complicated organisms such as humans. Why is this probably true?
2. Compare methods of locomotion, digestion, and sensitive response in amebas, paramecia, and euglenas.
3. Once a person has become infected with the malarial parasite, at what stage in the development of the illness would you consider treatment most possible?
4. How are protozoa important in a pond?

19

The Fungi

A **LIST** some general characteristics of fungi.

B **DESCRIBE** the characteristics of each of the four classes of fungi.

C **DESCRIBE** the life cycle of a bread mold.

D **LIST** some useful characteristics of fungi.

E **DESCRIBE** the unique life cycle of slime molds.

F **DISCUSS** some diseases caused by fungi.

G **DESCRIBE** the structure of a mushroom and discuss its function.

19-1 | Mushrooms are typical examples of fungi. *(HRW Photo by Russell Dian)*

What Are Fungi?

Fungi grow everywhere. You can find them on rotting fruit, between your toes as athlete's foot, or on the damp ground of a forest. Fungi are plantlike in many ways, but they are not green. They have cellulose cell walls but lack chlorophyll and cannot make their own food. They are **heterotrophs,** which means they must depend on other organisms for their food. Fungi use both animals and plants as sources of food. In fact, many species of fungi compete with humans for the same foods. If two oranges are on a table, and one is slightly moldy, which will you choose to eat? If you leave the moldy orange, the fungus wins.

Farms have had to learn how to deal with fungi that threaten their crops. Farmers plant fungus-resistant crops and even fumigate the soil in an effort to prevent fungal disease. **Mycologists,** scientists who study fungi, are employed to find new ways of protecting both animals and plants from fungal diseases such as ringworm, Dutch elm blight, potato blight, and some forms of asthma.

Although many fungi are troublesome, many others are helpful. Baker's yeast is a fungus used in making bread.

myco = fungus

Many cheeses owe their flavor to fungi. The powerful anti-bacterial agents called antibiotics are derived from fungi.

Some fungi, such as wheat rust and corn smut, are parasites and live off living organisms. Most fungi are **saprophytes.** They live off the bodies of dead organisms or nonliving products, such as wood.

The most important role of fungi, essential to all life on earth, is as decay organisms. In the decay process digestive enzymes are secreted by fungi. Complex molecules are broken down into simpler ones. Some of the molecules are absorbed by the fungi and used as food, but many of these simple molecules are released into the soil and atmosphere. These molecules can then be taken in and used by green plants as nutrients. Thus saprophytic fungi supply nutrients to living plants. The fungi, together with decay bacteria, serve as a bridge between the dead and living. They enable organic matter to be recycled continually. In this way they are absolutely vital to life on earth.

sapro = rotten, decaying
phyta = plant

Eumycophyta: The True Fungi

All of the true fungi are classified in the phylum *Eumycophyta* (YOO-MY-KAH-fuh-tuh). **These organisms have cell walls but no chlorophyll, and are usually composed of threadlike filaments that secrete digestive enzymes.** The true fungi are simple in basic structure. Yeasts, such as the dried baker's yeast you use in making bread, are unicellular. All of the other of these fungi form long filaments of cells called **hyphae** (HIFE-ee). If you hold a piece of moldy bread or moldy orange rind up to the light, you can see these thin, glistening filaments. A single hypha is a long tube containing the living cytoplasm of the fungus. Sometimes the tube is hollow along its entire length, and sometimes it has cross walls. The cell wall of a hypha is made of cellulose, so some structures of certain fungi can be hard and woody.

A thick mass of interwoven hyphae filaments is called a **mycelium,** as can be seen in figure 19-2. Sometimes the filaments are pressed so closely together that they form the solid bodies of mushrooms or the bracket, or shelf, fungi you sometimes see growing on rotting logs or tree trunks. These solid structures are "fruiting bodies." They contain the spore-producing organs of the fungi. Fungi produce spores by the billions, and the wind distributes them all over the earth.

The method of spore production is an important feature in the life cycle of any fungus. In fact, **fungi are classified**

19-2 | The water mold, *Saprolegnia,* on a dead fish. The cottonlike mass is mycelia. Note that it is made of individual filaments. *(Allan Roberts)*

according to the type of reproduction bodies they produce. There are four different classes of fungi:

- *Phycomycetes* (FIKE-oe-MY-SEE-teez) have spore containers called **sporangia** at the ends of long filaments.
- *Ascomycetes* (ASK-oe-my-SEE-teez) produce spores in fingerlike spore sacs called **asci**.
- *Basidiomycetes* (buh-SID-ee-oe-SEE-teez) produce spores at the ends of club-shaped hyphae called **basidia.**
- *Deuteromycetes* (DOO-tuh-ROE-MY-SEE-teez) produce spores on simple hyphae.

Phycomycetes: The Sporangia Fungi

Some of our most common molds are Phycomycetes, the fungi that form long, hollow, tubelike hyphae without cross walls. These hyphae resemble the long strands, or filaments, of certain algae. Phycomycetes reproduce sexually, as well as producing asexual spores in sporangia. In sexual reproduction, two nuclei unite and form a zygote, or **zygospore.**

Some common Phycomycetes are common bread mold, water mold that you may see on aquarium fish, potato blight, and tomato blight. The following discussion of the life cycles of bread mold will illustrate some of the main characteristics of the Phycomycetes.

Bread Mold   One of the most familiar molds is *Rhizopus nigricans,* or bread mold. If you rub dust on a piece of moist bread, put the bread in a covered dish and wait a few days, bread mold will form. The mold can form from a single spore on the moist bread. The hyphae grow very quickly into a fluffy white mycelium.

When you look through a microscope you will see several different kinds of hyphae in the mold. Those that spread over the surface of the food supply are called **stolons** (STOW-lonz). At intervals along the stolons, clusters of shorter hyphae reach down into the food supply like roots. These **rhizoids** (RY-zoidz) secrete enzymes that act on the sugar and starch in the bread. The digested foods, along with water, are then absorbed by the rhizoids. The flavor, odor, and color spots produced by bread mold result from the action of its enzymes.

After a few days, black knobs appear among the hyphae of bread mold. Each knob is a spore case, or *sporangium.* More than 50,000 spores develop in each sporangium.

When a sporangium matures, it breaks open and releases its spores. The spores are carried away by air cur-

phycos = seaweed (resembling seaweed)
myceto = fungus

ascos = cup, sac

deutero = secondary

rhizo = root

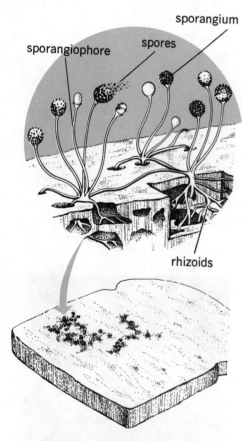

sporangium

sporangiophore   spores

rhizoids

19–3 | The structure of bread mold. Note the rootlike rhizoids extending into the bread. Note the sporangium, typical of the Phycomycetes.

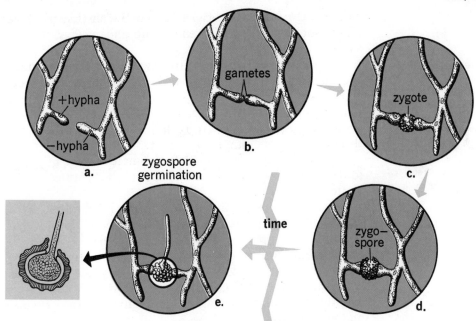

a. +hypha −hypha

b. gametes

c. zygote

d. zygo−spore

time

e. zygospore germination

19-4 | Sexual reproduction in bread mold requires two different mating strains.

rents. If a spore lodges on a food supply in a suitable environment, it **germinates.** That is, the spore becomes active and forms hyphae that branch out and form a new mycelium.

Bread mold also reproduces sexually by a form of **conjugation.** Although the reproductive hyphae all look alike, they actually are two different mating types. These types can be called *plus* and *minus*.

In sexual reproduction the hyphae form short, specialized side branches. The tip of a *plus* branch meets the tip of a *minus* branch during conjugation. Cross walls form behind the end tips, leaving each tip as a gamete cell. The two gametes then fuse and form a zygote. These zygote develops a thick wall and matures into a *zygospore*, which enters a dormant period.

After from one to several months, if conditions permit, the zygospore germinates. In some cases it produces a single stalk that bears a sporangium and spores. In other cases, a short, branching hypha grows from the zygospore. A cluster of rhizoids grows from this hypha sporangium, and spores then develop.

Other Phycomycetes The Phycomycete known as *late blight fungus* is a plant parasite that causes tremendous damage in plant crops. This fungus diease caused the great famine in Ireland from 1845 to 1847 by destroying nearly the whole potato crop. The blight fungus hyphae grow

Facts & Figures

In the 1830s the population of Ireland was approximately eight million. By the mid-1840s, following the destruction of the potato crop by potato blight, two million Irish had emigrated, two million had died of starvation, and four million were in dire poverty.

Facts & Figures

In 1970 the United States lost one sixth of its corn crop to southern corn leaf blight.

between the leaf cells of the host plant and destroy the plant. Blight can also infect the potatoes themselves as well as the leaves.

Instead of germinating directly, a late blight fungus sporangium may release **zoospores.** Zoospores are single cells with *flagella*, or tails. When dew or rain wets the plants, the zoospores swim around and infect new plants. A single zoospore produces a hypha, which enters the plant through some opening in the plant.

The same blight can also infect tomatoes. Late blight of tomatoes is common in some of the southern states in the United States.

If you have pet goldfish you might be familiar with *water molds* of the genus *Saprolegnia*. Some of these water molds are saprophytes that live on the bodies of dead fish, insects, and other animals in water. Other water molds are parasites. They invade the tissues of living fish and other water animals. Such parasites rob the host of food, and usually kill it. They are a great problem in lakes, streams, and aquariums.

You can usually see *Saprolegnia* growing as a white fluffy mycelium on the body of the diseased fish. The hyphae are tubelike and hollow. The water molds are unusual in that they produce sporangia that release motile zoospores in the water. The zoospores have whiplike flagella that move them through the water. They are capable of producing a new colony of hyphae.

Ascomycetes: The Sac Fungi

Ascomyetes are the fungi that reproduce sexually by producing spores called *ascospores* **in special thin-walled, fingerlike sacs called asci** (singular, *ascus*). The asci usually line the inside of the colored, cuplike fruiting bodies. You can sometimes find these fruiting bodies on damp, rotting logs lying on the forest floor. You cannot see the main body of the mycelium, which is spread throughout the wood. The hyphae that make up the fruiting bodies have cross walls.

Ascospores result from the union of two nuclei in the ascus. The zygote goes through three divisions, which result in eight separate ascospore cells in each ascus. When released, the spores can be carried in the air to new locations. Some Ascomycetes also reproduce asexually by producing large numbers of spores called **conidia.**

Ascomycetes are among the most serious disease-causing fungi. Dutch elm disease destroys thousands of elms each year in the United States. American chestnut blight has almost completely destroyed a once common

19–5 | Brightly colored cups of some ascomycetes hold many saclike asci that contain spores. *(M. D. L. Fogden, Bruce Coleman)*

tree. Other Ascomycetes such as apple scab, and brown rot in peaches, attack food crops.

Yeasts One of the best known Ascomycetes is not associated with disease but with bread baking. This is yeast. *Yeasts* are microscopic, one-celled Ascomycetes. They do not have hyphae but can reproduce sexually and have asci. The sexually produced ascospores have thick walls that enable yeasts to survive extremes of temperature or prolonged drying. When environmental conditions make it possible for the ascospores to become active, they reproduce asexually by budding.

When bread is being made, only a small number of the dormant yeast cells, the ascospores, are added to a large amount of wet dough. The yeast cells become active and begin the budding when placed in a warm area.

A bud begins as a small knob pushing outward on the side of the yeast cell. The small bud pinches off from the large cell. It then grows in size and forms its own buds. Under ideal conditions yeast cells can bud very rapidly. As they reproduce, they use nutrients to grow and reproduce.

Bread dough rises because bubbles of carbon dioxide are trapped in the dough. Sugar that is added to the dough is broken down by yeast into alcohol and carbon dioxide through the process of *fermentation*. You can smell the alcohol in the rising dough. When the dough is cooked, the yeast cells die, and the alcohol is burned off by the heat.

There are many different species of yeasts. Some are found naturally on the surfaces of grapes and other fruits and in the nectars of flowers. Others are found in soil, milk, and animal excretions. Some cause disease in humans, insects, and certain protozoa.

Powdery Mildews The powdery mildews are also Ascomycetes. These disease-causing fungi appear as a white powder on the leaves of roses, grapes, clover, apples, wheat, and other plants. Their hyphae destroy plant cells by penetrating them and digesting their contents. Powdery mildews produce enormous numbers of conidia, which account for the white powery coat on the leaves. They can completely destroy a crop.

Other Ascomycetes The *morel* is an Ascomycete that looks like a spongy mushroom. It is prized for its flavor. Another tasy ascomycete, the *truffle,* is imported from France. Neither of these fungi can be cultivated, so they are expensive delicacies.

Certain Ascomycetes live in close association with algae

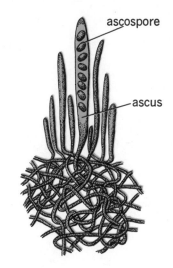

19–6 | In the Ascomycetes, ascospores develop in an ascus.

19–7 | The morel, or sponge mushroom, is a highly prized edible fungus. *(Alvin E. Steffan, National Audobon Society)*

in a plant called a *lichen*. The small cups that contain the asci can be seen on these primitive plants.

Basidiomycetes: The Club Fungi

Basidiomycetes, the "club fungi," get their name from the club-shaped reproductive hyphae, called basidia (singular, *basidium*). The basidia produce spores called **basidiospores.** Mushrooms and bracket fungi are the most prominent Basidiomycetes. This class of fungi includes also puffballs, rusts, and smuts.

Mushrooms Mushrooms seem to pop up all over, especially after a warm rain in the autumn or spring. This sudden appearance of mushrooms is a good example of how fast a fungus grows. Mushrooms are actually the reproductive bodies of the fungus.

Mushrooms first become visible to us as small, round knobs, called buttons, that poke up above the decaying litter on the soil surface. The mature mushroom has a stalk, or *stipe*, supporting an umbrella-shaped *cap*. At first, the cap is folded down around the stipe. After breaking through the ground surface, the cap begins to open. A ring, or *annulus*, remains where the cap and stipe were joined.

In most cases the cap contains many *gills* radiating from the stipe like spokes. On the sides of each gill are thousands of the club-shaped hyphae, basidia.

19–8 | The development of a mushroom. The inset is an enlargement of a gill.

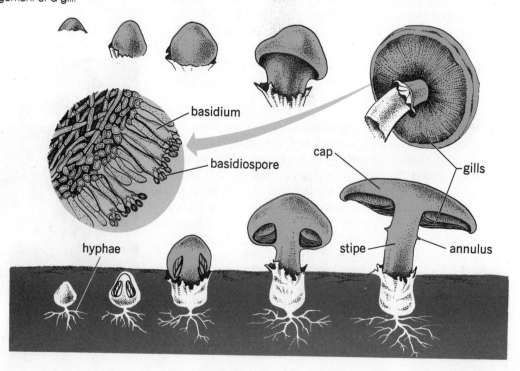

basidium

basidiospore

hyphae

cap

gills

stipe

annulus

Each basidium at first contains two nuclei, which originated from two different parent fungi (two different genetic strains). The two nuclei fuse, or unite into one. This nucleus divides twice in the process of meiosis to produce four nuclei. Each nucleus then enters a separate cell, and so four separate basidiospores are formed. A single mushroom may produce as many as ten billion spores. The spores drop from the basidia onto the ground or are carried away by air currents. If a spore lands in a suitable environment, it germinates and forms a new mycelium.

When a mushroom spore comes in contact with a food source and germinates, it grows out in all directions through the soil and rotting surface litter. This silvery, growing mycelium forms a circle. As the mycelium increases in size, the hyphae in the center of the disk die out. When the reproductive bodies of the mushrooms appear, they form on the outer rim of the disk. Such a circle of mushrooms is called a *fairy ring*. Old superstitions said that fairies danced at night in a circle, and the mushrooms marked their path.

If you stand a short distance from the ring of mushrooms, you can see that the grass inside the ring is a darker green than that outside the ring. This is because nutrients, such as nitrates, are released as part of the process of fungal digestion. These nitrates and other nutrients are used by the green plants.

Many mushrooms are poisonous. If eaten, they produce severe and often fatal effects. Some people use the word *toadstool* to describe a poisonous mushroom. However, only an expert can safely tell a poisonous mushroom from one that is not poisonous. In some cases, even the experts cannot easily tell the difference. For this reason, it is a good idea not to eat a wild mushroom.

19–9 | A fairy ring. Hyphae grow out from the center. Reproductive bodies form at the outer edge of the circle. *(G. R. Roberts)*

Bracket Fungi   Bracket, or shelf, fungi on the sides of rotting boards or old trees often appear like plates sticking out of the trunks of the trees. The bracket is the reproductive portion of a fungus, as are mushrooms. Bracket fungi do not appear quickly, as mushrooms do. This is because of the compressed, woody cell walls of the bracket fungi. Rather than gills, bracket fungi have holes, or pores, on their undersurface. The basidia line the inside of the pores and produce basidiospores. The spores drop out of the brackets and are distributed by the wind.

Most of the mycelium of the bracket fungus is inside the wood of the tree or other food source. There digestion is taking place causing the wood to be broken down. Some of the nutrients are used by the mycelium; some will be used by other plants.

19–10 | Bracket fungi. Notice the dark bands. They are growth rings. Each ring represents a year's growth. *(R. E. Pelham, Bruce Coleman)*

19-11 | Life cycle of the wheat rust. The two hosts necessary for the completion of the life cycle are the common barberry bush and the wheat plant. *(courtesy of USDA)*

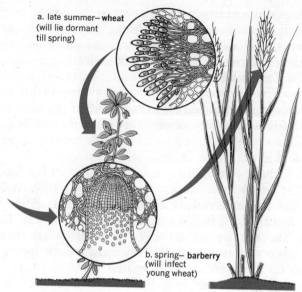

a. late summer– **wheat** (will lie dormant till spring)

b. spring– **barberry** (will infect young wheat)

Rusts *Rust fungi* cause many serious plant diseases. More than 2,000 known rusts attack flowering plants and ferns. Over 250 of these rusts are parasites on wheat, oats, barley, and other cereals. Rusts cause millions of dollars worth of crop damage each year.

Wheat rust is one of the best-known plant parasites. Its complex life cycle involves two host plants, wheat and the common barberry bush.

The rust appears on wheat in late spring or early summer, when the wheat is green and growing. Entire crops can be ruined. The rust mycelium spreads among the cells of wheat stem and leaves. Tiny blisters appear where hyphae grow on stems and leaves, and release spores. Carried through the air, the spores spread the disease rapidly by infecting other plants. Walking through an infected field, a person is soon covered by the red spores.

Later in the summer when the wheat is ripening and turning yellow, a new spore stage begins. The same hyphae that produced red spores now form black spores. The black spores remain inactive, or dormant, through the winter on the wheat stubble or on the ground. In early spring they begin a complex series of changes during which the barberry bush is infected. More spores are formed in the barberry bush. Released into the air, these spores infect wheat, completing the life cycle of the rust. Knowledge of an organism's life cycle helps scientists suggest the most efficient means for eliminating the disease. In the case of wheat rust, the disease can be controlled by eliminating the barberry bush.

Smuts The *smuts* cause great damage to corn, oats, wheat, rye, barley, and other grain plants. One of the most familiar smuts is *corn smut*, which infects young corn plants. Some weeks later a gray, slimy swelling appears on the ear, tassel, stem, or leaf of the plant.

Corn smut can be controlled by burning infected plants, plowing the corn stubble under, and destroying unused stalks and leaves. The life cycle of the corn smut does not involve a second host as does wheat rust. To prevent damage to crops the smut fungus itself, must be attacked.

Deuteromycetes: Imperfect Fungi

Biologists have observed some form of sexual reproduction in all members of the three classes of true fungi that have been discussed in this chapter. However, sexual reproduction has not been observed in all fungi. Some fungi may lack a sexual stage. **A fungus that is observed to lack a sexual stage is classified as a deuteromycete, or imperfect fungus.**

Most imperfect fungi are important parasites of plants or animals. Several diseases of grains, tomatoes, citrus fruits, lettuce, cabbage, beans, and apples are caused by imperfect fungi. Deuteromycetes also produce several skin infections in human beings. Among these are ringworm and athlete's foot.

Penicillium and Aspergillus Perhaps the most famous of all fungus is the Deuteromycete *Penicillium*, from which the antibiotic pencillin is derived.

Fungi of the genus *Penicillium* often form blue-green molds on open jars of jam and on oranges and lemons. They also appear on bread, meat, leather, and cloth. Molds of the genus *Aspergillus* are also common on these foods. Both fungi are often seen together. Both reproduce asexually by producing great numbers of *conidia*. Short, aerial hyphae grow from the surface mycelium. The hyphae branch, often like the fingers on a hand, to become **conidiophores,** special hyphae that produce conidia. Long lines of conidia appear like beads as they pinch off at the ends of the conidiophores. A mold growing on a piece of bread can produce billions of conidia, which are usually transported by air. The various shapes of conidiophores aid scientists in classifying these fungi.

Some species of *Penicillium* are used in making cheese. The flavors of Roquefort and Camembert cheeses are due to the action of certain enzymes secreted by *Penicillium* molds.

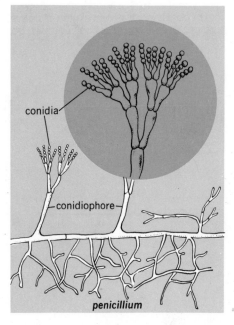

19-12 | Conidiophores and conidia of *Penicillium.*

myxo = slime

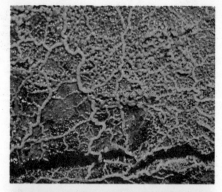

19–13 | (top) A plasmodium of a slime mold, shown at about two and one half times natural size. Under certain conditions, the plasmodium becomes inactive, and clusters of stalked sporangia develop. *(top: Hugh Spencer; bottom: Thomas Martin, Ralpho Guillumette)*

Phylum Myxomycophyta

Members of the phylum *Myxomycophyta* (MICK-suh-MY-KAH-fuh-tuh) are known as *slime molds*. In some ways, they are like giant masses of amebas. Thus, they might be classed as Protozoa. However, they also form sporangia and spores, like the fungi. **The confusion whether to classify them as plants or animals is avoided by placing the slime molds in their own protist phylum, the Myxomycophyta.**

The body of a slime mold is called a **plasmodium.** It is a mass of protoplasm with many nuclei and no cell walls. A plasmodium often appears as a slimy network of living matter. Somewhat like an ameba, it flows along on forest soil, dead leaves, or a rotting log. As it moves, it takes in bits of organic matter and digests them in food vacuoles.

After an active period, the plasmodium becomes inactive. Clusters of stalked sporangia, often delicate and beautiful, rise up. Spores are released and carried away in the air. Spores that reach wet surroundings germinate and release one or more tiny cells. Each cell has two flagella. Such cells may act as gametes and fuse in pairs. This fused pair of cells develops rapidly into a new plasmodium. In some cases, many pairs of cells unite and form the plasmodium.

Summary

Mushrooms and athlete's foot, pencillin and Dutch elm disease are all fungi, or their products. Fungi are organisms with vastly contrasting qualities. They are plants, but they have no chlorophyll. Farmers are constantly at war with fungi that threaten their crops, yet fungi are absolutely vital to life on earth. As organisms of decay, they enable organic matter to be continually recycled.

Since fungi cannot carry on photosynthesis, they are *heterotrophs*. Some, such as wheat rust or corn smut, are parasites and live off living organisms. Most fungi are *saprophytes*.

Fungi produce spores in various types of reproductive bodies, and are classified according to the types of reproductive bodies they produce. There are four classes: Phycomycetes, Ascomycetes, Basidiomycetes, and Deuteromycetes.

heterotoph	rhizoid
mycologist	germinates
saprophyte	conjugation
hyphae	zoospore
mycelium	ascospore
sporangium	conidia
asci	basidiospore
basidia	conidiophore
zygospore	plasmodium
stolon	

1. Describe the general characteristics of true fungi.
2. Why must fungi live in contact with a food supply?
3. Name the four classes of fungi.
4. Describe the mycelium of true fungi.
5. Name the kinds of hyphae of bread mold.
6. Describe two methods of reproduction that occur in *Rhizopus.*
7. List several ways in which fungi may be harmful.
8. How are the products of yeast fermentation used commercially?
9. Outline the life cycle of wheat rust.
10. Describe the reproductive structure of a mushroom.
11. Describe the plasmodium stage of a slime mold.
12. What is the difference between perfect and imperfect fungi?

1. Sweet cider will ferment rapidly in a warm place even when it is in a tightly closed container. Explain.
2. Describe ways to control various plant diseases caused by fungi.
3. In what respects could slime molds possibly represent a link between different protist phyla?
4. Under what conditions can fungi grow best?

20

The Algae

A **DESCRIBE** the characteristics of algae.

B **DESCRIBE** the various methods of reproduction in algae.

C **LIST** the six divisions of algae and describe their characteristics.

D **EXPLAIN** the reproductive cycle of spirogyra and oedogonium.

E **EXPLAIN** how algae are important.

F **DISCUSS** how chromosome number relates to an alga life cycle.

G **DESCRIBE** how lichens illustrate mutualism.

20–1 | Algae, the dominant vegetation in waters. (© Robert W. Mitchell, Earth Scenes)

The Grasses of Many Waters

If you've ever walked near a pond, lake, or ocean, you've seen *algae.* Water moss, scum, and seaweed are popular terms for different kinds of algae.

Algae (singular, *alga*) have been called the "grasses of many waters." Algae are as common in water as grasses are on land. For another, the algae are just as important in an aquatic environment as the grasses are on the land. **Because they carry on the process of photosynthesis, algae are the main food producers in water environments.** They also serve as food for many tiny animals such as insect larvae or small shrimp. These in turn serve as food for larger animals such as fish. Thus, directly or indirectly, most water organisms depend on algae for life.

In addition, the photosynthesis of algae is the greatest producer of atmospheric oxygen. The microscopic, floating algae of the ocean, called *phytoplankton,* are estimated to produce over 50 percent of the earth's atmospheric oxygen. The total amount of photosynthesis carried on by phytoplankton is far greater than that of all the plants living on dry land. Thus all life depends on algae for food and particularly for oxygen.

phyto = plant
plankton = wanderers

252

In the future, humans may depend even more directly on algae. As human populations continue to increase, algae increasingly may be used directly as food for the growing numbers of people. Many people, especially the Japanese, use algae as food. One species of brown algae and several red algae are used as food in Japan. *Algin*, a product of brown algae, is used throughout the world to make ice cream and marshmallows smooth and creamy. Small quantities of algae are added to poultry and cattle food in underdeveloped countries.

What Are Algae?

All algae have cell walls and chlorophyll, so they are clearly plantlike. **Algae have tissues that lack specialization, and exhibit characteristics of both plants and animals. They are classified in the kingdom Protista because of these traits. However, algae are considered more plantlike than animallike.** The blue-green algae are *prokaryotes* (they do not have an organized nucleus) and are sometimes classified along with bacteria in the kingdom *Monera*.

In many species the algae are microscopic single cells. Some single-celled algae form groups of cells called *colonies*. A common colony form is a filament, a long string of algae cells arranged like beads on a thread. Some algae are slippery, because they have a jellylike sheath of slime around their cells. That is why algae sometimes slip through your fingers when you pick them up.

Not all algae are tiny. In some species, like the seaweed kelp, a single alga can be over 30 meters (99 feet) long. An underwater bed of kelp looks like a forest of swaying ribbons.

No matter how complex an alga such as kelp might look, it is extremely simple when compared with most land plants. Algae do not have the highly specialized tissues or organs found in higher plants. They have no roots, stems, or leaves. They lack highly developed food- and water-conducting tissue, and the supportive tissue of most land plants. Each alga cell retains a high degree of independence. The body of a plant that lacks highly organized tissue is called a **thallus.**

Where Do Algae Live?

Most algae are aquatic. They live in freshwater or are marine (live in salt water). Many factors affect the growth

pro = before

20-2 | The largest seaweed is kelp. It grows along the coast in colder waters. Each leaf-like structure is called a *blade*. (Runk, Schoenberger, Grant Heilman)

zoo = animal

of algae. These factors include minerals in the water, temperature of the water, amount of light, and the oxygen and carbon dioxide supply. Different species of algae thrive under different conditions. Algae are found in nearly all bodies of water. They can live in the meltwater of snowbanks as well as in the water of hot springs.

Some algae grow attached to rocks in fast-flowing rapids or waterfalls. Others thrive in slow or quiet water. Most species live near the surface, where they get the most light. Marine algae tend to live near the shore. They can be seen attached to rocks or floating in tidal pools at low tide. Some species live at depths of 150 meters (165 yards) or more.

Not all algae live in water. One type of algae, called *Protococcus*, looks like green powder or dust on the sides of trees or on moist soil. One unusual environment where certain species of algae are found is on the hair of the three-toed sloth, a South American mammal.

Some algae live inside other organisms. There is a one-celled species that lives inside certain paramecia. Other species live in the bodies of freshwater sponges, water snails, and other organisms. Usually, algae do not harm the organisms in which they live. In fact, they are often helpful, supplying food through the process of photosynthesis.

Methods of Reproduction

Many different forms of reproduction are carried on among the algae. Most species reproduce in more than one way. Often reproductive methods are determined by environmental conditions. Reproduction may be *asexual* or *sexual*. Unfavorable conditions, such as insufficient nutrients and unfavorable temperature, often initiate sexual reproduction. This is because the new combination of genes may allow the organism to adapt to the changed environmental conditions.

Asexual Reproduction

Many one-celled algae reproduce asexually by cell fission. Two new algae result. Another form of asexual reproduction of algae is carried on through specialized cells called ***zoospores.*** Zoospores have flagella and therefore are *motile*, or capable of movement. A zoospore can swim away from a parent plant. After a time the zoospore germinates. It goes through a series of cell divisions that result in a new colony being formed in a new area.

In a colony of algae, the colony grows by divisions of individual cells. Colonies can increase in number by a mechanical separation of cells called ***fragmentation.*** A colony itself may be broken apart by water currents, passing fish, or animals feeding on it. No new cells are produced, but the number of colonies is multiplied. All of the cells of a colony have little or no dependence on one another. No harm is done to individual cells by fragmentation. Each fragment of the original colony can continue to grow on its own. Fragmentation occurs often and is a major factor in the spread of colonies through water environments.

Sexual Reproduction

Sexual reproduction in algae, like sexual reproduction in other organisms, involves the production of *gametes*, or sex cells. Some algae produce gametes that are alike in size, form, and ability to move. These gametes are called **isogametes.** Other species of algae produce two types of gametes, male and female. These gametes are called **heterogametes.** The male gamete (sperm) is the smaller, motile gamete. The female gamete (egg) is the larger, nonmotile, or stationary, gamete.

iso = equal

hetero = different

The gametes fuse, or unite, in the process of fertilization to produce a zygote. The single-celled zygote forms a tough outer coat and is called a **zygospore.** The zygospore may survive drought or winter conditions that would kill other algae cells. Under favorable conditions the zygospore germinates and gives rise to a new colony. In some algae there is an intermediate step in this process in which a single zygospore produces several zoospores. These zoospores then swim freely about before germinating and starting a new colony.

zygo = forming

Haploid and Diploid Number in Algae

A typical colonial alga such as a filament is made of cells that have a haploid number (n) of chromosomes. The cells reproduce by mitosis, and the filament grows in length.

When sexual reproduction occurs, the filament cells produce gametes that are also haploid. With fertilization, a diploid (2n) zygote results. When the zygote germinates, meiosis reduces the number of chromosomes, and the cells of the new filament are haploid. The life cycle is then repeated. The haploid produces the diploid, the diploid produces the haploid. The haploid and diploid conditions alternate. The alternation of haploid and diploid phases is called **alternation of generations.**

Classification of Algae

While all species of algae contain chlorophyll, the green color of some groups is masked by other pigments. **The differences in color, cell structure, and type of reproduction**

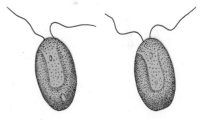

isogametes

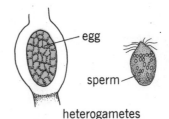

egg

sperm

heterogametes

20–3 | In some species of algae all the gametes are the same (isogametes). Other species form two types of gametes, male and female (heterogametes).

are all considered in the classification of algae.

There are about 30,000 species of algae. In the system of classification used in this book the algae are placed in six phyla according to pigments, or color. These organisms will be considered as protists.

cyano = blue

chloro = green

chryso = gold

pyro = fire

- *Cyanophyta* (SY-un-NAH-fuh-tuh), or *blue-green algae.*
- *Chlorophyta* (kloar-AH-fuh-tuh), or *green algae.*
- *Chrysophyta* (krih-SAH-fuh-tuh), or *yellow-green algae,* golden-brown algae, and diatoms.
- *Pyrrophyta* (py-RAH-fuh-tuh), or *fire algae,* mainly dino-flagellates. Pyrrophyta is mainly composed of asymmetrical motile cells.
- *Phaeophyta* (fee-AH-fuh-tuh), or *brown algae.*

rhodo = rose

- *Rhodophyta* (roe-DAH-fuh-tuh), or *red algae.*

In certain systems, euglenas and related organisms are classified as forms of algae. These organisms are placed in a seventh phylum, the *Euglenophyta* (yoo-gluh-NAH-fuh-tuh). *Euglena* was discussed in the chapter on Protozoa (Chapter 18).

Cyanophyta: Blue-Green Algae

Have you ever seen a pond or stream with a greenish tinge to the water? No matter how closely you look, you cannot see individual organisms, you see only the green color. The chances are that the color is due to blue-green algae. They can be found in almost every ditch or pond.

There are about 1,500 species of blue-green algae. They are among the most primitive organisms on earth; they are prokaryotes. Scientists have never observed sexual reproduction in this group. They seem to reproduce only asexually, by fission. Their chlorophyll is spread throughout the cell rather than being contained in structured chloroplasts. Because they are prokaryotes, Cyanophyta are sometimes classified as *Cyanobacteria.*

phyco = seaweed

The phylum name *Cyanophyta* refers to the blue pigment *phycocyanin* (FIKE-oe-SY-uh-nin). This pigment, along with chlorophyll, gives the blue-green algae their color. Actual colors of different species of *Cyanophyta* range from bright blue-green to nearly black. A few species even have a red pigment. One such species sometimes appears in great numbers in the Red Sea, which may explain how the sea got its name.

Blue-green algae are important because they are one of the few groups of organisms that can "fix" nitrogen. They can take nonusable nitrogen gas from the air and convert it into a usable form of nitrogen. This nitrogen later becomes available to other organisms. The blue-green algae that grow in rice fields, for instance, help supply the rice plants with usable nitrogen compounds.

Three Blue-Green Algae   These common blue-green algae will give you a good idea of the range of traits seen in this phylum.

One genus is *Nostoc* (NOSS-tock). You can find it on mud or sand near lakes or ponds, usually just where the ripples lap the shore. A *nostoc* colony looks like a small ball of jelly, ranging in size from a pinhead to a marble. Within this jellylike sheath are many tangled filaments made of individual cells. Each filament looks something like a string of pearl beads.

From point to point along a filament are **heterocysts.** These are empty cells with thick walls and pores at either side where they meet other cells. They may be spores that have lost their content and no longer function. Filaments of *Nostoc* usually fragment between a heterocyst and a normal cell.

The only known form of reproduction in *Nostoc* is simple fission. When a cell divides, two small cells of equal size result, and the filament grows in length.

A relative of *Nostoc* is *Anabaena* (AN-uh-BEE-nuh). The cells and filaments of these two algae are much alike. However, *Anabaena* filaments occur singly rather than in groups. Another difference is that *Anabaena* produces true spores. Each spore is a large, oval cell protected by thick walls and containing much stored food. Mature spores separate from the parent filament and may germinate in new

20–4 | Two common blue-green algae. (top: 600X; bottom: 400X) In what ways are they similar? How do they differ? (both: © 1979 T. E. Adams, Peter Arnold)

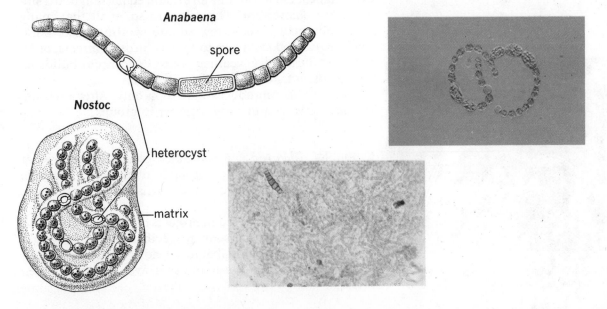

Anabaena

spore

Nostoc

heterocyst

matrix

locations. These spores also can resist the severe conditions of winter and germinate in the spring.

A third example of a blue-green alga is the *Oscillatoria* (AH-suh-luh-TOAR-ee-uh). This alga forms filaments made of many thin, disk-shaped cells. Each filament looks somewhat like a stack of coins.

If you watch *Oscillatoria* under a light microscope for any length of time, you will notice it move. It moves back and forth with a gentle swaying motion. The cause of the swaying motion, or oscillation, has never been explained.

Chlorophyta

The *green algae* of the phylum *Chlorophyta* vary from one-celled forms to colonies made of many cells. Most forms live in fresh water, though many live in the ocean. Some live in strange environments, such as salt lakes or hot springs. **The green algae are by far the largest group of algae, with about 20,000 species.**

Green algae are more complex than blue-green algae. A definite nucleus with a nuclear membrane is present. Therefore, they are *eukaryotes*. Chlorophyll and other pigments are organized in chloroplasts. Some species reproduce asexually, either by fission or by forming spores. Sexual reproduction, involving either isogametes or heterogametes, also occurs.

Protococcus One of the most common of the green algae is *Protococcus*. *Protococcus* cells are spherical, or slightly oval-shaped. Each contains an organized nucleus and a single, large chloroplast. The cells are so small that many thousands may cover a few square centimeters of bark. They are carried from tree to tree by birds or insects, or by the wind during dry weather. Since *Protococcus* builds its own foods, it takes no food from the tree.

Protococcus reproduces by fission only. After division, the new cells tend to cling together in groups.

Chlorella *Chlorella* is a one-celled green alga somewhat like *Protococcus*. It is of special interest to biologists because some species live in cells or tissues of protozoans, sponges, and jellyfish.

Chlorella has been used in projects designed to grow and harvest algae as a food source, specifically as a flour substitute. Since it is impossible to get rid of the green color in *Chlorella*, most people will not use it. Would you eat green bread?

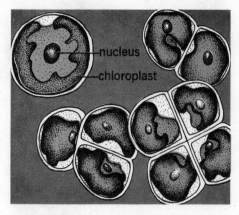

20-5 | Cells of the green alga *Protococcus* occur singly or in colonies of two or more.

Spirogyra   During the spring or fall, almost any quiet pond will have bright green masses of threadlike *Spirogyra* (SPY-ruh-JY-ruh). The cells of this green alga form filaments from a few centimeters to one half meter long. Under a microscope, the cells appear almost transparent, joined end to end like stacked water glasses.

Under the light microscope each cell is seen to have one or more spiral chloroplasts winding from one end of the cell to the other. On these chloroplasts are small protein bodies, called **pyrenoids,** surrounded by layers of starch grains. The nucleus is held near the center of the cell by radiating strands of cytoplasm. Most of the cytoplasm lies near the cell wall, leaving a large central vacuole filled with water and dissolved substances. A thin jellylike sheath around each cell makes *Spirogyra* filaments slippery to the touch.

On sunny days, photosynthesis takes place at a rapid rate. Oxygen bubbles stream from the cells and collect among the filaments. If enough oxygen builds up, masses of *Spirogyra* float to the surface. At night, the oxygen dissolves in the water, and the masses sink again.

Spirogyra reproduces asexually by fission. The cells always divide crosswise, thus adding to the length of the filament.

Spirogyra also reproduces sexually by conjugation. This process occurs when the weather does not favor normal growth by fission. It is most likely to be seen in late spring or early fall.

Conjugation begins with two filaments lined up next to each other. A small knob grows out from each cell until it meets the knob of the cell opposite it. The tips of the knobs dissolve, leaving a hollow tube between the two cells. The content of one cell flows through the tube and unites with the content of the other, producing a zygote. Thick walls develop around the zygotes, after which they are known as *zygospores*.

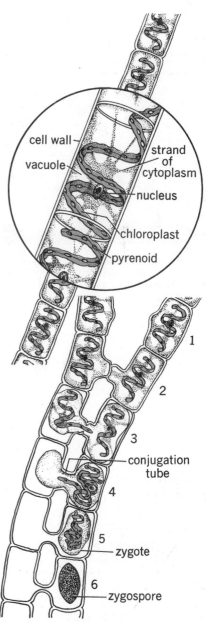

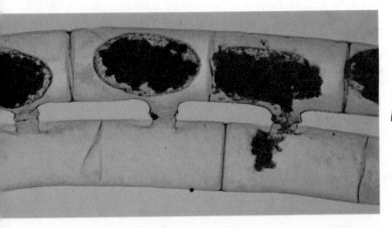

20-6 | Filaments of the green alga *Spirogyra.* The structure of a single cell can be seen at the top. Conjugation is shown below. Explain what is happening in each of the numbered steps in the sequence. *(Carolina Biological Supply Co.)*

When conditions favor growth, the zygospore becomes active, goes through the process of meiosis, and develops into a new *Spirogyra* cell. A new filament builds up by simple cell division.

Desmids One of the most interesting forms of green algae are the *desmids*. These organisms make up a large portion of ocean phytoplankton. Desmids are unicellular and occur in both fresh and marine waters in many different shapes. Most have two equal halves, connected by a narrow isthmus that contains the nucleus. In asexual reproduction the halves separate, and each produces another half.

20-7 | An electron micrograph of desmids. Each half is called a *semi-cell*. (1,000X) *(Courtesy of Dr. Pickett-Heaps)*

Oedogonium *Oedogonium* (OE-duh-GOE-nee-um) is a common green alga that grows on rocks and other objects in quiet freshwater pools. It has single filaments held in place by a special cell called a **holdfast.** Each cell has a single chloroplast made of many joined strands. Any cell above the holdfast can change its content into a large, single zoospore. This zoospore moves through the water by means of a ring of flagella. Upon reaching a suitable spot, it becomes a holdfast and gives rise to a new filament.

Only certain cells in a filament take part in sexual reproduction. Further, these cells form *heterogametes* that are clearly different sexual types. Several cells in an *Oedogonium* filament may develop into large, single eggs. Each of these special cells is called an *oogonium*. In most species, two sperms form in each of several shortened cells grouped together in the filament. Each of these cells is an *antheridium*. Eggs and sperms develop in the same or different filaments, depending on the species.

The sperm looks like a tiny zoospore. Soon after leaving the antheridium it swims to the oogonium and enters through a small pore. The egg is fertilized and becomes a zygote. After a time, the oogonium wall breaks apart. The released zygote forms a thick wall and becomes a zygospore. After a dormant period, the zygospore divides by meiosis to produce four zoospores. Each of these can produce a new filament. **In exhibiting an alternation of generations, the only diploid cell (2n) is the zygospore. All the other cells are haploid (n).**

Chrysophyta: Yellow-Green and Golden-Brown Algae

The Chrysophyta are a varied group of algae, including motile and nonmotile unicellular forms, and colonial filamentous and nonfilamentous species. They are found on soil and in fresh and marine waters. Diatoms represent 16,000 of the 16,600 species of Chrysophyta.

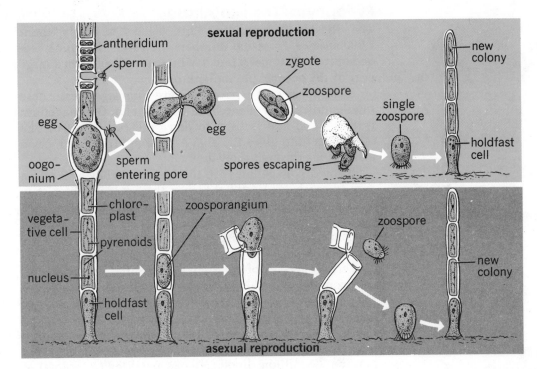

20-8 | Sexual and asexual reproduction in the green alga *Oedogonium.* Note that in this alga, sexual reproduction involves heterogametes.

Diatoms   Most diatoms are unicellular planktonic algae. A few are colonial. Their cell walls contain silica, which is the main ingredient of glass. So, silica gives diatoms a glasslike quality. The hard walls have etched lines and grooves in them that can be seen under a light microscope. They give diatoms a distinct beauty. Designs of diatoms have been copied by people who design jewelry. The cell walls are unusual also in that they form two halves called *valves.* The top valve overlaps the bottom valve like a lid on a pill box.

Asexual cell division in diatoms is simple. The cell is duplicated, the valves separate, and each daughter cell becomes a new top valve. You can see in figure 20-9 that the daughter cell derived from the bottom valve is smaller than the daughter cell of the covering valve. With each division a smaller bottom valve is formed. This explains why diatoms of the same species are different sizes. Eventually a limit in size is reached, and asexual division stops. At this stage, sexual reproduction usually occurs.

When diatoms die, the protoplasm and inner walls decay. The clear outer walls of silica remain and settle to the bottom of the lake or sea. Over centuries, these shells build up as layers of *diatomaceous earth.* Some layers formed in ancient times are now on dry land. One such California deposit is over 450 meters (495 yards) thick.

20-9 | Diatoms come in a variety of shapes and sizes. Note the silica valves (60X) (© Lester V. Bergman Associates)

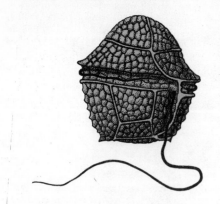

20-10 | A dinoflagellate, *Peridinium*.

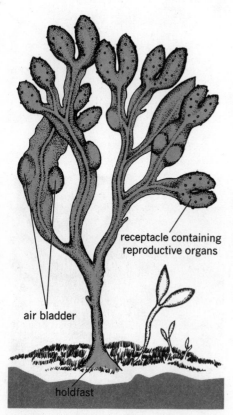

receptacle containing
reproductive organs

air bladder

holdfast

20-11 | *Fucus,* a brown alga. The gas-filled air bladders serve as floats. *(D. P. Wilson)*

Pyrrophyta: The Fire Algae

The division *Pyrrophyta*, "fire algae," has only about 1,000 species. In actual numbers, however, they rank second only to diatoms. A few live in water. They form a large part of the oceans' phytoplankton.

Most species of Pyrrophyta are *dinoflagellates*. These motile, unicellular algae have two flagella. One flagellum trails behind and is used to drive the cell forward. The other flagellum gives the alga a twisting, rotating motion as it moves through the water.

Many dinoflagellates are luminescent. They give off an eery greenish or bluish light when the water in which they float is disturbed at night. Oars dipped into the ocean will glow with these algae when they are present in sufficient numbers. This blue light is probably the reason they are called "fire algae."

Certain species of Pyrrophyta cause the red tides that occasionally occur along seacoasts. The red tide algae of the genus *Gonyaulax* produces a poison that is deadly to fish. Several epidemics of food poisoning, some causing death, have been traced to eating shellfish that contain large numbers of *Gonyaulax*. When a bloom occurs, there may be 70 million dinoflagellates per liter (2.1 pints) of water, and a single bloom may stretch for miles. The algae cells contain a red pigment and in high concentrations give the sea water a red color. The loss of fish to *Gonyaulax* can be massive. Red tides seem to occur at definite intervals and are part of recorded history. The cause of the red tides are not known. They may be due to a high concentration of nutrients and minerals occurring at the proper temperature to favor the reproduction of these algae.

Phaeophyta: The Brown Algae

Most brown algae live in the colder ocean waters. Attached to rocks, they grow at depths of a few meters to 15 meters (49.5 feet) or more. All brown algae are multicellular, and they vary a great deal in form and size.

Algae such as kelp (the largest brown algae) and *Fucus*, or rockweed, are among the most complex algae. They show some cell specialization and tissue development, although not of the complexity seen in higher plants. Their color is due to a golden-brown pigment that masks the green chlorophyll.

Reproductive organs are located on the very ends of the blades as can be seen in figure 20-11. When mature, the male structures release great numbers of sperm, and the female structures release eggs. Fertilization occurs and later the zygote germinates to produce a new thallus.

Another common brown alga is *Sargassum*. This is the

seaweed found in such abundance in the Sargasso Sea southeast of Bermuda. It had been suggested that Sargassum is there because of the lack of moving water in that area. It is the "dead" area in terms of Atlantic circulation. In this "dead" area Sargassum grows to such a great extent that it piles up. It is thought that early sailors, when they saw this piled-up seaweed, thought it was the sea dragons they had heard about. In many places brown algae are used as fertilizer. Off the west coast of Ireland kelp has for centuries been collected from the seashore and carried to the stony fields to help build soil.

Rhodophyta: The Red Algae

Red algae make up another phylum of seaweed. Nearly all of the 2,500 species live in the sea. Some live at depths of 150 meters (495 feet) or more. Most are less than 30 centimeters (12 inches) in length. They have various amounts of red pigment along with the green chlorophyll. Red algae grows at greater depths than most of the other algae. The red pigment absorbs blue light that can penetrate to those depths.

The red algae lack motile gametes. Otherwise their life cycles are similar to those of the brown algae.

Japan cultivates several edible species of red algae. Some substances derived from red algae are used in making beer and medicine. Agar, the jellylike substance used as a medium on which to grow bacteria, is derived from red algae. Red algae called coralline algae have hard calcareous cell walls. They are the largest contributors to coral reefs in tropical waters, contrary to the common belief that coral animals alone make up the reefs.

Lichen: Two Life Forms in One

For a long time the lichen (LIKE'n) was considered an individual plant. With the invention of the light microscope, it was found to be a combination of two plants—an alga and a fungus. The alga is usually a species of Cyanophyta. The fungus is one of the Ascomycetes. The fungus depends on the algae cells for food. The algae cells depend on the ability of the hyphae, or filaments, of the fungus to hold water. **Both the alga and fungus benefit by living together. In fact, neither could survive alone in the environments where lichens live.** A relationship in which two different species live in close association is called *symbiosis*. When both organisms benefit from this relationship, it is called **mutualism.** In a lichen both species benefit from the association. This, then, is an example of mutualism.

20–12 | *Chrondrus crispus*, also called Irish moss. Carrageenin, a gel used in many food products is derived from this alga. *(Walter Dawn)*

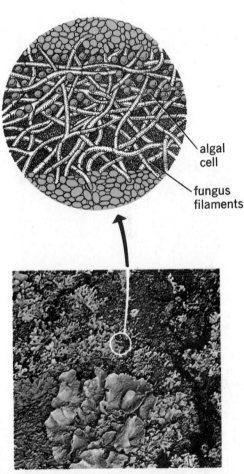

algal cell

fungus filaments

20–13 | A lichen is two kinds of organisms. This symbiotic relationship is called mutualism. *(Dennis Brokaw)*

Summary

The algae, once thought of as simple plants, are now usually classed as protists. They are among the most common and widespread forms of life. Most live in water, although some live in other environments.

Some algae live as single cells, others in colonies made of many cells. All contain chlorophyll and carry on photosynthesis. Many different methods of reproduction are seen among the algae. These methods range from asexual cell fission to sexual reproductions by means of heterogametes. Many forms reproduce by more than one method.

In their water environments, algae are important as sources of both food and oxygen. They are sometimes used as soil fertilizers and in other ways. Some types are harmful, such as the dinoflagellate that causes "red tides."

Biologically Speaking

algae
phytoplankton
thallus
zoospore
fragmentation
isogamete
heterogamete

zygospore
alternation of generations
heterocyst
pyrenoid
holdfast
mutualism

Questions for Review

1. List the general characteristics of algae.
2. List the six divisions of algae and briefly outline the characteristics of each.
3. Describe conjugation in *Spirogyra*.
4. How does diploid and haploid number relate to the life cycle of *Spirogyra?*
5. List several characteristics of desmids. How do they differ from diatoms?
6. List three ways people benefit from algae.
7. Explain the relationship between algae and fungi in a lichen.

Applying Concepts

1. A colony of 50 algae cells is not a 50-celled plant. Explain.
2. Compare *Spirogyra* with *Oedogonium*. Which is more specialized? Why?
3. Why are blue-green algae considered the most primitive algae?
4. Why hasn't the opportunity for harvesting algae been fully investigated and developed?

UNIT 3

1. Use your library to prepare an oral or written report on viruses and how they are used in genetic engineering.

2. Construct a model of a phage, complete with DNA, neck, and "legs."

3. Take a small sample of water and sediment from an aquarium or a pond. Use a microscope and identify as many different kinds of protozoa as you can.

4. Try to grow a slime mold using oatmeal as a source of food.

5. Make spore prints of the wild mushrooms that grow in your area. Find the best procedure for making these prints.

6. Look around your neighborhood for algae. Make a list of the places in which you find them and write a brief report on your findings.

7. With the help of a microscope and resource books, try to identify the algae that you find in a stream or pond near your home.

8. Obtain fresh sloke or dulse (a health food store may have it). Cook the seaweed for three hours (or 45 minutes in a pressure cooker) and then make seaweed soup, using this recipe.

> 1 cup cooked sloke or dulse
> 6 cups milk
> juice of 1 lemon
> 2 cups mashed potatoes
> 1 tablespoon butter (melted)
> pepper

Simmer the milk, cooked seaweed, and potato together for about 20 minutes, then either beat well or liquefy. Season to taste, add the melted butter and the lemon juice, and beat again. Heat and serve hot. (Fitzgibbons, *A Taste of Scotland*, Avenue Books, New York, 1970)

Related Readings

Books

Boettcher, Helmuth, *Wonder Drugs: A History of Antibiotics.* J. B. Lippincott Co., Philadelphia. 1963. An entertaining history of the "wonder drugs" and the medical discoveries of the last century.

Christensen, Clyde M., *The Molds and Man* (Second Edition). University of Minnesota Press, Minneapolis. 1965. A general account of the fungi and their impact on humans.

Dixon, Bernard, *Magnificent Microbes.* Atheneum, New York. 1976. The book lives up to its title. Well illustrated.

Kavaler, Lucy, *The Wonders of Fungi.* The John Day Company, Inc., New York. 1964. The story of fungi as both destroyer and saver of people, from prehistoric days to the present-day age of wonder drugs.

Schneider, Leo, *Microbes in Your Life.* Harcourt, Brace Jovanovich, Inc., New York. 1966. A good book for background information, includes a discussion of techniques used in microbiology.

Silverstein, Alvin and Virginia, *Cancer.* The John Day Co., New York. 1972. This book explains the various forms of cancer, gives the symptoms, and explains the possible causes and treatments of cancer.

Wheeler, Margaret F., and Wesley A. Volk, *Basic Microbiology.* J. B. Lippincott Co., Philadelphia. 1973. Microbiology treated not only in terms of the categories of micro-organisms but also in terms of the application of this knowledge to everyday life.

Articles

Cooper, Max D., "The Development of the Immune System," *Scientific American,* November 1974. A detailed study about the highly diversified cells that defend the body against foreign substances.

Echlin, Robert, "The Blue-Green Algae," *Scientific American,* June 1966. Deals with the identification and environmental importance of the blue-green algae.

Lamb, I. M., "Lichens," *Scientific American,* October 1969. A general account of lichens as an example of symbiotic mutualism.

Zahl, Paul A., "Where Would We Be Without Algae," *National Geographic,* March 1974. A dramatic article concerned with life's dependence on the algae.

MULTICELLULAR PLANTS

Ages ago certain green algae may have undergone changes that enabled them to survive on land. Some plants, such as the moss, never did completely adapt to a land environment. Most mosses still live in wet areas; mosses cannot reproduce without water. Other plants, such as the seed plants, have become fully adjusted to life on land. These are the plants, grasses, and trees that now dominate the land.

21

Mosses and Ferns

A EXPLAIN the development of the first land plants.

B DESCRIBE the structure and life cycle of moss.

C DESCRIBE the characteristics common to club mosses, horsetails, and ferns.

D DESCRIBE liverworts and their life cycle.

E DISTINGUISH bryophytes from tracheophytes.

F EXPLAIN the life cycle of the fern.

G EXPLAIN how alternation of generations applies to the life cycles of plants.

21–1 | What adaptations enable these plants to live out of water? *(Manuel Rodriguez)*

The First Land Plants

Some of the plants that lived in aquatic environments already had the ability to survive in the partial absence of water. These survived and reproduced in areas that became drier. This change from an aquatic environment to land is actually a change from living in water to living in a gaseous environment. Water and air are drastically different environments. This change of environment is thought to have taken place over millions of years.

The first land plants are thought to have existed first on shores or in marshy areas where periods of dryness occurred. These first land plants probably had many characteristics of water plants and depended on water for some functions.

Plants that are adapted to live on land have developed specialized tissues and structures to protect against water loss. The bark of an oak tree and the waxy coating on leaves are examples of structural adaptations to retain water. The leaf of an oak tree needs water, and it cannot absorb it as a water plant does. A system of tubes, however, transport water. Such tubes are adaptive for plants to live completely on dry land.

The Bryophytes: Mosses and Liverworts

bryon = moss
phyta = plant

The bryophytes are a good example of land plants that still retain many of the characteristics of simple water plants. The bryophytes were among the first land plants, but they never underwent changes that would enable them to adapt completely to life on land. For example, mosses and liverworts, the two main classes of bryophytes, never developed the transport system of tubes called **vascular tissue.**

If a plant is going to be tall and reach into the atmosphere, it has to have conducting tissue to carry water up to the leaves. Because they do not have these vascular tissues, bryophytes cannot transport water any great distance. Instead, water passes from cell to cell. This is one reason that plants like mosses never grow to be very tall. Also, the bryophytes never developed the thick-walled supporting cells that hold up land plants and help them resist the effects of strong winds. In addition, bryophytes do not have a sexual reproductive cycle independent of water. The sperm cells of bryophytes have to swim through water to fertilize eggs. In contrast, the higher seed plants often use wind-blown pollen to carry the sperms to eggs.

Despite these limitations, bryophytes are widely distributed. They are most abundant in temperate and tropical climates. They do not compete with the *tracheophytes*, plants with vascular tissue, but they can live side by side with them. In fact, both ferns and seed plants often provide the shade that many mosses need for survival. In such places as the windswept arctic tundra, and above the tree line in mountain areas, bryophytes cover more area than other plants.

tracheo = vessel

Mosses

The word *moss* is often used incorrectly. Most of the plants called water mosses are actually algae; reindeer moss is actually a lichen. Spanish moss, which hangs from trees in the southern United States, is actually a seed plant related to the pineapple.

Mosses are very small, green, leafy plants that are often overlooked. However, after you recognize their distinguishing characteristics and become aware of the plants, you will find them growing in a variety of places.

Mosses can grow in almost any moist, shady area. They grow in the shady cracks of sidewalks, on rooftops, in gutters, on the sides of trees, or on moist, shaded soil.

A clump of moss is really a group of tiny individual

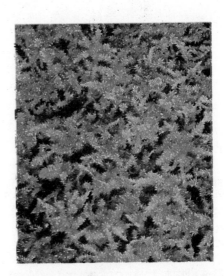

21-2 | Sphagnum moss. *(Carolina Biological Supply Co.)*

21-3 | A clump of *Polytricum* moss showing stalks and capsules. *(William E. Ferguson)*

plants. Each plant has a slender stemlike structure usually less than 3 centimeters (1.2 inches) long, with lots of thin fragile leaves around it. These leaves are really simple structures only one cell thick. Each leaf has a central rib.

At certain times of the year you can see another part of the plant growing on top of the green leafy moss. This part consists of a long, thin stalk. At its tip is a bump or swelling. The bump is actually a capsule that contains spores. The stalk with the capsule may be brown or green. It grows out of the top of the green leafy part of the plant. These spore-producing structures are not found on every moss plant.

If you take a moss plant out of the ground you will see a cluster of hairlike filaments coming out of the bottom of the plant. These are called **rhizoids.** Rhizoids serve the same purpose as roots in tracheophytes. They absorb water and minerals, and anchor the plant. Unlike roots, rhizoids are simply cellular filaments without specialized tissues. Since bryophytes lack vascular tissue, mosses do not have true leaves, stems, or roots.

The Life Cycle of Moss Mosses have a two-part life cycle with an alternation of generations. That is, a haploid generation alternates with a diploid generation as described in Chapter 20. Mosses and liverworts both have a multicellular haploid generation that reproduces sexually. This plant is called a **gametophyte.** The gametophyte plants of the moss are the green leafy plants that are most conspicuous. At the very tips of the gametophyte plants are the structures that contain reproductive organs. Male organs, which produce sperms, are called **antheridia** (an-thuh-RID-ee-uh). Female organs, which produce eggs, are called **archegonia** (ahr-kih-GOH-nee-ah). In some species of moss both organs can be on the same plants; in other species the organs are on different plants.

When morning dew or rain water covers the moss, and the antheridia are mature, large numbers of sperms are released. The sperms swim to the mature archegonia. Some reach and enter the female archegonia. Several sperms may swim down the long necklike structure of a single archegonium, but only one sperm fertilizes the single egg at the base. The diploid (2n) zygote is formed after the egg is fertilized. The zygote is the first cell of the diploid generation.

A long stalk develops from the zygote and grows out of the archegonium. A capsule develops at the end of the stalk. Both stalk and capsule make up the diploid **sporophyte.** During the growth period, the sporophyte is supplied nutrients by the leafy gametophyte.

Inside the diploid sporophyte capsule, spores are

gametophyte generation (haploid, n)

spores (n)

meiosis

sperm + eggs (n)

sporophyte generation (2n)

fertilization

zygote (diploid, 2n)

21-4 | Plants, including mosses and liverworts, show alternation of generations. The basic features of this cycle are shown here.

formed by the process of meiosis. Thus spores are haploid. When the capsule turns brown and crisp, its top breaks off and the spores are released. The spores are carried by air currents. If they land in a suitable moist place, they germinate.

When a spore germinates, it develops a horizontal green filament called a **protonema** (pro-toe-NEE-muh), which closely resembles an alga filament. As the protonema grows, small buds appear along its length. When the buds develop into the gametophyte (haploid) plants, the cycle is complete.

proto = **first**
nema = **thread**

The Importance of Mosses

Mosses are among the first plants to grow in the cracks of rocks or on freshly exposed soil. In time they add their organic material to the soil and enrich it. Eventually enough soil accumulates and is rich enough for other plants to grow.

21–5 | Life cycle of the moss. Note that alternation of generations occurs. After fertilization, a sporophyte grows out of the female gametophyte. Spores form at the top of the sporophyte and fall to the ground. These germinate and grow into a new generation of gametophytes which reproduce sexually.

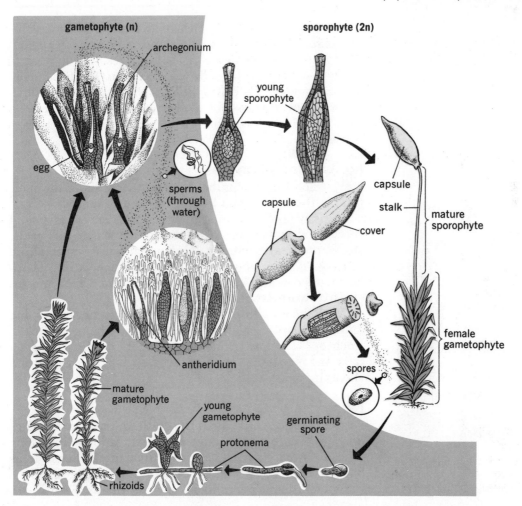

gametophyte (n)

archegonium

sporophyte (2n)

young sporophyte

egg

sperms (through water)

capsule

capsule

stalk

cover

mature sporophyte

antheridium

mature gametophyte

young gametophyte

protonema

germinating spore

spores

female gametophyte

rhizoids

21-6 | Marchantia, a common liverwort. *(Carolina Biological Supply Co.)*

Liverworts

Liverworts are less familiar to most people than are the mosses. These small plants grow in wet places, often muddy areas near streams or on ground or rocks continually exposed to mist or spray. As in mosses, the gametophyte plant is the most noticeable stage of the liverwort.

Liverworts have an alternation of generations similar to that of mosses. They also have an interesting way of reproducing asexually. If you were to look closely at the surface of the gametophyte you would find small cuplike structures. Inside the cups are tiny flat multicellular plates called **gemmae.** If a raindrop makes a direct hit in the cup or if water covers the cup, the gemmae are washed out. They can be carried some distance from the parent plant before growing into a new liverwort.

The Tracheophytes

The term *tracheophytes* applies to all plants that have tube-like tissues that conduct water and nutrients throughout the plant. Vascular tissue is of two types. Tissue used to conduct water in a plant is called **xylem.** The tissue conducting nutrients is called **phloem.** Both xylem and phloem occur together in cablelike strands called *vascular bundles.* Vascular bundles are visible most easily as veins in leaves.

Early Tracheophytes

Early tracheophytes probably appeared at about the same time as the mosses and liverworts. The adaptation of vascular tissue allows plants to live in drier environments. A specialized system of tissue resulted consisting of roots, stems, and leaves. Such vascular plants with specialized tissue gained an independence from surface water. Vascular plants can also grow in bright sunshine where mosses and liverworts would perish.

With the passage of hundreds of millions of years, many different vascular plants developed. The major groups of tracheophytes now include the ferns, club mosses, horsetails, and plants that produce seeds, such as evergreens and flowering plants.

Ferns

Ferns are found throughout the earth. In the United States they are usually found in woodlands, meadows, and along roads or stream banks. Generally they are in moist areas but they can also be found in direct sunlight. They have the roots, stems, and leaves of all vascular plants. Fern leaves

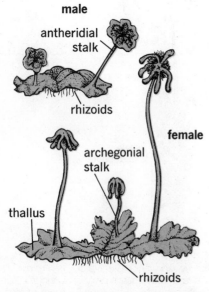

male
antheridial
stalk

rhizoids

female

archegonial
stalk

thallus

rhizoids

21-7 | Female and male liverwort plants.

are called *fronds.* Although some species of fern become treelike, the majority are closer to the ground, usually no more than 1 meter (3.3 feet) high.

The Life Cycle of the Fern Tracheophytes also have an alternation of generations. At certain times of the year colored, beadlike structures appear on the undersurface of the fern fronds. They are the *sori,* (SOR-i) or asexual (diploid) reproductive bodies of the fern. Each *sorus* contains numerous *sporangia,* saclike structures in which the haploid spores are found. As a sporangium dries, it bends slowly backwards and then springs forward. The spores are thrown out from under the fronds. Spores may be carried by wind or water to different locations.

When a spore lands on moist soil, it germinates, forming the first cells of the gametophyte (haploid) generation. More cell divisions form a short filament, which soon puts out the *rhizoids.* The tip of the filament broadens into a sheet of cells. After several weeks of growth, this becomes the heart-shaped *prothallus.* The prothallus is the gametophyte generation of the fern plant. This stage of the fern is rarely seen since it is usually only 1 or 2 centimeters (0.4 to 0.8 inches) in width. Because all its cells contain chloroplasts, the prothallus can photosynthesize.

Eventually, multicellular sex organs develop on the underside of the prothallus. The archegonia that form usually contain one egg at their base. The base is embedded in the tissue of the prothallus. Knob-shaped antheridia develop at the same time. These begin to protrude among the

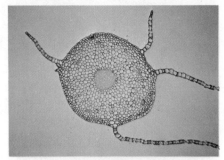
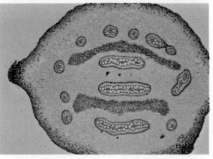

21-8 | (top) A cross section of a moss stem shows no vascular tissue. (bottom) A cross section of a fern stem shows vascular bundles. *(top: William E. Ferguson; bottom: Carolina Biological Supply Co.)*

Facts & Figures

In tropical zones some ferns grow to a height of 10 meters (33 feet).

21-9 | Diorama of a forest of giant club mosses and horsetails typical of Pennsylvanian and Mississippian periods during the Carboniferous age. *(American Museum of Natural History)*

21–10 | Tree ferns. These are small relatives of the tree ferns that were abundant some 300 million years ago. *(W. H. Hodge, Peter Arnold)*

21–11 | Life cycle of the fern. The gametophyte, which is so small you can hardly see it, develops on the ground.

rhizoids. There the prothallus is only one cell thick. When mature, each antheridium contains several motile sperms.

When the eggs and sperms are mature, water becomes a necessity if fertilization is to occur. Even the slightest film of water is enough to allow fertilization. The sperms are set free and swim along a watery path to enter the open archegonia. A zygote is formed when a sperm fertilizes an egg. This is the first cell of the sporophyte generation.

After fertilization, the zygote begins cell division. It grows and fills the arechegonium, and soon it is a sporophyte embryo. As the embryo grows, an aerial portion grows upward to become a frond. An underground, horizontal stem, the ***rhizome,*** and a root system grow downward into the soil. During the growth of the embryo, the prothallus withers away. Once established, the rhizomes grow in all directions and send up more fronds. The result is the familiar clump of ferns. Although the fronds may die

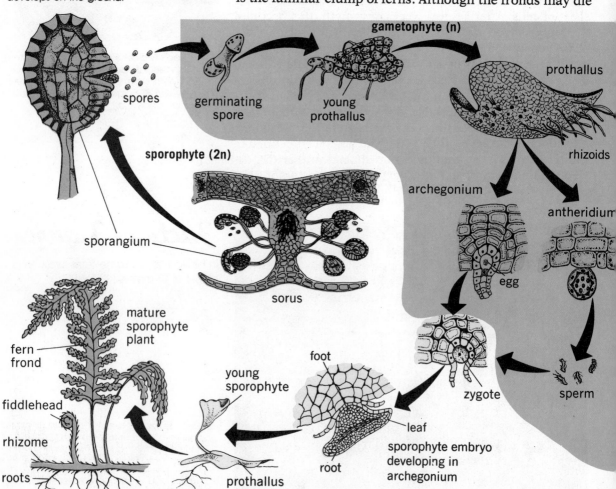

in winter conditions, the rhizomes survive. They can then produce more fronds in the spring.

The sporophyte is larger than the gametophyte and may grow for years. In contrast, the gametophyte prothallus is small and shortlived, surviving only for a few weeks.

Club Mosses and Horsetails

Club mosses (Lycopodophyta) and horsetails (Equisetophyta) have life cycles similar to those of ferns. The conspicuous bodies of these plants are sporophytes. The gametophytes are often small and difficult to find. All species produce asexual spores, and may have cone-like, spore-bearing structures at the tips of their branches. They all have vascular tissue.

Despite their name, club mosses are not closely related to mosses. They are vascular plants that look something like mosses. Club mosses of the genus *Lycopodium* are small, low-lying plants with erect branches 6 to 8 centimeters (2.4 to 3.2 inches) high. Most species are evergreen, and their branches resemble those of pine trees. For this reason they are often used as Christmas decorations and are called ground pines. However, they are neither mosses nor pines.

Most horsetails grow on wet swampy areas. Some grow well in drier areas, especially around railroad embankments. The stems consist of hollow cylinders. In some species, a cone containing sporangia forms on special fertile shoots. In other species some stems are *vegetative*, meaning that they do not produce reproductive structures. These vegetative stems appear as a bushy type of plant. The stems have silicon, giving them a rough, gritty texture. For this reason they are also called "scouring rushes."

The life cycle of the horsetail resembles that of the fern or club moss. The horsetails all belong to a single genus. Their ancestors were present in great numbers and in a variety of genera during the Carboniferous period. Some fossils show that giant treelike horsetails existed during this period, 300 million years ago.

21–12 | This club moss, *Lycopodium*, is related to the ferns because of similarity in reproduction. *(Russ Kinne)*

21–13 | Horsetails are sometimes called scouring rushes. Some horsetails produce bushy, green vegetative shoots. The conelike structures are asexual reproductive bodies that produce spores. *(left: Albert Towle; right: Carolina Biological Supply Co.)*

Summary

Land plants are thought to have developed much later than water plants. Plant adaptations, such as specialized tissues and structures, protected them against water loss. The *bryophytes* (mosses and liverworts) are a good example of land plants that still retain many of the characteristics of simple water plants.

Ferns, on the other hand, are *tracheophytes*. This means that they have tubelike tissues that conduct water and nutrients throughout the plants. Ferns, the earliest tracheophytes, were abundant about 300 million years ago. They were able to live in drier environments than the mosses and liverworts.

Biologically Speaking

vascular tissue	gemmae
rhizoid	xylem
gametophyte	phloem
antheridia	fronds
archegonia	sori
sporophyte	prothallus
protonema	rhizome

Questions for Review

1. Describe two characteristics that limit the size of bryophytes.
2. Describe the life cycle of the moss, naming the different structures of each stage.
3. Describe the gametophyte of a liverwort.
4. At what stage does a fern develop from a germinating spore?
5. In what way are ferns, like mosses, dependent on water during sexual reproduction?
6. How are the club mosses and horsetails similar to the ferns?
7. How are the diploid and haploid numbers related to the moss life cycle?
8. How does alternation of generations apply to the life cycle of a fern?

Applying Concepts

1. Give possible reasons for the abundance of mosses in regions with extreme climatic conditions, for example, tundra and alpine areas.
2. Compare the sporophyte plant of a moss and a fern and explain the ways in which the fern is considered to be more advanced.

The Seed Plants

A **DESCRIBE** the main characteristics of gymnosperms and angiosperms.

B **DISTINGUISH** between monocot and dicot plants.

C **DESCRIBE** the function of each vegetative organ of a flowering plant.

D **DESCRIBE** the function of specialized plant tissues.

E **DISTINGUISH** an herbaceous plant from a woody plant.

F **DEFINE** annuals, biennials, and perennials.

22–1 | Conifers were thought to have been the first seed plants. Juniper trees have seeds in the form of berrylike structures. *(Derek Fell)*

A Rise of Seed Plants

Fossil evidence indicates that seed ferns probably developed during the Devonian period of the Paleozoic era and became more numerous during the Carboniferous period. Today seed ferns are extinct, but they may have been the ancestors of today's seed plants.

When the Mesozoic era dawned around 200 million years ago, the earth's climate grew warmer and drier. Biologists think this accounts for the gradual disappearance of the seed ferns during the Triassic period. At this time, other seed plants gained in number. Among these were the conifers, predominant in the Mesozoic era. Flowering plants, the most complex of the seed plants, probably first developed in the Jurassic period of the Mesozoic era. They spread rapidly throughout the Cretaceous period. They are the dominant form of vegetation on earth today.

Why were seed plants so successful? Seed plants are better adapted to life on land. They have vascular conducting tissues and, unlike the bryophytes, they do not require water for fertilization. Their male gametes are carried by air and other means. After fertilization, seeds develop

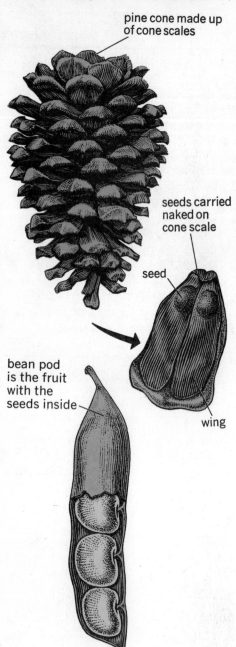

pine cone made up
of cone scales

seeds carried
naked on
cone scale

seed

bean pod
is the fruit
with the
seeds inside

wing

22–2 | The bean is an example of an angiosperm; the pine cone is an example of a gymnosperm. The bean seed is enclosed in a ripened ovary, or fruit, whereas the pine seed lies exposed on a cone scale.

directly on the parent plant; nutrients are furnished by the parent.

Alternation of Generations in Seed Plants

Most of the plants you see around you are sporophytes. They all have diploid (2n) cells.

The male gametophyte in seed plants has been reduced to a pollen grain and pollen tube with three nuclei. The female gametophyte is a small, eight-nuclei embryo sac that lies within the sporophyte parent plant. With fertilization the haploid (n) sperm unites with the haploid (n) egg, and a zygote of diploid (2n) number is formed. The zygote develops into a sporophyte embryo. At maturity the seed containing the embryo is eventually released from the parent plant. It then develops into a new, diploid (2n) sporophyte plant.

What Is a Seed?

In one sense, a seed is a packaged plant. Everything the plant needs to begin growing is wrapped in one or more protective coats. Inside the seed is a new plant, or *embryo*, complete with embryonic leaves, stem, and root. The embryo is surrounded by stored food. The protective coat of the seed prevents drying so that seeds can lie dormant for months, some even for years. A seed may be carried with the wind, float on water, or ride on the fur of an animal or the feet of a bird. Seeds can also be transported when a bird or other animal eats fruit containing a seed. Later when eliminated from the digestive tract, the undigested seed is in a new location. When the seed lands in soil where it gets warmth and moisture, its coat softens. The embryo grows as it absorbs water. Cell division occurs at a rapid rate, and soon the embryo sends a root into the earth and a leafy shoot into the air.

Classification of Seed Plants

Seed plants, like other tracheophytes (the ferns, club mosses, and horsetails), are vascular plants. Their ability to form seeds, however, separates them from the other tracheophytes. They are generally classified in two groups: **gymnosperms** and **angiosperms.** A brief description of the plants included in each plant division follows.

Gymnosperms

- *Cycadophyta.* Palmlike plants called cycads. About 100 species.

- *Ginkgophyta.* An ancient type of tree that was abundant in preglacial times. Only one species survives.
- *Coniferophyta* (conifers). Includes pine, spruce, yew, juniper, and other evergreens. Many have cones. About 600 species.

Angiosperms

One division includes all flowering plants, about 250,000 species.

The Gymnosperms

In gymnosperms, seeds develop without a protective wall. The seeds of many gymnosperms are exposed to the air. They are on the surface of a cone scale, unlike seeds of an apple, for instance.

Only about 700 different species of gymnosperms are alive today. These are the cycads, the ginkgo, and the conifers.

The Cycads The cycads are about 100 species of plants that resemble some ancient fossil plants. One kind of cycad is called the sago palm. They live in subtropical and tropical parts of Florida, the West Indies, and Mexico, and in certain areas of Australia, Africa, and Asia.

The Ginkgo The ginkgo tree is the only surviving species of the *Ginkgophyta,* once a prominent group. The ginkgo is a large tree, sometimes as high as 30 meters (100 feet) or more, and with a trunk up to one and a half meters (about 5 feet) thick. Its leaves are unique; they are fan-shaped with two lobes.

Ginkgo trees are either male or female. Male trees produce pollen contained in short, conelike *catkins.* The female trees produce the seeds, which develop in fleshy orange or yellow fruitlike berries 2.5 cm (1 inch) wide. They look like plums or large cherries and have a foul odor. Each contains a single, almond-flavored nut. Once many species of Ginkgoales grew all over the world, but by the last glacial age, a million years ago, they could only be found in what is now China. For centuries they were planted in Chinese temple gardens. Later they were brought to Japan. Today they are quite common in the United States. Even so, the ginkgo is still among the rarest of all living plants. It is the single surviving species of an order that flourished at the time of the dinosaurs.

The Conifers Familiar trees such as pines, spruce, firs, and sequoias are conifers. Most conifers, like those mentioned, produce woody, seed-bearing structures called

22-3 | A cycad. While it resembles a palm tree in appearance, the cycad reproductive structure is like that of gymnosperms. *(Albert Towle)*

gymno = naked
sperm = seed
angeion = case, capsule

22-4 | The leaves of a ginko tree resemble the leaflets of the maidenhair fern. *(Walter Dawn)*

cones. Some conifers however, such as the yew and juniper, produce seeds in cones that resemble berries.

Most conifers are trees, but some species of yews and junipers are shrubs. As a group, the conifers probably go back to the Carboniferous age. Today they are the most widespread of the gymnosperms. There are huge forests of conifers in North America. Some grow in rocky or sandy soils not suitable for many broad-leaved trees. Others thrive in swamps and bogs and around lake edges. They flourish from Alaska to the Gulf of Mexico. They are found in all the major mountain regions, along the Great Lakes, and along the ocean coasts. These forests serve as the main source of supply for lumber and paper products.

Conifers grow larger and older than any other trees. One of the largest is a redwood in California, 100 meters (333 feet) tall with a trunk 10 meters (33.3 feet) wide. It is probably more than 4,000 years old. An even bigger conifer is the cypress called the "Big Tree of Tule," in Mexico. This tree is 15 meters (49.5 feet) thick and has probably been alive for more than 5,000 years.

Most conifers are evergreen. Two exceptions are the larch and the bald cypress. These trees lose their needles every fall. Conifer leaves are in the form of needles or scales.

Cones can contain either seeds or pollen. **Seed cones** are woody and take from several months to several years to develop. They produce pairs of winged seeds on the upper surfaces of shelflike cone scales. Seed cones come in all kinds of shapes and sizes. They are often helpful in identifying species of trees.

Pollen cones are smaller than seed cones. They can be found at the tips of branches, sometimes in clusters. These cones are yellow or red in color. Pollen cones stay on the tree only a few days after they have shed their pollen. Often pollen cones are seen only in the spring. Most North American conifers have both seed and pollen cones, but on separate branches of the same tree.

The Angiosperms: The Flowering Plants

Angiosperms include all flowering plants. Angiosperms probably branched off from the gymnosperm line during the Jurassic period of the Mesozoic era. They developed quickly, replacing much of the vegetation during the Cretaceous period. **Today angiosperms are the dominant plant life.** They grow in most areas not occupied by coniferous forests.

There are several reasons for the success of angiosperms. Genetic variations over the ages have resulted in many forms—trees, shrubs, and herbs. They also grow in

Facts & Figures

Conifers appeared 300 million years ago.

22-5 | Pine trees are the most widely distributed of the conifers. They are a source of rosin, turpentine, resin paper, and lumber. *(William E. Ferguson)*

Table 22-1 SOME FAMILIES OF MONOCOTS AND DICOTS

Monocot Families	Familiar Members	Dicot Families	Familiar Members
cattail (Typhaceae)	common cattail	beech (Fagaceae)	beech, chestnut, oak
lily (Liliaceae)	lily, onion, tulip, hyacinth	water lily (Nymphaea-ceae)	water lily, pond lily
grass (Gramineae)	cereal grains, bluegrass, sugar cane, bamboo, timothy	poppy (Papavera-ceae)	poppy, bloodroot
iris (Iridaceae)	flag, iris	rose (Rosaceae)	rose, apple, hawthorn, strawberry pear, peach, plum, cherry
palm (Palmaceae)	coconut palm, date palm, palmetto	maple (Aceraceae)	maple

various ways. Some are upright; others climb, creep, or float. More than any other group, angiosperms can grow and reproduce rapidly in a wide variety of environments. They live in all types of soils. They survive in most extremes of temperature, rainfall, and sunshine. In one form or another, they inhabit deserts, lakes, plains, marshes, mountain slopes, and arctic regions.

Monocots and Dicots Angiosperms include about 300 families and more than 250,000 species of flowering plants. The plants can be divided into two classes: *Monocotyledonae* and *Dicotyledonae*.

The basic difference between the two is the number of **cotyledons,** or seed leaves, that develop in the embryo plant. The cotyledon is the first leaf of the young plant. In many species the cotyledons act as the food supply to the seedling until it can synthesize its own food. In other species the cotyledon carries on the first photosynthesis for the plant. As the names imply, **a *monocot* plant has a single cotyledon, while a *dicot* has two.** As you learn more about flowering plants, you will find other differences between these two subclasses. The arrangement of their root and stem tissues differs. They have different patterns of leaf veins and number of flower parts.

Organs of Seed Plants

Each organ of a flowering plant has a special job. The root, stem, and leaves are **vegetative organs.** They carry out all

Facts & Figures

Flowering plants appeared 150 million years ago.

mono = **one**
di = **two**
cotyledon = **seed leaf**

Facts & Figures

There are 200,000 species of dicots and 50,000 species of monocots.

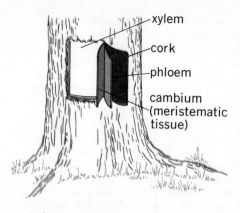

22-6 | The general locations of specialized tissue in a tree.

the processes necessary for life except sexual reproduction. They are not involved in forming seeds.

Roots   The *root* anchors the plant in the ground. It spreads through the soil to *absorb* water and soil minerals and conduct them to the stem. Many roots also *store* food for the plant until it is needed.

Stems   The *stem* is like a busy highway. It *conducts* water and minerals from the root up to the leaves. At the same time, it brings foods that have been manufactured in the leaves back down to the roots. The stem is also a storage place for some of this food. In addition, it produces the leaves and displays them to the light. The green stems of many plants even carry on photosynthesis.

Leaves   The *leaf* is the center of many of the plant's activities. In most plants, leaves are the chief organs of *photosynthesis*. Here also, gases are exchanged between the plant and air by means of *respiration* and photosynthesis. Much of the water absorbed by the root has a one-way trip through the plant to the leaves. From there, it passes into the air as water vapor. This process, called *transpiration*, will be explained in detail in Chapter 23.

Flowers   After the plant has grown for a time, it usually reproduces. **Flowers are plant organs that specialize in sexual reproduction.** Part of the flower grows into a **fruit,** which contains the seeds. The reproductive process that begins with the flower and leads to the fruit, seed, and embryo plant is the most highly evolved in the whole plant world.

Specialized Tissue in Seed Plants

The organs are able to function because they are composed of specialized tissues. In each tissue, the cells are slightly different. These differences allow each organ to carry out its special purpose. Similar tissues are found in both gymnosperms and angiosperms, but differences in cell structure, especially in the vascular tissues, are seen in these two groups. Let's look at the different kinds of plant tissues and what they do.

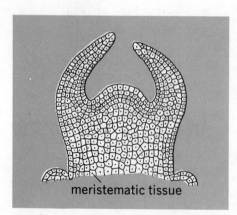

meristematic tissue

22-7 | Meristematic tissue on the tip of a stem.

Meristematic Tissue   *Meristematic tissue* is made of thin-walled cells that divide rapidly. Plant growth occurs only at the meristematic tissue. The *meristems* or growing points are found on the ends of branches and the tips of roots. They increase the length of these structures. **Cambium** is a cylinder of meristematic cells, usually only one cell in

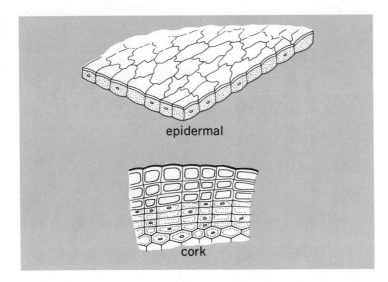

22–8 | Epidermal cells are usually one cell thick. The cork layer can be many cells thick.

thickness. It surrounds the stems and roots. Cell division of the cambium increases the diameter of stems and roots. The cells produced from the meristematic tissue become the permanent, mature, specialized cells of the plant.

Epidermal Tissue *Epidermal tissue* is the covering layer on the surfaces of roots, stems, and leaves. Epidermal cells protect the underlying tissues from injury and lessen water loss. In young roots, the epidermis absorbs materials for food.

Cork *Cork* is a covering tissue on the surfaces of woody roots and stems. Cork cells usually do not live very long. After they die, their cell walls form a protective covering that also lessens water loss.

Parenchyma *Parenchyma* tissue is made up of thin-walled cells that serve as storage cells in stems, roots, and fruits. The white storage tissue of the potato is made up of parenchyma cells that store starch. The soft white gummy tissue inside some stems is made of parenchyma cells. These cells are loosely packed and are quite large. Substances like starch and sugar are stored in parenchyma cells.

Chlorenchyma is parenchyma that contains chlorophyll. These cells are found under the epidermal tissues of leaves, flower petals, and some stems. They make up the primary tissue that carries on the process of photosynthesis. They are loosely packed, with many intercellular spaces. The spaces are important in the exchange of gases during photosynthesis and respiration.

epi = above
derma = skin

para = beside

enchyma = to pour in

chlor = light green

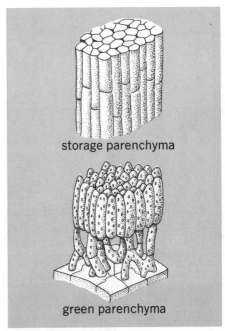

storage parenchyma

green parenchyma

22–9 | Parenchyma tissue. Green parenchyma is also called *chlorenchyma*.

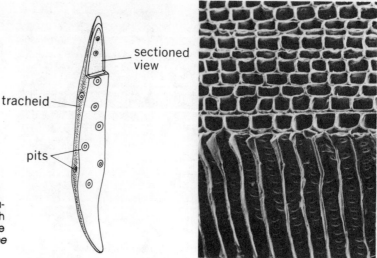

22–10 | (left) Note the thick walls of the tracheid. (right) A scanning electron micrograph shows how tracheids are arranged in the wood of a pine tree. (220X) *(Courtesy of the Institute of Paper Chemistry)*

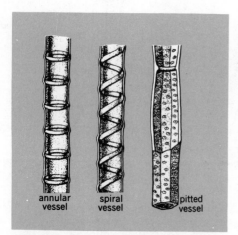

22–11 | Vessels of angiosperms. These tissues are usually dead and function only in conducting water.

Vascular Tissue *Vascular tissue* serves as the transport system of the plant. The water-conducting tissue is called **xylem.** The cell walls of xylem form the wood used in construction. The food-conducting tissue is called **phloem.**

The xylem of gymnosperms is composed almost entirely of **tracheids.** Tracheids are long, thick-walled cells with tapered ends. After the tracheid cells are formed, the cells die. Only the hollow, thick cell walls remain. Tracheids are considered a primitive type of conducting cell. They also serve as strengthening cells because of their thick, strong walls.

The conducting tissue in angiosperms contains some tracheids but they are more complex than that of the gymnosperms. Angiosperms have cells called **vessel elements,** which are hollow and thin-walled. These are connected end to end to form a tube called a **vessel.** The xylem of angiosperms consists of large numbers of these vessels. Water moves up the vessels and can move from one vessel to another through holes in their sides.

Unlike xylem, *phloem* is made of living cells. In angiosperms the phloem consists of cells called **sieve-tube elements.** The ends of these cells have perforated plates. Protoplasm strands pass through these plates to unite the cells with one another. This forms a continuous **sieve tube** that conducts sugar and protein down the stem.

Companion cells are smaller cells that lie alongside the sieve tubes. Nuclei of companion cells are thought to control the activities of the sieve tube cells. The phloem in gymnosperms is similar, but the sieve tubes are less specialized because they lack the sieve plates.

Strengthening Tissue   *Strengthening tissues* are found in roots and stems and in the stalks and large veins of leaves. Tracheids function as supporting cells in both gymnosperms and angiosperms. **Wood fibers** in angiosperms are similar to tracheids but are longer and taper more at the ends. They function only for strength. **Sclerenchyma** is a strengthening tissue that can be fiberlike, round, or starlike in shape. The fibers are elongated cells with tapered ends. Walls of this tissue are thick and tough. A type of sclerenchyma forms most of walnut shells.

scler = hard

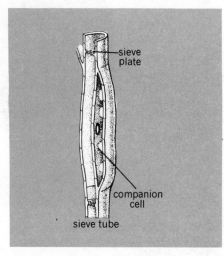

Woody and Herbaceous Plants

Plants are often described as either *woody* or *herbaceous*, depending on the kind of tissues they have. Cutting the stem of a woody plant is difficult. The stem has woody tissue almost all the way through. In contrast, cutting through an herbaceous stem is easier. The vascular, woody tissue is usually in thin strands or bundles that run the length of the stem. The inner tissue of the herbaceous plant is usually soft and pulpy; sometimes it is moist and fleshy.

22–12 | Phloem tissue. Protoplasmic strands are not shown.

Woody plants tend to remain erect when water is lacking, while herbaceous plants tend to wilt or droop. Trees and shrubs are woody plants and tend to live a number of years, growing in diameter and height each year. Herbaceous plants are usually short-lived. Most garden flowers and vegetables are herbaceous.

Annuals, Biennials, and Perennials   Both woody and herbaceous plants can be grouped according to how long the plant body lives. Plants that live for only one season are called **annuals.** They grow from seed, produce flowers, then fruits and seeds, all in a single growing season. Only the seeds live until the following year. Typical annuals are garden flowers such as the zinnia, marigold, and pansy, and vegetables such as beans and peas. Cereal grains are also annuals.

annus = year

Biennial plants have a life cycle that lasts two growing seasons. During the first year, the roots, stem, and leaves develop, often in the form of a low ring or rosette. The stem grows in the second year, bearing more leaves, the flower, fruit, and seeds. After it produces the seeds, the plant dies. Several garden vegetables, such as beets, carrots, cabbages, parsnips, and turnips are biennials.

bi = two

Perennial plants live more than two seasons. They usually grow roots, stems, and leaves during the first year. They usually do not flower until their second or third season. Once growing, they usually continue to flower for several seasons. In temperate climates the portion of an her-

per = through

22–13 | (left) Herbaceous perennial. (right) Woody perennial. How often must each of these be planted? *(left: Matthew Stettler; right: Derek Fell)*

baceous perennial that is above ground may die. The roots or underground stems remain alive to produce new plants the following season. Delphiniums, lilies, columbines, and irises are some herbaceous perennials. Woody perennials include trees, shrubs, and many vines. The woody portions of these plants remain alive year after year.

Summary

The two largest groups of seed plants are the *gymnosperms* (mainly *conifers*) and *angiosperms* (flowering plants). Conifer leaves are in the form of needles or scales, and most conifers have cones. The angiosperms are the dominant plant life today.

The tissues of seed plants are specialized to perform special functions. The vast variety of seed plants makes it possible for them to grow in nearly all environments. The stems of some seed plants, trees, and shrubs are woody nearly all the way through. These plants tend to remain erect when water is lacking. Herbaceous plants have their vascular woody tissues in thin strands or bundles. Herbaceous plants tend to wilt when water is lacking.

Woody and herbaceous plants can be grouped according to how long the plant body lives. *Annuals* live only one season. *Biennial* plants have a life cycle that lasts two growing seasons. *Perennials* live more than two seasons.

gymnosperm
angiosperm
seed cone
pollen cone
cotyledon
monocot
dicot
vegetative organ
root
stem
leaf
flower
fruit
meristematic tissue
cambium
epidermal tissue

cork
parenchyma
chlorenchyma
vascular tissue
xylem
phloem
tracheid
vessel elements
vessel
sieve-tube element
sieve tube
companion cell
wood fiber
sclerenchyma
annual
biennial
perennial

Questions for Review

1. How do the reproductive organs of gymnosperms differ from those of angiosperms?
2. List the main functions of roots, stems, and leaves.
3. What two kinds of cones are produced by the conifers?
4. In what respects is meristematic tissue different from other plant tissue?
5. Describe the water-conducting tissue in gymnosperms. How does it differ from that of angiosperms?
6. What is the function of parenchyma tissue?
7. In what ways do phloem and xylem differ?
8. What are the differences between woody and herbaceous stems?
9. If we group flowering plants on the basis of duration of the plant body, what are the three groups?
10. How do monocots and dicots differ?

Applying Concepts

1. Discuss various ways in which angiosperms are better adapted than other kinds of plants in the struggle for existence on land.
2. How might the flowering plants of the future differ from those of today?

23

The Leaf and its Function

A **DISTINGUISH** a compound leaf from a simple leaf.

B **LIST** the structures of a leaf and describe its functions.

C **DESCRIBE** photosynthesis and respiration in plants.

D **DESCRIBE** water loss from leaves.

E **EXPLAIN** how the stomata of the leaf work.

F **EXPLAIN** why leaves change color and drop off in the fall.

G **LIST** some examples of leaf modification.

H **DISTINGUISH** between a monocot and a dicot leaf.

23–1 | The Norway maple has a typical dicot leaf. *(Derek Fell)*

The Leaf: A Specialized Food Factory

The leaf is a seed plant's food factory. It is where **photosynthesis** takes place. Leaves absorb sunlight and carbon dioxide through their surface openings. They get water through roots and stems. **The green cells of the leaves then use the light, carbon dioxide, and water to make food, primarily sugar.**

Some plants, such as maples or elm trees, lose their leaves each autumn. The stems form new leaves each year. Other plants, such as evergreens, keep their leaves. However, evergreens grow new leaves on young stems each year. Thus plants constantly renew their vital food factories.

Leaf Tissues

If you were to look at a cross section of a leaf under a microscope, you would see three different kinds of tissue. The top and bottom surfaces are covered with a single layer of cells, called **epidermis.** Between them are several layers of **chlorenchyma cells** (chlorophyll-containing cells), where photo-

epi = on
derma = skin

synthesis takes place. These layers are known as the ***mesophyll.*** Veins of various sizes run through the middle of the mesophyll. All the tissues fit together in a way that lets light in and allows gases to move in and out. All tissues and structures function together in photosynthesis.

meso = **middle**
phyll = **leaf**

The Leaf Epidermis

A single layer of epidermal cells forms the top and bottom layers of the leaf. In a cross-section view, these cells look like cubes or bricks. From the surface, you can see how their irregular shapes fit together like pieces of a jigsaw puzzle. Epidermal cells usually do not have *chloroplasts*, the organelles containing chlorophyll. **Their relatively thick walls form a layer that protects the more delicate cells beneath.**

plast = **molded**

Often the epidermis is covered by a thin, waxy film, the ***cuticle.*** The cuticle slows down the escape of water vapor and other gases from the leaf tissues. Most of the gases move in and out of the tissues through pores in the epidermis called ***stomata*** (singular, *stoma*). Stomata are slitlike openings into air spaces between cells of the mesophyll. Each stoma has two ***guard cells*** around it. The guard cells are modified epidermis cells. They have chloroplasts and thickened walls that are important factors in opening and closing the stoma. This keeps the water content in the leaf stable.

stoma = **mouth**

Stomata may occur in both top and bottom epidermal layers. If the plant holds its leaves in a horizontal position,

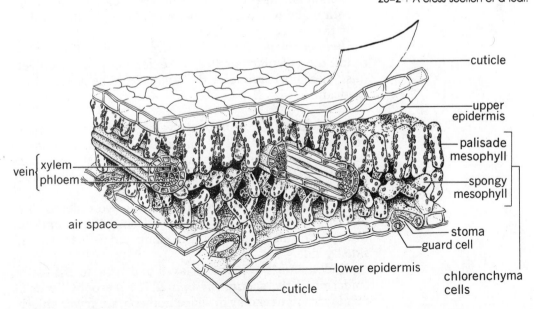

23–2 | A cross section of a leaf.

cuticle

upper epidermis

palisade mesophyll

spongy mesophyll

stoma
guard cell

chlorenchyma cells

lower epidermis

cuticle

air space

vein { xylem / phloem

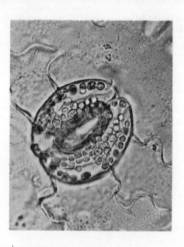

23–3 | A stoma. Unlike other cells of the epidermis, the two bean-shaped guard cells that surround each stoma, or opening, contain chloroplasts. *(Hugh Spencer)*

the stomata are usually on the underside. This is especially true of woody plants. In the floating leaves of water plants, all the stomata are on top. Stomata are also found on the epidermis of herbaceous stems and young shoots of woody plants. The vertical leaves of the iris have approximately equal numbers of stomata on both sides. Up to a thousand stomata may be found on each square centimeter of epidermis.

Many leaf surfaces feel velvety, fuzzy, or wooly because they have **epidermal hairs.** Actually the hairs are outgrowths of epidermal cells. They may help reduce water loss by reducing evaporation. Many leaves contain glands that secrete oily or sticky substances on the surface, which also reduce water loss.

Leaf Veins Veins are made of supporting and conducting tissues gathered together in **fibrovascular bundles.** One or more of these bundles enter the blade through the *petiole.* The large leaf veins in a plant of the class Dicotyledonae branch again and again, forming a network all through the mesophyll. The network is so fine that each cell is no more than a few cells removed from a vein.

A large vein has a zone of **xylem vessels** on the upper side and **phloem sieve tubes** on the lower side. As veins branch out, they get smaller and have less vascular tissue. Some may have only one xylem vessel that ends in the middle of the mesophyll. Xylem vessels carry water and minerals to leaf tissue. Phloem cells carry food from the leaf that was made in the leaf cells.

Small- and medium-sized veins are enclosed in a **bundle sheath** made of elongated **parenchyma cells,** thin-walled cells that make up soft tissue.

Sclerenchyma fibers (plant-strengthening fibers) surround the vascular bundles and extend out to the epidermis. These fibers reinforce the bundles and help strengthen the leaf.

The Mesophyll Except for the veins, the whole leaf blade between the two layers of epidermis is made up of **mesophyll cells.** Mesophyll cells are thin-walled cells that contain many chloroplasts. They make up the main photosynthetic tissue of the leaf.

The mesophyll cells are arranged in two different layers. Directly beneath the upper epidermis is the **palisade mesophyll.** This layer is made of elongated cells that stand side by side.

Underneath the palisade layer and next to the lower epidermis is the **spongy mesophyll.** The mesophyll cells of this layer are irregular in shape and contain fewer chloro-

Table 23-1 SUMMARY OF STRUCTURE AND FUNCTION OF LEAF TISSUE

REGION	TISSUE	FUNCTION
epidermis	epidermal cells	protect the upper and lower surface of the leaf
	cuticle	prevents excessive loss of water and gases
	stomata	regulate passage of air and water vapor in and out of the leaf
	guard cells	regulate opening and closing of stoma
mesophyll	palisade mesophyll	most active area of photosynthesis, greatest concentration of chloroplasts
	spongy mesophyll	active area of photosynthesis, provides air passages
fibrovascular bundle	xylem vessels phloem sieve tubes	conduct water and minerals conduct dissolved food substances

plasts. They are arranged very loosely with plenty of space between cells. These open spaces lead to the *stomata*, in the lower epidermis. The branching veins, large and small, run through the spongy mesophyll.

Photosynthesis and Respiration

Photosynthesis usually starts when the first rays of the morning sun penetrate the leaf. **As glucose is produced by photosynthesis** (as described in Chapter 6), **the leaf cells use some of it for respiration.** The excess glucose is stored as starch grains in the mesophyll cells. Starch storage is at a maximum, usually, at about mid-afternoon. The mesophyll cells then convert the starch back into glucose. This sugar, dissolved in water, enters the phloem sieve tubes of the leaf's veins. Still in solution, it moves through the petiole to the plant stem. There the phloem transports it to other parts of the plant. It may be used in cell respiration, or it may be stored in roots, tubers, seeds, fruits, or various other regions of the plant. This transport of glucose extends into the night. By morning the leaf cells are low in starch and photosynthesis begins again.

Respiration in plants goes on day and night. Respiration in plants is like that of other aerobic (oxygen-using) organisms. Glucose and oxygen, the two products of photo-

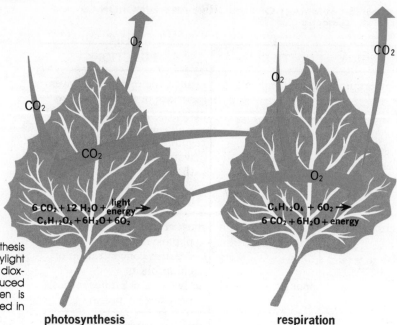

$$6 CO_2 + 12 H_2O + \text{light energy} \rightarrow$$
$$C_6H_{12}O_6 + 6H_2O + 6O_2$$

$$C_6H_{12}O_6 + 6O_2 \rightarrow$$
$$6 CO_2 + 6H_2O + \text{energy}$$

photosynthesis   **respiration**

23–4 | Gas exchanges due to photosynthesis and respiration. Under normal daylight conditions, five to ten times more carbon dioxide is used in photosynthesis than is produced in respiration. Also, much more oxygen is released in photosynthesis than is required in respiration.

Facts & Figures

The leaf surface of a large oak equals about one-half acre.

synthesis, are used in respiration. Glucose serves as fuel in respiration. When combined with oxygen, the glucose is broken down into simple molecules. The energy made available from this breakdown of glucose is used to make ATP. ATP is the high-energy molecule plants use for all energy-consuming processes.

Respiration produces not only ATP. It also produces two by-products. One is carbon dioxide, and the other is water. They pass out through the stomata. Both of these products are also used in photosynthesis.

Table 23-2 COMPARISON OF PHOTOSYNTHESIS AND RESPIRATION

PHOTOSYNTHESIS	RESPIRATION
food accumulated	food broken down (oxidized)
energy from sun stored in glucose	energy of glucose released by oxidation
carbon dioxide taken in	carbon dioxide given off
oxygen given off	oxygen taken in
produces glucose from PGAL	produces CO_2 and H_2O
goes on only in light	goes on day and night
occurs only in presence of chlorophyll	occurs in all living cells

Water Loss in Plants

During the growing season water continuously streams up through the roots and stem to the leaves. About one percent of the water is used in photosynthesis and other processes of the plant. The rest escapes from the leaves, mostly through the stomata, as water vapor. The process in which water is lost from plants is called *transpiration.*

As a result of transpiration, leaves are cooled. Also, the loss of water out of the leaves helps to pull water through the plant.

As water enters the leaf through the veins, it goes from the xylem vessels into the mesophyll. Some of this water is absorbed and used by the cells, but much of it evaporates. It diffuses through the spaces between the spongy mesophyll cells. From there, it passes out into the air through the stomata. As this happens, more water moves in through the veins to replace the water that is lost.

Function of Stomata   **The opening and closing of the stomata control the rate of transpiration.** In most plants the stomata are opened during the day and closed at night. They may also close during the day on hot afternoons or when the plant wilts. The change in the shape of a stoma's guard cells causes the stoma to open and close. When the banana-shaped guard cells absorb water from nearby epidermal cells, their water vacuoles fill. This increases their internal pressure, or *turgor.* The increased turgor makes the thinner, outer walls of the guard cells bulge. The thicker, inner walls around the opening are pulled into a crescent shape, and the stoma opens. Water evaporating through the walls of the guard cells reduces turgor pressure. This makes the guard cells shrink. As they get smaller, their inner walls straighten and the stoma closes.

Arrangement and Structure of Leaves

Important influences are light, temperature, and the supply of water and carbon dioxide. Often light is the most limiting factor. **Leaf structure and arrangement are all adaptations to different environments.** Environments vary in their effect on how the process of photosynthesis will be carried out in the leaf.

Leaf Structure   A leaf is an outgrowth of the stem. Many leaves have flattened, broad, green blades, as seen in figure 23–4. Leaf blades have many sizes and forms. The edges, or leaf margins, may be smooth, toothed, or indented. The tips and bases of the blades also have many different shapes. These differences are often helpful clues to the plant's identity.

trans = **across**
spiration = **breath**

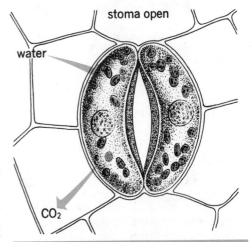

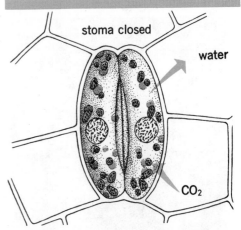

23–5 | Changes in the concentration of carbon dioxide and carbonic acid in the guard cells affect enzyme action on sugar and starch. This results in water movement and turgor change that open and close the stoma.

23–6 | The leaves of the Pilea are arranged so that they receive maximum sunlight. *(W. H. Hodge, Peter Arnold)*

bi = two
pinna = feather

Facts & Figures

There are about 650 species of deciduous trees in the United States.

23–7 | Maple tree showing autumn coloration. *(Derek Fell)*

The blade is attached to the stems by a stalk, or **petiole.** Usually there is a slight bulge at the base of the petiole where it joins the stem. This is called a **node.** Many leaf petioles have two small leaflike outgrowths called **stipules** at their base. Some of these stay on all season, while others fall off soon after the leaf develops. Some leaves lack petioles entirely; these leaves are called *sessile* leaves.

Simple and Compound Leaves When each leaf blade is single, even if it is deeply indented, it is *simple*. A simple leaf, such as the maple leaf, has one blade and one petiole. In many leaves, though, the blade has several parts called *leaflets*, so it is called a *compound* leaf. Like the veins of a leaf, leaflets grow in either a **palmate** or a **pinnate** pattern. When the leaflets fan out from the base at the petiole, they are *palmately compound*. You can see these leaves on buckeye and horse-chestnut trees, and in lupine, poison ivy, Virginia creeper, and some clovers.

Leaflets of a *pinnately compound* leaf branch out from one central stalk. You can see this in the leaves of the pea, rose, walnut, and hickory. Sometimes the leaflets themselves are divided into little leaflets. Then they are *bipinnately compound*. You will find them on the honey locust and the Kentucky coffee tree.

Venation of Leaves The petiole contains long, tubelike structures called **veins.** The veins branch out in various directions when they reach the blade of the leaf. Large veins look like ribs on the underside of the leaf. The pattern the larger veins take as they branch throughout the blade is called the **venation** of the leaf.

When a leaf has *parallel venation*, the large veins are parallel with the edge of the leaf and with each other, as in monocotyledons such as corn, lilies, irises, and orchids. The veins of dicotyledons branch and rebranch to form a netted pattern. These netted patterns take several forms. One form is the *palmate venation* of leaves like sycamore and maple leaves, which have large veins that spread out from the end of the petiole like the fingers on a hand. Another pattern is *pinnate venation*, which resembles the structure of a feather: One large vein, called the **midrib,** runs the length of the blade. Small veins branch out from the midrib to the leaf's edge. You can see this pinnate net venation in the leaves of elms, willows, and apple trees.

Leaf Fall and Coloration

At the end of the growing season, leaves fall naturally from many woody plants in temperate climates. Trees that lose their leaves seasonally are called *deciduous trees*. When

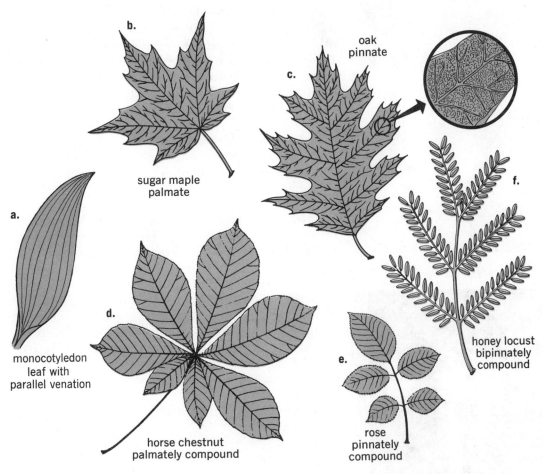

23-8 | Form and size of blade, venation, and compounding are often used as a basis for identification in plants.

autumn comes, the parenchyma cells across the base of the petiole form a weak zone called the ***abscission layer.*** The abscission layer is formed in response to environmental factors such as daily light period. After the abscission layer forms, only the petiole's fibrovascular bundles keep it attached to the twig. The slightest jar from rain or a gust of wind can make the leaf fall. Then a thin layer of cork cells seals the scar where the leaf was attached.

Some deciduous trees such as some oaks never lose their leaves in the fall. The leaves dry, but they stay on the tree. They fall gradually during the winter and the following spring. Evergreens, including most conifers, keep their needlelike green leaves all winter. They slowly drop off during the next season, after they have been replaced by new shoots and leaves.

Leaves are green during their growing season in the late spring and summer. This is because the chloroplasts con-

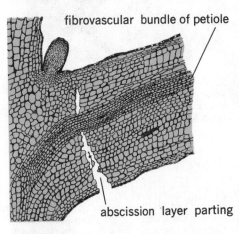

23-9 | During autumn, the cells of the abscission layer separate.

tain chlorophyll. The chloroplasts have two other pigments as well. One is a yellow pigment called **xanthophyll;** the other is an orange pigment called **carotene.** In a green leaf these are masked by the chlorophyll. **As fall arrives, the temperature becomes too cold for plants to make any more chlorophyll. Light destroys whatever chlorophyll is left. Now the yellow and orange pigments that were hidden become visible.**

Cool nights and sunny days in the fall cause many leaves to form the red pigment **anthocyanin.** This is the pigment that turns the leaves of many woody plants red in the cool spring and fall.

Leaf Modifications In hot, wet regions leaves tend to be broad and flat. They expose a large amount of surface area to light. In hot, dry climates where plants must not lose precious water through transpiration, leaves are often small. The needles on a cactus are examples of leaf adaptations to a desert environment. In cacti the stems are the main organs of photosynthesis.

Leaf modification results in structures that perform a variety of functions. **Tendrils** are long, springy modified leaves (and stems) that coil and twist around supporting objects. You can see them on pea plants, morning glories, and greenbrier. The protective scales on the buds of winter twigs are also modified leaves, and the onion bulb is made of layered leaves.

Some of the most unusual leaf adaptations have developed in plants such as the sundew, Venus' flytrap, pitcher plant, and bladderwort. Their leaves are all designed to capture insects. Therefore the plants are called **insectivorous** plants. Insectivorous plants contain chlorophyll and synthesize their own carbohydrates. They do not need the insects as food. Because these plants usually grow in the kind of soil where nitrates are scarce, they must digest insects that contain nitrogen products in order to get the nitrogen supplement their diet requires.

vorous = eats greedily

23–10 | The cactus, *Cereus giganteus,* stores water in its thick, fleshy stem. The leaves are reduced to spines to prevent water loss. *(Carolina Biological Supply Co.)*

23–11 | The Venus' flytrap (left) and the pitcher plant (right) are insectivorous plants. These plants have special adaptations which allow them to digest insects which become trapped between their leaves. *(Carolina Biological Supply Co.)*

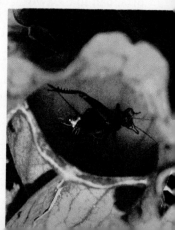

The leaves are the focal point of all the structures and processes of plants. It is the leaves that absorb light and use its energy to make food. The absorption of water and minerals, the arrangement of leaves on stems, and the flat end leaf blade are all adaptations for photosynthesis.

Leaves are adapted to a variety of environments. In dense jungles leaves are often very large, taking light and allowing large amounts of water to move through and out of the plant. In deserts, where the plant must conserve water, the leaves are small and thick or are modified, such as needles on cacti.

As cold weather approaches, many leaves do not continue to replace their chlorophyll. The red and yellow pigments they contain become visible. At the same time, changes occur in the abscission layer. This makes the leaf fall. Other plants have leaves that are modified to help them catch and digest insects as part of their food.

Summary

photosynthesis
epidermis
chlorenchyma cell
mesophyll
cuticle
stoma
guard cell
epidermal hair
fibrovascular bundle
xylem vessel
phloem sieve tube

bundle sheath
parenchyma cell
sclerenchyma fiber
mesophyll cell
palisade mesophyll
spongy mesophyll
transpiration
turgor
petiole
node
stipule

palmate
pinnate
veins
venation
midrib
abscission layer
xanthophyll
carotene
anthocyanin
tendrils
insectivorous

Biologically Speaking

1. How is leaf shape an adaptation for function?
2. Name two functions of a leaf's veins.
3. Distinguish venation of monocots from dicots.
4. What is the function of the cuticle of a leaf?
5. Describe the structure of guard cells and their relation to a stoma.
6. Explain why leaves change color.
7. Explain how wilting can occur in a leaf.
8. How do plant photosynthesis and respiration differ?
9. Why do some leaves fall with a season change?

Questions for Review

1. Cells in the mesophyll of a leaf are thin-walled and arranged loosely. Why is this important in the activities of the leaf?
2. Discuss the different structural differences in leaves that allow them to live in their environment.

Applying Concepts

24

Roots and Stems

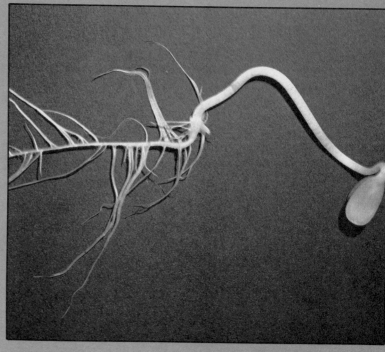

24–1 | Embryo plant showing new shoot and roots. *(William E. Ferguson)*

Roots

Did you ever try to pull up a dandelion root by hand? Very often it can't be done. This is because the main dandelion root grows straight down and anchors the plant in the soil. Roots have a variety of forms, but they all serve the same function. They absorb water and minerals from the soil to supply the entire plant. They also anchor the plant.

Roots and Root Systems

Root systems vary in form, shape, and size. Many environmental factors such as type of soil, amount of moisture, and temperature, affect the growth of roots. Land plants may have as much root system below the ground as they have stem and branches above ground. The roots of most plants do not grow as deep into the earth as their stems grow high above ground. The roots of large trees grow only about 2 meters (6.6 feet) below the soil surface. However, roots usually spread wider than the branches above them.

When a seed germinates, the first root pushes downward into the soil from the lower end of the embryo plant. This is called the ***primary root.*** In some plants the primary root keeps growing and forms the major root of the system. If the primary root is the major root, it is called a ***taproot.*** It can reach water supplies that are deep in the ground. Oak and hickory survive on dry hillsides because of their long taproots.

Some plants have taproots that get thick and fleshy and serve as underground storehouses for food. Beets, radishes, carrots, turnips, and parsnips are examples. Many of these plants are grown as root crops.

Roots growing out from the primary root are called ***secondary roots.*** In plants such as the grasses, secondary roots quickly outgrow the primary root. These roots are called ***fibrous roots.*** Fibrous root systems are usually shallow and spread through a large area of soil. The tangled mass of their threadlike roots also hold soil particles together.

Growth of Roots

When a root tip grows, it increases in length only. If you were to study a young root tip, you would find that it has many parts. These are the ***root cap, meristematic region,*** and ***elongation region.*** These areas are shown and described in figure 24–3.

How does the growing root tip force its way through soil without becoming completely torn? Its cells give off carbon

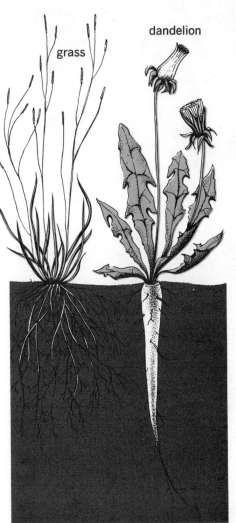

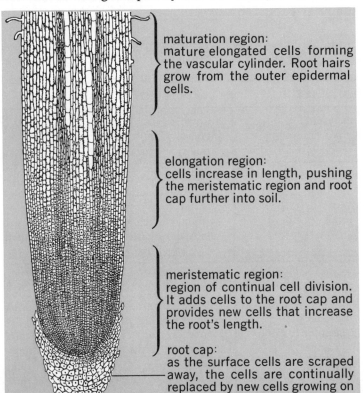

maturation region:
mature elongated cells forming the vascular cylinder. Root hairs grow from the outer epidermal cells.

elongation region:
cells increase in length, pushing the meristematic region and root cap further into soil.

meristematic region:
region of continual cell division. It adds cells to the root cap and provides new cells that increase the root's length.

root cap:
as the surface cells are scraped away, the cells are continually replaced by new cells growing on its inner surface.

24–2 | Compare and contrast the fibrous root system of the grass with the taproot system of the dandelion. Which acts as the better soil binder?

24–3 | Major regions of a root tip. Note the blunt, thimble-shaped root cap. This cap protects the delicate meristematic region from injury by soil particles.

a.

b.

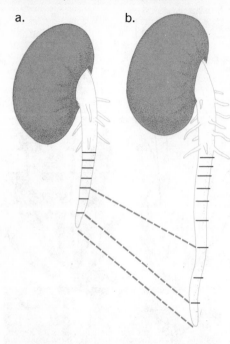

24-4 | In order to locate the elongation region, the young root in *a* was marked with ink at intervals of one millimeter (0.04 inches) from the tip back. The same root is shown in *b* after 24 hours of growth. Notice the region in which elongation has occurred.

24-5 | Stages in the development of root hairs from epidermal cells of a young root.

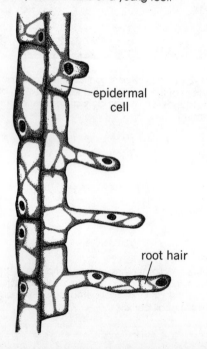

epidermal cell

root hair

dioxide during cellular respiration. The carbon dioxide gas reacts with water in the soil to form *carbonic acid.* This weak acid dissolves certain minerals in the soil and makes it easier for the root tip to move forward.

The most noticeable feature of the **maturation region** is the growth of **root hairs.** A root hair is a tiny fingerlike extension of a single epidermal cell. You need a microscope to see the root hair's origin in the epidermis of the roots, but you can see the fuzzy hairs themselves with a hand lens. Root hairs cover an area about 25 to 50 millimeters (1 to 2 inches) long. As roots grow and move forward, new root hairs sprout continually. Older ones farther from the root tip die and fall off. The root hairs serve a very important purpose. As the root tip grows, the hairs constantly push into new soil. They greatly increase the surface area for absorption. **The thin outer membranes of root hairs take in the water and minerals needed for the plants to survive.**

Primary Root Tissue   The first tissues that develop in a young root are called **primary tissues.** Primary tissue adds length to the root. It establishes the growth pattern of the plant. These tissues form three concentric layers of the root: the **epidermis,** the **cortex region,** and the **vascular cylinder.** The primary root tissues and their functions are summarized in Table 24-1.

**Table 24-1 SUMMARY OF ROOT TISSUES AND THEIR
SPECIAL FUNCTIONS**

TISSUE	FUNCTION
epidermis root hairs	absorption and protection increase in absorptive area of epidermis
cortex endodermis	diffusion of water and minerals to vascular cylinder and storage of food and water boundary layer separating cortex from vascular cylinder controls movement of water into xylem.

vascular cylinder
   pericycle
 	
   phloem
   vascular cambium
 	
   xylem
	
	 origin of secondary roots and formation of cork cambium
	 conduction of food materials
	 formation of secondary xylem and phloem, resulting in growth in diameter
	 conduction of water and dissolved minerals upward to stem and leaves.

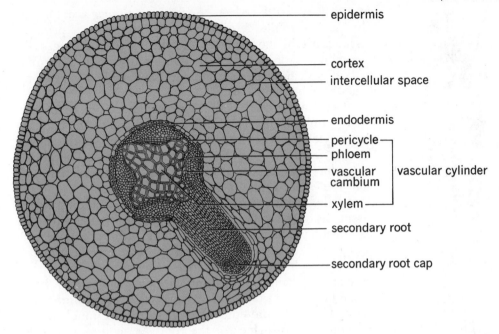

epidermis

cortex
intercellular space

endodermis
pericycle
phloem
vascular cambium } vascular cylinder
xylem

secondary root

secondary root cap

24-6 | Cross section of a young buttercup root. From what tissue does the secondary root arise?

Water and dissolved minerals pass easily through the epidermis and spaces of the cortex region. In many roots the parenchyma cells that make up the cortex store starch and other food substances.

The inner boundary of the cortex is formed by a single layer of cells called the **endodermis.** It is believed to control the flow of water and minerals into the central core of the root. Usually water can pass freely through the internal tissue of a plant. Cellulose is very permeable to water. Water, therefore, can pass freely through cell walls, between cells, and through the living cells themselves. The endodermis tissue, however, restricts the flow of water. There is a waxy waterproof strip between the endodermal cells that prevents water movement. The endodermis is like a special brick wall. Water can flow easily through the bricks but not through the mortar between the bricks.

endo = inside

On the inner side of the endodermis is a ring of parenchyma cells. This is called the **pericycle.** In most roots it is usually one cell thick. The pericycle is the first layer of the *vascular cylinder*. It is made of **xylem, phloem,** and **vascular cambium.** In the cross section of many roots of woody plants, such as trees and shrubs, the primary xylem appears star-shaped. The phloem is located between the arms of the xylem. Secondary growth is due primarily to the activity of the vascular cambium.

peri = around
vas = vessel

longitudinal section

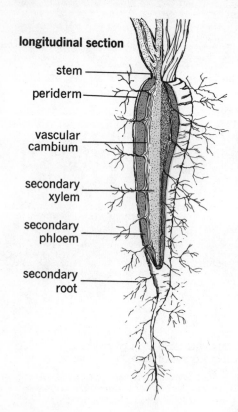

- stem
- periderm
- vascular cambium
- secondary xylem
- secondary phloem
- secondary root

cross section

- periderm
- secondary phloem
- vascular cambium
- secondary xylem
- secondary root

24–7 | Tissues of a fleshy root. As you study the tissue in the longitudinal section of the carrot root, locate the same tissues in the cross section.

Secondary Root Tissue   *Secondary tissues* account for the increase in diameter of roots and stems. Once primary tissue is established in trees and shrubs, secondary growth occurs and soon becomes the dominant growth. The great bulk of an oak tree is secondary tissue. Only a very small amount is primary tissue.

Secondary growth begins with rapid division of the vascular cambium layer, adding xylem tissue to the core. As more xylem cells are added, the cambium gradually moves farther from the star-shaped primary xylem. The added secondary xylem rounds out the central core of tissue so that the entire xylem is a rounded cylinder.

While the inner surface of the cambium is adding xylem tissue, its outer surface is forming phloem tissue. With this expansion the primary phloem, along with the endodermis and part of the cortex, is crushed or pressed by the growing secondary phloem. During each growing season, another ring of phloem is added along with the new xylem.

In later stages of secondary growth a **cork cambium** is formed beneath the epidermis. It forms the tough water-resistant outer surface of the root. **As soon as the corky layer is formed, the root can no longer absorb water. However, it still conducts water, stores food, and anchors the plant. The young tips of the roots continue to grow, establish new primary tissue, and absorb water and minerals.**

Modified Roots

The root tissues that have been discussed are similar in most roots, but root structure varies widely. The environment sometimes has a marked effect on modifications in roots. The bald cypress tree of the southern United States is a good example. It often grows in swamps. With its roots submerged in shallow water, the lateral roots produce upright growths called cypress "knees." It is thought that these knees may aerate the underwater roots. They do not form when the bald cypress grows in drier places.

Many plants, especially in the tropics, grow *aerial roots.* Tropical orchids, for instance, live on trees. They absorb water from dew, rainwater, and the damp air. Dust, fragments of bark, and other debris collect around the tropical orchid's roots. The plant gets enough minerals from these sources to survive.

In some plants, *adventitious roots* develop from the stem. Sometimes they even develop from the leaves. On corn stalks you may see circles of roots that grow from the lower joints of the stem. In this case these adventitious roots are called *brace roots* or **prop roots.** They push into the ground to help the underground root system support the corn stem. If soil is piled around the stem, more brace roots grow from the lowest joint still above the soil. Even the corn plant's soil roots are adventitious. They also grow from the stem, replacing the short-lived primary root.

Another tree with brace roots is the huge banyan which grows in warm climates. Roots grow down from its branches and penetrate the soil. These roots serve as extra trunks and help support wide-spreading limbs.

Poison ivy, English ivy, and other vines grow clusters of roots from their stems. These roots cling to trees or walls and anchor the stems. These adventitious roots are called *climbing roots.* Such plants also have ordinary soil roots to absorb water and minerals.

Stems

While part of the embryo plant forms the root, another part develops into the stem. The stem and its leaves are called the *shoot.* In most plants the stem and leaves rise into the air to make up the visible part.

Stems, like roots, grow in many different shapes and sizes. The trunks of huge forest trees that tower hundreds of feet in the air are stems. Some stems live only a few weeks; others grow for centuries. **Stems have a variety of functions. They expose the leaves to sunlight. They conduct food and water, store food, and sometimes go through the process of photosynthesis.**

Vascular tissues present in the root extend through the stem. **The xylem and phloem of a root and stem are continuous.** Food made in the leaves moves down the stem to the root. Food also moves up to the stem to supply the seeds, growing tips, and other tissues. In the spring a tree stem conducts food stored in the stem and root to the buds, growing leaves, and flowers.

Growth in a Stem

A pattern similar to that seen in the root is established in the stem of woody plants. Growth is rapid in the meristematic tissue at the tip of the stem. The newly formed cells then elongate, and the shoot apex moves forward, increasing the length of the stem. When the newly formed cells have reached their full size, they mature into primary tissue such as xylem, phloem, cortex, and epidermis. Thus there are three regions along the length of a growing stem, just as in the growing root: the meristematic region, the elongation region, and the maturation region where primary tissue is formed.

Since the tip is where the stem grows in length, a tree limb 2 meters (6.6 feet) above the ground will still be only

24–8 | The lateral roots of this cypress tree are called "knees." They help support the tree in its swampy habitat and aerate its underwater roots. *(Alan Pitcairn, Grant Heilman)*

Facts & Figures

Some giant redwood trees lift water 121 meters (399 feet) at the rate of 46 meters (152 feet) an hour.

two meters above the ground 50 years later. The tree will have become taller, but that additional length will have come at the *tips of the stems*.

Primary tissue in a stem is similar to the root except that the xylem and phloem are arranged in vascular bundles. The only difference between a stem and a root in secondary tissue is that the ring of vascular bundles gradually becomes a cylinder in a stem.

Parts of a Woody Stem

The trunk of a tree is a good example of a large, woody stem. It is very similar in structure to a large root. A large tree trunk half a meter in diameter may represent over 50 years of growth. If you look at a cross section of a trunk, four regions can be recognized: **pith, wood** (xylem), **cambium,** and **bark.**

Pith Pith is part of the primary tissue formed by a young shoot. When first formed, it consists of loosely packed parenchyma cells that are used for storage. During secondary growth the pith is surrounded by the secondary growth of the xylem.

In a trunk the pith is a tiny region, a few millimeters in diameter. With age its cells fill with tars, and it becomes nonfunctional.

Wood Wood contains fiber cells that support the tree. It has structures called **vascular rays** that conduct water horizontally in the stem.

One of the outstanding features of the xylem in a tree trunk is its annual rings. In the spring the cambium produces xylem vessels with a large diameter. Later in the summer, fewer and smaller xylem vessels are formed. The *spring wood* thus appears lighter than the more dense *summer wood*, hence the light and dark rings. You can tell the

24–9 | (top) The spruce illustrates the *excurrent* growth habit. In this tree, the lateral branches arise from the trunk, which acts as a central shaft. (bottom) In contrast, the oak illustrates the *deliquescent* growth pattern, in which the trunk is divided into several large main branches. *(Herbert Weihrich)*

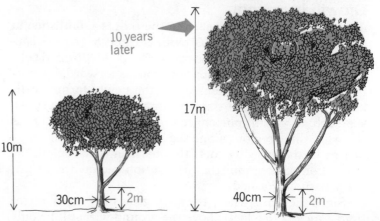

24–10 | A tree increases in length only at the tips of its branches. Secondary growth increases its diameter but not its height.

10 years later

10m

30cm

2m

17m

40cm

2m

age of a tree by counting its dark (or light) bands. You can also tell something of the history of the environment by the tree rings. A wide, light band means good growth and plenty of spring rain. A very narrow band means a poor growing season. Poor growth might be caused by drought, insect damage to leaves, or fungal disease. If a tree is bent or leans a certain way for a number of years, it will show that stress in its annual rings.

As a stem increases in diameter the older, more central wood no longer conducts water. Its xylem cells become clogged with resin, gum, and other deposits. These deposits give the wood a dark color. Such hard, dark, inactive wood is called *heartwood*. The active, lighter, functional wood is called *sapwood*. The heartwood is nonconducting, but it still serves to support the tree.

Cambium　It forms during the first growing season and is responsible for the secondary growth of xylem and phloem. During each season of growth, the cambium forms more xylem, which increases the diameter of the stem. On its outer edge the vascular cambium forms new phloem also. The new phloem crushes and replaces the older phloem. Phloem, therefore, does not accumulate year after year.

Bark　The active phloem may occupy somewhat more than half the thickness of the bark. If the phloem is cut all the way around the tree, the tree will die. This procedure is called **girdling.** It is sometimes used to kill unwanted trees. This was done by early colonists in order to clear fields. The tree dies because the phloem can no longer supply food to

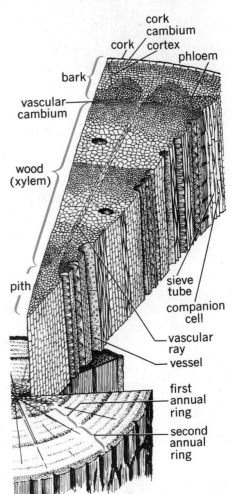

24–11 | The tissues of a three-year-old dicotyledonous stem.

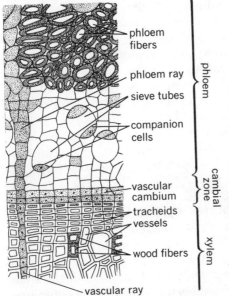

24–12 | A portion of a cross section of a woody stem in the region of the vascular cambial zone. Cells formed by division of cambium cells grow and differentiate into xylem cells on one side of the cambium layer and phloem cells on the other.

its roots. The roots then die of starvation. Animals often girdle trees. Since the inner bark transports food, it is this layer that insects and gnawing animals use for food.

Outside the phloem the next layer of bark is the *cortex.* It can be a fairly thick layer in young stems. Sometimes its cells have chlorophyll so that the cortex appears green when the thin epidermis is peeled away.

The *cork cambium* is a layer of meristematic cells. The cork cells build up a thick layer on the outer side of the stem. The cork cells soon die and become air-filled pockets. **Cork keeps water and gases from leaving the stem tissue. It protects the inner stem from insects, fungi, and other parasites. It also protects the stem from physical damage and injury from low temperatures.** A thick cork layer may give a tree some protection against fire. As weather wears away the outer cork, the cork cambium produces new cork cells.

Dicotyledonous Stems

Plants with woody stems are in the class *Dicotyledonae.* These trees can live hundreds of years. **The stems of herbaceous, or fleshy, dicots such as clover, buttercups, and beans live only a short time.** This is because their vascular cambium is active only a few months, so that only a small amount of secondary tissue is formed before the stem dies. Herbaceous stems, therefore, are rather soft, with tissues similar to the primary tissues of most woody trees and shrubs. The typical herbaceous dicot stem contains a large central area of pith: large, thin-walled storage cells. The xylem and phloem are confined to vascular bundles (strands) which run the length of the stem. They are arranged in a circular pattern around the pith. A thin layer of cambium separates the xylem and phloem within each bundle. The xylem is always on the inside, close to the pith, and the phloem is on the outside of the cambium. Rapid division of cambium cells lying between the vascular bundles results in a complete ring of cambium tissues linking the vascular bundles.

Outside the ring of vascular bundles is the cortex. The cortex cells often contain chloroplasts and carry on photosynthesis. The epidermis is usually very thin rather than corky and thick.

Monocotyledonous Stems

The corn stem is typical of a plant of the class *Monocotyledonae.* It differs from the stem of an herbaceous dicotyledon in several ways. **The fibrovascular bundles of monocotyledons are scattered throughout the stem. There is no clearly defined cortex.** It also lacks cambium.

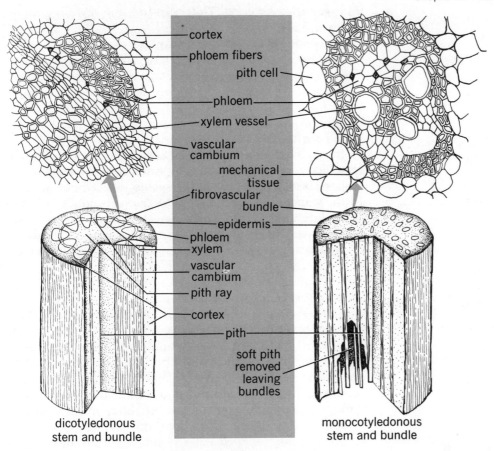

cortex

phloem fibers

pith cell

phloem

xylem vessel

vascular cambium

mechanical tissue

fibrovascular bundle

epidermis

phloem

xylem

vascular cambium

pith ray

cortex

pith

soft pith removed leaving bundles

dicotyledonous stem and bundle

monocotyledonous stem and bundle

24-13 | Compare and contrast the sections of the herbaceous dicotyledonous (bean) stem and fibrovascular bundle with those of the herbaceous monocotyledonous (corn) stem and bundle.

The corn stem is covered by a thick-walled epidermis. Just beneath the epidermis lies a thin layer of sclerenchyma cells. These add strength and hardness to the outer region.

In these stems, pith is the most abundant tissue. Many fibrovascular bundles are scattered throughout the pith. A ring of thick-walled sclerenchyma cells surrounds the whole bundle.

Since monocotyledonous stems do not have a vascular cambium, their growth in diameter is limited. So, this kind of stem does not allow the plant to develop into a tree form as do many dicots. A few monocots, such as palms, are tree-like. Their stems are slender and are composed of strengthening tissues unlike the xylem of dicots.

The Winter Twig

One of the most outstanding features is the shield-shaped *leaf scars.* The leaf scars mark the places on the twig where

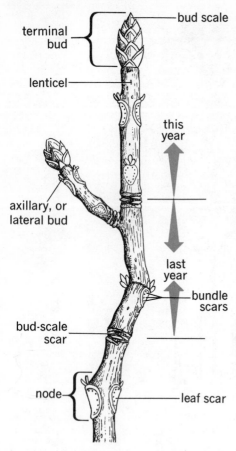

24-14 | The external structure of a woody stem.

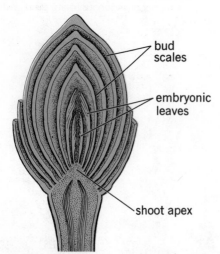

24-15 | A longitudinal section through the terminal bud of a woody plant.

last year's leaves grew. They also mark a *node,* a growth region, on a stem.

By looking closely at a leaf scar, you can see tiny bumps, or dark dots, within the scar. These are the **bundle scars.** They mark the place where the vascular bundles entered the petiole, where the leaf attached to the stem. The shape of the leaf scars and the arrangement of their bundle scars are unique for each species of plant. These features are often used to help identify a plant.

Immediately above each leaf scar is a tiny bud. This is an *axillary,* or **lateral bud. The buds contain embryonic structures which emerge in the spring.** These buds are not all the same. Some produce leaves, some produce flowers. Some lateral buds will form new branches. Some buds, called *mixed buds,* will produce shoots, leaves and flowers.

By looking at the overall arrangement of the leaf scars on the stem, you can tell the arrangement of next spring's leaves. For example, some leaves grow in opposite pairs. Others grow in a spiral pattern around the stem.

The **terminal bud** is the end, or top, bud on the twig. The terminal bud, like the other buds, is covered by **bud scales.** These hard scales are actually modified leaves. They protect the inside of the bud from drying out and from winter ice. At the center of the terminal bud are an embryonic stem and leaves. If you cut a terminal bud lengthwise through the middle, you can see the different parts of the embryonic stem. At the tip of the stem, deep inside the bud scales, is a cone-shaped mass of meristematic tissue, the *shoot apex.* It is here that young cells divide rapidly at the beginning of the growing season, when buds enlarge.

When growth occurs in the spring, the bud scales will drop away and leave a scar that goes completely around the stem. This is called the *terminal bud scale scar.* **By measuring the distance between two bud scale scars, you can tell how much a stem grew in any particular year.**

The shoot growing from a terminal bud makes the stem longer. Shoots from some lateral buds form branches. The terminal bud grows more than lateral buds. This is called **apical dominance.** The terminal bud thus maintains its position of being farthest out on the stem during each growing season.

Modified Stems

Not all stems are upright and leaf-bearing. Underground stems called **rhizomes** grow horizontally through the soil. Most rhizomes are thick and fleshy and are used by the plant to store starch. Rhizomes produce erect, leaf-bearing branches and roots at their nodes all along their length. One rhizome can give rise to many plants.

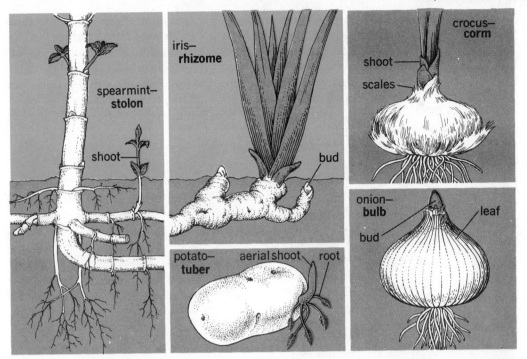

spearmint—
stolon

shoot—

iris—
rhizome

bud

potato—
tuber

aerial shoot   root

crocus—
corm

shoot—

scales—

onion—
bulb

leaf

bud

24–16 | Five types of modified stems. Why are they stems rather than roots?

The **stolon** is a slender, modified stem that grows into the air and then arcs, or curves, downward. When it touches the ground, it sends down roots and establishes a new plant. Some plants, such as strawberries and crabgrass, can reproduce and spread very rapidly this way. A swollen area of a stolon is called a **tuber.**

A **corm** is a short, thick, underground stem enclosed in several thin scale leaves. Its fleshy tissues store food. In some plants a corm grows a new aerial shoot every growing season. In others, such as the gladiolus, a corm grows only one aerial shoot in the plant's lifetime. During the growing season lateral buds at the nodes produce new corms that will grow during the next season.

Another kind of modified stem is a **bulb.** A typical example of a bulb is an onion. The bulb consists of a short central stem and bud surrounded by layers of thick fleshy leaves. The leaves contain stored food. In the spring the bud and stem use this food for growth.

Summary

You may think of a plant as growing *up*, but actually it grows in two directions, both up and down. The tips of the roots and the tips of the stems are the areas where plants increase in length.

These growth areas form specialized tissues. Though root tissues develop somewhat differently than stem tissues do, the vascular tissues of root and stem are continuous with one another. They form the supporting tissues and the food- and water-conducting tissues of the plant. Xylem carries water and dissolved minerals from the soil up to the highest branches and leaves. Phloem carries dissolved foods from the leaves down to the roots and to other regions, such as the seeds and fruits.

Biologically Speaking

primary root	xylem	girdling
taproot	phloem	cortex
secondary root	vascular cambium	cork
fibrous root	secondary tissue	leaf scar
root cap	cork cambium	node
meristematic region	aerial root	bundle scar
elongation region	adventitious root	lateral bud
maturation region	prop root	terminal bud
root hair	climbing root	bud scale
primary tissue	shoot	apical dominance
epidermis	pith	rhizome
cortex region	wood	stolon
vascular cylinder	cambium	tuber
endodermis	bark	corm
pericycle	vascular ray	bulb

Questions for Review

1. Describe the difference between primary and secondary root tissue.
2. Describe taproot and fibrous root systems.
3. List the primary tissues of a root, from outside to inside, and give the function of each.
4. Give some examples of adventitious roots.
5. Distinguish between terminal and lateral buds.
6. How can you tell how much a certain twig grew last year?
7. Describe two branching habits related to apical dominance.
8. Name the bark tissues of a woody stem.
9. Explain the role of vascular cambium in the growth of annual rings in a stem.
10. Describe three structural differences between dicotyledonous stems and monocotyledonous stems.
11. Name and describe three types of modified stems.

Applying Concepts

1. Discuss the various advantages of taproot and fibrous root systems.
2. Discuss the reasons why carving initials in a tree might kill the tree.

25

Water Relations in Plants

A **DESCRIBE** the importance of water to plants.
B **DEFINE** the terms loam, topsoil, and humus.
C **EXPLAIN** how water and minerals are absorbed and transported in plants.
D **DESCRIBE** how food is transported in plants.
E **DESCRIBE** turgor pressure and its function in plants.

25–1 | What determines the type of plant life in an area? *(Stephen J. Krasemann, Peter Arnold)*

The Water Cycle in Relation to Plants

Water maintains the life-supporting relationships plants have with two very different environments: the soil and the atmosphere. This relationship can be thought of as a cycle.

Water vapor in the atmosphere enters the soil as rain. Minerals in the soil are dissolved in groundwater, which then enters the bodies of plants. This water unites the soil with the plants. As the water passes through plants, it performs a wide number of chemical and physical functions. The cycle is complete when water leaves the plant as water vapor and returns to the atmosphere.

Soil and Water

Soil is a mixture of mineral particles and organic particles. Water and air are in the spaces between the particles. Most soil also contains a large community of living organisms. These include bacteria, molds and other fungi, protozoa, and a great variety of worms, bugs, and other animals.

Many of these animals aerate the soil. They also make the soil more fertile by adding organic wastes. Nitrogen-fixing bacteria make the nutrient nitrogen available to plants.

Soil texture is determined by the nature and size of the mineral particles in the soil. These particles can be anything from large gravel to sand, silt, or clay. Often the different particles are mixed to form a soil called **loam.** Loam is valuable for growing crops. The best loam contains about 40 percent sand, 40 percent silt, and 20 percent clay.

Much of the organic matter found in soil lies in the upper region, called **topsoil.** Topsoil is made of decaying roots and soil organisms, plus the decayed bodies of plants and animals on the soil surface. This decaying organic matter is called **humus.**

The spaces between the soil particles are important because they help make soil suitable for plants. Sandy soils have large spaces. Water passes through this soil rapidly. Clay soils are packed closely, with small spaces. Water moves very slowly through clay. Organic matter mixed with the mineral particles loosens the soil and increases the number of spaces.

Most of the water that sinks into the soil passes through the spaces between the soil particles. Eventually, it gets down to the water table. This is the level at which water is standing in the ground. It is usually too far down for plants to reach.

The small spaces around soil particles often hold water. This is called **capillary water.** Following a rain, capillary water moves through these spaces from the higher to the lower regions in soil. As the soil dries, the capillary water moves up again into the dried-out region. Even when the surface of the soil is dry, quite a lot of capillary water remains in the spaces around soil particles. This is the water that roots can absorb.

Typical land plants are rooted in the soil and extend their branches and leaves into the atmosphere. Roots of some plants help keep soil particles in place so that the soil is not washed away by moving water.

Plants and Water

Water performs a wide variety of functions in plants as well as in other organisms. When plants undergo photosynthesis, water molecules supply the hydrogen that combines with carbon dioxide to make sugar. The oxygen of the water molecules forms oxygen gas during photosynthesis. This oxygen is used to break down the sugar and supply energy to plant cells. Sugars, amino acids, hormones, minerals, gases, and other substances are transported throughout the plant in a water solution. Most important, water is the

topsoil:
humus, minerals,
rock particles

subsoil:
leached minerals,
rock particles

soil material:
lies in solid
bedrock

25-2 | A soil profile. The topsoil and subsoil are called true soil. Water cannot penetrate bedrock and so it builds up forming a saturated region, the water table.

medium in which all of the chemical reactions of life occur. **Because water has so many functions in different parts of the plant, plants have developed mechanisms for transporting large quantities of water.**

Water is so important that the amount of rainfall in an area determines what types of plants can grow there. In dry environments plants must conserve water. It is the crucial factor needed to turn many deserts into groves of fruit trees or vegetable farms.

Absorption

Root hairs are special projections from the epidermal cells of roots. **The main function of root hairs is to absorb water.** These long, delicate, fingerlike projections grow between soil particles, where capillary water is available. The walls of root hair cells are very thin. Water can pass freely through the cell walls and membranes to enter the cytoplasm of the root hairs.

Salts from rocks dissolved in water form mineral ions such as potassium, calcium, magnesium, and phosphorus. **These minerals are used in plants for the processes of photosynthesis, respiration, and cell division.**

How Roots Absorb Water

Water in the cytoplasm of root hairs contains large amounts of dissolved minerals, sugars, amino acids, and other substances. In general, the soil has a greater concentration of water than it has dissolved minerals. Water, therefore, flows by osmosis from the soil into the root hairs. Osmosis is the passive movement of water discussed in Chapter 6. Because the movement is passive, the plant does not have to use energy in the process.

Cells of the root cortex also contain a large amount of dissolved substances, so they, too, take in water by osmosis. Once in the cortex, the water flows easily through the cell walls of the cortex to the xylem tubes deeper in the root. The water would stop flowing if the root filled with water. However, as water enters the root hairs on the outside of the root, water moves up xylem tubes on the inside of the root. The movement of water is continuous. Pressure is created by the movement of water molecules in the process of osmosis. This is called *osmotic pressure.*

How Roots Absorb Minerals

The concentration of minerals is less in the surrounding groundwater than in the root hairs. Mineral ions, therefore, do not move simply from the soil water into the root hairs

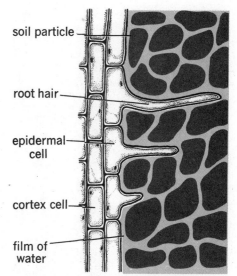

soil particle

root hair

epidermal cell

cortex cell

film of water

25-3 | Water is absorbed by the root hair by osmosis. Some form of active absorption, which involves the use of energy to absorb water, is probably also used by the root hairs or the cortex cells.

as do water molecules. The root hairs absorb dissolved minerals from soil water by **active transport.**

Active transport is a process in which a cell uses energy to transport, or move, another substance from one place to another. Oxygen and high-energy molecules are used in the process.

The cell membrane of the root hairs and young tissue near the root tip appear to be the sites where active transport occurs. The activity of the membrane seems to determine which ions are transported into the cells and at what rate. Once the mineral ions are inside the root hairs, active transport is also used by the cortex cells to move the minerals into the xylem tubes.

Translocation

Inside the xylem tubes dissolved minerals are lifted with water from the root and distributed to all parts of the plant. The movement of water, minerals, and food within a plant is called **translocation.**

Water Movement Up the Stem

The function of the xylem is to conduct water from roots to leaves. The conducting tubes are either **vessels** or **tracheids.** Both are hollow, nonliving tubes of microscopic diameter. Vessels are arranged somewhat like packed soda straws placed end to end. Tracheids are arranged so that one overlaps the other. **Both vessels and tracheids provide a series of tubes for water movement.** Vessel elements are more efficient than tracheids in conducting water. Vessels are found only in angiosperms, the flowering plants.

It has been estimated that a single cottonwood tree 45 meters (150 feet) tall can move over 1,800 liters (about 500 gallons) of water from the soil to the atmosphere on a breezy, sunny day. How can a plant lift such large quantities of water to such heights? Several features of plant structure must be understood.

A plant does *not* force water through empty xylem tubes. Water continually fills the xylem tubes from the time they are first formed in a young plant. As the plant grows in height more xylem cells are formed, which makes the column of water grow in height.

When a well-watered plant is cut off close to the ground, water can often be seen flowing from the stump. Nothing in the nonliving xylem tubes can account for the flow. So, what causes this water pressure?

Osmotic pressure caused by water continually entering the root hairs is part of the answer. However, osmotic pres-

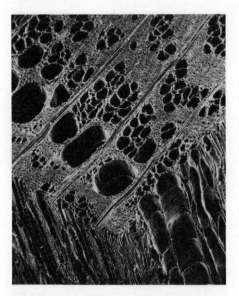

25-4 | A scanning electron micrograph of the wood of an elm. Note the structure of the vessels. (95x) *(Courtesy of the Institute of Paper Chemistry)*

sure alone cannot account for the water pressure observed in cut stems.

The cells of the root are thought to actively transport water just as they do minerals. There is some evidence for an active system of transport in the endodermis cells of the young root. Recall that these cells surround the vascular core containing the xylem. The endodermal cells contain stored food which might be used to supply energy for active transport. Such a system could force water from the cortex into the xylem. The waterproof layer between the walls of endodermal cells could possibly prevent water in the xylem from flowing back into the cortex. The actual chemistry for this active transport is not understood entirely.

Thus both osmotic pressure and active transport could account for the internal pressure within root cells. The pressure of water within the root, *root pressure,* aids in maintaining the column of water and in moving water up the plant.

Capillarity is another possible factor in water conduction. If you place a small tube in a liquid, the liquid in the tube rises higher than the water level of the container. This is because the liquid is attracted by surface forces along the sides of the tube. The smaller the tube's diameter, the higher the liquid rises. In very small capillary tubes, the liquid may go up many centimeters.

Two physical properties of water are also involved in maintaining the column of water and moving it up the xylem. These properties are *adhesion* **and** *cohesion.*

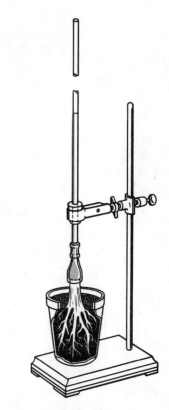

25–5 | Demonstrating root pressure. Water rises a considerable distance in a glass tube attached to the stump of an actively growing plant.

Adhesion

Adhesion *Adhesion* is the force of attraction between *unlike* molecules. Water droplets, for example, cling to your hands because of adhesion. Xylem tubes are extremely small in diameter. Each tube holds relatively little water. The water attracted to the walls of the tube by adhesion helps to maintain the column.

ad = **toward**
hesion = **clinging**

Adhesion aids in supporting the water column all the way up to the leaves. The tubes end in the mesophyll (middle layer) of the leaves. The water then spreads throughout the middle layer and clings to the walls of the mesophyll cells. The water wetting the mesophyll cells and the water in the columns is continuous. Adhesion in the middle layer, therefore, is effective in helping to keep the column from collapsing.

Cohesion

Cohesion *Cohesion* is the attraction between *like* molecules. Cohesion explains why a cup of water can be filled just above the brim without spilling. As pointed out in

co = **together**

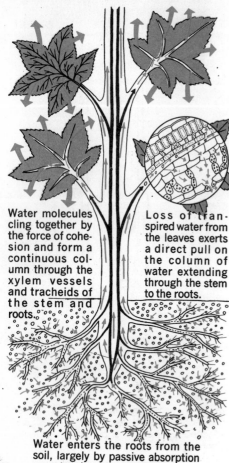

Water molecules cling together by the force of cohesion and form a continuous column through the xylem vessels and tracheids of the stem and roots.

Loss of transpired water from the leaves exerts a direct pull on the column of water extending through the stem to the roots.

Water enters the roots from the soil, largely by passive absorption as water rises through the plant.

25-6 | Trace the water from root hairs, through the plant, and out the leaves.

Chapter 3, water is a polar molecule. One end of the molecule is positive, the other end is negative. Water molecules have a strong attraction to each other. The positive end of one molecule attracts the negative end of another molecule. This attractive force between water molecules helps keep columns of water from breaking apart or collapsing.

Cohesion also helps explain how water *moves up* a plant stem. In the process of evaporation in the leaves, water molecules are pulled away from the upper surface of the columns of water. When water molecules are pulled from the tops of the columns, an upward pull due to cohesion is felt all along the column. This pulling action helps account for water being lifted up the xylem tubes. As water evaporates and escapes from the leaves in the process of *transpiration*, more water moves from the soil into the root hairs. Thus a continuous stream of water flows up through the plant.

Transpiration causes a negative pressure in the water column as water evaporates from the leaf. This **transpiration pull** accounts for more water moving up the stem. Factors that increase evaporation such as higher temperature and wind also cause an increase in transpiration pull.

Translocation of Food

Food, such as dissolved sugars and amino acids, is required by all living plant cells. Food, especially sugars, is made primarily in leaves. **Food dissolved in water is actively transported from the leaves through the phloem throughout the plant.**

Phloem is composed of elongated cells that form sieve tubes. Unlike the xylem's hollow tubes, the phloem is composed of living cells. The cytoplasm of the phloem's sieve tube cells is interconnected so that a continuous column of cells extends from leaves to roots. In the fall of the year the dominant movement of sap, the food dissolved in water, is downward. This food is stored in the roots, stems, or other storage organs of plants during the winter. In the spring the sap in woody plants rises from the food storage areas to the newly forming tissues of the stem. In annuals the food may move up the stems in the fall to be stored in the fruits and seeds.

Active transport plays a role in food translocation. Experiments show that oxygen is utilized in the process of translocation of food. This indicates that active transport is involved in movement of food substances through the plant. Experiments also show that sap moves under pressure through the phloem. However, the exact mechanisms involved in this food translocation are not known.

Turgidity

When water enters a cell by osmosis or active transport, the water vacuole of the cell swells. The water inside the cell exerts a pressure against the rigid cell wall. This water pressure is called **turgor pressure.** It supplies most of the support for herbaceous plants. When flowers or vegetables are picked, they lose turgor. Sprinkling them with water will delay wilting.

Wilting and Loss of Water   Sometimes, on a hot day, the rate of transpiration in a plant may exceed its rate of absorption. This can occur even though the soil is not particularly lacking in water. When this occurs the plant suffers a temporary loss of water. With a decrease in water, the cells lose their turgor pressure, the leaves droop, and the plant loses its firmness. This is called **temporary wilting.**

In the evening, the temperature goes down and the humidity rises. Thus the rate of transpiration decreases and, as a result, the plant builds up its water supply again. Thus temporary wilting does not really damage a plant. However, if it happens often, it can stunt the plant's growth.

Real injury to plants happens when there is not enough soil water, or when the roots are destroyed. For example, roots of plants will rot if they are overwatered. A lack of soil water over a long period of time causes **permanent wilting.** This cannot be corrected by a decrease in the rate of transpiration. Permanent wilting usually occurs during droughts.

25-7 | Plants sometimes lose water through special stomata along the edge of the leaf. It is thought that this water loss is due to root pressure. This process is called *guttation (Walter Dawn)*

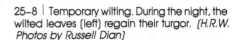

25-8 | Temporary wilting. During the night, the wilted leaves (left) regain their turgor. *(H.R.W. Photos by Russell Dian)*

Summary

Soil, plants, and atmosphere are linked together by water. Water is recycled continually, passing from soil to plants to the air and then back into the soil. Water is the medium in which all of the chemical processes of life occur.

Water carries minerals from the soil to plants. It transports the food that the plants' leaves produce.

Special chemical, physical, and biological forces help move water through plants. Osmotic pressure causes water to flow through root hairs into the roots of plants. A system of active transport pushes water into the xylem vessels. There the forces of adhesion and cohesion help draw it up through the stem to the leaves. The water then leaves the plant through the process of transpiration.

Biologically Speaking

loam	active transport	adhesion
topsoil	translocation	cohesion
humus	vessel	transpiration pull
capillary water	tracheid	turgor pressure
root hair	root pressure	temporary pressure
osmotic pressure	capillarity	temporary wilting
		permanent wilting

Questions for Review

1. What are some of the important plant processes that require water?
2. Explain the importance of soil texture to the growth of plants.
3. What forces are involved in passive water absorption by root hairs?
4. What process is used by a plant's root cells to absorb minerals?
5. List three factors believed to be involved in translocation of water through the xylem of stems.
6. Explain how cohesion and adhesion help in the translocation of water.
7. How is turgor pressure involved in supporting soft plant tissue?
8. Account for temporary wilting of nonwoody plant tissue.

Applying Concepts

1. Discuss the difference between the transport of sap and the transport of water.
2. Compare the conditions under which roots take in water by active and by passive absorption.
3. Heavy equipment is used in logging. What effect might such equipment have on soil?

26–1 | A dwarf plant shown with another plant of the same species.
(© Derek Fell)

Plant Growth and Responses

A **LIST** some environmental factors that affect plant growth.
B **EXPLAIN** photoperiodism and dormancy in plants.
C **LIST** the basic types of plant hormones.
D **DISCUSS** how plant hormones affect plant cells, tissues, and structures.
E **DESCRIBE** the various forms of tropic response.
F **DISTINGUISH** between nastic movement and tropic responses.

Growth

In previous chapters you learned that meristematic tissue is the region of cell division. Plants grow only where meristematic tissue is located. If so, what makes a root grow into the soil and a shoot grow up into the air? Why do some plants develop flowers in the summer and others develop flowers in the fall? There are environmental external and internal factors within the plant that cause these effects.

While considering these effects, it is important to remember that the genes a plant inherits are significant influences in how a plant grows. Within the same species of plant, dwarf varieties grow less under the same environmental conditions that promote good growth in a tall variety.

External Influences on Growth

Plants grow in response to certain environmental factors such as light, temperature, and moisture. Moisture was discussed in Chapter 25. Let's now examine light and temperature as important factors that influence plant growth.

Facts & Figures

In 1630 Johann van Helmont planted a five-pound willow branch in 200 pounds of soil. After five years of a water diet, the plant had gained 164 pounds, and the soil had lost only 2 ounces.

Facts & Figures

Carolus Linnaeus, the Swedish botanist who set up the basis for the classification system used today, could tell the time of day by the different openings and closing of wildflowers such as daisies, primroses, and wild roses.

photo = **light**

26-2 | (top) The flower of the night blooming cactus at night, and (bottom) during the day. (Allan Roberts)

Light Have you ever seen plants that sprout in a basement or under a porch? Such plants, exposed to little or no light, are a pale, whitish yellow. They lack chlorophyll, and their stems are usually abnormally long with leaves that are poorly developed and far apart.

The chemistry and structure of different leaves on the same plant may be affected in different ways by light. The leaves on the tips of branches are exposed to bright light. They contain more sugar because of increased photosynthesis in bright light. Leaves in direct sun usually contain less water and are thicker but smaller than the shaded leaves farther down the stem. They also may have more than one layer of palisade cells, a thicker cuticle, and more conducting tissue. A thicker cuticle and more conducting tissue supply leaves in direct sun with increased water. Since these leaves are exposed they transpire more and therefore lose more water than shaded leaves. Shaded leaves contain more water, less food, and also contain more of the widely spaced mesophyll cells. These leaves also are larger and present more surface area to the light.

Photoperiodism Have you ever noticed the sudden appearance of bright red poinsettia flowers in stores during certain holiday seasons? These flowers are forced to bloom at certain times by artificially controlling the length of time the plants are exposed to light and dark. Actually it is the length of darkness rather than the length of light that stimulates the flowering response. Response of plants to varying periods of light and darkness is *photoperiodism.*

As you may know, the number of hours of daylight and darkness changes with the seasons. On March 21 and September 22, day and night each last exactly 12 hours. In the northern hemisphere, the shortest day of the year is December 21. After that, every day has a few more minutes of light until June 21. Between June 21 and December 21, the daylight hours get shorter.

Many plants produce flowers during the spring or fall, when there is less daylight than in summer. These *short-day plants* include poinsettias, chrysanthemums, ragweeds, most asters, and goldenrod.

Long-day plants grow stems and leaves while there is less daylight. They bloom in late spring and early summer when there is more daylight. Among them are the iris, the hollyhock, clover, beets, and radishes.

A third group of plants are hardly affected by the length of days and nights. First they grow, then they flower, with little response to the photoperiod. These *day-neutral* plants include tomatoes, corn, carrots, zinnias, carnations, marigolds, and daffodils.

Temperature Plant growth and reproduction are influenced also by temperature changes. The days and nights in early spring and fall are cooler on the average than the days and nights of early summer. All plant processes tend to react to variations in temperature. These processes include photosynthesis, translocation, respiration, and transpiration. If temperatures are too low or too high, plant growth will slow or stop. Somewhere between is an *optimum temperature* which is best for plant growth. **Most plants grow best between 10°C and 38°C (50° and 100.4°F).** Plants may survive brief periods of temperatures above or below the optimum, but long exposure to temperature extremes will eventually stunt growth and may even kill them.

Dormancy in Plants

In many parts of the world there are seasons when temperature, water supply, or light is unsuitable for growing. Many plants then become inactive, or *dormant.* Woody plants stay alive since their tissues are protected by bark or the scales on winter buds. Herbaceous perennials die above the ground, but their underground parts survive in a dormant state. Annual plants die, but their seeds will live to grow in the next season.

Internal Influences on Growth

Plant growth is affected not only by external factors such as light and temperature. **Growth is also regulated by the internal influence of *hormones.*** Hormones are chemical substances produced within the plant. Their production may be influenced by external conditions. This interplay of environment and hormones make growth-control mechanisms complex. Hormones are produced in certain parts of the plant and then translocated to other parts where they influence the division, elongation, and maturation (specialization) of cells.

Three types of plant hormones are *auxins, gibberellins,* and *cytokinins.*

Auxins The most widely studied plant hormones are called *auxins.* They mostly cause cells to get longer and larger. They also act in the development of flowers, fruits, and seeds. Auxins are really *growth regulators* since they may either speed up or slow down the growth process. Large amounts of auxins are produced in growing parts of plant organs. These include the tips of shoots and roots, young leaves, flowers and fruits, and in cambium cells. Auxin is then translocated from these places to other parts of the plant.

Different parts of the plant react differently to auxins.

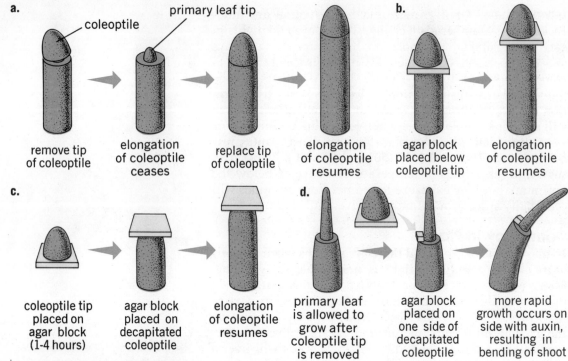

a.

coleoptile

primary leaf tip

remove tip of coleoptile

elongation of coleoptile ceases

replace tip of coleoptile

elongation of coleoptile resumes

b.

agar block placed below coleoptile tip

elongation of coleoptile resumes

c.

coleoptile tip placed on agar block (1-4 hours)

agar block placed on decapitated coleoptile

elongation of coleoptile resumes

d.

primary leaf is allowed to grow after coleoptile tip is removed

agar block placed on one side of decapitated coleoptile

more rapid growth occurs on side with auxin, resulting in bending of shoot

26–3 | Four experiments demonstrating the presence and action of auxin in the tip of an oat coleoptile. The coleoptile is a sheath like structure covering the shoot of grass seedlings. (a) The tip of the coleoptile is removed and no further growth occurs. (b) Auxin can pass through nonliving material and still exert an effect. (c and d) Agar absorbs auxin and exerts an effect on the coleoptile.

A relatively high concentration of auxin seems to stimulate stem growth but inhibit root growth.

Auxins are responsible for *apical dominance,* mentioned in Chapter 24. In apical dominance auxins influence the overall branching pattern of a plant. Auxins produced in the terminal buds of stems move downward and inhibit the growth of lateral buds. Removal of the terminal bud allows lateral buds to grow, causing more branching and making a plant appear more bushy.

Commercial Uses of Auxin Preparations   The most common weed killer used in the United States is a synthetic auxin called 2,4D. This compound is similar to a natural auxin but has chlorine atoms added to the molecule. Such compounds are called chlorinated hydrocarbons, and these do not exist as hormones in nature. 2,4D is used on lawns to kill broad-leaved plants such as dandelions. The dandelions absorb the compound, develop abnormally, and die. The narrow-leaved plants (monocots) such as grass are unaffected by this compound. Since corn is a monocot, 2,4D is used to control weeds in corn fields.

Other types of auxins are sprayed on fruit trees to prevent fruit from falling off before it is mature. This makes it possible to harvest the fruit all at one time. The auxins work by preventing the *abscission layer* from forming.

Remember that the abscission layer is also formed across the base of the leaf petiole in the fall. This causes trees to drop their leaves.

Ordinarily, pollination and fertilization must take place before fruit and seed develop. The use of certain auxins can stimulate the fruit development without pollination and fertilization. By using auxins, growers have produced seedless watermelons, cucumbers, and tomatoes. Some seedless fruits, however, such as bananas and navel oranges, develop naturally without either pollination or the use of auxins.

Gibberellins   This group of growth hormones was discovered in Japan when fungus-infected rice plants grew abnormally long. In 1935 the substance causing the abnormal height was isolated and named *gibberellin*, after the fungus. Later it was discovered that other gibberellins are made by more complex plants.

Gibberellins, like auxins, promote an increase in the length of plants. They also promote cambium activity in woody plants. Gibberellins may act together with auxins.

Cytokinins   *Cytokinins* are another group of plant-regulating substances, usually regarded as hormones. Some biologists disagree, however, because cytokinins are not translocated after they are produced.

While auxins and gibberellins cause cell enlargement and development, cytokinins influence cell division.

26-4 | Effect of gibberellin on fruit growth. These grapes are larger than "normal" grapes using gibberellin. *(Abbott Laboratories)*

Careers

Horticulturists work in greenhouses, orchards, or gardens. They grow plants and usually improve plants to increase crop yield and quality.

Training beyond high school is usually necessary either at a vocational school or junior college.

26-5 | Plants can be grown to fit almost any specification. What means does the horticulturist have to grow plants larger? smaller? fuller? *(Courtesy Brooklyn Botanic Garden. HRW photo by Ken Karp)*

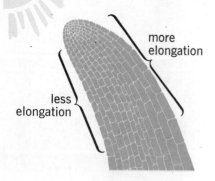

sun

more elongation

less elongation

26-6 | Why did this shoot grow toward the light?

Plant Responses to Stimuli

So far, you have been learning about plant growth. Growth is a general response to various internal and external factors. Now some particular plant responses to specific environmental stimuli will be discussed.

Tropisms

A directional growth response that is directly related to an environmental stimulus is called a **tropism** (TROPE-iz'm). External stimuli include light, gravity, contact, water, and chemicals. A tropic response is said to be *positive* if growth is toward the stimulus. It is said to be *negative* if growth is away from the stimulus. Tropic responses are growth reactions that are related to plant survival and adaptation to environmental conditions.

Phototropism A familiar tropism is **phototropism** (foe-TOE-troe-PIS'M), the response of plants to light. This tropism is seen when a plant on a windowsill bends toward the light. This is a *positive tropic response*. The stem bends because of uneven cell elongation. The cells on the shaded side tend to elongate more than those on the bright side. This causes the stem to grow unevenly and bend.

How does this happen? The most common explanation is that the auxin is translocated away from the light to the shady side. High concentration of auxins causes cells of stems to elongate which causes the shady side to grow more. This uneven growth bends the stem toward light.

Roots show *negative phototropism*. Consider a germinating seed that is lying on the soil surface. The root emerges. One side of the root will be exposed to light, the other side, next to the soil, will be more shaded. Auxins are more concentrated on the dark side. The cells on the dark side will then be slow in growing because high concentrations of auxins inhibit elongation of root cells. This is a negative reaction to the auxin. The cells on the light side will elongate normally. The root will therefore bend away from the light and toward the soil.

Geotropism

Geotropism Gravity also affects stems and roots in opposite ways. We call this reaction **geotropism** (jee-OH-troe-PIS'M). If you plant a seed upside down, the root will still grow down and then shoot will grow up. Why? Again it is the effect of auxins.

Suppose a seed is placed on its side and it germinates and grows in the dark. Which way will the stem and root grow? (See figure 26-8.)

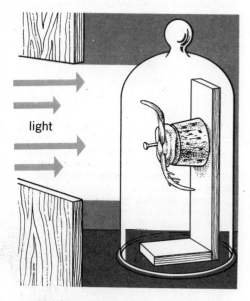

light

26-7 | An explanation of the role of auxins in controlling phototropic responses. Auxin accumulates on the shaded side of the plant. Here, the auxins promote normal cell elongation in the stem but prevent normal cell elongation in the root. Cells on the lighted side of the stem fail to elongate normally and the stem grows toward the light source. Root cells on the shaded side are prevented from elongating so the lighted side grows more. This makes the root grow away from light.

As auxins are secreted in the roots and the shoot, gravity makes them gather on the lower side. The underside of the stem will grow faster because of the higher auxin level, making it bend upward. On the lower side of the root, though, the auxins have a reverse effect. The root cells with the auxins will not elongate as much as the cells on the upper side. This growth bends the root down. Of course, if both root and stem are growing vertically, the auxin distribution is equal on both of their sides.

Thigmotropism   *Thigmotropism* (thig-MOE-troe-PIZ'm) is the positive response of a plant structure to contact or touch. The tendrils of climbing plants curl around any object they touch. When a tendril touches an object, would the auxins concentrate on the touch side or the opposite side of the tendril? They would concentrate on the side opposite the touch, so the tendril would curve around the object.

Nastic Movements

Other kinds of plant reactions to external stimuli are called **nastic movements.** These are different from tropic responses in several ways. First, nastic movements are independent of the direction of the stimulus. Nastic movements are seen in the way flowers or leaves close at certain times of the day. They may also occur when the temperature reaches a certain point. Morning glories open in the morning. When dusk brings cooler temperatures, the flowers close until sunrise. The flowers of the night-blooming cereus, a cactus, do just the opposite. They stay closed all day but open to the darkness of evening.

Nastic movements are *turgor movements*. Tropic responses are growth movements. Tropic responses are slow, often taking days for a visible change to occur. Nastic movements happen quickly, within a few minutes or hours. Also, they are reversible; a flower that closes will open again. Tropic growth responses do not reverse. Once the plant has grown a certain way, those cells do not change.

A good example of an almost immediate nastic response to touch is shown by the plant *Mimosa pudica*. This sensitive plant has compound leaves. The leaflets are normally in the horizontal position. If a leaf is touched, a reaction occurs within three to five seconds. The stimulated leaflets will fold upward and the petiole droops. After having folded, the leaflets return to the original position as turgor returns to normal.

The mechanism is very complex. Epidermal hairs receive the touch stimulus. Sudden loss of turgor causes the petiole to droop.

26–8 | An explanation of the role of auxins in controlling geotropic responses. Auxin accumulates on the lower side of the plant. Because cells on the upper side of the stem fail to elongate normally and because cells on the lower side elongate more than average, the stem grows upward. By contrast, the excess accumulation of auxin on the lower side of the root inhibits normal elongation. Cells on the upper side of the root elongate more normally. The result of this difference in growth makes the root turn downward.

26–9 | Nastic responses to touch in the sensitive plant. (top) Normal position of the leaves and leaflets. (bottom) Position of the same leaves and leaflets after they had responded to a touch stimulus. *(Walter Dawn)*

Another example of this turgor is the Venus' flytrap. As you learned in Chapter 23, its leaves will close suddenly to trap an insect in a nastic response. Similarly, the changes you can see in flowers such as sunflowers, when they "follows the sun," are nastic and caused by turgor changes.

Summary

Environmental factors have a great deal of influence on how a plant grows and adapts to its immediate surroundings. Environmental factors such as light, temperature, gravity, touch, and water affect plants through the growth substances called hormones. Three general types of hormones are well known. They are *auxins, gibberellins,* and *cytokinins.* By understanding how these hormones affect cells, we can explain some of the simple responses that are observed in plants. These include how a plant grows towards light, why roots grow down and stems up, and why a tendril curls around a fencepost.

Biologically Speaking

photoperiodism	auxin	phototropism
optimum temperature	gibberellin	geotropism
dormant	cytokinin	thigmotropism
hormone	tropism	nastic movement

Questions for Review

1. Name several environmental factors that influence plant growth and development.
2. Give examples of how flowering plants exhibit photoperiodism.
3. What are day-neutral plants?
4. What is meant by the term *optimum temperature* for plants?
5. Describe the various ways that some plants survive periods of dormancy.
6. List three groups of plant-growth hormones.
7. Name three different tropic responses in plants.
8. Distinguish between a nastic movement and a tropic response.

Applying Concepts

1. How do auxins relate to tropisms?
2. Discuss experimental evidence that auxin is secreted near the tip of an oat coleoptile and translocated to the tissue below the tip.
3. Explain several ways in which our knowledge of auxins has benefited agriculture and other businesses.

Plant Reproduction

A **DESCRIBE** vegetative reproduction in plants.

B **LABEL** the parts of a flower and know their functions.

C **LIST** some agents of pollination.

D **EXPLAIN** the process of fertilization.

E **DESCRIBE** the formation of a seed.

F **LIST** the characteristics of different types of fruits.

G **EXPLAIN** how germination occurs and list the stages of germination.

27–1 | How are flowers adapted to their one function? *(Animals Animals, © D. R. Specker)*

Reproduction in Flowering Plants

The fact that plants cannot move around as animals do presents certain problems in reproduction. Flowers are the reproductive structures of angiosperms, the flowering plants. Elaborate systems of pollination have developed to bring sperm and egg together for fertilization. Other systems and structures enable the seeds and fruits to be dispersed at a distance from the parent plant.

As with other plants you have studied in this unit, angiosperms have an asexual reproductive stage as well as a sexual reproductive stage. In the process of asexual reproduction part of the root, stem, or leaf becomes detached and develops into a new plant.

Vegetative Propagation

Asexual reproduction occurs during a plant's growing stage, or *vegetative* stage. The process therefore is called *vegetative reproduction.* .It is, however, more commonly referred to as **vegetative propagation.**

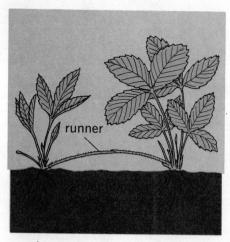

27-2 | Vegetative propagation in the strawberry plant.

Annual plants do all their vegetative growing in a single season. Perennials keep adding new vegetation year after year. So, vegetative reproduction occurs mostly in woody and herbaceous perennials.

The strawberry is a good example of natural vegetative propagation. The parent plant forms modified stems, or stolons, called runners, that grow along the ground. The tips of the runners form shoots and *adventitious* roots that develop in an uncommon area of the plant. These give rise to new plants. A single parent plant can produce many new plants in a single season. In this way one plant may create a whole strawberry patch by itself.

Sometimes aerial shoots rise from horizontal stems growing underground near the surface. The small tree or shrub of the sumac plant does this. It produces clusters of new plants from its own rootlike structures. Trees such as the osage orange, lilac, and white poplar produce whole groves in this way.

A few kinds of plants exhibit an unusual type of vegetative propagation. Bryophyllum plants develop new plants along their leaf edges. Such new plants form between the coarse teeth of the thick, fleshy leaves. The plantlets drop to the ground and continue to grow. Because this kind of reproduction is both unusual and interesting to watch, people often have bryophyllum as a houseplant.

Artificial Vegetative Propagation

People have learned to propagate many plants vegetatively. If you grow plants, you know that you can cut off part of a plant, put it in water, and grow another entire plant from it. These parts of plants, whether they are leaves, roots, or stems, are called *cuttings.*

Cuttings These pieces can be from several centimeters to 30 centimeters (1 foot) or more long. In the case of woody perennials, the cutting should have several nodes and lateral buds or leaves. The lower end of the cutting is buried in damp sand or loose soil. The cutting is successful if it produces adventitious roots of its own within several weeks. You can propagate many woody plants such as pussy willows this way.

Newer methods have been developed to make cuttings even more reliable. Growth-regulating hormones, particularly auxins, are sometimes used to start cell division and to make roots develop.

Layering Many forms of *layering* are used in artificial propagation of many plants. In one method, a rose stem is bent to the ground. All but the tip is covered with sand or soil. The buried part will grow roots, and a stem will grow up from the tip. When the new plant is strong, it is cut away from the parent rose bush and planted in another place. This process is called *simple layering*. It is useful for growing plants with strong roots, such as climbing roses.

Mound layering is used in propagating woody shrubs. The shrub is cut back to allow more growth of the lateral buds. The lower part of the shrub is covered with a mound of soil. New stems and adventitious roots grow from the buds near the base of the shrub. These can be removed and set out alone.

Grafting One of the most widely used methods of propagating woody plants is by **grafting.** Grafting is really splicing two stems together. The rooted part is called the *stock*. The cutting that is joined to the stock is called the *scion*. The scion is the plant the grower wants to propagate by joining it to a healthy stock.

A graft is successful only when the vascular cambiums of the stock and the scion are placed in contact with each other. Also, the graft must be made when the scion is dormant. This allows the cambium to unite before shoots develop. For this reason grafts are usually prepared during the winter.

Budding *Budding* is a specialized form of grafting. A bud is used as the scion instead of a branch. A strong bud, together with the surrounding bark and its active cambium, is removed. The bark of the stock is loosened by a T-shaped cut. Then the piece of bark attached to the bud is slipped into the cut. The vascular cambiums of scion and stock are united. The stock is wrapped with tape to hold the bud and prevent drying.

Budding is usually done in the summer or fall, depending on the species. When a shoot grows from the bud in the spring, the stock is cut off above the spot where the bud was added. The growing terminal shoot is then the graft.

Pears, plums, apples, and peaches are all produced commercially by budding. Seeds of these fruits do not always develop into the same quality. In order to insure a constant high-quality crop, vegetative propagation is the favorable method. In woody perennials, budding is an easier form of propagation than cuttings.

Sexual Reproduction

Plants can propagate by vegetative means during the growing season. However, in order for most species to survive, they must reproduce sexually. Sexual reproduction results

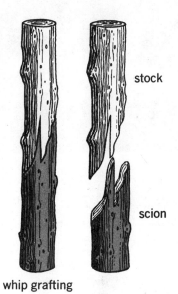

whip grafting

27-3 | Grafting. The cambium of stock and scion must be in contact.

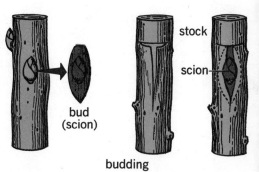

budding

27-4 | Budding. Tape is usually added so that the bud does not dry out.

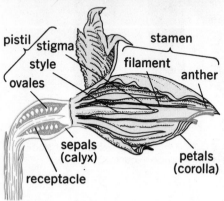

27–5 | Flower parts of a complete flower. Compare the cross-section of the flower at the top to the labeled drawing of the same flower below. *(top: G. R. Roberts)*

in seeds, and seeds carry genetic traits into the next generation.

You may recall that the diploid, or 2n, number represents a complete set of chromosomes. Chromosomes carry the hereditary material, genes, of the organism. Certain diploid cells located in the reproductive organs divide by meiosis to produce sex cells, sperm or egg. The sex cells contain nuclei with a haploid, or n, number of chromosomes. Sexual reproduction always involves the union of two haploid (n) cells, one male cell and one female cell, to form a diploid (2n) zygote.

Seeds usually have combinations of traits from different parent plants. Variations come about through the different recombinations of chromosomes and genes during the union of gametes. These variations, no matter how slight, may adapt a species to conditions in a changing environment.

Flowers are specialized for the single purpose of sexual reproduction. They do not have meristematic tissue to continue the growth of the shoot. However, flowers do start the development that leads to the formation of fruit and seed.

Flowers vary greatly in appearance. Some are large and colorful, like roses, lilies, and tulips. Other flowers, like those of grains, grass, and some trees, are not usually noticed, but they still contain the same reproductive organs. The essential parts of flowers are not the bright petals.

Flower Parts

Typical flowers, such as tulips or apple blossoms, have many parts. Some of these parts are *nonessential.* They are not involved directly in the process of reproduction. Flowers all grow from a flower stalk whose tip is the **receptacle.** The outer ring of floral parts is formed by several leaflike **sepals** (SEEP'lz). They are usually green. All the sepals form the **calyx** (KAY-licks). The sepals protect the rest of the flower in the bud stage. They also help support the other parts when the bud opens.

Inside the calyx is the **corolla** (kuh-RAH-luh), which is usually made of one or more rings of **petals.** The petals are often brightly colored. In some flowers, such as the tulip, both calyx and corolla are the same color. This makes it difficult to tell that both parts are there.

In the center of the flower are the two kinds of *essential* parts directly involved with reproduction. They are the **stamens** and the **pistil.** Each stamen is a slender stalk or filament with a knobby sac at the end called an *anther.* The anther produces colored grains called **pollen,** which contain the male sex cells.

The pistil usually is shaped like a flask. It has a sticky top called a *stigma* to which pollen adheres. Just below the stigma is a slender stalk, the *style*. The swollen base of the pistil contains the *ovary*. Inside the ovary the female sex cells, the *ovules*, are formed. There may be from one to several hundred ovules, depending on the kind of flower. The ovary later develops into a fruit and the ovules become seeds.

Pollen Formation   If you look at a cross section of a developing anther on a large stamen, such as in a lily or tulip, four chambers can clearly be seen. These chambers are called *pollen sacs*. While the flower is developing, each pollen sac is filled with cells with large nuclei. Each nucleus contains a complete set, or diploid (2n) number, of chromosomes.

As the anther grows, each of these cells goes through meiosis forming four cells. Each cell, called a **microspore,** has a haploid number of chromosomes and will eventually become a pollen grain. The nucleus then divides so that each pollen grain has two nuclei. One is the **tube nucleus.** The other is the **generative nucleus.** The wall of the pollen grain thickens to reduce water loss and to protect against damage.

micro = small

There are millions of these pollen grains in each pollen sac. As the anther ripens, the wall between the paired pollen sacs disappears. The pollen grains are ready for dispersal.

Ovule Formation   While pollen grains are forming in the anthers, changes are occurring in the ovary at the base of the pistil. An ovary may contain one or many ovules,

27–6 | The development of pollen grains in an anther.

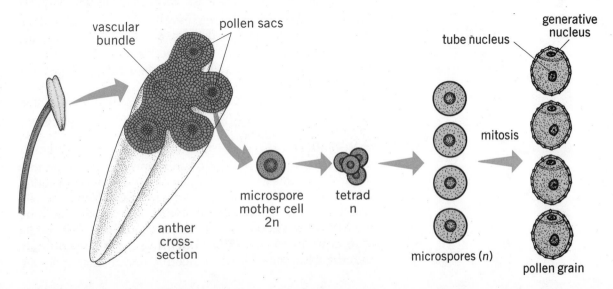

vascular bundle

pollen sacs

anther cross-section

microspore mother cell 2n

tetrad n

microspores (*n*)

mitosis

tube nucleus

generative nucleus

pollen grain

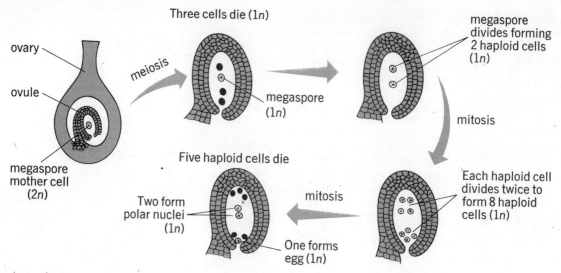

Three cells die (1n)

ovary

ovule

megaspore
mother cell
(2n)

meiosis

megaspore
(1n)

megaspore
divides forming
2 haploid cells
(1n)

mitosis

Each haploid cell
divides twice to
form 8 haploid
cells (1n)

Five haploid cells die

Two form
polar nuclei
(1n)

mitosis

One forms
egg (1n)

27–7 | Development of an ovule within the
ovary at the base of a pistil.

mega = large

depending on the species of plant. Each ovule develops into
a seed after fertilization. Each mature ovule contains a cen-
trally located egg cell.

The formation of an ovule and egg is shown in figure
27–7. The following are the steps of egg development:

- the *megaspore mother cell* divides by meiosis and
  produces four haploid (n) cells. Three of these cells die.
- The surviving haploid cell, the **megaspore,** enlarges and
  becomes an *embryo sac.*
- The haploid nucleus in this large cell divides three times
  to produce eight haploid nuclei.
- The eight nuclei are arranged so that a group of three
  nuclei are at either end of the embryo sac and two nuclei,
  called **polar nuclei,** are in the center.
- The nuclei at each end develop cell membranes and are
  now considered cells.
- One of the three cells closest to the ovule enlarges and
  develops into an egg.

The mature ovule is now ready for pollination and fertilization.

Pollination

Pollination is the transfer of pollen from an anther to a
stigma. Pollen is transferred by wind, insects, or other
agents. Have you ever wondered why some flowers have a
fragrance or are exceptionally beautiful while others are
not? Flowers have colorful petals and fragrances to attract
insects needed to transfer pollen from one flower to another. For example, while collecting nectar from a flower,

pollen clings to a bee. When collecting nectar from another flower, the bee transfers the pollen to the sticky stigma.

Pollen may also be transfered from anther to stigma within the same flower. In this case *self-pollination* occurs. If flowers on two separate plants are involved, it is called *cross pollination.*

Each flower is adapted structurally to its method of pollination. For example, wind pollinated flowers are often in clusters near the ends of branches. Usually there are no petals, and the anthers are extended on long filaments. Even a slight breeze is enough to disperse the pollen. These flowers, like the hayfever-causing ragweed, the willow, and corn, lack the insect-attracting features found in other flowers.

Although it is true that bees are most important in pollination, other insects are also agents in pollination. These insects include certain flies, moths, butterflies, and beetles. The hairy bodies of bees, however, make them especially good pollinators.

The best known bird agent of pollination is the hummingbird. Its long tongue reaches down into the flowers as the bird hovers outside or even enters the large flowers. Pollen on the hummingbird's feathers may then be transfered to other flowers.

Fertilization

What happens after a pollen grain lands on the surface of the pistil's stigma? Follow figure 27–8 on page 335 during the following discussion. First, a chemical from the pistil causes the pollen grain to form a pollen tube that grows into the stigma surface.

Both the tube nucleus and the generative nucleus enter the pollen tube as it grows and advances down the style. On entering the pollen tube the generative nucleus divides by mitosis to form two sperm nuclei. Farthest along the tube is the tube nucleus which is followed by two sperm nuclei. When the tube reaches the opening of the ovule, it digests part of the embryo sac's thin wall. The tip of the tube breaks open, and the two sperm nuclei enter the embryo sac. At this time the tube nucleus disintegrates.

One of the two sperms unites with the egg in fertilization. This produces the fertilized egg, a diploid zygote. The zygote develops into an embryo plant.

The second sperm nucleus also has a function. It unites with the two polar nuclei in the embryo sac to form the **endosperm nucleus.** The endosperm nucleus is a triploid (3n) nucleus. It divides many times and forms a mass of nuclei. Later, thin walls form around each of the nuclei, and the endosperm tissue is formed. The endosperm serves

endo = within

as food-storage and supplies the embryo with nourishment.

While the embryo and endosperm grow and develop, the cells of the outer layers of the ovule develop thick walls. The layers eventually form the outer seed coat. The seed coat protects the embryo and endosperm against water loss and damage. While the ovule forms a seed, the ovary wall aids in developing a fruit.

Alternation of Generations in Flowering Plants

Recall that *alternation of generations* refers to a multicellular diploid (2n) stage alternating with a multicellular haploid (n) stage. The diploid stage, called the *sporophyte*, alternates with the haploid, or *gametophyte*, stage. The moss is a good example of a plant with these two plainly visible stages. In angiosperms the main body of the plant—the roots, stem, leaves, and flowers—makes up the sporophyte generation. All of these tissues are composed of diploid (2n) cells. The male gametophyte is represented by the pollen grain which contains two haploid (n) nuclei. The female gametophyte is the embryo sac. This consists of the egg, five other haploid cells, and two polar nuclei.

You will recall that in lower plants, like certain algae and moss, the gametophyte generation is dominant. It is represented by a prominent body. The sporophyte is reduced. In the complex seed-producing plants, the sporophyte is dominant and the gametophyte generation is reduced to a few cells. The overall evolutionary trend in nature has been toward a more complex sporophyte body and a much reduced gametophyte stage.

From Flower to Fruit and Seed

Fertilization brings a sudden end to the work of the flower. The sepals, petals, and stamens wither. Hormones cause the plant to use all its energy for developing the ovary and the ovules inside it. The ovary and its contents ripen. In many plants, parts like the receptacle or the calyx get larger and become part of the fruit. **So we can define a *fruit* as a ripened ovary, with or without associated parts. A *seed*, though, is a matured ovule enclosed inside the fruit.**

Like flowers, fruits vary in structure. Notice how different the biological meaning of fruit is from the grocery-store word. Some fruits are fleshy such as apples, oranges, tomatoes, and squash. However, kernels of corn, a hickory nut,

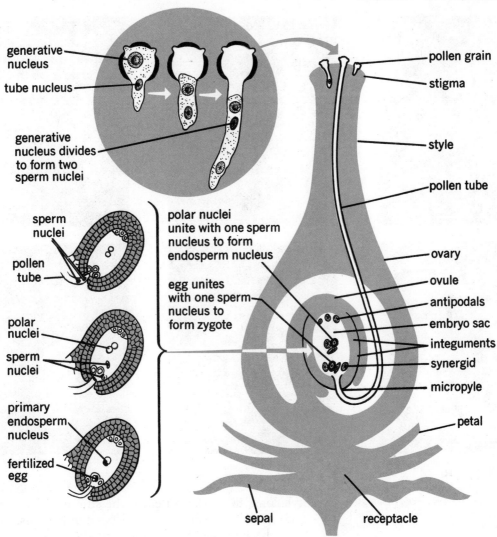

generative nucleus

tube nucleus

generative nucleus divides to form two sperm nuclei

pollen grain

stigma

style

pollen tube

sperm nuclei

pollen tube

polar nuclei unite with one sperm nucleus to form endosperm nucleus

egg unites with one sperm nucleus to form zygote

polar nuclei

sperm nuclei

primary endosperm nucleus

fertilized egg

ovary

ovule

antipodals

embryo sac

integuments

synergid

micropyle

petal

sepal

receptacle

27-8 | Growth of the pollen tube and double fertilization.

beans in a pod, or a burr that sticks to your clothes are fruit just as much as the fleshy, juicy kind.

Seeds

There may be many seeds inside one fruit. **Each seed is made up of a tiny living embryo, stored food, and the seed coats.** The young plant is nourished by the stored food from the time it starts to grow until it can produce its own food by photosynthesis. The food is stored in tissues called *cotyledons.* The division of angiosperms into monocotyledons and dicotyledons is based on how many cotyledons there are in the seed. Monocot plants have one, while dicots have two cotyledons in their seeds.

Not all seeds have the same kinds of food stored in their

mono = one
di = two

27-9 | Development of a peach from flower to fruit. *(a: John Colwell, Grant Heilman; b, c, d: Runk, Schoenberger, Grant Heilman; e: Grant Heilman; f: Robert Barclay, Grant Heilman)*

cotyledons. In a grain of corn, the starch and protein are stored in the endosperm. The cotyledon has oils and proteins. The endosperm fills most of the corn seed. Some seeds have a large endosperm. Some, like the bean, show none at all at maturity.

A Dicot Seed Bean seeds are usually kidney-shaped. The outer seed coat, or *testa,* is smooth. On the concave edge, there is an oval scar called the **hilum** (HILE'm), which marks where the bean was attaced to the pod wall. Near one end of the scar is a tiny pore, the **micropyle.** This was the small opening in the wall of the ovule through which the pollen tube grew.

The bean seed lacks an endosperm. The two large cotyledons that occupy most of the volume of the bean seed are a source of starch as well as proteins and oil. When the seed germinates, the stored food will be used rapidly by the growing embryo.

external

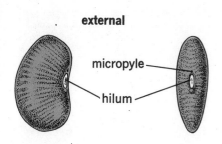

micropyle

hilum

epicotyl

cotyledon scar

hypocotyl

radicle

seed coat

cotyledons

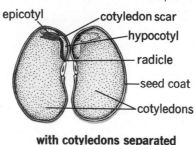

with cotyledons separated

27–10 | The structure of a bean seed.

If you soak a dried bean, you can take off the seed coats, and the cotyledons will come apart easily. The large fleshy white lobes are attached to the embryonic axis which lies close to the inner curve of the bean. The embryonic axis lies between the two cotyledons and resembles a tiny plant. It consists of an **epicotyl,** a **hypocotyl,** a **radicle,** and the two cotyledons.

hypo = upon

The plumule is that part of the embryonic axis that consists of the first pair of leaves. The hypocotyl is the embryonic stem. Cotyledons attach below the hypocotyl area. As you will learn, the hypocotyl has a special function during germination. The radicle is the embryonic root.

A Monocot Seed   Each kernel of corn is a complete fruit. It can be compared to the bean pod instead of to the individual bean seed, but each grain of corn has only one seed.

The micropyle is covered by the fruit. However, you can see where the corn fruit was attached to the cob. On one side of a corn grain a light-colored oval area shows through the fruit coat. This is where the embryo is located. Near the top of the kernel is a tiny point called the *silk scar*, where the style was attached.

If you cut a grain of corn lengthwise right through the embryo, you can see the internal parts. The endosperm fills most of the seed. In the sweet corn you eat, the endosperm

27–11 | The structure of a kernel of corn.

external

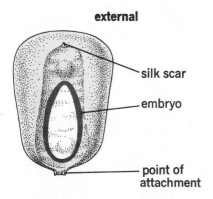

silk scar

embryo

point of attachment

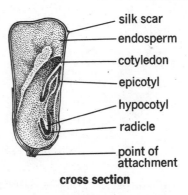

silk scar

endosperm

cotyledon

epicotyl

hypocotyl

radicle

point of attachment

cross section

Table 27-1 CLASSIFICATION OF FRUITS

TYPE	STRUCTURE	EXAMPLES
	Fleshy Fruits	
pome	outer fleshy layer developed from calyx and receptacle; ovary forms a papery core containing seeds	apple, quince, pear
drupe	ripened ovary becomes two-layered—outer layer fleshy, inner layer hard, forming stone or pit, enclosing one or more seeds	plum, cherry, peach, olive
berry	entire ovary fleshy and often juicy; thin-skinned and containing numerous seeds	tomato, grape, gooseberry
modified berry	like berry, but with tough covering	orange, lemon, cucumber
aggregate fruit	compound fruit composed of many tiny drupes clustered on single receptacle	raspberry, blackberry
accessory fruit	small and hard; scattered over surface of receptacle; edible portion formed from enlarged receptacle	strawberry
multiple fruit	compound fruit formed from several flowers in a cluster	mulberry, pineapple
	Dry Fruits (open when ripe)	
pod	ovary wall thin, fruit single-chambered, containing many seeds; splits along one or two lines when ripe	bean, pea, milkweed
capsule	ovary containing several chambers and many seeds; splits open when mature	poppy, iris, cotton, lily
	Dry Fruits (remain closed when ripe)	
nut	hard ovary wall enclosing a single seed	hickory nut, acorn, pecan
grain	thin ovary wall fastened firmly to single seed	corn, wheat, oats
achene	similar to grain, but with ovary wall separating from seed	sunflower, dandelion
winged fruit or samara	similar to achene but with prominent wing attached to ovary wall	maple, ash, elm

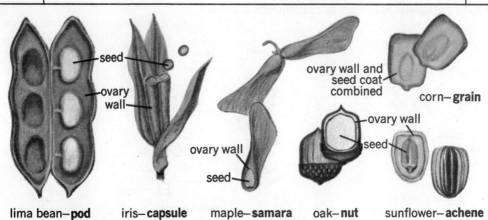

lima bean—**pod**   iris—**capsule**   maple—**samara**   oak—**nut**   sunflower—**achene**

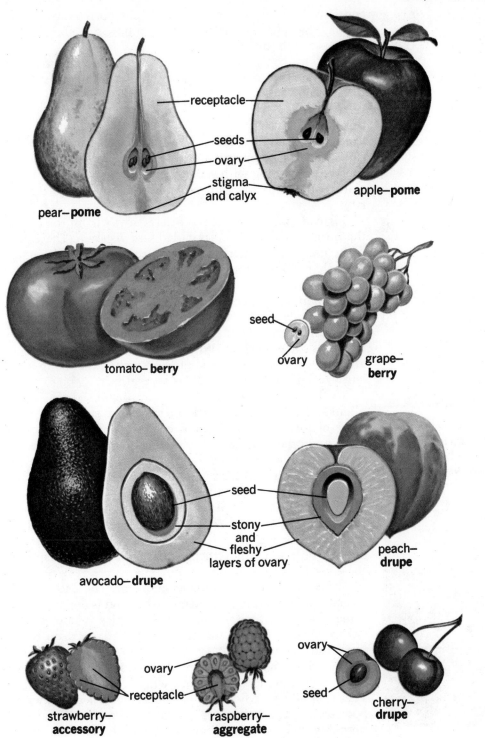

receptacle

seeds

ovary

stigma and calyx

pear–**pome**

apple–**pome**

tomato–**berry**

seed

ovary

grape–**berry**

seed

stony and fleshy layers of ovary

peach–**drupe**

avocado–**drupe**

ovary

receptacle

strawberry–**accessory**

raspberry–**aggregate**

ovary

seed

cherry–**drupe**

27–12 | Types of dry and fleshy fruits.

contains both starch and sugar. Field corn stores only starch. The field corn embryo does not have any starch, but it does contain protein.

Corn has only one cotyledon which lies against the endosperm. It is attached to the plumule and to one side of the hypocotyl.

Seed Dispersal

What would happen if seeds just fell to ground and grew right next to the parent plant? All those seedlings would soon be competing with each other and the parent for sun, water, and minerals. Not many would survive to maturity.

Instead, many seeds are scattered away from the plant that produced them. This is called *seed dispersal.* There are many means of scattering seeds. In some plants, dispersal is mechanical. In others, the dispersal is helped by agents such as wind, water, or birds.

Mechanical dispersal happens in pods like the bean and pea. The pods often twist as they ripen and dry. Eventually the strain makes them burst, with enough force to throw the seeds some distance. When the fruits of a touch-me-not are ripe, they open at the slightest touch and curl up violently, often throwing the seeds several feet.

In these cases only the seeds are dispersed. In other plants, though, the fruit plays a role. The sweetness and color of grapes, cherries, and other fleshy fruits attract birds and other animals. The seed coats protect the seeds from being digested. Then the seeds usually pass unharmed through the digestive tracts of animals. In this way seeds may be dispersed over a very large area.

Animals help to disperse fruit and seeds in other ways, too. Many plants produce fruit with stickers or spines that easily catch on animal fur. If you've ever found beggar-ticks or burrs on your clothes, then you probably helped disperse these seeds.

Water also serves as a dispersal agent. The fruit of the coconut palm is often washed out to sea. If it is deposited on some beach, it may germinate to produce a new palm. Other shoreline plants, like the grassy sedges, drop their fruits into the water.

The *wind* is a familiar agent of dispersal for seeds. Some seeds have long, loose hairs or "wings" attached to them. These help the seed float to a new location. When milkweed pods split open, their seeds are carried like this. You have probably helped dandelions by blowing off their fluff. Some trees, such as the maple, ash, and elm, have seeds with tiny propellerlike wings that whirl them away from their parent plants.

Facts & Figures

When coconut palms are grown from seeds, it takes 3 to 6 months for them to germinate, 8 to 10 years before they bear fruit, and 15 to 20 years before they are in full production.

27–13 | What are the adaptations of these seeds for seed dispersal by wind? *(G. R. Roberts)*

The Germination Process

If you have ever planted seeds you know that the appearance of the tiny green shoot is always something of a delight. Although each species has its own requirements for germination, plants do have basic needs. **The process of germination requires right amounts of moisture, oxygen, and heat.**

Before a seed germinates, it absorbs water. This softens the seed coat and makes the seed swell. At the time of germination the cotyledons contain stored water as well as food.

The first structure to emerge from the seed is the radicle. It grows downward in a geotropic response to gravity. It quickly develops into a primary root. Shortly afterwards, root hairs are absorbing water from the soil.

The following is a description of the germination of a bean as seen in figure 27–14. While root development is going on, the stem is growing toward the surface. When the hypocotyl emerges from the seed, it forms a crook or arch. By its own growth it moves up through the soil. It is usually able to survive some bruising as earth is moved aside. The plumule is protected at this time by the cotyledons. When the hypocotyl reaches the surface, its arch straightens out. The embryonic leaves emerge from the cotyledons and are spread to the sun.

Facts & Figures

During forest fires the cones of jack pine and lodge pole pine spring open and free the seeds for germination. The cone scales are glued together by resins that melt in the heat of a forest fire.

27–14 | Germination of a bean seed.

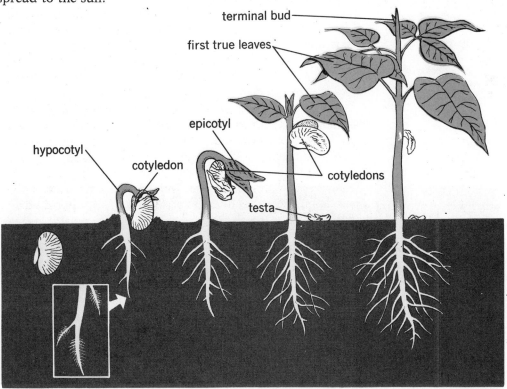

terminal bud

first true leaves

epicotyl

hypocotyl

cotyledon

cotyledons

testa

All this growth requires food, water, oxygen, and energy. The seedling absorbs oxygen for respiration from the atmospheric oxygen dissolved in water in the soil. That is one reason soil must be loose and well aerated as well as moist for germination of seeds.

Food from the cotyledons is absorbed by the shoot as it grows. The starch in the cotyledon is converted into sugar through the action of the enzyme *amylase*. The sugar, along with other nutrients, is then used by the growing shoot.

As stored food is used, the cotyledons shrink in size. The shoot gets larger. As the plant grows and starts producing its own food, the cotyledons shrivel and drop off.

With the unfolding of the embryonic leaves, the plant begins photosynthesis. Growth in the apical meristem occurs with rapid cell division and elongation of the stem. By this time all plant surface areas above ground are usually green and carry on photosynthesis. If the new plant can make sufficient food before the cotyledons are completely shriveled, it will survive. If not, it will die. Once the plant is established, the stem continues to grow and new leaves appear.

Germination and growth of a corn seedling are seen in figure 27–15. With the addition of water, the corn kernel swells. The presence of water also activates digestive enzymes, and digestion of the endosperm begins. The rad-

27–15 | Germination of a kernel of corn.

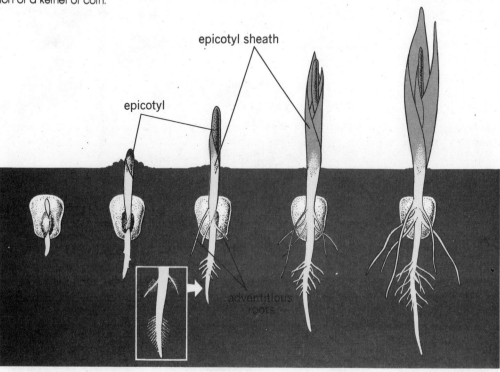

epicotyl sheath

epicotyl

adventitious roots

icle emerges and grows downward. The plumule, protected by a sheath, the **coleoptile,** grows toward the surface.

coleo = sheath

The corn kernel remains underground, and its endosperm and cotyledon continue to supply food to the growing embryo plant. The radicle rapidly forms a primary root, but branch roots soon develop from it and eventually from the bottom of the stem.

When the coleoptile breaks through to the surface, the leaves of the tightly rolled plumule emerge and unroll. The stem continues to grow and forms the corn stalk.

Dormancy in Seeds

Many seeds go through a period of rest before germinating. During this period, called *dormancy,* the chemical activity of living cells is slowed to a minimum. The length of time a seed remains dormant depends on the species and the environmental conditions. Some seeds, such as maple seeds, can germinate almost at once after falling from the tree. Some seeds can remain dormant for only one year while others can remain dormant for over hundreds of years and still germinate when conditions are correct.

Dormancy is useful because it enables a seed to withstand unfavorable conditions like drought, and the cold of winter. Seeds are the only form in which annuals survive the winter months in cold climates. These seeds remain dormant only from one growing season to the next.

One factor that accounts for dormancy is a thick, hard seed coat like those of the lotus and locust plants. The seed coats of such seeds must be worn away or must decay before germination occurs. Another factor is chemical inhibitors, which may prevent germination. Such chemicals may break down when subjected to periods of cold. Or, once formed, they may be destroyed at a certain rate so that a definite amount of time has to pass before germination occurs.

The ability of seeds to germinate is called **viability.** Seed viability depends on conditions during dormancy and on the amount of food stored in the cotyledons and endosperm. Ideally, seeds should rest in a cool, dry place. Warmth and moisture shorten the period of viability.

Facts & Figures

The oldest seeds to be germinated successfully are lotus seeds found in a peat bog in Asia. They have been dated at about 1,000 years old. They were still viable because the seeds were protected by an especially hard seed coat that is impervious to water.

Summary

Plants can reproduce in two ways, by vegetative reproduction and sexual reproduction. Vegetative reproduction produces many plants rapidly. Sexual reproduction is also effective and has the advantage of introducing genetic variety into a population.

The flower is the most highly specialized reproductive body in plants. The pistil consists of stigma, style, and ovary. An ovary can have one or more ovules. The stamens consist of anther and filament. The anther produces pollen grains. Pollination is the transfer of pollen from the anther to the stigma. Pollination is followed by development of a pollen tube, fertilization, and the maturation of the fertilized ovule into a seed.

Seeds germinate when conditions favor seedling survival. The embryonic plant in the seed includes the epicotyl, hypocotyl, and radicle. These three tissues develop into the leaves, stem, and root of a young plant using the food stored in the cotyledons.

Biologically Speaking

vegetative propagation	stamen	seed
	pistil	cotyledon
cutting	pollen	testa
layering	microspore	hilum
grafting	tube nucleus	micropyle
budding	generative nucleus	plumule
receptacle	megaspore	hypocotyl
sepal	polar nuclei	radical
calyx	pollination	coleoptile
corolla	endosperm nucleus	dormancy
petal	fruit	viability

Questions for Review

1. Describe some methods of vegetative reproduction.
2. Distinguish stock from scion in a graft. How must these be placed for the graft to be successful?
3. What purpose is served by the sepals and petals?
4. Describe the parts of the stamen and the pistil.
5. List three common agents of pollination.
6. Describe the growth of the pollen tube and double fertilization.
7. What part of the seed is produced from the zygote? from the endosperm nucleus?
8. What is the biological meaning of the term *fruit?*
9. Describe several ways seeds are dispersed.
10. How do dicot and monocot seeds differ?
11. List the stages in the germination of a bean.

Applying Concepts

1. Discuss the importance of vegetative propagation in farming and other businesses.
2. A seed will not germinate unless it has enough water to soften the seed coats. How is this a safeguard against germination during unfavorable conditions?

1. Write a paper or give an oral report on one of the following topics.
    A. An interview with a florist on the use of plant hormones, light, and temperature control to influence plant responses.
    B. A research paper on the pros and cons of synthetic auxins in agriculture or lawn care.
2. Learn how to press and preserve plants. Get information from your library or teacher and start your own collection of leaves and/or flowers.
3. Ask your lumber yard dealer for pamphlets or information on the uses of various hard and soft woods. Use samples of these woods to design a display.
4. Make a bulletin board display of the life cycle of a gymnosperm in your area. Collect and display the cones and seeds and a sprig of the tree's leaves.
5. Get a section of a log about four or five centimeters thick. Label all the parts: pith, xylem, phloem, and so on. Also interpret the growth rings and display the log with your findings.
6. Using information from your library, construct a terrarium (a miniature garden). Use moss as your base, or "carpet," plant.

Books

Anderson, A. W., *How We Got Our Flowers*. Dover Publications, Inc., New York. 1966. A fascinating history of the common flowers of America.

Bold, Harold C., *The Plant Kingdom* (3rd ed.). Prentice-Hall, Inc., Englewood Cliffs, NJ. 1970. A broad presentation of the main features of structure, physiology, and reproduction in the plant kingdom.

Heiser, Charles B., Jr., *Seed to Civilization, the Story of Man's Food*. W. H. Freeman and Co., San Francisco. 1973. An interesting account of progress in production of food.

Hutchins, Ross E., *Plants Without Leaves*. Dodd, Mead and Co., New York. 1966. A description of these plants by a well-known biologist, who explains their uses and odd ways of survival.

Page, Nancy M., and Richard E. Weaver, *Wild Plants in the City*. Quadrangle/The New York Times Book Co., New York. 1975. An easy-to-understand handbook about plants that grow in city environments.

Rahn, Joan Elma, *Alfalfa, Beans and Clover*. Atheneum, New York, 1976. This book deals with basics of plant classification. It also contains information on economic botany, cooking, history, and unfamiliar cultures.

Wendt, Frits, and the Editors of Life Magazine, *The Plants*. Time-Life Books (Time, Inc.), New York. 1963. A picture-essay book that answers most of the questions biology students ask about plants.

Wilson, Carl L., and Walter E. Loomis, *Botany*. Holt, Rinehart and Winston, Publishers, New York. 1971. An excellent text in botany which incorporates all the newer knowledge in this field.

Wohlrabe, Raymond A., *Exploring the World of Leaves*. Crowell, New York. 1976. Discusses all aspects of leaf biology. Tells how to collect and mount leaves and suggests several experiments.

Articles

Cook, R. E., "Long-Lived Seeds," *Natural History*, February, 1976. An interesting article on this fascinating topic.

Epstein, Emanuel, "Roots," *Scientific American*, May 1973. An interesting article describing the structure and function of the root.

Galston, Arthur W., "Bios: New Ways to Increase Man's Food," *Natural History*, October 1973. The article explains how the reaction of plants to light and darkness affects crop yield.

Galston, Arthur W., "The Language of the Leaves," *Natural History*, January 1973. Discusses the mechanisms of leaf movement.

Galston, Arthur W., "Sex and the Soybean," *Natural History*, October 1978. This interesting article discusses many topics mentioned in this unit, including flowering, auxins, and grafting.

Spencer, Patricia W., "The Turning of the Leaves," *Natural History*, October 1973. A clear presentation of chemical and physical changes causing leaves to change.

5

INVERTEBRATES

Unicellular organisms are considered to be in the phylum Protozoa. Multicellular animals are called metazoans. They are divided into two groups: those that have backbones are called vertebrates; those that do not have backbones are called invertebrates. More than 95 percent of all members of the animal kingdom are invertebrates. They have many diverse forms and ways of life that you will learn about in this unit.

28

Sponges and Coelenterates

A **UNDERSTAND** the division of labor among cells.

B **RECOGNIZE** the general pattern of development of multicellular organisms.

C **DESCRIBE** the types of symmetry.

D **DESCRIBE** the characteristics of Porifera.

E **DESCRIBE** the characteristics of Coelenterata.

F **DESCRIBE** the different types of cells of *Hydra*.

G **DISCUSS** coral reef formation.

28-1 | A pair of pink vase sponges. *(Dave Woodward/Taurus Photos)*

The Advantages of Association

meta = after
zoa = animal

Protozoans live as single cells. **Metazoans** are organisms made up of many cells. Is the multicellular condition an advantage over the single-celled condition? Think about a single person shipwrecked and alone on a deserted island. This one individual must gather food, make clothes, build a shelter, and perhaps protect himself or herself. It would be much easier if ten people were stranded. One person could become an expert at hunting food, another at cooking, another at carpentry, and so forth. Together, then, each member specializes in a skill. Yet, they function more efficiently than one person performing all the tasks. Multicellular organisms have the same advantage. Each individual cell is highly developed in a special skill.

An increased number of cells can divide the labor. In metazoans, certain cells specialize in functions that benefit all the cells. The adaptation of a cell for a particular use is called *specialization.*

While division of labor allows cells to specialize, it also makes them more dependent on each other. This is called *interdependence.* A one-celled ameba can live by itself in a pond. But an isolated muscle or bone cell certainly could

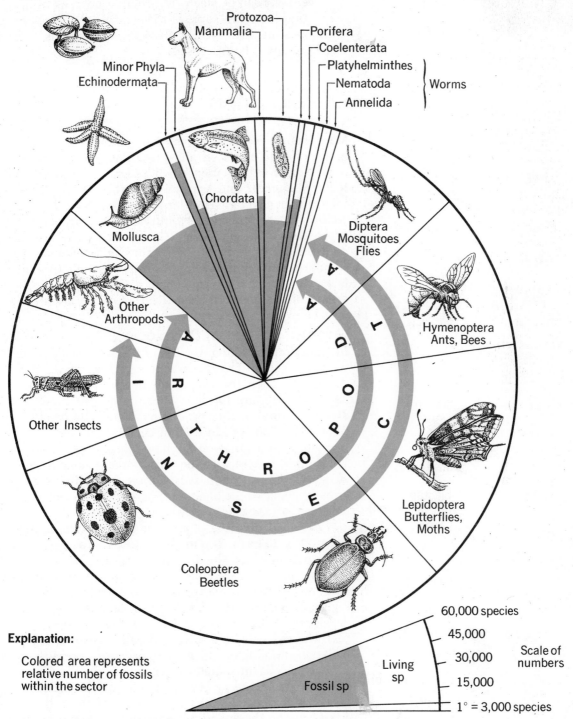

Explanation:

Colored area represents relative number of fossils within the sector

60,000 species

45,000

30,000   Scale of numbers

Living sp

15,000

Fossil sp

1° = 3,000 species

Relative numbers of known species (living and fossil) of various animal phyla.

28-2 | Relative numbers of known species (living and fossil) of various animal phyla.

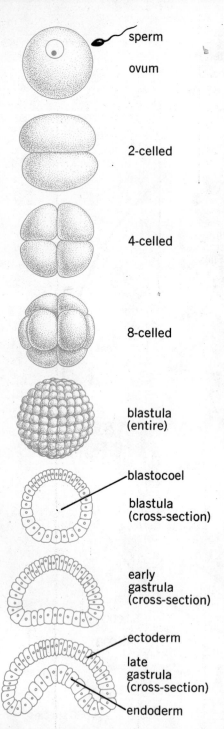

sperm

ovum

2-celled

4-celled

8-celled

blastula
(entire)

blastocoel

blastula
(cross-section)

early
gastrula
(cross-section)

ectoderm

late
gastrula
(cross-section)

endoderm

28-3 | Development in a sea urchin. Note that the total size does not change from zygote to gastrula. Only the number of cells has changed.

not live in a pond by itself. The highest degree of cell specialization occurs in some of the *vertebrates*, animals with backbones. In this unit the *invertebrates*, animals without backbones, will be discussed.

Development

Many examples of *asexual reproduction*, where a spore or a group of cells break off and grow into another complete organism, have been mentioned. In Unit 2 you studied *sexual reproduction* and learned how the gametes pass on information through DNA. You learned how the genetic code of the egg and sperm combine to determine the characteristics of the offspring. This genetic code also gives instructions to the zygote about the way in which a multicellular animal will develop from the zygote. **Development is the study of how a zygote forms a complete multicellular organism and how cell specialization comes about.**

General Pattern of Development

In sexual reproduction, the life of a new individual begins with *fertilization*. The sperm unites with an ovum, forming the *zygote*. Then the zygote divides by mitosis and two daughter cells are formed. After a time, each cell again divides by mitosis, thus producing a total of four cells. Successive divisions produce eight cells, sixteen cells, thirty-two cells, and so on. Soon a hollow sphere of cells is formed. This hollow sphere with the cells on the outside is called a **blastula.** The process is *blastulation*. There is little or no growth in size of the blastula. Therefore each cell is much smaller than the original zygote.

Continued dividing of cells of the blastula causes an indentation to form. You might picture this as a punctured basketball in which the air would escape. You could push your fist into the basketball, causing an indentation. The point at which the infolding begins is called the **blastopore.** Figure 28-3 shows these developing cells. At this stage of development the mass of cells is called a **gastrula.** The process whereby cells fold inward is called *gastrulation*. Gastrulation is an important process because it sorts the total number of cells into outside cells and inside cells. The outer cells are the **ectoderm.** The inner cells are the **endoderm.** If you look at figure 28-3 you will see that the cells of the ectoderm and the endoderm have different environments. Their position in relation to other cells and to either the outside or the "pushed-in" cavity are quite different. All the cells are destined to form specific structures.

Germ Layers

Cells of the endoderm will form the lining of the gut or alimentary tract. Cells of the ectoderm will form part of the skin, the brain, hair, and nails as well as other tissues. In mammals, ectoderm cells will form the **epidermis,** or outer layer of skin, of metazoans in general. But both ectoderm and endoderm cells will form other tissues as well. Because the ectoderm and endoderm will give rise to specific structures in the metazoan, they are called **germ layers.**

In many metazoans, a third layer forms. It is the **mesoderm.** It may form in one of two ways. The genetic code of the organism determines how the mesoderm is formed. In clams, snails, and oysters, for example, dividing cells split off near the point where the ectoderm joins the endoderm. The cells continue to divide and form the *mesoderm.*

In the vertebrates and in some invertebrates, the mesoderm forms in another way. Cells of the endoderm form pouches. Continued cell division causes the pouches to become larger. These cells form the mesoderm. Figure 28-4c shows how these pouches arise from the innermost part of the endoderm.

Cells of the mesoderm form such structures as muscles. Other important functions will be described as you continue the study of biology.

The cells of the three germ layers continue to divide and rearrange into groups. The groups of cells will then form the specific tissues and organs of the multicellular organism. Growth occurs as the cells continue to divide and become larger.

All metazoans do not show these exact stages of development. But this is a basic pattern that will be referred to throughout the text.

28–4 | (a and b) In clams, snails, and oysters, the mesoderm arises from cells where the endoderm and ectoderm meet. (c) In vertebrates and some invertebrates, the mesoderm is formed from cells of the endoderm inside the hollow cavity, or primitive gut.

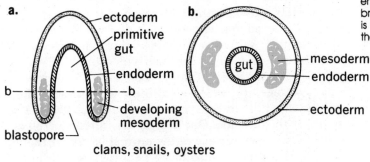

clams, snails, oysters

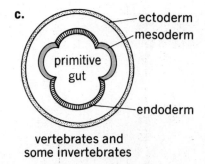

vertebrates and
some invertebrates

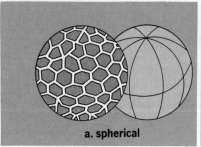
a. spherical

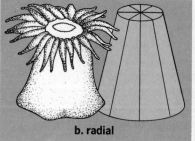
b. radial

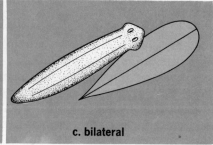
c. bilateral

28-5 | Three types of symmetry.

Symmetry and Similarities

Similarity of structure is important in classification. **The general form of each organism is called its *symmetry*.** The ameba has no definite shape, so it is said to be *asymmetrical*. It orients itself to the environment by moving in any direction with its pseudopods. Most sponges grow in colonies without a definite shape. They also may be thought of as asymmetrical. An organism with *spherical symmetry* meets the environment on all its surfaces. Organisms with spherical symmetry often have no effective method of locomotion, and they float on or near the water's surface.

Most organisms are affected by gravity, however. The sea anemone, for example, has tentacles at one end and a basal disk for attachment at the other. The sea anemone has *radial symmetry*. Its tentacles radiate like spokes of a wheel from a *central disk*. Imagine a line drawn right through the mouth and the center of the body. This line would be the *central axis* of the sea anemone. Some sponges, most coelenterates (hydra, anemones), and most adult echinoderms (sea urchin, sand dollar) are radially symmetrical.

Actively moving organisms are better adapted for their way of life by having *bilateral symmetry*, which means "two-sided shape." Animals with this kind of symmetry are similar on two sides. They can be divided in half by a plane passing through a longitudinal axis, from the center of the upper surface, to the center of the lower surface. The two halves of a bilaterally symmetrical animal are the right side and the left side. One side is the mirror image of the other. **The upper surface of the animal is *dorsal*, the lower surface is *ventral*. It also has a definite front, or anterior, end, and a hind, or posterior, end. All vertebrates and many invertebrates have this kind of symmetry.** In humans, dorsal is your "back," ventral is your "front."

Many organisms with bilateral symmetry have a concentration of nerves and sense organs at the anterior end.

Thus, as they move forward, they can sense the environment and react quickly to changes. This is a great advantage for survival.

The Animal Phyla

As you continue to study living things, look for similarities in characteristics. These similarities are important for understanding how animals survive and adapt to changing conditions. For example, the backbone is a characteristic used for separating animals into two groups—the vertebrates and the invertebrates.

Other characteristics are used for dividing these two groups into smaller units. **Similar characteristics among animals can indicate two things. They may point to evolutionary relationships. They may also mean that different animals have adapted in the same ways to stay alive.** As you read about the various animals, ask yourself these questions: What are the structural features that make this animal part of its group? Where does the animal live? What are its organic needs, and how does it satisfy them? How does the environment affect this animal? How does this animal affect other living things in the environment?

Ten large animal phyla will be discussed. You may want to use a classification table in the Appendix reference and review. It lists the important characteristics and some typical examples of each group. Only the largest and most important phyla will be discussed. The first one is the sponge phylum, *Porifera*, (puh-RIF-uh-ruh), which includes some of the simplest animals.

Phylum Porifera: The Sponges

Most sponges are marine; that is, they live in the sea. But there are a few freshwater species. Living sponges can be almost any color, from white and gray to any shade of red or yellow, even purple and black. Some sponges live singly. Others crowd together in colonies that form a crustlike layer over rock surfaces. Individual sponges can be as small as a centimeter (0.4 inches) or as big as two meters (6.6 feet) across.

A simple sponge has a hollow body. The body wall is formed of two layers of cells separated by a layer of jellylike substance. Loose cells, and *spicules* (SPI-kyoolz) are found in the jelly layer. The spicules are noncellular skeletal

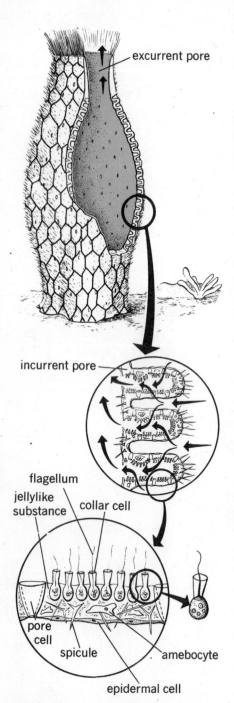

28–6 | Water is continually drawn into the sponge by the flagella of the collar cells. It passes through small pores into the cavity of the sponge and out through the osculum.

structures that help support the body of the animal. These spicules are secreted by living cells. Sponges are classified according to the material forming them. The spicules of some sponges are made of silicon, others of calcium carbonate (lime). A third group of sponges is supported by a fibrous network of tough, flexible material called *spongin.* Many sponges have spongin and spicules.

Sponges are often referred to as loose masses of cells. They have no organs and no true tissues. And though they have two cell layers, these layers are not formed from definite germ layers. However, their cells are interdependent enough to justify the classification of these animals as multicellular organisms.

How Sponges Acquire Food

When you first look at a living sponge, you may mistake it for a plant. Animals are usually thought of as chasing, catching, and eating their food. A sponge, though, is **sessile** (SESS-ill). This means that it is permanently attached to something by its base. **Organisms that are radially symmetrical, such as the sponge, are adapted to a sessile existence.** If sponges are anchored to one place, then how do they get food? Sponges act as living filters. They remove small food particles and oxygen from the water that they pump through their bodies.

If you put a drop of India ink near a sponge and observe its cells through a microscope, you would be able to see how water circulates through the sponge's body. You would see ink particles being taken into the sponge's body through small *incurrent pores.* The ink would reappear as though being forced out from a larger *excurrent pore,* also called the osculum (OSS-kyu-lum). The sponge moves water through itself in currents. Because of the many pores, the sponges are in a phylum called Porifera, which means "pore-bearing."

The sponge is able to control the size of its **osculum.** This action controls the rate of water flow or even stops it. Sponges feed mainly on organic particles. They may also take in diatoms, small protozoans, and bacteria. The food material is drawn into them along with the water. Carbon dioxide and other wastes leave through the osculum.

The sponge's inner layer has many unusual cells with curious collars that have flagella sticking through them. These are called **collar cells** or *choanocytes.* The flagella of these collar cells set up the currents that draw water into the sponge. As bits of food enter, they are caught by the collars. The food then passes into the collar cell. Food vacuoles are formed and enzymes digest the particles. The digested food is absorbed by special cells called **amebocytes.** The amebocytes wander through the jellylike layer, carrying digested food and oxygen to other cells. They also carry wastes and carbon dioxide to the collar cells for disposal.

Reproduction in Sponges

Sponges reproduce asexually in two ways. They may form **buds.** These are groups of cells that enlarge, but stay attached to the parent for a time before breaking off to live separately. Another method may occur during periods of freezing temperatures or drought. Groups of cells become surrounded by a heavy coat of organic matter. They contain little groups of amebocytes and a few spicules. When the parent sponge disintegrates, they remain and are called **gemmules** (JEM-yewlz). When growing conditions improve, each gemmule can develop into another sponge. Reproduction by gemmules is usually found in freshwater species.

Sponges can also reproduce sexually by producing eggs and sperms. The sperms are shed into the water and enter another sponge through the incurrent pores. They are taken in by the cytoplasm of the collar cells. Then the sperms are carried to the egg by the carrier amebocyte. The fertilized egg develops into a flagellated larva, which escapes from the sponge. After swimming around for a while, it settles and grows into another sponge.

Sponges are able to regrow missing parts when damaged. This is called *regeneration*. The ability of sponges to regenerate is quite remarkable. Some sponges may be cut and the pieces strained through a silk mesh. The individual cells will then form clumps that can grow into new sponges. Ability to regenerate a new organism is closely associated with the ability to reproduce asexually. Forming a new organism from a group of cells is the same principle in both processes.

Phylum Coelenterata

If you have ever been stung by a jellyfish, you have already been introduced to one of the coelenterates. Many of these creatures bob around in the ocean, dangling long stringy tentacles under a floating, inflated sac. Their phylum, *Coelenterata* (suh-LEN-tuh-RAH-tuh), also includes the hydroids, corals, sea fans, sea anemones, and the Portuguese man-of-war. The size of the members of this phylum range from microscopic to the largest jellyfish of the North Atlantic. These may be four meters (3.2 feet) across. Coelenterates live singly or united in colonies. All coelenterates live in the water and most are marine. The cells of coelenterates are more highly specialized than those of the sponges. They form the two germ layers ectoderm and endoderm.

The Hydra

A genus that shows characteristics typical of the coelenterate phylum is *Hydra*, a common freshwater genus. Different species are white or brown. Some appear to be green because of algae living beneath their outer cells. The *Hydra* live in quiet ponds, lakes, and streams.

Hydras vary in size from a centimeter, including tentacles, up to about four centimeters (1.2 inches). They attach themselves to rocks or water plants with a sticky secretion from the cells of their **basal disks.** Sometimes hydras leave one place of attachment and move to another. They may secrete bubbles at their bases and float upside down to the surface. They sometimes move by means of a peculiar somersaulting motion.

The body of a hydra has two cell layers separated by a jellylike material called **mesoglea** (MEZ-o-GLEE-uh). The outside cell layer is the **epidermis.** It was formed from the *ectoderm* during development. The inner layer of cells is the **gastrodermis.** It was formed from the *endoderm.* The saclike body of the hydra has a single opening, the mouth. **Tentacles** surround the mouth and are armed with stinging cells. The stinging cells contain structures called **nematocysts** (NEM-et-uh-sists). Only the coelenterates have these spearlike nematocysts. If a person is stung by a jellyfish, the poison from the nematocysts causes red welts to form.

How the Hydra Acquires Food The hydra waits for a small animal to come into contact with one of its tentacles. At once several nematocysts explosively discharge, throwing tiny hollow barbs into the victim's body. Each barb is attached to the tentacle by a thin thread. The combined strength of many threads prevents the hapless victim from escaping. At the base of each barb is a small poison sac that releases poison and paralyzes the prey.

As soon as the animal stops moving, the tentacles bend inward. They push the victim through the hydra's circular mouth and into its hollow body. This space is lined with specialized *gastrodermal* cells. Some of the cells secrete digestive enzymes that partly break down the prey. The partly digested food is taken in by the lining cells, which complete the digestion process. Because of these functions, the space is called a *gastrovascular cavity.* Undigested particles then leave through the mouth.

The mouth and digestive cavity of the coelenterate are more complex than the feeding structures of the sponge. They allow a greater range in the types and sizes of food that the animal can use. The cells discharge metabolic wastes directly into the water. Gases are also exchanged directly between the water and the cells in respiration.

epi = on, upon

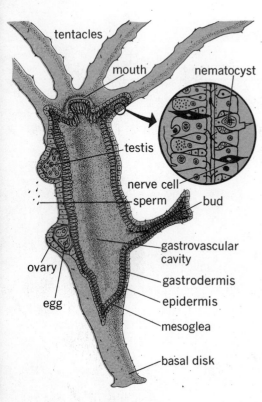

28-7 | The external and internal structure of the hydra. Note the two layers of cells with a jellylike material between.

Sensitivity in the Hydra Now you know about one coelenterate reaction that shows higher specialization than the more primitive sponge. The hydra's tentacles work together to catch food and push it into its mouth. The tentacles and the entire body will contract suddenly if you touch the hydra with a needle. The stimulus applied to one tentacle will travel to cells of the other tentacles and the body through a series of nerve cells. This **nerve net** lies in the mesoglea. The hydra does not have a nervous system like those in higher animals. And the hydra does not have a brain. Also, unlike higher animals which conduct nerve impulses in one direction, hydra nerve cells conduct impulses in all directions.

The nerve net is a primitive type of nervous system. Since a hydra's general reaction to strong stimulus is withdrawal, it is called a negative reaction. When it senses food, it goes toward the food, which is a positive reaction.

How the Hydra Reproduces The hydra can reproduce asexually by forming *buds*. A bud starts as a knob growing out from the side of the adult. Later, the knob develops tentacles. After it has grown, the bud separates from the parent to live on its own. In this method of reproduction, the bud is a small outgrowth of epidermis and gastrodermis, capable of becoming a new organism.

Like the sponge, the hydra is able to regenerate. If a hydra is cut into pieces, most of the pieces will regenerate the missing parts and become whole animals.

Sexual reproduction usually occurs in the fall. Eggs are produced along the body walls in little swellings called *ovaries*. Motile sperm cells are formed in similar swellings called *testes*.

The egg is fertilized in the ovary. The zygote divides and grows into a ball of cells with a hard, protective cover. Then it leaves the parent. It goes through a rest period before forming a new hydra.

Two Ways of Life

Coelenterates have two different types of body forms. The hydra is a good example of the **polyp** (PAHL-uhp) form. Its tubular body has a basal disk at one end and tentacles at the other. The second form is bell-shaped and freeswimming, like the jellyfish. This is called a **medusa.** A medusa swims by a jerky kind of jet propulsion. It does this by taking water into the bell and then forcing it out.

Aurelia, a common jellyfish, is an interesting example of a coelenterate whose life cycle includes both medusa and polyp forms. The medusa reproduces sexually. It has protective tentacles that hang from a scalloped edge. The male

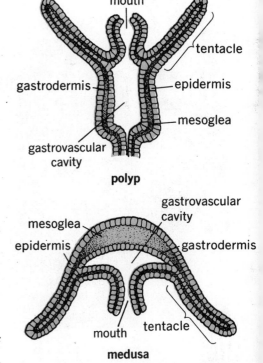

28–8 | Compare the body plans of the sessile polyp and the free-swimming medusa.

28-9 | Life cycle of *Aurelia*.

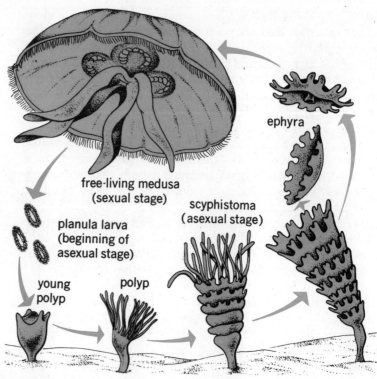

free-living medusa
(sexual stage)

ephyra

scyphistoma
(asexual stage)

planula larva
(beginning of
asexual stage)

young
polyp

polyp

28-10 | Compare the sea anemone (top) and hydroid (bottom) with the diagrams in figure 28-9. (top: R. Mariscal, Bruce Coleman; bottom: Allan Power, Bruce Coleman)

medusas shed sperms into the sea. Some of the sperms enter the gastrovascular cavity of a female. Here they fertilize eggs that have been released by the female. For a short time the zygotes are protected by folds of tissue surrounding the mouth.

The young are released in the form of small, oval-shaped, ciliated larvae called *planulae* (PLAN-yuh-lee). After a planula swims around for a time, it attaches itself to a rock or seaweed. It develops tentacles and begins feeding. At this stage, it is considered a polyp. As it grows, more polyps are formed from buds at its base. During the fall and winter, the polyp elongates and has several horizontal divisions, until it looks like a pile of saucers. One by one, starting from the top of the pile, the saucers break loose and swim away. On their own, they become sexually reproducing adult medusas.

Other Coelenterates

Coral polyps are the only coelenterates of economic importance. Their skeletons, also called coral, are used as jewelry, in flower arrangements, and as pure decoration. The body of the coral animal is a small, flowerlike polyp. Most coral polyps live in colonies. They form skeletons from lime, which they take out of the sea water. They cement their own skeletons to the skeleton of the polyp next to

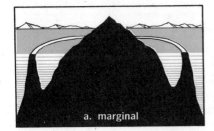
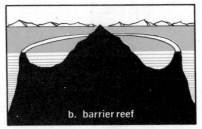
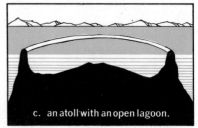

a. marginal   b. barrier reef   c. an atoll with an open lagoon.

28–11 | Three different kinds of coral reefs: a. marginal; b. barrier reef widely separated from the land; c. an atoll with an open lagoon.

them. When a coral animal dies, its skeleton remains. This serves as a point of attachment for another polyp. Lime skeletons of coral build up this way. A single mass may eventually support several thousand animals, all living on top of skeletons of their ancestors. Some species build solid masses. Others create delicate, complicated, fan shapes.

Over a long time, large coral reefs build up. They are most often found in warm, shallow oceans. There are three types of coral reefs. One is the *marginal type* or *fringing type* reef, which forms close to a beach. A second is the *barrier type*, which forms a ring around an island with a wide stretch of water separating it from the beach.

The Great Barrier Reef off the northern coast of Australia runs for about 2,000 kilometers, (1,200 miles) parallel to the coast, and is about 80 kilometers (48 miles) wide. The third type of coral reef is a ring called an *atoll*, which has an open lagoon in the middle. The other two types of coral reef are actually stages in the formation of the atoll.

Storms on the Pacific Coast may leave beaches covered with bluish animals that look like membranes five to eight centimeters long. They belong to the genus *Velella*, and are called purple sails or by-the-wind sailors. The Portuguese man-of-war, or *Physalia*, is related to them. **Both these organisms are basically colonies of polyps. Each polyp has a special job in the colony.** The other polyps are suspended from it. This large polyp float keeps the coelenterate colony near the surface, where the wind moves it through the water. Some polyps in the colony digest food caught by other polyps. Still others specialize in forming gametes. The Portuguese man-of-war is found mainly in tropical and semitropical waters. But it is also found in the Gulf Stream, which occasionally takes it all the way to the English coast. The Portuguese man-of-war may be dangerous to swimmers because of its painful sting.

28–12 | *Physalia*, the Portugese man-of-war, is a colonial coelenterate. *(Runk, Schoenberger, Grant Heilman)*

Summary

	PORIFERA	COELENTERATES
Body Types	asymmetrical	radial symmetry; polyp, medusa
Type of Life	marine, freshwater sessile as adults	marine, freshwater sessile, free swimming
Organization	no true tissue, specialized cells	no true organ systems, gastrovascular cavity
Digestive System	none, no mouth	digestive sac, mouth
Reproduction	asexual—budding, gemmules sexual—egg and sperm formation	asexual—budding sexual—egg and sperm formation

Biologically Speaking

metazoan	symmetry	bud
specialization	dorsal	gemmule
blastula	ventral	basal disk
blastopore	spicule	mesoglea
gastrula	sessile	gastrodermis
ectoderm	incurrent pore	tentacle
endoderm	excurrent pore	nematocyst
epidermis	osculum	nerve net
germ layer	collar cell	polyp
mesoderm	amebocyte	medusa

Questions for Review

1. How does the multicellular condition permit efficient division of labor?
2. What are the differences between blastulation and gastrulation?
3. Name and define the kinds of symmetry.
4. What structural features make sponges dfferent from coelenterates?
5. Describe regeneration in sponges and in coelenterates.
6. In what ways are the *Aurelia* and hydra similar? How are they different?
7. How is a coral reef made? List three types.

Applying Concepts

1. Compare the ways in which cell specialization is similar to division of labor in human societies.
2. Is a sponge more primitive than a hydra?

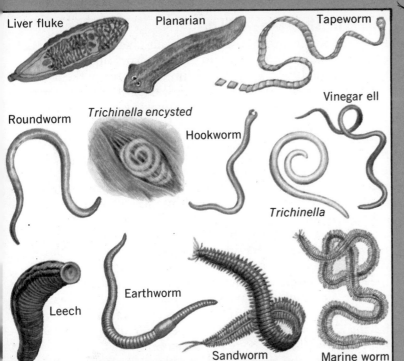

Liver fluke   Planarian   Tapeworm

Roundworm

Trichinella encysted

Hookworm

Vinegar ell

Trichinella

Leech

Earthworm

Sandworm

Marine worm

29–1 | Examples of common worms.

The Worms

A **IDENTIFY** the characteristics of *Planaria*.

B **DISTINGUISH** between free-living and parasitic organisms.

C **IDENTIFY** the characteristics of roundworms.

D **EXPLAIN** regeneration in *Planaria*.

E **EXPLAIN** the relationships of *Ascaris*, Trichina, hookworm, and tapeworm to humans.

F **DESCRIBE** the physiology of the systems of the earthworm.

G **DESCRIBE** the development and importance of the coelom.

Phylum Platyhelminthes

About 20,000 species of worms have been classified. This number is very small when compared to all the known species of animals. Many worms play an important role among living things. This book deals with three major worm phyla: flatworms, roundworms, and segmented worms. The least complex worms are included in *Platyhelminthes* (PLAT-ee-hel-MINTH-eez), or flatworm, phylum. During development they have an ectoderm and endoderm like coelenterates. However, flatworms form the third germ layer, the *mesoderm*, during development. **Organisms with only ectoderm and endoderm such as the coelenterates form tissues. But animals with all three germ layers develop organs and organ systems.** This is true for all the other animals you will study, including human beings. The flatworm phylum is divided into three classes: *Turbellaria*, *Trematoda*, and *Cestoda*.

Animals of the class Turbellaria are free-living. Members of the other two classes of Platyhelminthes are *parasitic.* They get their nourishment from living in another organism called the *host*. The parasitic worms make up the largest number of metazoan parasites.

platos = flat
helminthos = a worm

The Parasitic Way of Life

Parasites living inside the body of another animal have characteristics that make them different from those of their free-living relatives. Their size is limited by that of the host. Intestinal parasites usually have hooks or suckers so they can cling to the walls of the host's intestines. In this way, they are surrounded by digested food and they merely absorb nutrients from it. Some parasites are protected from being digested by a thick *cuticle* not found in the free-living organisms. The cuticle is a thick nonliving layer secreted by the epidermis. Other parasites do not have a cuticle, but instead are protected by a thick layer of cells called a *tegument.*

Certain systems are not found in parasitic worms. The tapeworm, for instance, has no digestive system. Sometimes it is said that these worms have *degenerated*. That is, they do not develop organs or tissues that animals of comparable complexity have developed. To the parasite, though, this is adaptive. It is really a specialization by *not* having a digestive system. The tapeworm adapted to having more room in its body for developing eggs.

The passing of eggs to new hosts is a problem for internal parasites. Because of this, complicated life histories are an adaptive feature of parasites. At the larval stage, they may be free-living or live within another organism. The life histories of some common parasitic worms will show how parasites infect other animals and thereby reproduce more of their species. See figure 29-5 on page 365.

The Planarian

A free-living organism is one that is not a parasite. The most common examples of the free-living flatworms are the planarians. These members of the class Turbellaria are aquatic. Planarians are often found under stones in freshwater ponds and streams. They can be collected by tying a piece of liver to a rock and lowering it into a pond. After a few hours, the rock can be removed and placed in a jar of pond water. The following day, you probably will find many planarians on the sides of the jar.

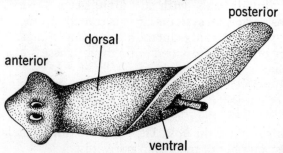

29-2 | The planarian is an animal showing bilateral symmetry.

Planarians are small, usually less than one centimeter (0.4 inches) long. Their color ranges from black or brown to white. They are bilaterally symmetrical, blunt at the anterior and pointed at the posterior. The two **eyespots** at the anterior end have led to the planarian's nickname of "the cross-eyed worm." These eyespots are *photosensitive*. That is, when light strikes the eyespots, it stimulates nerves. The animal senses the light and avoids it.

The **pharynx** (FARE-inx) is a tube on the ventral surface of the planarian. When extended, this tube sucks up microscopic particles, including tiny organisms. Planarians are called scavengers because they clean the water in which they live by eating organic matter. This food is drawn into the digestive cavity and enters one of three branches of the intestine. It then passes along to one of the side branches.

Food is digested in the cavity of the intestine and within the cells lining the intestine. Cells lining the intestine take in the food particles and digests them in food vacuoles. The digested food then diffuses to the various body tissues. Indigestible materials are eliminated through the pharynx and the mouth opening. Since the planarian has no separate circulatory system, cellular wastes are collected by tubules that branch throughout the animal. The wastes leave by the several tiny excretory pores on the surface of the worm's body.

The nervous system of the planarian is more highly developed than that of the animals you have studied so far. A mass of nerve tissue that functions as the brain lies just under the eyespots at the anterior end. Many nerves from this anterior region lead directly to the brain. In organisms with bilateral symmetry, this arrangement of nerves is very important. As the worm moves, its anterior end is the first part exposed to chemicals, water currents, touch, light, and heat. So the planarian can test the environment into which it is moving. If the conditions are not good, it can move in a different direction. **Concentration of receptors (receivers of stimuli) and nerves at the anterior end is called *cephalization*. Cephalization is of great survival value to bilateral organisms in the way that they respond to their environment.**

Two *longitudinal nerves* run along either side of the body near the ventral surface. They are connected by *transverse nerves*. This makes the nervous system look like a ladder. Many small nerves also run from the surface of the planarian to the longitudinal nerves. This nervous system allows the animal to be coordinated in its movements. Planarians respond to stimuli anywhere on their bodies.

If you watch planarians in a dish or an aquarium, you

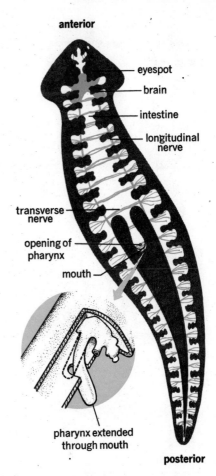

anterior

eyespot
brain
intestine
longitudinal nerve

transverse nerve

opening of pharynx

mouth

pharynx extended through mouth

posterior

29–3 | The digestive and nervous systems of a planarian.

cephalic = head

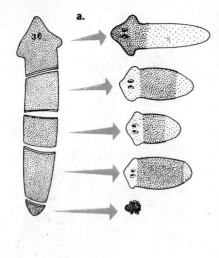

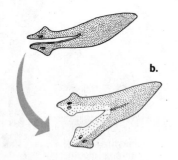

29–4 | Regeneration in the planarians. (a) Each section except the last will form a new head. (b) Another animal is shown forming two heads. This animal will complete the separation and become two planarians.

will see that they move in two different ways. In one, the anterior end moves from side to side. In another, the whole body moves forward in a gliding motion due to tiny muscle contractions. This movement is aided by cilia on the ventral surface.

Planarians reproduce asexually by fragmentation and sexually by gametes. Each animal has both the male and female reproductive organs in its body. This kind of an animal is called **hermaphroditic.** Cross-fertilization occurs and the eggs are shed in capsules. There are usually ten or fewer eggs per capsules. These capsules are often attached to rocks or twigs in the water. The tiny planarians hatch in two or three weeks.

Many species of planarians have the same remarkable ability to regenerate missing parts that the sponges and coelenterates have. Some planarians will grow into complete new worms from almost any part. If you cut one into anterior and posterior sections, the anterior part will grow a new tail while the posterior will grow a new head. A small section of the tail, however, does not regenerate.

A planarian can develop two heads if it is cut lengthwise halfway down the body. But soon it divides completely into two animals. Very little is known about how this happens. In general, the more complex the organism, the more specialized tissue the organism has, and the less it is able to regenerate lost parts. Crabs can grow new claws, and lizards replace lost tails. Humans can grow new skin and some muscles, but not new organs.

The Flukes

Flukes are in the class Trematoda. These are parasites that live in many animals, including humans. Flukes differ from planarians in that adult flukes have no external cilia. Flukes have thick teguments and one or more *suckers* for clinging to the tissues of the host. An anterior sucker surrounds the mouth, which opens to a short pharynx. The fluke's nervous system is similar to the planarian's but there are no special sense organs. Most flukes have a highly developed reproductive system and are hermaphroditic. Another difference between a fluke and a planarian is that a fluke has a **uterus.** The uterus is a long coiled tube where the many eggs are stored. When the eggs are ready to be released, they are discharged through the *genital pore.*

Flukes have complicated life histories. Part of their lives are spent in snails and another part in one or more other hosts. The sheep liver fluke lives as an adult in a sheep's liver and gall bladder. Its eggs pass from the gall bladder to the intestine. If the eggs fall into the water after they pass through the sheep, they hatch into young worms called **lar-**

vae (singular, *larva*). There are several larval stages, as you can see in figure 29-5. The larvae first enter the body of a certain kind of snail. In the snail, they go through several stages and increase in number by asexual reproduction. Then they leave the snail and climb blades of grass at the water's edge where they form **cysts.** If a sheep eats the grass with these cysts, the fluke enters its liver, and the cycle starts again.

The liver fluke makes its host sick. It causes irritability, inflammation, and swelling. Cows with liver flukes produce less milk.

Other types of flukes may live in animal blood, intestines, or lungs. They are often found externally on the gills of fish and in cavities of other vertebrates that live in the water.

The blood fluke, *Schistosoma*, causes one of the major diseases of the world. More than 200 million people are infected with this parasite. These flukes live as adults in the blood stream of a human. They do not form cysts. The eggs have sharp spines that damage tissue. For a time the larva develops inside a snail. Therefore the snail is called the secondary host. Humans are infected when the larvae pass through the skin while bathing, or in drinking water that contains the larvae.

29-5 | The life cycle of a sheep liver fluke.

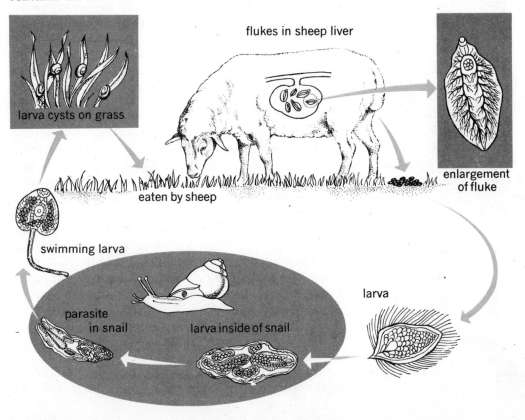

flukes in sheep liver

larva cysts on grass

enlargement of fluke

eaten by sheep

swimming larva

parasite in snail

larva inside of snail

larva

Although flukes in humans are most common in the Orient, they are also found in other places. Cuba has had epidemics of flukes among its residents. On the Gulf Coast of the United States, farmers have suffered economic loss due to flukes infecting many cows, pigs, and sheep. The best way to control flukes is to eliminate one of the hosts in their life cycle. Which host would you try to eliminate?

Tapeworms

The best-known parasitic flatworms are tapeworms, members of the class Cestoda. An adult tapeworm has a flat, ribbonlike body that is grayish white. It has no cilia. The knob-shaped head is called a *scolex.* The scolex has suckers, and some species have a ring of hooks. But there is no mouth or digestive structures. Adults usually are attached to intestine walls, where nutrients bathe them. The digested food is absorbed through the tapeworm's body.

Below its slender neck, a tapeworm has many nearly square sections. These body sections are called *proglottids* (proe-GLOT-idz). A tapeworm may grow to ten meters (33 feet) in length. The tapeworm grows by adding new sections at the anterior end, so the oldest ones are at the posterior end. The proglottids basically are masses of reproductive organs. Tapeworms are hermaphroditic. Cross-fertilization is the most common method of reproduction in tapeworms, but self-fertilization is known to occur. The eggs formed in a proglottid are also fertilized there. When the eggs mature, the proglottid breaks off and passes out in the host's feces. These proglottids may be eaten by an animal such as a pig or cow. In the body of the new host, the eggs hatch into larvae that burrow into the muscles and form cysts.

Tapeworms may enter the human body as cysts. If meat from an infected animal is eaten undercooked, the living cysts can enter the stomach. Each cyst contains a fully developed scolex. When the cyst reaches the intestine, the scolex breaks out. It then attaches to the intestinal wall and begins to grow.

Since tapeworms rob their hosts of nutrients in the form of digested food the hosts may lose weight and energy. Tapeworms are not as common in humans today because there are new ways to detect the parasites and treat people for them. Meat is also inspected more carefully for tapeworm cysts.

Phylum Nematoda

Members of the phylum *Nematoda* (nem-uh-TOE-duh) are called roundworms or nematodes. Nematodes are the most

29–6 | The structure of a tapeworm. The tapeworm attaches the hooks of its scolex to the intestinal wall.

hooks
sucker
scolex
scolex
testes
sperm duct
genital pore
vagina
ovary
proglottid

widespread and numerous of all multicellular animals. They are long, slender, smooth worms, which are tapered at both ends. They can be as short as one-fifth of a millimeter (0.008 inches) or as long as 130 centimeters (72 inches). Roundworms live in soil and in fresh or salt water. Many live as parasites in plants and animals. The parasitic roundworms include the hookworm, trichina worm, pinworm, whipworm, *Ascaris*, and guinea worm.

More than one-third of the human population supports parasitic roundworms. Although this occurs mostly in the warm regions of the world, this fact makes roundworms very important. There are harmless roundworms, too, like the vinegar eel which is found in nonpasteurized vinegar.

Like the flatworms, roundworms are bilaterally symmetrical. They develop from three germ layers: ectoderm, endoderm, and mesoderm. But they are more complex than the flatworms. Their digestive system is a tube with an opening at each end. Their bodies are long and tubeshaped. The roundworm is able to take food in through the mouth and digest it. As the food moves along through the tube, the usable parts are removed. Undigested material is passed out through the opening in the posterior end, the **anus.** The flatworm has only one opening for both taking in food and elimination of undigested food. But **the roundworm's body arrangement of a tube within a tube has two openings. This allows all its material to move more easily and efficiently through the digestive tract.**

A large roundworm that may live in the intestine of pigs, horses, and sometimes people is *Ascaris*. The females, growing as long as 30 centimeters (12 inches), are larger than the males. *Ascaris* eggs enter the human body in contaminated food or water. Passing through the stomach, they hatch a few hours after they reach the small intestine. The larvae then bore into the intestinal wall, beginning a ten-day trip through the body. Once in the bloodstream, they are carried to the lungs. From there, they travel through the air passages to the throat, where they are swallowed and returned to the digestive tube. There they spend about two and a half months developing into adults. After the female has been fertilized, the eggs are surrounded by a thick, rough shell, and leave through the genital pore of the female worm. As many as 200,000 eggs may be produced each day. The eggs leave the host's body with the feces, and the cycle is repeated. *Ascaris* is usually harmless to humans. But when many adult worms twist together and block the intestine, results may be fatal. Also, larvae in the host's lungs can cause an illness similar to pneumonia.

The *hookworm* is a far more serious health menace than *Ascaris*. It is widespread in southern United States and in

Facts & Figures

Several billion soil nematodes may live in one acre of farmland.

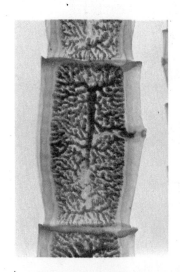

29-7 | A tapeworm proglottid. Compare this photo with the diagram of the proglottid in figure 29-6. *(Courtesy of Carolina Biological Supply House)*

all semitropical and tropical regions. Hookworm larvae develop in the soil. They enter the body by boring through the skin of the feet. When they enter the blood vessels, they travel through the heart to the lungs. Like *Ascaris*, they pass through the air passages and the throat, then they are swallowed and pass to the intestine. They use their jaws to attach to the intestinal walls. Nourished by the blood they suck, the larvae grow into adult worms.

The victim's loss of blood lowers vitality by producing anemia. A typical host may become quite sluggish. And if young enough, the host may suffer from retarded growth.

The hookworms reproduce by means of fertilized eggs which leave the host with the feces. If the eggs land in warm, moist soil, they develop into tiny larvae that begin the cycle again.

Three factors can contribute to the spread of this disease: 1. careless sewage disposal; 2. warm soil; and 3. going barefoot. Public health agencies have reduced the number of cases in the United States.

One of the most dangerous parasitic worms is the *trichina*, or *Trichinella*. This roundworm spends the first part of its life as a cyst in the muscles of pigs, dogs, cats, or rats. If uncooked scraps of meat from an infected animal are fed to a pig, the scraps will probably have cysts. In the pig's intestine, the larvae grow into adult worms, mate, and produce microscopic larvae. These pass into the blood-

29-8 | (a) *Ascaris,* a parasitic roundworm, with sideviews of a female and male. (b) Compare the mouthparts of *Ascaris* (right) to that of the free-living marine roundworm *Pseudocella* (left). Internal organs are similar in both.

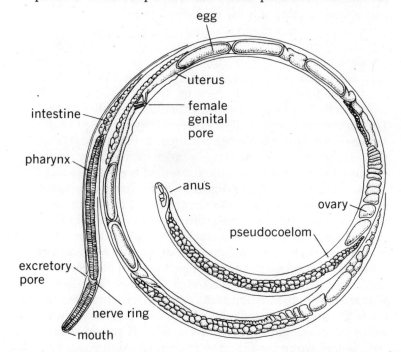

a.

b.

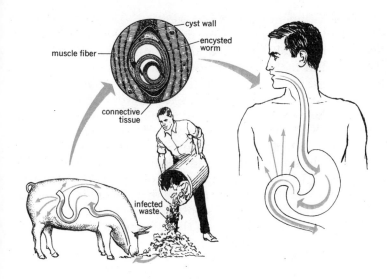

29-9 | The life cycle of the trichina worm. Follow the path of infection that leads to the man.

stream to muscles, where they again form cysts. The same thing happens when a human eats undercooked infected meat. The cysts are released and the larvae mature in the intestine. Each worm produces about 1,500 cyst-forming larvae. The cysts form in the muscle, causing a disease called **trichinosis.**

It should now be clear that it is important to know about parasitic worms. They cause disease, multiply rapidly, and are widespread. Many are spread because of poor sanitary conditions. But the eggs can be killed by proper sewage disposal. Careful inspection and thorough cooking of meat are other ways to avoid these parasites.

Phylum Annelida

Segmented worms have the most complex body structures of all the worms. These invertebrates belong to the phylum *Annelida*, which has four classes. Most segmented worms live in salt water, although some live in fresh water. Others, including common earthworms, live in soil. Because segmented worms are common, biologists often study them.

annellus = little ring

An earthworm has approximately 100 segments. If you examine an earthworm, its segments can easily be seen. You can also see that the anterior end is darker and more pointed than the posterior end. It does not have a separate head, or any visible sense organs. The crescent-shaped mouth is at the anterior end, underneath a kind of upper lip called a **prostomium** (proe-STOME-ee-um), which is a spe-

pro = before, in front of
stomatos = mouth

cialized segment. At the posterior end, the vertical *anus* opens from the intestine. Earthworm segments 32-37 have a distinct swelling called the **clitellum** (kli-TELL-um), involved in the worm's reproduction.

Each segment, except the first and last, has four pairs of bristles, or **setae** (SEE-tee), on the bottom and side surfaces. The earthworm uses the setae for moving and for clinging to the walls of its burrow, as anyone hunting for bait to go fishing has found out. An earthworm moves by pushing the setae of its anterior segments into the soil, then shortening its body by using a series of *longitudinal* muscles that are found throughout the length of its body. Then the worm pushes the setae of its posterior end into the soil, and withdraws the anterior setae. Next, it pushes itself forward by tightening the *circular* muscles, which make its body longer.

The earthworm consists of many cells. But it also has many different kinds of specialized cells. Each group of cells has the same job, so each group makes up one kind of *tissue*. Each tissue is grouped with others in larger structures called *organs*. Each organ has a definite job to do, too. In the earthworm, a whole series of organs work together to carry on a basic body process. These groups of organs are called *systems*. Systems are groups of organs working together to perform a function. The earthworm has several well-developed systems: the digestive, circulatory, excretory, nervous, muscular, and reproductive systems.

The Earthworm's Digestive System Below the prostomium is the mouth of the earthworm. Since it has no jaws or teeth, the earthworm uses its muscular *pharynx* to suck

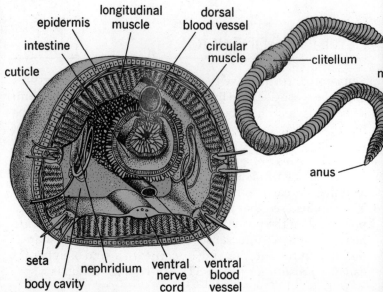

prostomium
mouth cavity
brain
pharynx
ventral nerve cord
ventral blood vessel
esophagus
aortic arches (hearts)
seminal receptacles
seminal vesicles
nephridium
crop
dorsal blood vessel
gizzard
intestine

epidermis
longitudinal muscle
dorsal blood vessel
intestine
circular muscle
cuticle
clitellum
anus
seta
body cavity
nephridium
ventral nerve cord
ventral blood vessel

29–10 | The external and internal structure of the earthworm. (left) The anterior portion is dissected to show the well developed nervous and circulatory systems. (right) One of the abdominal segments is shown in the cross section.

in soil containing food. The food particles and soil go through a long *esophagus* into a round organ called a **crop.** The crop stores the food temporarily. Then it is forced into a very muscular organ called the **gizzard.** The gizzard contracts and expands, causing grains of sand and food to rub together. In this way, the food is ground up. Food is digested in the **intestine,** which stretches from segment 19 to the end of the worm. Here enzymes chemically break down the food. Then the digested food is absorbed by the blood circulating through the intestine walls. As in flatworms and other metazoans, the earthworm's digestive system can be thought of as a tube within a tube.

eso = inner, within
phago = to eat

The complicated organs of the digestive system take up most of the anterior half of the earthworm's body. The earthworm ingests large amounts of soil, which has organic matter in it. The useless inorganic matter goes through the worm with no change. This is often left on the surface of the ground in the form of *castings.* As the earthworms feed, they loosen the soil, making it easier for air and water to enter. Its wastes also add to soil fertility. If there were no earthworms, the soil could not support crops, grasses, and other plants.

The Earthworm's Circulatory System After the earthworm has digested the food, the blood in the circulatory system carries the products of digestion to all the cells of the body. In the lower animals you have studied, the digested food had only a short distance to go to reach all the cells. But in higher forms, the distances are greater. More food material is needed by the many specialized cells at work in the body. The higher forms of animals have special transportation tissue for this. It is the circulating fluid called **blood.**

The earthworm's blood moves through a closed set of tubes, or vessels. Therefore earthworms are said to have a closed circulatory system. Blood flows forward to the anterior end inside a *dorsal blood vessel* and returns to the posterior end in a *ventral blood vessel.* Small tubes connect the dorsal and ventral vessels all through the worm. In segments 7 through 11, the pairs of tubes are large and muscular. They alternately contract and relax, keeping the blood flowing. Although they pump blood, they are not true hearts. So they are called **aortic arches.**

Respiration and Excretion A thin skin enables the earthworm to absorb oxygen and give off carbon dioxide. The skin is protected by a thin *cuticle,* which is secreted by the epidermal cells. The skin is kept moist by a mucus also secreted by the epidermis. **A moist surface is necessary for oxygen and carbon dioxide to pass through the membrane.**

If the worm dries out in the sun, it will die because this gas exchange can no longer take place.

Cell activities produce metabolic wastes containing nitrogen. These wastes are removed to the outside of the body by little tubes called **nephridia.** There are two nephridia in each segment except the first three and the last. Each nephridium does the same kind of work that a kidney tubule does in a human.

nephros = **kidney**

The Earthworm's Sensitivity

The nervous system coordinates the earthworm's movements. It sends impulses received in the sense organs to certain other parts of the body. In segment 3, there is a very small nerve center. Two nerves run from the center around the pharynx, forming a connecting collar. Then they join together to become one long *ventral nerve cord.* In each segment, there are enlarged nerve centers, called **ganglia.** Three pairs of nerves branch out from each ganglion. Though the earthworm does not have eyes or ears, it is sensitive to light and sound. Certain cells in its skin are sensitive to these stimuli. And the impulses are carried to the muscle. That is why earthworms react so quickly when you hunt them at night with a flashlight.

Earthworm Reproduction

Earthworms are hermaphroditic. Each earthworm produces both eggs and sperm. But the eggs of one worm must be fertilized by sperms from another. Sperms are produced by two pairs of testes found

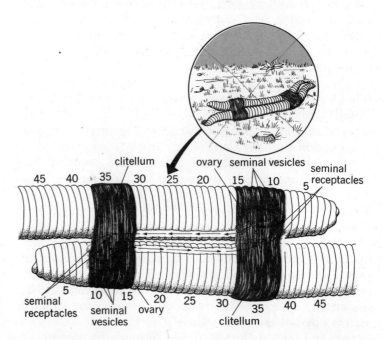

29-11 | Reproduction in the earthworm. Even though the earthworm has reproductive organs of both sexes, it exchanges its sperms for those of another earthworm. As shown, the sperms travel from the seminal vesicles of one worm to the seminal receptacles of the other.

in segments 10 and 11. The testes lie in sacs called *seminal vesicles.* Sperms leave the testes and are stored in the seminal vesicles. A sperm duct carrries the sperms to the male genital pore on segment 15.

Eggs are produced in a pair of small ovaries in segment 13. The eggs leave the ovaries and mature in the body cavity of the worm. The eggs are then collected by a ciliated funnel. They are carried by *oviducts* to the female genital pore on segment 14.

Figure 29-11 shows how sperms pass from one worm to the other. The sperms enter the *seminal receptacle* through openings in segments 9 and 10. There they are stored until eggs are laid. When the eggs are mature, they are released into a slime ring which is secreted by the clitellum. As the ring moves forward, eggs are deposited in it. Then the seminal receptacle releases the sperms onto it that it has been storing. Fertilization occurs, and the slime ring continues to move forward. When the slime ring slips off the body, it becomes the cocoon in which the young worms develop.

The Leech: Another Segmented Worm

The leech, or blood sucker, is an annelid found in streams and ponds. It is an external parasite on fish and other animals that live in the water. It may also attach to the skin of humans when they are swimming or wading. A leech is able to suck blood when it attaches its posterior sucker to some vertebrate. It applies the anterior sucker to the skin and makes a wound with little jaws inside its mouth. The salivary glands of the leech secrete a substance that prevents blood from clotting while it feeds. Leeches were used medicinally in the Middle Ages and in later years. It was then believed that blood loss was supposed to heal the sick by letting out what was thought to be "bad blood."

The Development of the Coelom

Certain similarities among worms have been pointed out. But sometimes these *patterns* are not clear until the animals are compared. One theory is that **the more similar the body plans of two groups, the closer the relationship.**

An important characteristic in grouping animals is the type of body cavity or ***coelom*** (SEE-lom) in the adult. Flatworms are bilaterally symmetrical, but they do not have a body cavity between their internal organs and the body wall. Their tissues have been formed from all three germ layers. But in development, the *mesoderm* completely fills the space between the ectoderm and the endoderm. Cell wastes and nutrients diffuse from cell to cell. The planarians are **acoelomate.**

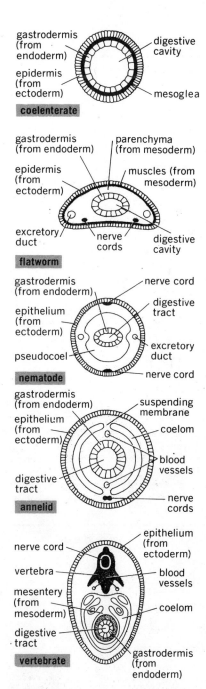

29-12 | General body plans of organisms of five representative animal phyla. Notice the germ layers forming the various tissues.

Because of their size, large animals could not have a solid structure like that of flatworms. This kind of structure would not be efficient. **The majority of animals have a coelom.** It is a fluid-filled cavity with room for looped digestive organs. The coelom aids in circulation of food and oxygen and the removal of wastes. As you saw in the earthworm, it also serves as a place where eggs develop. The true coelom develops between two layers of mesoderm. The coelom has a membrane lining made of specialized cells that suspend the intestines within it. Earthworms are *coelomate.*

There are animals that are grouped between the *acoelomates* and the *coelomates.* These animals have a *pseudocoel* (SOO-doe-seel), or false coelom. This cavity is different from the coelom. It is not lined with the specialized cells. Also, the internal organs are free within the cavity instead of being suspended by a membrane. **Nematodes are *pseudocoelomates.*** Compare the cross sections of the organisms in figure 29-12 on page 373. You will see patterns in general body plans of the organisms you have been studying.

pseudo = false

Summary

	PLATYHELMINTHES	NEMATODA	ANNELIDA
Body Types	flat, unsegmented bodies	round, unsegmented bodies	body divided into segments
Type of Life	many parasitic	some parasitic	majority *not* parasitic
Organization	3 germ layers form many organ systems	3 germ layers form many organ systems	3 germ layers form many organ systems
Body Cavity	acoelomate	pseudocoelom	true coelom
Digestive System	open at one end only	mouth and anus	mouth and anus
Reproduction	asexually by fission; sexually–hermaphrodite with cross-fertilization	sexual, definite male and female	sexually–hermaphroditic with cross-fertilization
Circulation	none	none	5 pairs of aortic arches, large dorsal vessel, small ventral vessel
Nervous System	2 longitudinal nerve cords	2 nerve cords, one dorsal, one ventral	one large ventral nerve cord with ganglia in the adult

Biologically
Speaking

parasitic	proglottid	aortic arch
cuticle	anus	nephridia
tegument	trichinosis	ganglia
eyespot	prostomium	seminal vesicle
pharnyx	clitellum	seminal receptacle
cephalization	setae	coelom
hermaphroditic	esophagus	acoelomate
uterus	crop	coelomate
larvae	gizzard	pseudocoelomate
cyst	intestine	
scolex	blood	

Biologically Speaking

1. What is the importance of the three germ layers of cells found in flatworm development?
2. How does the planarian test its environment?
3. In what ways are the flatworms more complicated than the sponges and coelenterates?
4. Where are nematodes found?
5. In what unusual ways does the tapeworm show specialization?
6. Describe the life cycle of *Ascaris*.
7. Describe how the trichina worm reaches the human body.
8. Describe the way the earthworm moves.
9. Describe the route of food through the digestive system of the earthworm, naming the organs involved.
10. What is the difference between coelomates and acoelomates?
11. What are the two kinds of body cavities found in worms?

Questions for Review

1. Describe the path followed by *Ascaris* through the human body, naming all the structures through which it goes. At what stages are symptoms of disease most likely to be present? At what stages is treatment most likely to be effective?
2. What measures should be taken in trying to control parasitic worms?
3. Symptoms of tapeworms in an animal usually include loss of weight and general fatigue. Account for these conditions.
4. Trichinosis can become a hopeless disease. Why is it almost impossible to treat?

Applying Concepts

30

Mollusks and Echinoderms

A **IDENTIFY** the common characteristics of the phlylum Mollusca.

B **DESCRIBE** how mollusks differ from each other.

C **IDENTIFY** the parts of a bivalve mollusk.

D **IDENTIFY** the characteristics of the echinoderms.

E **EXPLAIN** a water-vascular system.

F **DESCRIBE** how the starfish gets food and reproduces.

30–1 | A sea scallop swims away from its predator, the starfish. (D. P. Wilson)

Phylum Mollusca

You are probably familiar with some members of the phylum *Mollusca*. This phylum includes clams, oysters, squids, and snails. Some of these mollusks are called shellfish. However, they are not fish, and many mollusks do not even have shells. Some mollusks are aquatic. They live in fresh water and marine environments. Some mollusks, such as slugs and snails, are terrestrial. That is, they live on land. Many are adapted to live buried in sand or mud where oxygen concentration might be too low for more active animals. There are more species of mollusks than any other phylum except the phylum *Arthropoda*, which includes insects.

Since earliest recorded time, mollusks have been used by human beings. They served our ancestors as food, money, dyes, tools, buttons, and weapons. Many people collect mollusk shells from all over the world for their beauty alone. High concentrations of shells, or their fossils, may lead engineers to oil deposits. These are *index fossils* which may indicate an underlying source of oil. Many fossil remains are mollusks mainly because their shells left imprints in rock.

The Binding Link

Perhaps you are wondering why such diverse organisms as clams, squids, and snails could all be in the same phylum. You already know that structural similarities are used in classification. Biologists compare more than the adult forms of animals. You have seen that the development of germ layers and the coelom are important characteristics used for grouping animals. Animals are also thought to be related when their juvenile forms, the larvae, develop in similar ways. **Animals classified as mollusks all go through a stage of larval development in which they look the same.** The larval stage of the mollusk is called a **trochophore** (TROCK-uh-FORE). The trochophore has a tuft of cilia at one end and a ciliated band around its middle. In a free-swimming larva, the cilia move the larva through the water and bring food to the larva's mouth. In terrestrial mollusks as well as many marine forms, the trochophore larvae are not free-swimming. They pass through their larval stage within the egg membranes.

Animals of the phylum *Annelida* also have a trochophore larval stage. For this reason, biologists believe that segmented worms and mollusks are related.

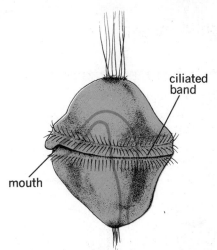

30–2 | The trochophore larval form is found in the development of both mollusks and annelids. An outline of the digestive tract is shown in blue.

The Mollusk Body Plan

The soft body of an adult mollusk has a *head, foot,* and *visceral* (VISS-uh-rul) *hump.* Inside the visceral hump are the digestive organs, reproductive organs or gonads, excretory glands, and heart. A true coelom, formed from mesoderm, is found in the mollusks. The coelom surrounds the heart, gonads, and excretory organs.

The visceral hump is covered by a *mantle.* The mantle is a thin membrane that secrets the calcium carbonate shell found in most species. The mantle hangs down over the sides and back of the body, forming a space called the *mantle cavity. Gills* are in this cavity. They are the respiratory organs of the aquatic mollusks. Undigested materials pass from anus to mantle cavity before leaving the animal.

The *foot* of a mollusk is a large muscular organ used in locomotion. The type of foot, the kind of shell, and the presence or absence of a shell are important characteristics. They are used to classify the mollusks. You will be studying three of the six classes of the phylum Mollusca.

- *Gastropoda* (ga-STROP-uh-duh), or stomach-footed, single-shell mollusks.
- *Pelecypoda* (pell-uh-SIP-uh-duh), or hatcher-footed, two-shell mollusks.
- *Cephalopoda* (SEF-uh-LOP-uh-duh), or head-footed mollusks.

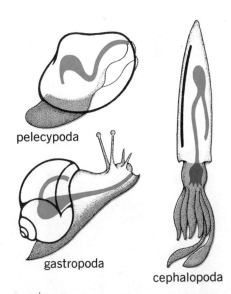

30–3 | Mollusk body plans. The *shells* are in black, the *digestive systems* in red, and the *foot* in blue. Note that the foot in Cephalopoda has become tentacles.

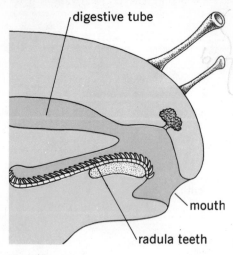

digestive tube

mouth

radula teeth

30-4 | A snail showing the rasplike *radula*. Both snails and slugs damage garden and greenhouse plants.

gaster = belly, stomach
podos = foot

30-5 | Some examples of gastropods are (left) the land snail, (middle) garden slug, and the most beautiful mollusk, (right) the nudibranch mollusk, also called a seaslug. *(left: William E. Ferguson; middle: © George K. Bryce, Animals Animals; right: Z. Leszczynski, © Animals Animals)*

Mollusks with One Shell: Gastropods

Aquatic and terrestrial snails, slugs, conches, and abalones are placed in the class Gastropoda. Most of these animals have only one shell. The land slugs and sea slugs of this class do not have shells but are like other gastropods in many ways.

The land snail has adapted to survive outside water. Its mantle cavity acts as a modified lung. Oxygen diffuses through the thin membrane that lines the cavity. This lining must be kept moist for gases to be exchanged. Air is most moist during the evening, night, and early morning. So it is during these times when snails are most active.

When the air is drier and cooler, snails become inactive. They retreat into their shells. Mucus secreted by glands in the foot forms a seal that hardens in the air. The dried mucus also attaches the shell to the hardened seal. This helps prevent water loss.

Land snails travel very slowly, about three meters (9.9 feet) an hour. When the snail is active, the mucus produced by the glands in the foot secretes a layer of slime on which the snail moves. Muscles in the foot contract in a wavelike rhythm, pulling the snail along. The snail's eyes are on the tops of two tentacles, which vanish upon touch by being pulled into themselves much as the toe of a sock disappears when you turn it inside out.

Slugs look like snails that have lost their shells. If you look closely at a slug, you can see the opening to the mantle cavity which is sometimes seen at the lower edge of the mantle. This opening is used in respiration. The animal is able to save moisture within the mantle chamber by controlling the size of the opening. Like land snails, slugs are usually active at night. They leave trails of slime wherever they go.

Both snails and slugs can do damage by feeding on garden plants. The best way to see the feeding mechanism of a gastropod is to watch freshwater snails in an aquarium. Watch to see a snail open its mouth and scrape the glass

with a tonguelike structure called a **radula** (RAJ-uh-luh). The word *radula* means "scraper." The snail's radula actually files algae from the glass walls of the aquarium. It is with their radulas that snails and slugs harm garden plants.

Mollusks with Two Shells: Pelecypods

pelekys = hatchet

Mollusks such as clams, oysters, scallops, and mussels are called *bivalves* because their shells have two halves, called **valves.** A hinge connects the two valves, so they can be opened and closed by the animal. Each valve has three different layers made of materials secreted by the mantle. The smooth, shiny layer next to the mantle is the *pearly layer.* If a grain of sand or the cyst of a parasitic worm gets caught in the mantle, this layer builds up around the object and forms a pearl. Oysters make the ones used as jewelry. The middle layer is made of calcium carbonate crystals and is called the **prismatic layer.**

The outer layer is called the **horny outer layer,** and is very thin. Perhaps you have seen this layer on a dried shell. It looks like shellac or varnish, and it can be peeled off. The hinge connecting the valves is also made of this hornlike material.

Bivalves are placed in the class Pelecypoda. The name refers to the shape of the mollusk's foot. Figure 30–6 shows how a clam puts its foot into the sand. Once the muscular foot is in the sand, blood swells the end. This causes the end of the foot to spread out to form a hatchet-shaped anchor. Then, the long muscles of the foot contract. The mollusk is pulled down into the sand or mud. As some of you may know, clams can dig very quickly!

A clam usually stays partly buried. Its valves are kept partly opened, with two *siphons* extended into the water. Water flows into the mantle cavity through an **incurrent siphon.** The water circulates over the gills. Next, the water flows past the anus where wastes are given off. Then the water leaves the animal through an **excurrent siphon.**

As water passes over the gills, two things happen. First, oxygen is taken in, and carbon dioxide diffuses out. Second, small particles of organic matter stick to a thin layer of mucus on the gills. Cilia on the surface of the gills carry the food-bearing mucus to the dorsal surface and forward to the mouth. Here two leaflike folds direct the food into the mouth. Animals that feed in this manner are called *mucus feeders.* They are scavengers, feeding on dead and decaying organic matter and the many microscopic protists living on the bottom of a body of water.

Clams, oysters, scallops, and mussels are all edible bivalves. They feed on microscopic organisms by filtering

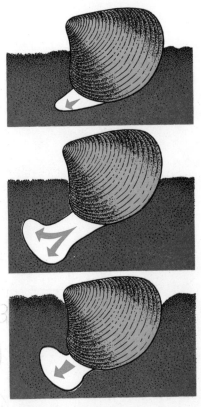

30–6 | Note how the clam's hatchet-shaped foot helps the clam to dig into sand.

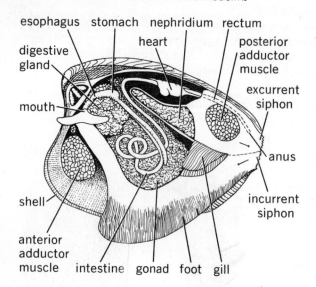

esophagus   stomach   nephridium   rectum

digestive gland

heart

mouth

posterior adductor muscle

excurrent siphon

anus

shell

incurrent siphon

anterior adductor muscle   intestine   gonad   foot   gill

30–7 | (left) A diagram of a partially dissected clam showing its internal structure. (right) A photograph of a clam with one valve removed. *(William E. Ferguson)*

water through their bodies. Because of water pollution, areas of some shorelines are closed to mollusk fishing. Also, some of the organisms mollusks eat are poisonous to humans, like the algae in a "red tide." When you eat raw mollusks, it is wise to be sure that they are from an uncontaminated area.

If you have eaten steamed clams, you know that even after they have been cooked and have opened up, you still have to pry their two shells apart. You are tearing two large muscles, the anterior and posterior *adductor muscles*. These muscles can pull shells tightly shut when the clam is alive. You can recognize dead clams at the market if their shells stay open all the time. Their adductor muscles do not counter the opening action of the hinge.

Mollusks have an open circulatory system through which blood goes from the heart, to tissues, to *nephridia* (nuh-FRID-ee-uh), to gills, and back to the heart. There also is a part of the circulatory system that goes to and from the mantle. Large amounts of water are excreted from the nephridia.

Bivalves have a well-developed nervous system with several large ganglia. Sensory cells at the edge of the mantle respond to light and touch.

Only a few Pelecypod species are hermaphroditic. Other species have individuals that are either male or female. Gametes are swept out of the bivalve through the excurrent siphon. Fertilization occurs in the surrounding water. In some freshwater species fertilization is internal.

cephalic = head

Head-Footed Mollusks: Cephalopods

Octopus, squid, cuttlefish, and chambered nautilus are placed in the class Cephalopoda. These animals are quite different from each other in appearance. The octopus has no shell. The squid and the cuttlefish have an internal shell. But the members of this class have common characteristics. They are all bilaterally symmetrical. The head is well-developed, and they have large complex eyes. The cephalopods have jaws as well as a *radula*. Perhaps the most obvious similarity is that the foot is divided to form several tentacles. And the tentacles usually have suckers for grasping prey and moving along the bottom of the marine environment. The cephalopods are the most complex mollusks.

The giant squid is probably the largest invertebrate in the world. It may grow to be 18 meters (59.4 feet) long and weigh 1,800 kilograms (3,960 pounds). A very large type of octopus that lives along the Pacific Coast has a body about 30 centimeters (1 foot) long.

Phylum Echinodermata

The common brittle star, starfish, sea cucumber, sea urchin, and sand dollar are members of the phylum *Echinodermata*. Echinoderms (ee-KINE-o-derms) begin life as free-swimming bilaterally symmetrical larvae. But as adults, they have radially symmetrical bodies covered with spines. The radial symmetry of echinoderms is very different from that of coelenterates. The bodies of most echinoderms have five sections. For this reason, biologists usually refer to the echinoderm body shape as **pentaradial.** In some echinoderms, like the sea urchin, the spines covering the body are long. Some spines, like those of the sand dollar, are very short. All echinoderms are marine. Some live deep in the ocean, and others live in shallow tide pools.

The starfish, or seastar, is one of the most familiar echinoderms. The starfish will be described in order to identify the characteristics of echinoderms. These animals have a skeleton made of calcium carbonate plates. An *epidermis*

30–8 | The octopus (top) and squid (bottom) have well-developed eyes. They can move by expelling a jet of water from their excurrent siphons. *(top: Jane Burton, Bruce Coleman Inc.; bottom: Runk, Schoenberger, Grant Heilman)*

echinos = prickle; sea-urchin

derma = skin

30–9 | Some examples of common echinoderms. (a) sand dollar; (b) sea cucumber; (c) sea urchin; (d) brittle starfish. Echinodermata is the only major phylum composed entirely of marine animals. *(a: Douglas Faulkner; b: J. Foott, Bruce Coleman; c: William Ferguson; d: Steve Earley, Animals Animals)*

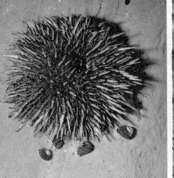
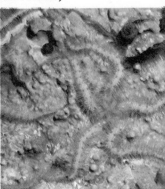

a   b   c   d

30–10 | The *tube feet* of the starfish are part of the water-vascular system. *(James H. Carmichael, Bruce Coleman)*

endon = within

ab = away from

30–11 | This aboral view of a partially dissected starfish shows the location of some of its internal organs.

covers the plates, so truly the skeleton is inside the animal. An internal skeleton is called an **endoskeleton.**

Starfish normally have five rays, or arms, radiating from a central disk. In a groove on the lower side of each movable ray are two rows of **tube feet.** These are part of a **water-vascular system.** Echinoderms are coelomates. The cavity surrounding the internal organs of the starfish and the water-vascular system are both part of the coelom. During development they are formed from the *mesoderm.*

The water-vascular system is found only in echinoderms. It is made of several structures. Figure 30–11 shows the tube feet connected to the *radial canal.* Each radial canal leads to the circular *ring canal,* in the central disk. The stone canal connects the ring canal to the *sieve plate* on the surface. In a pentaradial animal like the seastar, the surface on the opposite side of the mouth, or *oral* surface, is called the **aboral** surface. The anus of the seastar also opens on the aboral surface.

The starfish uses its water-vascular system to effectively open clams and oysters for food. When it presses its tube feet against the mollusk's shell, water is forced out the sieve plate and the starfish's feet grip by suction. When water comes back into the canals, the tube feet release their grip. The starfish begins its feeding process by arching over its prey. It firmly grips both valves with its tube feet, exerting a steady pull. The adductor muscles of the clam tire and the valves open. Then the starfish turns its stomach inside out through its mouth. The stomach may pass through the tiniest opening between the mollusk's valves. Enzymes secreted by the stomach then digest the mollusk's body. The clam is actually digested while in its own shell.

Less complex aquatic animals often have simple systems of gas exchange and excretion. In starfish, outpocket-

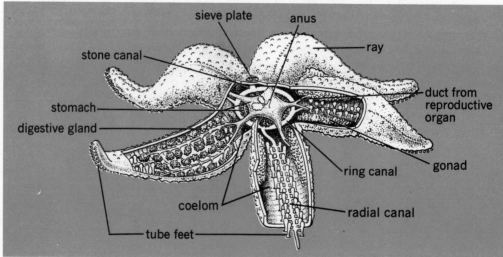

ings on the aboral surface serve as both respiratory and excretory organs. Wastes are excreted and gases are exchanged through these outpocketings by diffusion.

Starfish have nerve cords that follow the pentaradial system of their bodies. The nervous system is basically a *nerve ring* with a *radial nerve* to each arm. At the end of each arm is a light-sensitive *eyespot*.

Starfish are natural enemies of oyster fishers. An adult starfish can eat eight to twelve oysters a day. But oyster fishers who try to destroy starfish by tearing them to pieces and throwing them back in the water are only multiplying their troubles. **A starfish ray that is still attached to part of the central disk can regenerate its missing parts to become a whole new animal.**

Normally, starfish reproduce sexually. They are either male or female. Starfish shed their sperms and eggs into the water during the reproductive season. Thus, fertilization is external since it takes place outside the body. Female starfish can produce as many as 200 million eggs in one season. These may develop into free-swimming, ciliated larvae, complete with mouths, digestive tracts, and anuses. These are *bipinnaria* larvae, which are shown in figure 30–12. After swimming for a while, the larvae settle down to a solid surface and grow into adults.

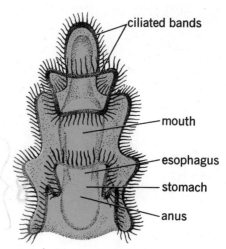

30–12 | A free swimming larva of an echinoderm called a *bipinnaria.* It is similar to the larva of some of the lower chordates (animals with backbones).

bi = two
pinna = feather, wing

Summary

	Mollusks	Echinoderm (example: starfish)
Body Types	Head, foot, visceral hump containing vital organs.	Radially symmetrical, spines on aboral surface. Endoskeleton.
Type of Life	Aquatic—freshwater, marine. Terrestrial. Trochophore larvae stage.	marine bipinnaria larvae
Movement	foot; water expulsion	water-vascular system
SYSTEMS		
Digestive	radula; mucus feeders; digestive gland	extracellular digestion; digestive gland
Circulatory	open circulatory system	open circulatory system
Nervous	ganglia; light receptors	oral and radial nerve cords; eyespots
Excretory	nephridia	diffusion through outpockets on the aboral surface
Respiration	diffusion through gills, mantle	diffusion through outpockets on the aboral surface
Reproductive	Sexual—separate sexes, some hermaphroditic.	Sexual—separate sexes. Regeneration

Biologically Speaking

trochopore	radula	pentaradial
visceral hump	bivalves	endoskeleton
mantle	prismatic layer	tube feet
mantle cavity	horny outer layer	water-vascular
gills	incurrent siphon	system
foot	excurrent siphon	aboral

Questions for Review

1. What characteristics place clams, oysters, squids, and snails in the phylum Mollusca?
2. Describe the route of food from outside the clam to the digestive gland, naming the organs through which the food goes.
3. Describe how a clam gets its food.
4. Explain why you should be careful of what shellfish you eat.
5. In what ways do the cephalopods differ from the gastropods?
6. What structures of the echinoderms make them different from other invertebrate animals?
7. Describe the movement and feeding of starfish.
8. Why is it useless to try to eliminate starfish by tearing them up?

Applying Concepts

1. What structural similarities indicate a relationship between the mollusks and the annelids?
2. In what ways have the mollusks been of value to human beings? In what ways have they been pests?
3. In what ways are echinoderms adapted to their aquatic way of life?

The Arthropods

A **LIST** the characteristics of the arthropods.

B **EXPLAIN** the advantages and disadvantages of an exoskeleton.

C **DESCRIBE** the variations among arthropods.

D **NAME** and **GIVE EXAMPLES** of each major class of arthropod.

E **DESCRIBE** arachnids and some of their behavior.

F **DESCRIBE** the parts of a spider.

G **IDENTIFY** the parts of a crayfish.

H **DISTINGUISH** between millipedes and centipedes.

31-1 | The Sally light-foot crab is an example of an arthropod. *(Albert Towle)*

What Is an Arthropod?

You may already be familiar with many arthropods. Insects, including flies, fleas, and bees, are arthropods. Spiders, centipedes, crabs, shrimp, and lobsters are all arthropods. Some serve as food for humans, but they also compete with people for food. Many of you have probably enjoyed a shrimp dinner or had honey provided by bees. On the other hand, insects destroy millions of dollars worth of food every year.

Arthropods are found everywhere. They have adapted to every kind of habitat. Many live as parasites in or on other organisms, and some transmit disease. Mosquitos, for example, transmit malaria. Arthropods that live in water serve as food for fish and other animals. On land they have adapted to all areas and climates. One arthropod, the springtail, can even be found within the Antarctic snow and ice.

Seventy-eight percent of all species of animals are arthropods. The class *Insecta* makes up a large part of that percentage (see figure 28-2 on page 349). Arthropods are the most successful groups of animals on the earth because they are numerous and are able to live everywhere. Why

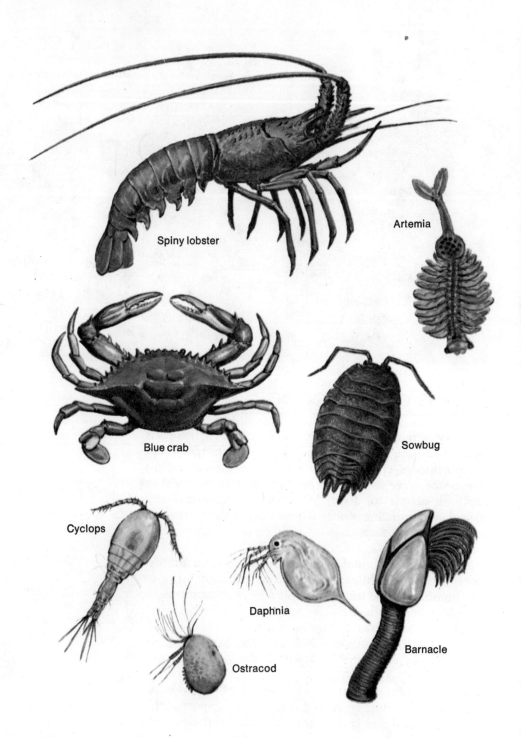

Spiny lobster

Artemia

Blue crab

Sowbug

Cyclops

Daphnia

Ostracod

Barnacle

31-2 | Various examples of the phylum Arthropoda.

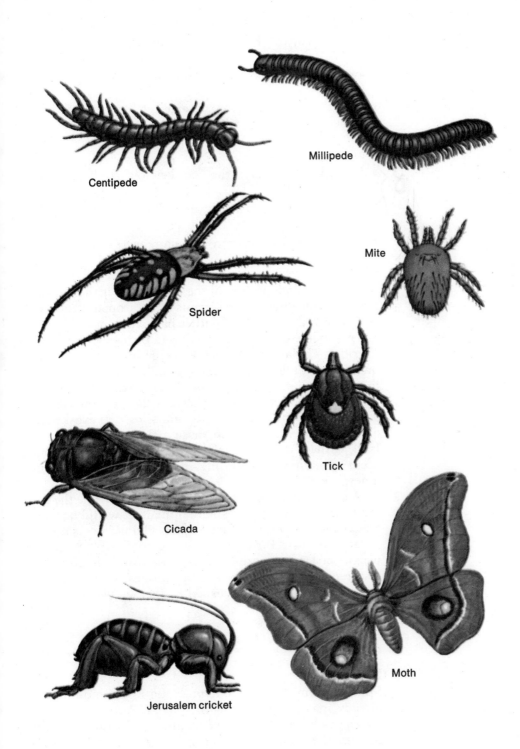

Centipede

Millipede

Spider

Mite

Tick

Cicada

Moth

Jerusalem cricket

are they everywhere? Why are they so numerous? To answer these questions you must first understand what an arthropod is. The phylum name *Arthropoda* means "jointed feet." All arthropods have these characteristics:

- Jointed **appendages,** including legs and other body outgrowths.
- A hard external skeleton, or **exoskeleton,** made of a substance called *chitin* (KITE'n). This differs from the *internal* support or skeleton in humans and other vertebrates.
- A segmented body; the exoskeleton is divided into parts.
- A dorsal heart; a heart located above the digestive system.
- A ventral nervous system; the main nerves are below the digestive system.

exo = outside

skeleton = dried body

An important adaptation of the arthropods is the *exoskeleton.* Like annelids, the epidermis of arthropods secretes a cuticle. But the arthropod cuticle has two layers. The inner layer is made of protein and *chitin* (a nitrogenous polysaccharide). The arthropod's outer layer may remain tough but somewhat flexible, as in the grasshopper. Or it may be made of calcium carbonate, as in the hard shell of a crab. The arthropod exoskeleton protects delicate internal organs and provides an anchor for muscles. The exoskeleton also prevents water loss in those arthropods that live on land. Growth of an animal with an exoskeleton can only occur by **molting,** or shedding, its old skeleton and forming a new one.

An exoskeleton does have its limitations. While the exoskeleton is ideal for very small animals, it would be a disadvantage for animals of larger size. Flying insects are not as large as birds. Birds' wings would not be able to lift the weight of large exoskeletons. A large exoskeleton would also require large and powerful muscles to move it. The animal would likely be crushed by its own weight.

Arachnids: Familiar Chelicerates

Spiders

Spiders are in the class *Arachnida* (uh-RACK-nid-uh). You already may be familiar with spiders. Perhaps you have seen a spider catch a fly. Spiders are very useful to humans because they destroy many harmful insects. All spiders use silk of some kind. Many are called *orb weavers.* They spin thin silklike threads into patterned webs. When a flying insect becomes trapped in the sticky web, the spider comes out from a hiding place along the edge.

The first pair of appendages in the spider are formed into hollow fangs. They are called **chelicerae** (ki-LISS-er-ay). When the fangs pierce the prey, poison from a gland flows through the fangs and paralyzes the victim. Some spiders wrap up their meals in more silken threads. The chelicerae are also used to suck the juices from their food. Not all spiders spin webs. Some stalk their prey as they roam.

The spider has no antennae. Its eyes are called simple eyes, and it has four pairs of legs. The *head* and *thorax* are joined to form a **cephalothorax** (SEF-uh-loh-THOR-aks). The second body division is the **abdomen.**

The second pair of appendages are the **pedipalps.** These are sensory appendages. In the male spider they are also used in reproduction. The four pairs of legs also are attached to the cephalothorax.

On the tip of the abdomen of many spiders there are three pairs of *spinnerets*. Each spinneret is composed of hundreds of microscopic tubes. The fluid silk is drawn out from the silk glands through these tubes. As it is drawn out, it hardens into a thread. The spider uses its silk to make webs, to build cocoons for eggs, and to build its nest. This thread sometimes acts as a guide to help the spider find its way back to the web. In many species, young spiders spin long silken threads that catch the wind and carry them to other places. This method of moving is called *ballooning*.

The spider respires through slitlike openings that take in air to a pair of sacs called *book lungs*. Book lungs are located on the lower side of the abdomen. The book lungs have several leaves, or plates, to expose a large surface to

31-3 | A longitudinal section of a female spider.

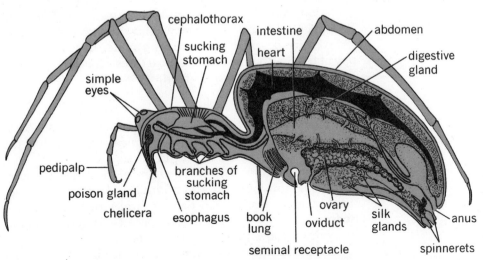

31-4 | Notice the characteristic hourglass marking on the ventral surface of the female black widow spider. Its round black abdomen is also a characteristic feature. *(Alan Roberts)*

Facts & Figures

The South American bird-eating spider may have a body 8.75 centimeters (3.4 inches) long and a leg span of 25 centimeters (10 inches).

the air. In addition to their book lungs, many spiders have openings in their abdomens that lead to air tubes called *tracheae* (TRAY-kee-ee). Tracheae are also used in gas exchange.

You can usually tell a mature male spider from the female just by size. The male is smaller. If both are the same size, the tips of the pedipalps of the male are much larger. When the male is mature, he transfers sperms to special sacs in these tips. The sperms are then placed in the *seminal receptacle* of the female by the male.

Spiders are solitary animals. When the male approaches the female, he must be careful that he is not mistaken for food. Interesting courtship behavior occurs before mating. Once mating has occurred, the male darts away. If he is not quick enough, the female's response will be to use him for food. When the eggs are laid, they are fertilized as they pass through the genital pore into a silken nest or cocoon spun by the female.

Among the best known spiders are the *tarantula* (teh-RANCH-el-uh), the *black widow*, and the *trapdoor spider* of the western desert. One interesting spider lives in the canopy of the South American tropical forest. It is large enough to catch small birds for its food.

Scorpions

Scorpions are also arachnids. Scorpions live in the southwestern United States and in all tropical areas. Unlike the spider, the abdomen of a scorpion is segmented, long, and ends in a poisonous stinger. The sting of the American scorpion is painful, but it is seldom fatal to humans. Some of the African scorpions can deliver fatal stings to humans. Scorpions may surprise a person because they often crawl into empty shoes to escape bright light.

The pedipalps of scorpions are in the shape of pincers.

They hold the prey while the poison from the stinger paralyzes it. Scorpions, like spiders, live solitary lives except during mating. As with the spiders, the male scorpion must escape the predatory impulse of the female after mating.

Mites, Ticks, and Other Arachnids

Mites and ticks are arachnids that often feed on humans and other animals. Many live as parasites on the skins of chickens, dogs, cattle, humans, and other animals. Some forms transmit disease, such as the Rocky Mountain tick, which can transmit Rocky Mountain spotted fever.

Harvest mites, or *chiggers*, are immature mites that attach themselves to the skin surface. They break the skin with their chelicerae and pedipalps to feed on blood. They are almost microscopic, so the first sign of them is swelling and itching.

Other arachnids more closely resemble spiders. The familiar *daddy-longlegs*, or *harvestman*, lives alone too. It travels through fields in search of its prey. Since it feeds on plant lice, the daddy-longlegs is an arachnid useful to humans.

31–5 | What are the characteristics that make the scorpion (top) and harvestman (bottom) different than spiders? *(top: William E. Ferguson; bottom: Ken Lewis, Animals Animals)*

Crustaceans: Mandibulate Arthropods

The edible lobsters and crabs are in the class *Crustacea*. But the vast majority of crustaceans are very small and even microscopic in size. Even so, they may occur in such tremendous numbers that ships' sonar equipment have misread the vast numbers of crustaceans for the bottom depth of the ocean.

Artemia, the brine shrimp, lives in tide pools and can survive in an environment with a high concentration of salt. Owners of tropical fish often buy its eggs and raise the shrimp for fish food. *Barnacles* are sessile crustaceans. They settle on a solid object when they are larvae. Then they produce a shell and use their feet to kick food into their mouths. Barnacles can gather on the hulls of ships in such large numbers that they slow down the ships. In order to get rid of barnacles, ships will often try to sail through fresh water. In fresh water barnacles die and drop off because they can't adjust to the lower salt content of the water.

If you have ever seen tiny brown specks zigzagging in the water, you may have been looking at *Daphnia* (water fleas) or *ostracods*. These are both crustaceans. Ostracods have hinged chitinous exoskeletons that contain lime. Their exoskeletons look like the shells of a clam. Another common tiny crustacean is the *copepod* (KOPE-uh-POD).

crusta = tough hard surface of a body, shell

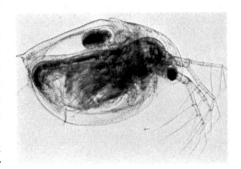

31–6 | Almost every body of water has crustaceans. The *Daphnia* is common in freshwater. *(Carolina Biological Supply House)*

Copepods are a very important part of the diet of many fish.

Interesting adaptations to land are found in terrestrial crustaceans such as the sow bugs and pill bugs. Since they have seven identical pairs of legs, these creatures are called *isopods*, or "same feet." Isopods have a series of platelike gills along the lower surface of the abdomen. The plates have tiny tubes to allow air to enter. These gills must stay moist for respiration to occur. So these animals usually live under stones and logs. Even if you do not live near the water where crayfish may be found, you can probably find isopods in your area. Terrestrial isopods can live for weeks in jars with slices of potato or carrot for food.

The Crayfish: Freshwater Crustacean

Crayfish make good subjects for study since they are large and easy to find. In some areas of the United States, they are called "crawdads." Except for a few details, crayfish are like lobsters. They live in nearly all bodies of fresh water that contain lime (calcium oxide). Lime salts are used by the crayfish to harden its tough, chitinous exoskeleton. The habit of digging holes in which to live has caused crayfish to become a nuisance. They may cause leaks in the banks of irrigation ditches.

Notice in figure 31-7 that the body of the crayfish can be divided into two regions. The first part is called the *cephalothorax*. As in the spiders, this region includes the head and the thorax. The *cephalothorax* of the crayfish is protected by a shield of exoskeleton called a **carapace** (KAHR-a-pays).

The second part of the crayfish body is posterior to the cephalothorax. It is the *abdomen*. Like the abdomen of the scorpion, it is divided into segments. But the abdomen of the crayfish has only seven segments, and it does not have a stinger.

Appendages of the Crayfish The anterior pair of appendages of the crayfish are the **antennules.** These contain the hearing and the balancing, or *equilibrium*, mechanisms. The large **antennae** are attached just behind the antennules. They are the organs of touch, taste, and smell. Behind the antennae are the **mandibles,** or true jaws. They crush and chew food. They are helped by two pairs of **maxillae** (mack-SILL-ee). Maxillae work from side to side instead of up and down. The second maxillae is called a "gill bailer." It has two flat plates that bail water over the gills. Maxillae are really leglike appendages that are adapted for chewing. They move sideways like the other legs. Refer to figure 31-7 as you read the following description of the other appendages of the crayfish. The first

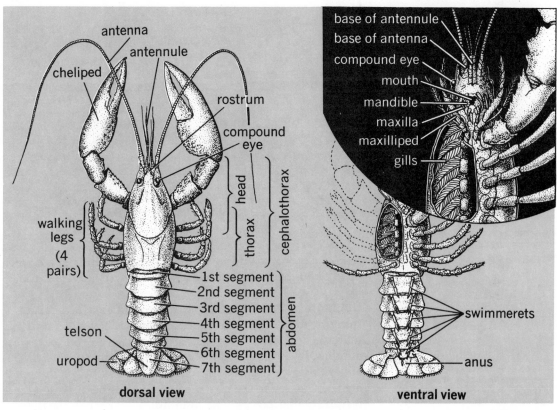

dorsal view

ventral view

31-7 | The crayfish, a common crustacean.

appendages of the thorax are three pairs of **maxillipeds** (mack-SILL-i-PEDZ). Maxillipeds, or "jaw feet," hold food while the crayfish is chewing. The next pair of appendages are the claws, or **chelipeds** (KEE-luh-PEDZ). These help to get food and to protect the crayfish. Behind the claws are the four pairs of **walking legs.** Feathery gills, for respiration, are attached to the appendages of the thorax. The delicate gills are protected under the carapace.

The appendages of the abdomen of the crayfish are called **swimmerets.** As you might expect, they are used for swimming. The female attaches eggs to the last three pairs of swimmerets. The sixth pair of abdominal appendages is developed into a flipper, or **uropod** (YOOH-ruh-POD). The middle of the tail is a flat, triangular structure called the **telson.** Strong muscles can whip the tail forward, causing the animal to shoot backward very rapidly.

Recall from Chapter 13 that organs in different animals that have similar functions are called analogous. The gills of a crayfish and the lungs of a human are analogous because they are the organs for respiration. But they are not homologous because they each have developed in a dif-

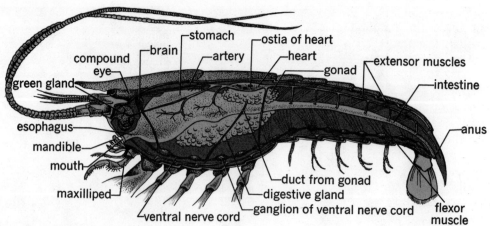

compound eye · brain · stomach · artery · ostia of heart · heart · gonad · extensor muscles · intestine · green gland · esophagus · mandible · mouth · maxilliped · ventral nerve cord · duct from gonad · digestive gland · ganglion of ventral nerve cord · anus · flexor muscle

31–8 | The internal structure of a crayfish. The term *gonad* refers to the ovary in the female and testes in the male.

ferent way from different structures. The gills have developed from legs, while lungs are outgrowths of the throat.

Nutrition in the Crayfish Crayfish will eat almost anything, dead or alive, that they can catch. They will eat plant material or dead organisms. They will even eat one another. In shallow water they may reach up to the surface and pull down algae with their chelipeds. Bits of the food are then passed to the maxillae and maxillipeds, which tear it into smaller pieces. The mandibles next crush the pieces of food before they pass through a short esophagus to the stomach. The stomach contains hard, chitinous teeth. When these have ground the food even finer, it is strained through folds of tissue in the stomach and mixed with digestive juices. Next, the digested food passes to the digestive glands and is absorbed. Undigested particles do not enter the digestive glands but pass directly to the intestine, and are eliminated through the anus. The crayfish also has excretory organs called **green glands.** These are located in front of the stomach near the base of the antennae. The green glands remove wastes from the blood.

Circulation in the Crayfish The heart of the crayfish pumps blood into seven large blood vessels called *arteries*. These arteries pour the blood over all the major organs of the body. The blood bathes the cells directly by flowing through the tissue spaces. Eventually it collects in one large lower cavity, the *sternal sinus*. From there, the blood is carried through vessels to the gills, where respiration occurs. Next, the blood goes through vessels to another large sinus, the *pericardial sinus*, which surrounds the heart. Blood enters the heart through three pairs of tiny pores called the *ostia*. When the heart contracts, valves

sinus = cavity or hollow

peri = around
cardio = heart

close off the ostia to prevent blood from flowing back into the pericardial sinus. **This type of circulation is called an *open system,* since the blood is not contained in vessels all through the body. In a closed system, the blood stays within vessels and does not bathe the organs directly.**

Respiration in the Crayfish   Respiration, or the exchange of oxygen and carbon dioxide, is more specialized in the more complex forms of animals. In protists, these gases diffuse through the plasma membrane. In worms, gases diffuse through the body wall. In the spiders, book lungs and tracheae serve in respiration. The thin-walled gills of the crayfish have many blood vessels. Gases diffuse through the thin wall between the blood and the flowing water. These gills are well adapted for the exchange of gases between the blood and the aqueous environment.

The gills are protected by the carapace. They are attached to the walking legs. As the legs move, the gills move and get supplied with air, or are aerated. The second maxillae keeps water flowing into the gill chamber and forward over the gills. The gill chamber can hold enough moisture to keep the crayfish alive for some time if it is taken out of the water.

The Nervous System and Sense Organs   The nervous system of the crayfish is similar to that in annelids, but it is more specialized. Nerves carry impulses from the eyes, antennules, and antennae to the brain. Two large nerves run from the brain to the ventral part of the crayfish's body. Here they unite to form a large double ganglion. They then continue together as the ventral nerve cord, which passes to the posterior end of the body. In each segment, the ventral nerve cord enlarges into a ganglion from which nerves run out to the appendages, muscles, and other body organs.

The antennae have receptors sensitive to smell and taste. The eyes are set on two short movable stalks. Each eye has more than 2,000 lenses. This type of eye is called a *compound eye.* The compound eye can detect movement. Many arthropods have compound eyes.

The antennae also have many sensory bristles that react to touch. These sensory bristles also grow all over the body, including the appendages. It is thought that these bristles may also react to sound waves.

A sac at the base of each antennule helps the crayfish keep its balance. The sac, called a *statocyst,* is lined with hairy receptor cells. Within each statocyst are grains of sand. If the crayfish becomes tilted, or upside down, sand grains stimulate the hairy receptor cells. This sends signals

31-9 | Regeneration. A crayfish growing a new claw. *(Allan Roberts)*

milli = thousand
diplos = double
podos = foot

to the brain along nerve fibers. The crayfish reacts by righting itself.

When the crayfish molts, the grains of sand are shed along with the old exoskeleton. Usually the crayfish replaces them with other grains.

Reproduction and Growth in the Crayfish   Crayfish usually mate in the fall. At this time, the sperms from the male are stored in small receptacles on the lower side of the female's body. In the spring, about one hundred eggs are laid. As they are laid, they are fertilized by the stored sperms. The fertilized eggs are covered with a sticky secretion so they will stick to the swimmerets. Swimmerets aerate the eggs. The eggs resemble a bunch of berries. The female carries these fertilized eggs and protects them for six to eight weeks, depending on the temperature and conditions of the water. When the tiny crayfish hatch, they look quite different from their parents.

Baby crayfish reach adult form by growing and molting several times. As the young crayfish begins to develop, the time span between moltings gets longer and longer. Most larvae molt seven times during the first year and about twice a year from then on. The average life span of a crayfish is three to four years.

When the crayfish is molting, the cells of the epidermis are dividing by mitosis. The cells of the epidermis secrete enzymes that actually digest the inner layer of the cuticle. Much of the digested material is absorbed by the cells of the epidermis to be used again. The space caused by the digested inner layer of the cuticle allows the crayfish to shed its covering. The crayfish quickly absorbs water from its surroundings and swells up to its new size. Then the cells of the epidermis produce a new cuticle. The lining of the stomach is also shed, including the teeth. As the lime is replaced, the exoskeleton hardens. Because it is helpless during molting, the crayfish usually goes into hiding until its new exoskeleton has hardened. **A crayfish will not grow in size until it molts again.**

A crayfish often loses or injures appendages during molting or fighting with enemies. It casts off an injured limb. A double membrane prevents much blood loss. Gradually, a whole new appendage grows to replace the lost one. This is another example of *regeneration* of lost parts.

Arthropods with Many Legs

Diplopods

Millipedes are mandibulates of the class *Diplopoda*. They really do not have a thousand feet! But if you have ever seen a millipede, you know that it has many legs. Each section of the body except the last two has *two* pairs of short legs. The short antennae and two clumps of simple eyes are located on the head. They use their maxillae and mandibles to chew decayed matter in the soil. They feed mostly on plants. Perhaps you have seen a millipede rolled up into a coil when you lifted a rock in the garden.

Chilopods

Centipedes are examples of this group of arthropod mandibulates. Centipedes are in the class *Chilipoda*. You may have seen these animals racing away when you disturbed a log or stone. They do not have 100 legs as their name implies. They may have as few as 15 pairs of legs, or as many as 175 pairs. Their bodies are more flattened than the millipedes. Each body section except the first one and the last two has one pair of jointed legs. Long antennae and two clumps of simple eyes are located on the head. Centipedes use the mandibules and maxillae to handle their food.

The appendages of the first segment of the centipede's body are poison claws. Centipedes eat other animals, such as earthworms. They also feed on many insects including cockroaches. Centipedes kill their prey with their poison claws, then they chew them apart with their mandibles. Most centipedes are not harmful to humans. In tropical regions, centipedes may be as long as 30 centimeters (12 inches). They may be kept as "pets" to control insect pests in houses.

31-10 | Compare the centipede (top) with the millipede (bottom). Note that the centipede just shed its exoskeleton. *(top: Z. Leszczynski, Animals Animals; bottom: Dr. E. R. Degginger)*

cheilos = lip

Summary

Subphylum	Class	Body Divisions	Appendages	Respiration	Examples
Chelicerata	Arachnida	2—cephalothorax, abdomen	no antennae 4 pairs of legs	tracheae, book lungs	spider, mite, tick, scorpion
	Crustacea	2—cephalothorax, abdomen	2 pairs antennae variable—may have 5 pairs of legs	gills	lobster, crab, water flea, sow bug, crayfish
	Diplopoda	head and numerous body segments	1 pair short antennae 2 pairs of legs on each body segment	tracheae	millipede
Mandibulata	Chilopoda	head and numerous body segments	1 pair long antennae 1 pair of legs on each segment except first one behind head and last 2	tracheae	centipede

Biologically Speaking

appendage	maxilla
exoskeleton	maxilliped
molting	cheliped
chelicerae	walking legs
cephalothorax	swimmeret
abdomen	uropod
pedipalps	telson
carapace	green gland
antennule	open system
antennae	compound eye
mandible	statocyst

Questions for Review

1. List three external characteristics of an arthropod that make it different from other animals.
2. What are some advantages and disadvantages of an exoskeleton?
3. How are arthropods similar to earthworms?
4. Name and give an example of four of the several classes of arthropods.
5. In what ways are spiders more like ticks than like crayfish?
6. What habits of spiders and scorpions make mating dangerous for the male?
7. What other animals besides the spiders are classified as arachnids?
8. How do a crayfish's gills carry on respiration?
9. To what stimuli is the crayfish sensitive, and what structures help in the sensitivity?
10. How does a centipede differ from a millipede?

Applying Concepts

1. What reasons can be given to explain why arthropods are so numerous?
2. Of what value is ballooning to the spider?
3. Why is it especially important for an animal such as the crayfish to have long antennae?

32-1 | A praying mantis feeds on other insects. *(Leonard Lee Rue III, DPI)*

Insects: The Most Common Arthropods

A **DESCRIBE** some characteristics of insects.

B **EXPLAIN** variations that permit insects to be so successful.

C **IDENTIFY** structural adaptations of the grasshopper.

D **IDENTIFY** several physiological variations among insects.

E **DISTINGUISH** incomplete from complete metamorphosis.

F **DESCRIBE** the social structure and behavior of bees.

A Vast Number of Species

Insects have lived on the earth for nearly 300 million years. They have survived many environmental changes during that time. Many other organisms have left only their fossils as signs that they ever existed. The phylum Arthropoda is the largest phylum in number of all classified animals. The class *Insecta* is, by far, the largest class in number in the phylum. So far, more than 675,000 species of insects have been recorded. It is believed that this is only half the insect species that really exist. The study of insects is **entomology.** Biologists in this field are known as *entomologists.*

entomon = **insect**

logos = **word or discourse**

What Is an Insect?

Insects belong to the class Insecta. They are not "bugs." A true bug is a member of only one order among all other insects. Insects are arthropods with three separate body regions. These are the *head*, the *thorax*, and the *abdomen*. The head bears one pair of antennae and the mouthparts. The thorax has three pairs of jointed legs and, when present, wings. The abdomen has up to 11 segments, but it

Facts & Figures

The largest prehistoric insect was a dragonfly that lived about 280,000,000 years ago. Fossil impressions of wings show that it had a wing span of nearly 69 centimeters (27.6 inches).

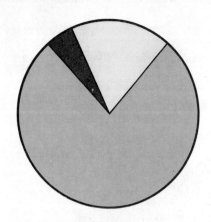

- ● insect arthropods
- ● noninsect arthropods
- ● nonarthropods

32-2 | Insects comprise nearly three quarters of all described species of animals.

32-3 | Can you see why camouflage is of adaptive value? *(Lynnae Pedersen, DPI)*

32-4 | Although this fly looks like a honeybee, it does not sting. Would this be of survival value to the fly? *(Walter Dawn)*

never has legs. Insects have separate sexes. The reproductive structures are usually on the eighth, ninth, and tenth segments. Insects breathe through branched air tubes called *tracheae*.

Like other arthropods, insects are protected by a chitinous exoskeleton. This exoskeleton forms a tough, but flexible and lightweight armor. This armor is coated with wax to help retain water. Insect joints are movable with a tough, membranous covering that helps hold skeletal parts together. As we have said before, the exoskeleton limits the size of a land organism. Therefore, most insects are small. This small size has survival value, since it allows the insect to use small spaces and feast on tiny food particles. They can find shade beside a pebble and hide in tiny spaces.

The colors and shapes of insect exoskeletons show great variety. Many insects are a color that blends with their environment. This helps hide the insect from its enemies. Many harmless insects look just like relatives that have poisonous stings. Of course, those insects that can bite or sting are also protected by the learned behavior of their enemies. An insect may also look like part of the plant in which it lives. For example, some insects look like leaves or twigs on plant stems.

Insects also survive because the different types can eat so many different kinds of food. They have developed specialized mouthparts. Some insects have strong jaws for chewing leaves. Some are equipped to pierce and suck plant juices. Others, like mosquitos, suck blood from animals. Some, such as butterflies, have siphoning tubes for getting nectar from flowers. Because of their nectar gathering habits, bees are the most important pollinators of flowers.

Many insects have developed wings and legs for great speed. Others, like the scale insects, have lost their legs through evolution. Some insects are adapted for an aquatic life. Others are adapted for burrowing in the ground.

You may have seen pictures of swarms of locusts or mayflies darkening the sky. One insect may produce thousands of offspring, but not all of them survive. Many factors help control this awesome rate of reproduction potential.

The Grasshopper: An Example Of An Insect

Because of such wide variation, there is no one typical insect. The grasshopper, though, makes a good example since it is relatively large in size and occurs in such large numbers.

The grasshopper is a member of the order *Orthoptera,* which means "straight-winged." When its wings are not being used, they lie in narrow, straight folds against the body. Like that of all arthropods, the skeleton is external. The exoskeleton differs from that of the crayfish since it has no lime. Instead, the grasshopper's exoskeleton is made mostly of light, tough chitin.

The grasshopper feeds on blades of grass. Its mouthparts are adapted for this type of food. The **labrum** is like an upper lip which keeps a blade of grass at right angles to the jaws. These rough-edged jaws are called **mandibles.** Posterior to the mandibles are the **maxillae.** This second set of jaws helps to hold and cut the food. Posterior to the maxillae is the **labium,** or lower lip. This organ also holds food between the jaws. It is thought that each mouthpart contributes to the success of this insect as a grass eater.

Grasshoppers include some of the most destructive insect forms. Migratory grasshoppers, often called locusts, have caused serious damage to crops and other vegetation on every continent. Accounts of locust plagues were recorded in the Bible. Occasional outbreaks still occur when insect populations increase greatly. These swarms may travel hundreds of miles causing destruction wherever they go.

32-5 | How are the grasshopper's mouthparts adapted to eating grass? *(William E. Ferguson)*

32-6 | Insects can do considerable damage to foliage. Note the difference between the damaged and undamaged trees. *(Runk, Schoenberger, Grant Heilman)*

pro = before, in front of
thorax = a breastplate, the chest

How the Grasshopper Moves The appendages that help the grasshopper move are located on the thorax. The thorax is divided into three segments. The head and first pair of walking legs are attached to the **prothorax.** The first pair of wings and the second pair of walking legs are connected to the **mesothorax.** The third segment is the **metathorax,** which has the second pair of wings and the jumping legs.

The grasshopper uses its wings to carry it for short distances over dry fields. It also flies for many miles when swarms migrate. The long, narrow anterior forewings are stiff. They protect the delicate underwings when the grasshopper is on the ground.

These outer wings also give lift when the grasshopper is flying or leaping. The thin underwings are posterior to the outer wings. These hind wings are like thin membranes, with many veins in them. These flying wings fold up like a fan when they are not in use.

The grasshopper uses its jumping legs for short distances. It jumps to escape enemies, to search for food, and to launch into flight. It uses both jumping and walking legs to climb plants in order to feed on tender leaves. When it uses its legs, the spines, hooks, and pads of each foot, or tarsus, help it to grip. The long joint next to the tarsus is the tibia. The large jumping muscles are in the heaviest part of the leg, the femur. The leg attaches to the body like a ball-and-socket joint. This provides more freedom of motion.

A Remarkable Respiratory Structure There are 10 segments to the grasshopper's abdomen. Each of these segments consists of two curved plates. The upper and lower

32-7 The external structure of a grasshopper.

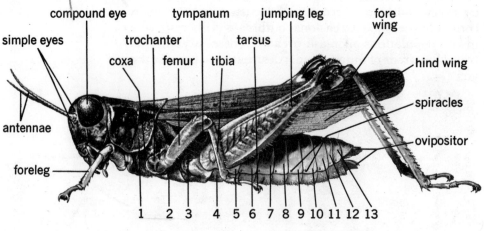

compound eye · tympanum · jumping leg · fore wing

simple eyes · trochanter · tarsus

coxa · femur · tibia · hind wing

antennae · spiracles

foreleg · ovipositor

1 2 3 4 5 6 7 8 9 10 11 12 13

1–prothorax   3–metathorax
2–mesothorax   4-13–segments of
                the abdomen

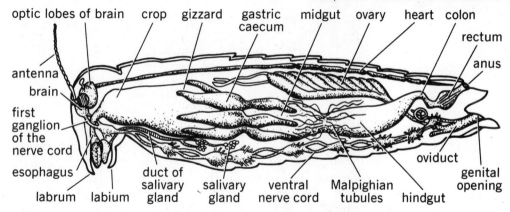

optic lobes of brain   crop   gizzard   gastric caecum   midgut   ovary   heart   colon

rectum

anus

antenna

brain

first ganglion of the nerve cord

esophagus

labrum   labium   duct of salivary gland   salivary gland   ventral nerve cord   Malpighian tubules   hindgut

oviduct

genital opening

32–8 | The internal structure of a grasshopper.

plates are joined together by a tough but flexible membrane. This membrane allows the whole segment to expand and contract when the grasshopper breathes. The same flexible membrane also joins each segment to the ones next to it. This allows the segments to move.

The first eight segments of the abdomen have pairs of tiny openings called **spiracles** (SPIR-uh-kulz). The thorax also has spiracles on its second and third segments. These openings lead to the **tracheae** (TRAY-kee-ee), or air tubes. The tracheae form a very complex network inside the grasshopper. Air is pumped in and out of the tracheae by the movements of the abdomen and wings. Oxygen quickly diffuses into the tissue, while carbon dioxide diffuses out through the tracheae. This is how the grasshopper respires.

Digestion, Excretion, and Circulation The grasshopper's mandibles can pinch off little pieces of grass which are then sucked into the mouth. As in many higher animals, **salivary glands** secrete juices that flow into the mouth. These juices moisten the food so that it can pass easily through an **esophagus** (ih-SAHF-uh-guhs) into the **crop.**

32–9 | The respiratory apparatus of a grasshopper.

air sac   tracheal trunks

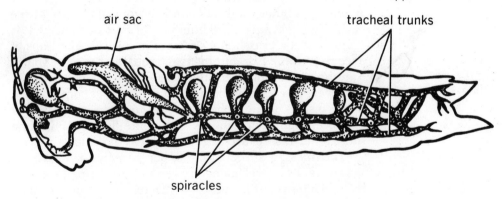

spiracles

The crop may store the food for a while. Grasshoppers may spit food out of the crop if injured or disturbed. Normally the food passes on to the **gizzard.** Here the food is shredded by plates of teeth containing chitin.

Thin plates screen the partly digested food before it passes into the large *midgut.* Outside the midgut are several double pouches, or *gastric caeca.* The exact function of these pouches is uncertain. However, enzymes are produced and pour into the midgut. These enzymes complete the digestion in the midgut. The bloodstream absorbs the digested food through the midgut wall. The undigested material in the midgut passes into the *hindgut.* The hindgut is made up of the *colon* and the *rectum.*

Cellular wastes are picked up by the blood. These wastes are collected by a series of tubes called **Malpighian** (mal-PIG-ee-un) **tubules.** The Malpighian tubules lie in the body cavity among other organs. They are bathed in blood, as are other body tissues. Here the wastes are concentrated and passed into the last part of the hindgut. Wastes leave the body through the anus.

The grasshopper's circulatory system is an open system, like that of the crayfish. The tubular heart is in the dorsal part of the body. This powerful muscle forces blood out its anterior end and through the **aorta.** From there it flows into the body cavity near the head. As blood flows from the head to the posterior of the body, it brings food to all of the organs. At the same time, the blood absorbs and carries away waste products. Finally, it returns to the heart.

The Grasshopper's Response to the Environment Each side of the grasshopper's first abdominal segment has a membrane-covered cavity called the **tympanum.** These are sensory organs for hearing. The antennae are sensitive to touch and smell. The grasshopper sees through two sets of eyes. The three **simple eyes** are just above the base of each antenna and in the groove between them. The large **compound eyes** bulge slightly from the front and sides of the head. They are made up of hundreds of six-sided lenses. It is thought that a grasshopper can see in several directions at once from all lenses, but focus is probably not very sharp. Entomologists consider most insects to be nearsighted. However, insects may be able to distinguish some colors. Some insects seem to be attracted to certain colors. For instance, night-flying moths seek white flowers. Flies and some other insects are attracted by red and blue.

The messages the grasshopper receives through its sense organs travel along nerves to certain parts of the body. Such parts, like muscles, then respond. Nerve centers called *ganglia* help direct the messages to the right places for coordinated reaction. The brain is actually several fused ganglia, with nerves going to the eyes, antennae, and other head organs. Other nerves go to the lower ganglia of the thorax and the abdomen. The most prominent parts of the brain are the **optic lobes.** They coordinate sight with muscle reaction through the nerves. Just move your hand toward a grasshopper and watch how fast it moves away from you! This complicated act is begun, controlled, and organized by the nervous system.

The Grasshopper's Reproductive Organs   In insects, the sexes are separate. The male produces sperm cells in the testes. The female produces egg cells in the ovaries. During mating, the male deposits his sperms into a special storage pouch in the female. This pouch is called the seminal receptacle. The sperms stay there until the eggs are ready to be fertilized.

The posterior segments of the female grasshopper have two pairs of hard, pointed organs called **ovipositors** (OE-vuh-POZ-it-erz). The female uses these to dig a hole and deposit the fertilized eggs. The fertilized eggs are protected by a gummy covering. One hundred or more eggs may be laid by each female in the fall. The eggs hatch the next spring.

A Successful Group

Insects are found in a great many places. You can find them at heights of 6,000 meters (3.6 miles) in the Himalayan mountains. Insects have been collected in the Antarctic, where temperatures drop to −65°C (−149°F), and in hot springs rising from deep in the earth's crust. Some insects live in pools of crude oil and there are some living on the surface of the ocean.

One reason for the success of insects has been the many different ways they have adapted. The differences among insects may be *structural.* Examples are the number, shape, or size of the appendages. Differences may be *physiological,* such as types of cells in its blood or the kinds of food it can digest. Methods of development are different for many insects, as you will soon see. Their high rate of reproduction is another reason for the success of insects. Differences may be *behavioral,* such as the way an insect reacts to light or moisture. Some insects are solitary and others, such as bees and ants, live in colonies.

These differences, or variations, do not mean that an

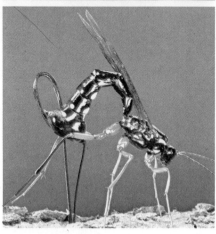

32–10 | Female insects often have specially designed ovipositors that they use to dig holes and deposit their eggs. *(top: William E. Ferguson; bottom: Oxford Scientific Films, Animals Animals)*

individual insect can live in all environments. However, variation permits different species of insects to adapt to the changing conditions in many environments.

Structural Variations

The three body sections of an insect permit specialization. The head, with its sense organs and the ability to turn, allows the insect to use its senses to detect what is going on in its environment. The head contains the "brain" for coordination of responses to the environment. Nerve cords passing from the brain form the ventral nerve cord with ganglia for further coordination of responses.

The mouthparts on the head are also specialized. Some insects, such as the butterfly, have mouthparts in the form of a long tube adapted for sucking up nectar from flowers. Other mouthparts, such as those of a mosquito, are used in piercing the skin of animals and sucking blood. The fly has lapping mouthparts. Still others, such as the grasshopper, have mouthparts in the form of strong mandibles. These are used in chewing and crushing plant material.

Adaptations in the form of various appendages of the thorax include legs for walking, legs for jumping, and legs for clinging to another animal. The wings, if present, are also attached to the thorax. The thorax, then, contains the "motor" parts of the insect. Large muscles for locomotion are in the thorax.

The third section of insects, the abdomen, specializes in reproduction. It ends with specialized structures for mating and depositing eggs.

Entomologists use these structural adaptations to group the insects into orders. Examples and characteristics of several insect orders are given in Tables 32-1 and 32-2 on pages 408 and 409.

Physiological Variations

Reproductive Potential One insect may produce thousands of offspring, but not all of them survive. The ability to produce so many eggs is an insect adaptation. Changing environmental conditions kill many, but some survive.

Digestion The mouthparts of each insect are specialized for taking in certain kinds of food. You saw, in the grasshopper, how the mouthparts were adapted for collecting, grinding, and taking in plant materials. Without special enzymes for chemically changing this plant material, the grasshopper would starve.

Enzymes in other insects, such as mosquitos, break down the chemicals in blood. If you were to feed blood to a

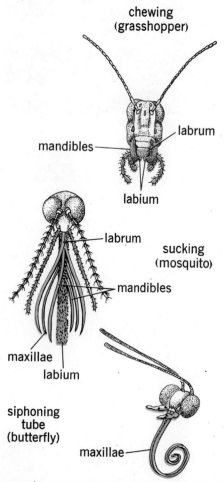

chewing
(grasshopper)

labrum

mandibles

labium

labrum

sucking
(mosquito)

mandibles

maxillae

labium

siphoning
tube
(butterfly)

maxillae

32-11 | Insect mouthparts adapted for different uses.

grasshopper, it would probably starve because it wouldn't have enzymes to digest this food material. On the other hand, fleas and lice live as external parasites on mammals and birds, feeding on their blood. **The enzymes for digestion of each type of food are physiological variations.**

Life History   Insects show several differences in the way in which they develop. **Most insects go through several distinct stages as they develop from egg to adult. This series of stages is called metamorphosis.** Grasshoppers, bugs, aphids, and termites go through an incomplete or *gradual metamorphosis.* It occurs in three stages: the *egg*, the *nymph*, and the *adult*. The nymph hatches from the egg, resembling the adult, but smaller. The nymph has no wings or developed reproductive organs. Most species molt five times in the nymph stage. Each time it becomes more like the adult.

Insects that go through *complete metamorphosis* include butterflies, moths, flies, and beetles. Each goes through four stages of development: *egg, larvae, pupa*, and *adult*. The eggs hatch into segmented larvae that look like worms. Different types of insects are called different names at this stage. They may be called caterpillars, grubs, or maggots. The larvae eat much and grow very fast. Their growth is by several molts of the larval cuticle.

Then they enter the pupal stage. The pupa is covered with a shell or case. From the outside, the pupa appears to be in a resting period. Inside the case, there is much happening. The tissues of the larva are changed into the tissues of the adult. When the shell opens again, out comes the butterfly or other adult insect. The change from caterpillar to butterfly or grub to beetle is a truly marvelous event.

Recently, biologists have been looking at the role of hormones in insect metamorphosis. **Hormones are chemicals secreted into the blood by a gland or organ in the body.** Hormones are carried to other parts of the body, where they control chemical reactions. When scientists studied the *Cecropia* moth, they found that hormones controlled metamorphosis. Many insects that go through complete metamorphosis have their pupal stage during the winter. This is a favorable adaptation because winter conditions are not good for active insects. Perhaps the cool temperatures affect the production of a brain hormone. This hormone stimulates a gland in the prothorax to produce a second hormone. The second hormone brings about the changes from pupa to adult moth.

In experiments with *Cecropia*, the brains of the pupae were removed. Such insects never went through metamorphosis to become adult moths. However, when a brain from

morphe = shape, form

Silverfish (1)

Mayfly (2)

Dragonfly (3)

Grass-hopper (4)

Cricket (4)

Termite (5)

Earwig (6)

Chewing louse (7)

Sucking louse (8)

Squash bug (9)

Aphid (10)

Cicada (10)

Table 32-1 COMMON INSECT ORDERS WITH INCOMPLETE METAMORPHOSIS

ORDER	MOUTHPARTS IN ADULT	ECONOMIC SIGNIFICANCE	EXAMPLES
Thysanura ("bristle-tail") 700* (1)	chewing	pests, feeding on starch in bindings and labels of books, clothing, paste in wallpaper	bristletails, silverfish, firebrats
Ephemeroptera ("for-a-day—wing") 1,500 (2)	adults do not feed	food for many freshwater fish	mayflies
Odonata ("toothed") 4,870 (3)	chewing	destroy harmful insects	dragonflies, damselflies
Orthoptera ("straight-wing") 22,500 (4)	chewing	damage crops, act as pests	grasshoppers, crickets, katydids, locusts, cockroaches
Isoptera ("equal-winged") 1,720 (5)	chewing	destroy wood in forests and buildings	termites
Dermaptera ("skin-winged") 1,100 (6)	chewing	damage crops and garden plants	earwigs
Mallophaga ("wool-eater") 2,680 (7)	chewing	most are parasitic on birds pests on poultry	chewing lice
Anoplura ("unarmed-tail") 250 (8)	sucking	parasitic on mammals parasitic on man transmit disease such as typhus	sucking lice
Hemiptera ("half-winged") 23,000 (9)	sucking	damage plants, act as pests, carry disease	squash bugs, all true bugs
Homoptera ("like-winged") 32,000 (10)	sucking	damage crops and gardens	aphids, mealy bugs, cicada

32–12 Common insect orders with no metamorphosis or with incomplete metamorphosis.

*Numbers indicate estimated number of species known.

Table 32-2 COMMON INSECT ORDERS WITH COMPLETE METAMORPHOSIS

ORDER	MOUTHPARTS IN ADULT	ECONOMIC SIGNIFICANCE	EXAMPLES
Neuroptera ("nerve-winged") 4,670 (11)	chewing	destroy harmful insects	dobsonfly, lacewing
Coleoptera ("sheath-winged") 276,700 (12)	sucking or chewing	destroy crops, act as pests, prey on other insects	weevils, ladybugs, ground beetles
Lepidoptera ("scale-winged") 112,000 (13)	siphoning	pollinate flowers, produce silk, damage clothing and crops	butterflies, moths
Diptera ("two-winged") 85,000 (14)	sucking, piercing, or lapping	carry disease, act as pests	flies, mosquitoes, gnats
Siphonaptera ("tube-wingless") 1,100 (15)	sucking	pests, feed on blood of birds and mammals, transmit disease such as bubonic plague	fleas
Hymenoptera ("membrane-winged") 103,000 (16)	chewing, sucking, or lapping	pollinate flowers, act as pests, parasitize other pests, make honey	bees, wasps, ants

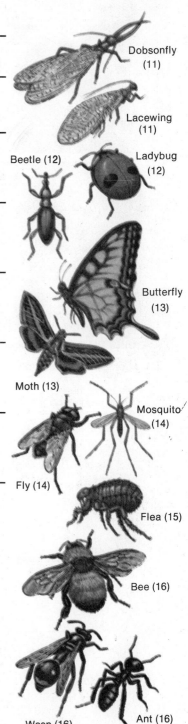

Dobsonfly (11)

Lacewing (11)

Beetle (12)

Ladybug (12)

Butterfly (13)

Moth (13)

Mosquito (14)

Fly (14)

Flea (15)

Bee (16)

Wasp (16)

Ant (16)

32-13 | Common insects orders with complete metamorphosis.

Table 32-3 Names of Insect Larvae

THE LARVA OF THE	beetle fly mosquito butterfly moth	IS CALLED	grub maggot wiggler caterpillar caterpillar

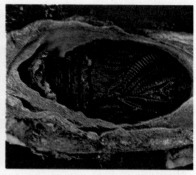

32–14 | Complete metamorphosis. Notice that the young of the *Cecropia* moth do not look anything like the adult. Can you think of any survival value in having two such distinct forms? *(Herbert Weihrich)*

a chilled pupa was planted in a pupa whose brain had been removed, metamorphosis did occur. In another experiment, a pupa was cut in half, and the ends were sealed. The anterior half, where the brain was, developed into an adult. The posterior end did not. Can you locate the hormone-producing organ?

Winter brings about the formation of a pupa, but a single unusual cold spell will not cause a young caterpillar to turn into a pupa. The biologists working with the *Cecropia* moth asked why. They found that when they removed a paired structure from behind the caterpillar's brain, the larva would form a pupa. Temperature did not seem to affect this process. It was decided that the paired structure produces a hormone in the larva. The hormone slows down or prevents metamorphosis. They called it a *juvenile hormone*, since it operates in the larval stage of the insect's development.

Adaptive Value of Complete Metamorphosis The process of complete metamorphosis is of value to species survival. A good example of this is the butterfly, or Lepidoptera. The sexes are separate. After mating, eggs are placed on or near material that will be food for the larva. Some eggs pass the winter in this stage. Normally, eggs are laid in the spring and develop into **caterpillars** the following summer.

Caterpillars have three pairs of jointed legs and several pairs of fleshy legs. They greedily devour plants, get large and fat, and molt several times. Since caterpillars need large amounts of food to grow so fast, they can do much damage to plants during this time.

When a caterpillar has grown large, it looks for a sheltered spot. Then it hangs with its head down, and becomes very quiet. Its body gets shorter and thicker. The exoskeleton splits down the back and falls off. Now the insect has become a **pupa.** While the butterfly pupa rests in a hardened brownish case, it is called a **chrysalis.** Moth larvae usually spin a strong case of silk called a *cocoon.*

Lepidoptera normally spend the winter in the pupal stage. The next spring the adult comes out as a butterfly or moth.

During their life history, the Lepidoptera have two very different sets of mouthparts. Thus the larvae and the adults have completely different diets. The larvae feed on leaves, while the adults suck nectar from flowers. This means the insect has a varied diet in its lifetime. It also means there is a good food supply during the time of most rapid growth. The adult serves to reproduce and disperse the species. **There is no competition for food between the young and the adult.**

Behavioral Variations

Variations in structure permit variations in behavior. Complex behavior is another reason for the success of insects. Such complex behavior is possible because of the development of (1) *complex sense organs*, (2) *jointed appendages*, and (3) a *brain*. The sense organs are stimulated both by the immediate environment and from a distance. These stimuli help insects escape from enemies, find food, find a mate,

Careers

Most entomologists are engaged in activities that direct efforts toward managing insect populations. They look for means to control harmful insects and try to increase the impact of desirable insects. Entomologists work in government agencies and other research centers such as in universities, and increasingly in "agribusiness."

As in many scientific careers, being an entomology technologist usually requires a bachelor's degree from college. To conduct much of the research requires an advanced degree.

32-15 | By collecting and studying the different stages of insects, a means for eliminating insect pests can be determined. (© Peter Arnold)

and find a good place for the eggs to develop. The brain is complex enough for the insects to organize information from the sense organs. They are also able to use this information to coordinate muscular responses. Insects also communicate with each other. One interesting means of insect communication involves the secretion of hormones. You may have seen a trail of ants walking across a wall or on the ground. Ants leave a trail that other ants can follow.

You have already seen how internal hormones affect metamorphosis. In addition, some chemicals are secreted outside the body. One group of these is called **pheromones.** Pheromones are substances that act as a chemical language between animals of the same species. The female gypsy moth secretes a pheromone that the male can detect with its antennae. This attracts the male to the female during mating time. Entomologists use this pheromone as bait to capture male gypsy moths. In this way, it is hoped that the gypsy moth population can be controlled.

Solitary Lives Many insects live solitary lives. They meet others of their species briefly for mating. One such interesting insect is the tarantula hawk. This is a large wasp. After mating, the female digs a burrow in the ground. With her stinger, she paralyzes other insects and drags them to her burrow. Her behavior is well coordinated. She can attack and paralyze the large spider, the tarantula, which is many times her size and weight. Using the powerful muscles of wings and legs, this insect can drag the paralyzed spider to her burrow. She then lays her eggs on the tarantula and kicks dirt to cover the burrow. When the eggs hatch, the immature forms feed on the paralyzed spider.

Insect Societies With the development of specialization, insects can do complex coordinated acts. They can even work together to change their environment by building many kinds of homes or nests. Some ants, for example, construct special passages to store grain. The fungus ant builds underground gardens where it grows a certain species of fungus.

Insects working together develop societies. Differences in body structure within the species allow for division of labor. Some of the insects are adapted for gathering food, some for protecting the home, some for tending the young, and some for reproduction. **Social insects** include the bees, ants, many wasps, and termites. These insects do not reason. They have specialized structures that are used in behavior patterns. The patterns are not taught to them. They carry out their jobs by *instinct*. As you can imagine, animal behavior studies are very interesting.

A Social Insect and Its Queen Bees, wasps, and ants are all examples of the order Hymenoptera. You can notice division of labor and individual variation more clearly in this order than just about anywhere else in the animal kingdom. Variation has brought about three distinct forms of bee: a queen, the drone, and the worker. The *queen bee* is nearly twice as large as the worker. She develops from special treatment of a fertilized egg. First, workers enlarge a wax cell where the egg is going to grow. When the grublike larva hatches, it is fed with extra helpings of *royal jelly*. This is a special high-protein food that the workers secrete. After five days, the larva becomes a pupa. Then the workers seal it into a large wax chamber. At the correct time, the old queen leaves the hive with a swarm of about half the population. She and her swarm will form a new colony, thus preventing overcrowding. After the old queen has left, the new queen emerges from her chamber.

A few days later, the young queen takes off on a special flight. During this flight, she mates with a *drone* (male bee). The queen receives several million sperms, which will fertilize all of the eggs she lays for the remaining three to five years of her life. When the queen returns to the hive, she begins laying eggs. She may lay as many as one million a year. This is her lifework. Although she is called a queen, she does not rule the hive. Instead she is its common mother.

Some of the eggs the queen lays are not fertilized. These haploid eggs develop into the males, or *drones*. The male bees are larger than the workers but smaller than the queen. They have broad, thick bodies, large eyes, and very powerful wings. Their tongues are not long enough to drink flower nectar, so they have to be fed by the workers. During the summer, a few hundred drones are tolerated in the colony. After all, one of them must function as a mate for the new queen. The rest, however, are of no use to the hive. This easy life has a price. When autumn comes, the honey runs low. The workers will no longer support the drones. The workers starve them or sting them to death. The drones' bodies can often be found around hives in early autumn.

The *worker bees* form the largest part of the hive population. They are undeveloped females, smaller than drones. The ovipositor is modified into a sting. This is a complicated organ. Two barbed darts, and strong muscles to operate them, are enclosed in a sheath. The darts are connected to a gland that secretes the painful poison delivered by the sting.

The workers carry on all the work of the hive except reproduction. They feed and care for the queen and drones. They nurse the hungry young larvae by feeding them partly

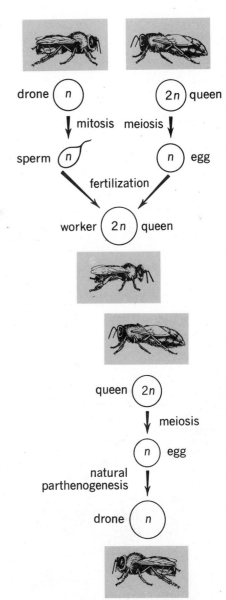

32–16 | Sex determination in the honey bee. Note that the drones are haploid because they develop from unfertilized eggs. In contrast, the workers and queen are diploid because they develop from fertilized eggs. Parthenogenesis is the ability to produce offspring without the egg being fertilized.

digested food from their own stomachs. The workers also clear dead bees and foreign matter out of the hive. If necessary, they fan their wings to bring fresh air into the hive. Thousands of workers are constantly bringing in nectar and pollen for the use of the colony. Workers born early in the season often work themselves to death in three or four weeks. Bees hatched in the fall may live for six months.

Worker bees are specialized in many ways for their tasks. Their mouthparts make efficient tongues for lapping up nectar. The workers' last four abdominal segments have glands that secrete the wax for making the comb. Their legs have many kinds of special structures. These include an antenna cleaner, pollen packer, pollen basket, and pollen comb.

The wax comb of the hive is built in six-sided cells arranged in two layers. There is no wasted space. It has the greatest amount of storage capacity for the least amount of building materials. Honey is stored in most of the comb's cells. There is one special section, called the brood comb. It is here that the queen lays one egg in each cell.

The bee makes honey from the nectar that goes straight into its crop. There, the sugars are changed into an easily digested form. Then the bee puts them into the comb cells. The honey is left to thicken by evaporation before the cell is sealed. It does not harm the bees if people take away some of their honey, as long as there is enough for the bees to use through the winter. About 15 kilograms (33 pounds) of honey will feed an average hive of 40,000 bees for an ordinary winter.

The Bees' Language Bees seem to communicate with each other by means of a complicated set of dances. When workers return to the hive, they can tell the other bees about the nectar they have found, what kind it is, how much there is, how far away and in which direction it is found. A bee communicates this information by dancing on

32–17 | a. The dancing bee makes the diameter of the "tail-waggling dance" upward on the vertical surface of the comb. This shows the bees that a source of nectar is located in a direction toward the sun. b. This dance shows that the nectar is located in a direction away from the sun. c. What message does this dance indicate?

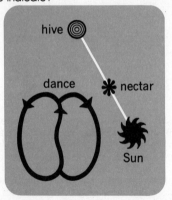

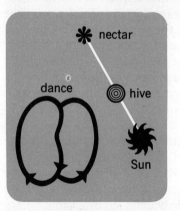

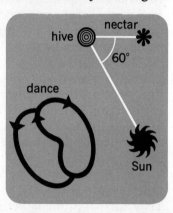

a

b

c

the vertical side of the comb. It dances in circles, going straight through the diameter of the circle every time around. The direction the bee takes on this cross-circle run shows where the honey is in relation to the sun.

The most interesting thing about this dancing is that the bee translates the angle between the direction of the sun and the food source into a vertical angle on the side of the comb.

The other bees watch the discoverer to find out where the food source is. They can tell how far the food is by the number of times the worker waggles its body on the way across the circle. The bees smell the kind of nectar. The more vigorous the dance, the more nectar there is. **This complex behavior allows for a coordinated society and increases the chances for species survival.**

GRASSHOPPER CHARACTERISTICS

Body Type	Segmented, three regions: head, thorax, abdomen
Type of Life	Terrestrial
Movement	3 pairs of legs, 2 pairs of wings
Development	Incomplete metamorphosis: egg, nymph, adult
SYSTEMS	
Skeletal	Exoskeleton made of chitin
Digestive	One-way digestive tube; esophagus, crop, gizzard, stomach and intestine (undigested food)
Circulatory	Open circulation, tubular heart and blood vessels (blood does not carry oxygen)
Nervous	definite nerve pathway; 2 ventral nerve cords, "brain," ganglia
Excretory	Malpighian tubules
Respiratory	Tracheae carry oxygen to cells by means of spiracles
Reproductive	Sexual—separate sexes Internal fertilization, external development

Summary

Biologically Speaking

entomology
labrum
mandibles
maxillae
labium
prothorax
mesothorax
metathorax
spiracles
tracheae
salivary glands
esophagus
crop
gizzard
Malpighian tubules

aorta
typanum
simple eyes
compound eyes
optic lobes
ovipositors
gradual metamorphosis
complete metamorphosis
caterpillar
pupa
chrysalis
cocoon
pheromones
social insect

Questions for Review

1. What is an insect?
2. Why are insects said to be a "successful" group?
3. What features separate the insect orders?
4. What is the chief difference between the respiratory system of the grasshopper and that of the human?
5. What are pheromones? How are pheromones used by social insects?
6. Of what survival value is metamorphosis?
7. What advantage do the social insects have over the solitary forms?
8. Do bees communicate with one another in the hive? Explain.

Applying Concepts

1. What theories explain why an insect resembles a thorn on a bush or why a fly looks like a bee?
2. What possible mechanisms account for the change in the amount of juvenile hormone that a *Cecropia* larva may produce? If you were a biologist studying the hormone balance in metamorphosis, how might you test your hypotheses?
3. What additional experiments might be performed to increase our understanding of communication among the bees?
4. How might pheromones be useful to farmers?

UNIT 5

1. Use clay to make models of early development. Be sure to include the egg, sperm, zygote, and 2-, 4-, 8-, 16-, and 32-celled stages.

2. Plan an experiment to observe regeneration in a planarian similar to that shown in figure 29–4 on page 364. After you cut them with a sharp razor blade, put the sections in small Petri dishes that contain pond water. Place the dishes in a drawer. Make observations and change the water every day. When the regenerated sections appear to be able to feed, place a small piece of raw liver in the water during the class period. Remove the liver when the water is changed. Keep careful notes of your observations and write a report on your findings. Report your results to the class.

3. Obtain a large starfish and dissect it to show the water-vascular system. Dissect one ray to show the gonads. Dissect another ray to show the digestive organs.

4. Many spiders can be kept alive in the laboratory and fed on mealworms. Design a "spider house" and plan which spiders would be suitable to keep. After receiving approval from your teacher, build and maintain the "spider house" for the classroom. Make notes on behavior you observe.

5. Pheromones have been used as bait to attract insects to other types of chemical traps. They have been used in the control of gypsy moths which are responsible for destroying hundreds of forest acres. Use your library to help you find out how these pheromones are obtained and used. Write a short report and explain your findings to the class.

6. Make an insect collection. Your teacher or the library will have information on the proper methods of mounting insects for study. Keep field notes showing dates and times of collection, weather conditions, and the location and activity of the insect at the time of collection. Be sure to label the insects. If you prefer, you may make an insect collection of only one order of insects. The order Coleoptera (beetles) would be a good one to select because they are so numerous.

Unit 5
Summary

Comparison of Invertebrate Systems

Phyla	Porifora	Coelenterata	Platyhelminthes
Symmetry	asymmetrical	radial	bilateral
Type of Life	sessile; marine, freshwater	sessile; free-swimming; marine, freshwater	free-living, parasitic, marine, freshwater
Systems	lack of organs	no true organ systems	some organ systems present
Digestive	none; no mouth	digestive sac; mouth	digestive; mouth only
Circulatory	diffusion only (water current system)	diffusion only	diffusion only
Excretory	diffusion only (water current system)	diffusion only	diffusion only
Nervous	none	nerve net	two longitudinal nerve cords
Respiratory	diffusion only	diffusion only	diffusion only
Reproductive: Asexual	budding, gemmules	budding	fission
Sexual	egg and sperm formation	egg and sperm formation	hermaphrodite; cross-fertilization

Nematoda	Annelida	Mollusca	Echinodermata	Arthropoda
bilateral	bilateral	bilateral	radial	bilateral
free-living; parasitic; terrestrial, marine, freshwater	free-living; terrestrial, freshwater, marine	free-living; terrestrial, freshwater, marine	free-living; marine	free-living; terrestrial, freshwater, marine; parasitic
most organ systems present	organ systems present	organ systems present	organ systems present	organ systems present
digestive tract; mouth and anus	digestive tract; mouth and anus	digestive tract	digestive tract, mouth and anus	digestive tract, mouth and anus
no specific system	dorsal and ventral vessels; 5 aortic arches	open circulatory system	open circulatory system	open circulatory system
canals with excretory pore	diffusion	system of tubules	outpocketings in aboral surface	green glands, nephridia
nerve ring; ventral and dorsal nerve cords	nerve cord with cerebral and other ganglia	nerve cords with cerebral and other ganglia	nerve ring, radial nerves	nerve cord with cerebral and other ganglia
diffusion	diffusion	diffusion through gills, mantle	diffusion	gills, aquatic trachea system, terrestrial
none	none	none	none	none
definite male and female	hermaphroditic—cross-fertilization	hermaphroditic, separate sexes	separate sexes	separate sexes

Related Readings

Books

Buchsbaum, Ralph, and Lorus J. Milne, *The Lower Animals: Living Invertebrates of the World*. Doubleday and Company, Inc., Garden City, New York. 1960. A complete discussion of each animal, with accompanying photographs.

Callahan, Phillip, *The Evolution of Insects*. Holiday House, New York. 1972. A readable account of insect evolution. The book is illustrated with excellent charts, diagrams, and black-and-white photographs.

Farb, Peter, and the Editors of Life Magazine, *The Insects*. Time-Life Books (Time, Inc.), New York. 1962. A beautifully colored picture-essay type book that effectively highlights the natural history of a wide range of insects.

Gertsch, Willis J., *American Spiders*. Van Nostrand Press-Reinhold Books, New York. 1949. This is an excellent presentation of the many common spiders in the United States.

Mash, Kaye, *How Invertebrates Live*. Elsevier Phaidon Press, Ltd. London. 1975. This is a very clear presentation of the development of invertebrates, their lives, and classification. It has many clear diagrams and beautiful pictures.

Mason, Herbert M., *The Fantastic World of Ants*. David McKay Co., Inc., New York. 1974. A very readable account of the ant world.

Articles

Conway, Morris and H. B. Whittington. "The Animals of the Burgess Shale." *Scientific American*. July 1979. This article describes many invertebrate fossils found in a rock formation in western Canada. These samples indicate an animal community in the mid-Cambrian. Some of the animals are considered to be ancestors of those living today.

Cooke, John A. L., "Unveiling the Black Widow." *Natural History*, February 1973. A very interesting article on the biology of the black widow spider.

Gilbert, Voss L., "Shy Monster, The Octopus." *National Geographic*, December, 1971. Discusses the natural history of the octopus, with many interesting photographs.

Gould, James L. "Do Honeybees Know What They Are Doing?" *Natural History*, June–July 1979. This article discusses the life and behavior of bees. Some evidence indicates that these insects learn.

6

Vertebrates

This unit introduces the most advanced of all animals—the vertebrates. All vertebrates have a spinal column made of bones called vertebrae. Inside the spinal column is the nerve cord. This cord is joined to a highly developed brain. This system makes it possible for the vertebrate to respond to stimuli in a very effective way for its own survival. This superior nervous system is the real key to the biological supremacy of the vertebrates.

33

Introduction to
the Vertebrates

A **LIST** the chordate
   characteristics.
B **NAME** the classes of
   vertebrates and give
   examples of each.
C **LIST** the structural
   characteristics of vertebrates.
D **NAME** the specialized
   systems found in the
   vertebrates.
E **LIST** and **DEFINE** the types of
   highly developed behavior
   of vertebrates.

33-1 | All vertebrates have a vertebral column. *Kenneth W. Fink, Bruce Coleman)*

Invertebrate Development: A Quick Review

In your study of Unit 5 you saw several body plans for invertebrate animals. In the protozoans, for instance, the specialization of a single cell is carried to the limit. The paramecium is an amazing single-celled organism, but it takes many cells to make a complex animal.

The sponges and coelenterates are made of large colonies of cells. In the endoderm and ectoderm you can see the beginnings of tissue. Flatworms and roundworms have several very efficient organs. These organs function in digestion, reproduction, excretion, and response.

Mollusks and clams have changed very little in many millions of years. They have the best possible protection for soft-bodied animals. Their shells are both a fort and a prison.

Arthropods, which include insects, have exoskeletons that combine protection with free movement. However, an exoskeleton would be too heavy on a big animal. Thus, the size of arthropods is limited.

Chordates: The Most Complex Form of Animal life

The phylum *Chordata* **includes the animals with which you are probably most familiar—cats, dogs, birds, fishes, and so on.** These animals are mostly *vertebrates*, animals with backbones. **Vertebrates are a subphylum of the phylum Chordata.** There are other subphyla that are interesting but of lesser importance. This chapter will deal mainly with vertebrates.

Three factors make chordates different from all other animals.

- **All chordate embryos have a stiff rod of specialized cells along the length of the dorsal side of their bodies called *notochord.*** Some primitive chordates have a notochord their entire lives. These primitive chordates include lamprey and hagfish. In most vertebrates the notochord appears only in the embryo. Early in life it is replaced by the ***vertebral column,*** or backbone.

- **All chordates have a tubular dorsal *nerve cord.*** It lies just above the notochord on the dorsal side. The anterior end of this nerve cord develops into a brain. The remaining part becomes the spinal cord. Together, the brain and the spinal cord make up the *central nervous system.*

- All chordates have either paired slits or pouches in the throat region at some time in their lives. In fish and amphibians, such as frogs, the slits form gill slits. In terrestial chordates the pouches develop into various structures in the throat.

- **The phylum Chordata consists of the three subphyla, Vertebrate, Urochordata and Cephalochordata.** Of the three subphyla, only the vertebrates of the subphylum Vertebrata are familiar to most of us. The other two subphyla are mainly marine animals. Biologists find them interesting because they can give us some idea of what the ancestors of present-day vertebrates may have been like.

noto = **the back**

uro = **tail**

cephalo = **head**

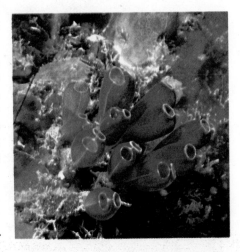

33–2 | Sea squirt. A member of subphylum Urochordata. It feeds on tiny animals and plants that are pulled into its body by a current. The sea squirt creates the current by beating its cilia. *(M. Timothy O'Keefe, Bruce Coleman)*

The Rise of Vertebrates

The subphylum Vertebrata includes animals with backbones. The presence of a strong, flexible support along the back is an advantage to land animals. With such a support, animals can lift themselves off the ground. This increases their mobility. In fish, especially large, rapidly moving fish,

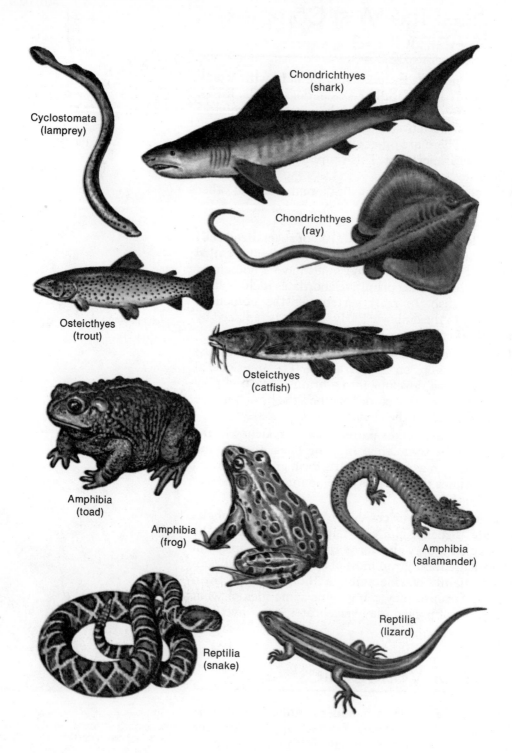

Cyclostomata
(lamprey)

Chondrichthyes
(shark)

Chondrichthyes
(ray)

Osteicthyes
(trout)

Osteicthyes
(catfish)

Amphibia
(toad)

Amphibia
(frog)

Amphibia
(salamander)

Reptilia
(snake)

Reptilia
(lizard)

33–3 | Examples of the various classes of vertebrates.

Reptilia
(alligator)

Reptilia
(turtle)

Aves
(cardinal)

Aves
(goose)

Mammalia
(horse)

Mammalia
(deer)

Mammalia
(seal)

Mammalia
(chipmunk)

the backbone forms a strong axis on which muscles can act.

When did the earliest vertebrates appear on the earth? From what chordate ancestors did they develop? There is no direct fossil evidence to answer these questions. This lack of fossil evidence may give us a small clue. Scientists believe that vertebrates may have evolved from soft-bodied chordates. Soft bodies would decompose without leaving an impression in rocks. The very first vertebrates probably lived about a half billion years ago, during the Odovician period. This seems likely because many vertebrate fossils were formed during the Silurian and Devonian periods that followed. Fossil records suggest that many vertebrate forms appeared and then disappeared during their early history.

Classes of Vertebrates

There are seven classes of modern vertebrates. They are listed here in order of increasing complexity. This may also have been the order in which they evolved.

- *Agnatha* (AG-nuh-thuh), jawless fishes, including lampreys and hagfishes.
- *Chondrichthyes* (kon-DRICKTH-ee-eez), sharks, rays, and skates.
- *Osteichthyes* (oss-tee-ICHTH-ee-eez), bony fishes.
- *Amphibia* (am-FIB-ee-uh), frogs, toads, and salamanders.
- *Reptilia* (rep-TILL-yuh), snakes, lizards, turtles, and crocodilians.
- *Aves* (AH-veez), birds.
- *Mammalia* (muh-MALE-yuh), mammals.

You will study these vertebrate classes in the chapters that follow. As you do, you will notice something interesting. There is a change from animals that live in the water to

ichthyes = fish

33–4 | *Amphioxus,* a member of the subphylum Cephalochordata, keeps its dorsal nerve cord, notochord, and gill slits throughout its life. It is about 5 cm (2 in.) long and lives in tropical and temperate coastal waters.

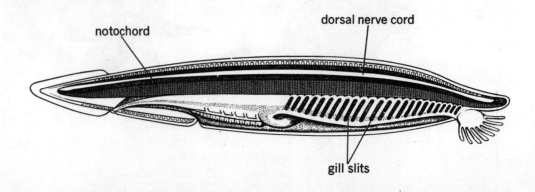

notochord

dorsal nerve cord

gill slits

those that live on land. This may have been the direction in the evolution of the vertebrates. You will also notice a movement toward more complex and efficient body organs. Finally, you will see that vertebrates can live successfully in all environments: land, water, and air.

Characteristics of Vertebrates

Vertebrates have many unique characteristics that make them different from other animals. **Vertebrates have an endoskeleton** (internal framework). It is made of *bone* and/or *cartilage.* It also consists of

1. **A vertebral column, or spine.** This is composed of cartilage or bony parts called *vertebrae.* This backbone, along with the skull, forms the *axial skeleton.*
2. **In most vertebrates there are two bony structures called girdles.** Girdles unite the extremities (arms or legs) with the axial skeleton. They are the anterior **pectoral girdle** and the posterior **pelvic girdle.**
3. **Limbs are attached to the pectoral and pelvic girdles.** They may be in the form of fins, legs, wings, or flippers. There are never more than two pairs. Both girdles and limbs form the *appendicular skeleton.*

Vertebrates have a body made up of a head and trunk. Many also have bodies with neck and tail regions. All vertebrates have an efficient **closed circulatory system.** This includes a **ventral heart** in the anterior part of the body. Their blood is partly composed of red corpuscles containing hemoglobin.

In most vertebrates there are 10 or 12 pairs of **cranial nerves** that extend from the brain, as well as **spinal nerves** that extend from the dorsal spinal cord.

They also have eyes, ears, and nostrils on the head. **Vertebrates have a food tube, or alimentary canal.** This tube is elongated and looped or coiled in the body cavity, or *coelom.* A liver and pancreas are also present.

Specialized Systems of Vertebrate Bodies

There are several vertebrate systems made up of many highly developed organs. They are listed here.

- *Integumentary system*—the outer body covering and special protective outgrowths. These include scales, feathers, and hairs.
- *Muscular system*—the muscles attached to bones for body movement and the muscles that form the walls of the heart, the digestive organs, and the blood vessels.

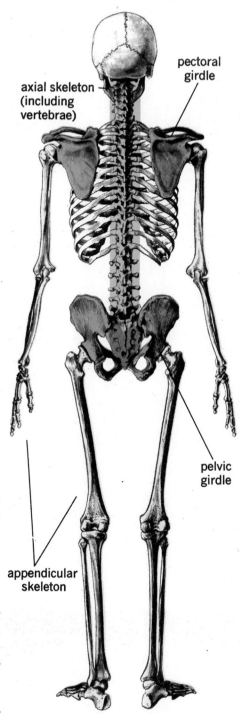

axial skeleton (including vertebrae)

pectoral girdle

pelvic girdle

appendicular skeleton

33–5 | Dorsal view of a vertebrate endoskeleton.

- *Skeletal system*—the bones and cartilage that make up the body framework.
- *Digestive system*—the many specialized organs that prepare food to be used by body tissues.
- *Respiratory systems*—gills or lungs and related structures used in exchanging gases between the animal and its environment.
- *Circulatory system*—the transportation system of the body. It includes the heart and blood vessels.
- *Excretory system*—organs that remove wastes from the body.
- *Endocrine system*—the glands that produce and secrete chemical regulators called hormones that help various organs and systems function in harmony.
- *Nervous system*—the brain, spinal cord, nerves, and special sense organs. This is a vertebrate's most highly developed system.
- *Reproductive system*—the male or female organs of reproduction.

Lines of Development in Vertebrates

Lampreys, sharks, rays, and bony fishes are adapted to live in water. Their limbs take the form of fins. Their gills can absorb dissolved oxygen from the water. Water flows over the gills through gill slits in the throat. Amphibians, as you will see, represent a transition from water life to land life. During the tadpole stage, a frog is like a fish with gills and a fin. As an adult, the frog can move on land and breathe the air.

The vertebrate heart and brain are more developed than those of invertebrates. Fish hearts have two chambers. One, the *atrium,* receives blood from the body. The other, the *ventricle,* pumps blood to the gills. Frogs have a three-chambered heart: two atria and one ventricle. They also have a more complex circulatory system. Birds and mammals have even more complex hearts with four chambers. They have two atria and two ventricles. One side of the heart receives blood from the lungs and pumps it to the body. The other side receives blood from the body and pumps it to the lungs. This type of heart is a kind of double pump. The human heart is this type of double pump.

The vertebrate brain also is highly developed. It is enclosed in a skull, or cranium. One brain region is called the **cerebrum.** The cerebrum is the center of instinct, emotion, memory, and intelligence. The more developed the vertebrate, the larger the relative size of this area of the brain. **The mammal brain has the biggest cerebrum in proportion to its body.**

The Complex Behavior of Vertebrates

Behavior is the way in which an organism responds to stimuli. The vertebrates' complex behavior depends on highly developed sense organs, nerve pathways, and organs specialized for nervous control. Protists and plants, on the other hand, do not have specialized nervous tissues. Their responses are limited to simple tropisms. Highly developed organs are the basis for the vertebrates' complex behavior.

Vertebrate behavior often is broken down into two different types. One type of behavior is *inborn*. The other type is *learned*.

Innate Behavior   Inborn behavior is called *innate behavior.* **Since innate behavior is inherited, its development is controlled by genes.** There are two kinds of innate behavior, **reflexes** and **instincts.** *Reflexes* are simple innate responses. A reflex is an automatic response to a stimulus. For instance, touching the surface of the eye or eyelid will cause blinking. Reflexes are involuntary. This means that the animal reacts to the stimulus without conscious control. Such responses usually protect the organism from harm.

Instincts are probably the most interesting innate responses. They are also the least understood. Instincts are often very complex. Yet they are unlearned and involuntary. **Animals act instinctively without any deliberate decision.**

33–6 | What kind of complex behavior is this baboon showing? *(John Dominis, Life Magazine)*

Self-preservation is a very basic instinct. It can be seen in all vertebrates and many invertebrates. In times of danger, an animal will respond to the "fight-or-flight" instinct. Have you ever cornered an animal that normally would flee? A squirrel can become vicious when cornered. It will bite and claw if it cannot escape from an enemy. In such a situation, a squirrel might defend itself against a human.

Scientists classify another instinct as **species preservation. Species preservation directs animal reproduction and the care of young.** This is what drives the Pacific salmon up the streams of the Northwest to their spawning beds. After they reproduce, the adult salmon die, but a new generation comes downstream to the ocean. Species preservation causes the sunfish to defend its nest when it would normally flee. In responding to an instinct, an animal behaves automatically without making a choice.

Learned Behavior **Vertebrates are capable of learned behavior as well as innate behavior.** This is due to their well-developed nervous systems. Learned behavior can be changed. A common form of learned behavior is called a *conditioned reaction.* **A conditioned reaction occurs when a specific behavior response always follows a particular stimulus.** If the results are pleasurable, or at least healthy, the animal will continue responding to that same stimulus in the same way. When humans condition animals to behave in certain ways, they do it by giving rewards or punishments for certain responses. As these continue, the desired responses become habits to the animals. Eventually, the animals are conditioned. This is how a dog learns to sit down or roll over at a given command. Even fishes in an aquarium can be conditioned to go to one certain corner of the tank when you approach. Just be sure always to feed them in that corner.

You can see instincts in all vertebrates. Most vertebrates are capable of some sort of conditioned behavior. *Intelligent behavior* is a more complex nervous activity. This sort of behavior involves problem-solving, judgment, and decision. Birds and some mammals have a limited degree of intelligent behavior. Human beings, however, are supreme among the vertebrates in intelligence. We are unique among living things in our ability to communicate by symbols in both speaking and writing.

With an understanding of the general characteristics of vertebrates, their systems, and lines of development, you are ready to study the vertebrate classes. You will study the least-developed to the most-developed living vertebrates. You will notice an increase in efficiency in the heart, respiratory organs, reproductive organs, and brain.

This progression has another interesting feature. Fossil evidence seems to show that vertebrates evolved in this order.

notochord	innate behavior
vertebral column	reflex
bone	instinct
cartilage	self-preservation
vertebrae	species preservation
axial skeleton	conditioned reaction
appendicular skeleton	intelligent behavior
cerebrum	

1. Name three unique characteristics of chordates.
2. Account for the lack of fossil evidence of vertebrate ancestry.
3. Name the seven classes of vertebrates in the order of their structural complexity.
4. Name 10 organ systems that make up the vertebrate body.
5. Explain why increase in the size of the cerebrum is an important evolutionary advancement.
6. Explain "innate behavior." Give examples.
7. In what ways are reflex actions important in the lives of animals?
8. Give an example of (a) a conditioned reaction in a vertebrate and (b) an intelligent act.

1. Discuss several structural characteristics that contribute to the success of the vertebrates.
2. Self-preservation and species preservation are instincts. Which is stronger? Give an example to support your answer.

The Fishes

A **DISCUSS** the characteristics of the three classes of fishes.

B **DISTINGUISH** sharks from bony fishes.

C **DESCRIBE** the external anatomy of a bony fish.

D **IDENTIFY** the internal systems of bony fishes.

E **EXPLAIN** reproduction in bony fishes.

34–1 | Sharks are one of the most primitive fishes. *(Flip Schulke, © Black Star)*

The Least Complex Vertebrates

Fish used to be the main source of protein for people in many parts of the world. Fish are part of an aquatic food chain that supports many animals, such as birds, seals, and sea lions. If the number of fish is reduced greatly, the number of a variety of other animals will be reduced also.

In addition to providing food for other animal life, fish have interesting behavior patterns. For instance, many fish make seasonal migrations; they perform complex mating rituals; they defend their territory, their nests, and their young. Although they are the least complex, fish are as diverse and puzzling as any of the other vertebrates.

The fishes consist of these three classes:

- *Agnatha:* The jawless fishes—a very small group that consists of the only vertebrates that live as scavengers and parasites. This class includes lampreys and hagfish.
- *Chondrichthyes:* These fish have skeletons of cartilage. This class includes sharks, rays, and skates.
- *Osteichthyes:* These are the fishes with bony skeletons.

Facts & Figures

There are 20,000 known living species of fishes.

a = without
gnathos = jaw

chondro = cartilage

ichthyes = fish
os = bone

The most familiar and the most complex fish are included in this class. Aquarium fish, common food fish such as cod, salmon, and perch are included in this class.

Let's look at each of these classes of fish.

Agnatha: The Jawless Fish

The jawless fish are the most primitive and oldest vertebrates. Fossil evidence indicates that they were present during the Ordovician period, about 500 million years ago. The only surviving members of this group, and the only vertebrate parasites, belong to the order *Cyclostomata*. These are the lampreys and hagfish. Each has a notochord which serves as the main skeletal support for the animal in its adult life. They also have some supporting cartilage in the throat region. Both freshwater and marine lampreys exist. The hagfishes are all marine and, although parasitic, live mostly as scavengers. The lamprey is more important because of its threat to our food supply.

cyclo = **circle**
stoma = **mouth**

Lampreys: The Blood Suckers of the Great Lakes

The lamprey has a thin body like that of an eel. The adult lamprey can be about 60 centimeters (24 inches) long and weigh about a half kilogram (about 1 pound). Its skin is soft, slimy, brownish-green, and blotched. The lamprey does not have paired fins. There are two single fins along the back plus a tail fin. The lamprey uses these fins to swim in a rippling manner. It has small eyes on each side of its head. On the top of the head, between the eyes, is a nasal opening. This opening leads to a sac containing nerve endings that aid in the sense of smell. There are seven oval gill slits on each side of the head. These openings lead to spherical pouches that contain many feathery gills. Water moves in and out of the gill slits and gases are exchanged.

The lamprey's head is very different from the head of other types of fish. Instead of jaws, lampreys have funnel-like mouths lined with sharp, horny teeth. In the center of the mouth is a rasping tongue with teethlike projections.

The lamprey uses its sucking mouth to attach to a fish. Then it tears a hole with its rasping teeth through the fish's scales. It sucks out blood and body fluids. Sometimes the lamprey may even suck out the internal organs of the fish. The injury it causes is not always fatal. Many fishes are

34-2 | The mouth of a sea lamprey. Note the circular, jawless mouth and rasping teeth. *(Russ Kinne, Photo Researchers)*

found with scars showing where they were attacked by lampreys. Lampreys feed mainly on lake trout, an economically important fish in the Great Lakes. When there are no trout, lampreys attack whitefish, pike, and other species.

Chondrichthyes: The Cartilage Fishes

Cartilage fishes have skeletons of cartilage rather than bone. It is thought that they developed early in the Devonian period, about 400 million years ago. Of the fishes that lived in the ancient seas, many cartilage fishes have survived relatively unchanged in great numbers.

Sharks

Sharks include the largest living fishes. The whale shark may grow to be over 15 meters (49.5 feet) long and can weigh as much as 18,000 kilograms (39,600 lbs). The great white shark may exceed 12 meters (39.6 feet) in length.

Sharks have *placoid scales*. Each placoid scale resembles a small tooth. It has a small spine covered by enamel. When you run your hand over a shark skin, it feels like sandpaper because of its many spiny scales.

The shark's body is torpedo-shaped. The long upper lobe of the tail fin is a characteristic of ancient fishes. This type of tail fin forces the head of the shark downward as it moves through the water. The mouth is a horizontal slit on the ventral side of the head. The jaws of most sharks are lined with several rows of razor-sharp, pointed teeth. When a tooth is lost, another one may move forward to replace it. The teeth slant backward to hold the food securely in the mouth. This, combined with great strength, makes the shark a fearsome hunter.

As the shark moves forward, water enters its opened mouth and passes over the **gills** inside both sides of the head. The water then goes out through the gills slits. Sharks can also pump water through their mouths by muscle action.

A shark can detect underwater vibrations of very low frequency from a long distance. The uneven swimming movements of an injured fish could cause such vibrations. These slight changes in water pressure are detected by a line of sensory cells called the **lateral line.** It is present on the sides of the shark. The shark then follows these vibrations to their source. Paired nostrils on the ventral surface of the shark lead to olfactory sacs. The water entering the olfactory sacs is continually tested for dissolved chemicals.

Facts & Figures

The largest fish ever caught on rod and reel was a white shark off the coast of Australia in 1959. It weighed 1,208.38 kilograms (2,664 pounds).

The two large, well-developed eyes above the mouth are used to see at close range.

Rays and Skates

Rays have broad, disc-shaped bodies with enormous lateral fins and whiplike tails. Rays swim with an undulating, or wavy, motion of these fins. They are usually bottom dwellers and feed on mollusks such as clams or oysters. Bottom-dwelling rays have flat, heavy teeth and strong jaws that can crush shells. Most rays are less than a meter (3.3 feet) long. The giant Manta ray, or devilfish, may be five or six meters wide. These giant rays are quite harmless to people and feed on the ocean plankton and small fish.

Most rays and skates are relatively harmless. One group of rays, the sting rays, have a tail with a venomous barbed spike. Trying to dislodge a fishhook from such a ray, or stepping on one, could result in a serious wound.

Skates are very similar to rays in basic body plan. They are more triangular and have a dorsal fin, which rays lack. Both rays and skates often can be found close to shore. They often lie on the bottom, half covered by sand. They take in water through two spiracles, bulblike structures on top of their heads. Water enters the spiracles, runs over the gills, and out through the gill slits on the ventral surface.

34-3 | The sting ray. Some species have a dorsal spine with venom glands. *(© Z. Leszczynski, Animals Animals)*

Osteichthyes: The Bony Fishes

True fishes belong to the class *Osteichthyes*. This means *bony fishes*. **Unlike the lamprey, shark, and ray, true fishes have bony skeletons.** Bony fishes first appeared in the Devonian period. Since the time they first appeared, bony fishes have increased steadily in number. Today they are the dominant vertebrates in both freshwater and marine environments. They are found in many forms and sizes. **Fishes are ideally adapted to life in water. In some form they live in practically every aquatic environment.**

External Features

Bony fishes have *gills* for respiration. Limbs take the form of *fins*. Most fishes have an outer covering of *scales*. Fish bodies are divided into three areas: head, trunk, and tail. Many people confuse the tail of the fish with the tail fin. The tail is a solid muscular part. The tail fin is an outgrowth of this region. In most fish, the body is streamlined perfectly. It is tapered at both ends, or spindle shaped. The lack of a neck is not a disadvantage to a fish. It can turn its body easily in the water.

At each side of the head is a crescent-shaped slit. This

34-4 | A skate. What features do you see in the photograph that would indicate that the skate is well adapted for living on the bottom of the ocean? *(Douglas Faulkner)*

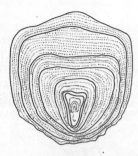

34-5 | Each season, as the fish grows, new rings form on its scales. Darker lines show where growth has stopped for that year. How old is the fish from which this scale came?

marks the back edge of the gill cover, or **operculum** (oe-PURR-kyoo-lum). This hard plate acts as a protective cover over the gills. By opening the rear edge of the operculum, you can see the gills lying in a large gill chamber. The four gills look like delicate combs. The edges of the opercula almost meet on the lower side of the fish. This marks where the head attaches to the trunk.

The Integument Fish *scales* are thin, flat discs of bone that grow from pockets in the skin. They overlap like shingles on a roof. Scales grow larger as the fish grows bigger, but they always stay the same in number. A young fish has the same number of scales as it will have when it is older. As scales grow, concentric rings form on them. As winter approaches, growth slows and the rings are closer together. To find out the age of a fish you can count the darker lines alternating with the lighter rings of the fish's scales. Each dark line represents one year.

Mucus, secreted by skin glands, seeps between the scales. It forms a covering that lubricates the fish body. This body slime helps fish glide through the water. It also makes the fish slippery to its enemies. Finally, this mucus forms protection against parasitic fungi, bacteria, and protozoans. If you pick up a live fish, wet your hands. Dry hands will scrape off some of this protective slime and expose the fish to parasites.

Many fishes are brightly colored. These colors often are arranged in stripes or spots. Much of the coloration is caused by pigment granules. These granules are located in special skin cells called **chromatophores** (krome-AT-uh-forz). Sometimes fish even change colors. Scientists think that this is an involuntary response to the environment.

A color change occurs when the pigment is rearranged within the chromatophores. When the pigment is dispersed within the cells, the fish is dark. When the pigment is concentrated in clumps, the fish is light in color. This helps a fish hide from its enemies. The ability to change color varies with species, size, and age. The length of time needed for the change also varies. Probably the flounder holds the "speed record" for color change. Its color can change to match a polka-dot background in just a few minutes. Most fish, however, take longer—even a couple of days—to change color.

Many fishes have a color pattern known as countershading. This pattern is a form of camouflage. Dark pigments on the fish's back tone down the bright light filtering through the water above. The dark colors on the dorsal side blend with the bottom of the body of water. Lighter colors on the ventral side blend with bright light on the surface

34-6 | Is this the dorsal or ventral surface of the flounder? (Russ Kinne, Photo Researchers)

when the fish is seen from below. For example, a flounder is white on its ventral surface, and sand-colored or dark on its dorsal surface.

Fins: Their Structure and Function Various kinds of fins develop from the trunk and tail. All are made of thin membranes, well-supplied with blood vessels. Fins are supported by *rays* and *spines*. Rays are very flexible but firm, rodlike structures that spread the fin out like ribs on a fan. Spines are stiff, bony, sharp structures that support the fins but also serve as a defense. The spikes that support the dorsal fin along the back of a perch, for example, discourage attacks. When the fin is lifted and spread, all the spines point towards the tail. This makes the fish difficult to swallow tail first.

There are two kinds of paired fins. These are homologous to the limbs of other vertebrates. The **pectoral fins** are nearest the head. These correspond to the front legs. The **pelvic fins** are posterior to and below the pectoral fins. These correspond to the hind legs. These pelvic fins act like oars when a fish swims slowly. They also aid in steering and keeping balance when the fish is resting. They are also used when the fish moves backward.

There are several single fins. The **caudal fin** grows from the tail. It helps push the fish forward.

The anterior and posterior dorsal fins help the fish to stay upright while swimming. The anterior dorsal fin has spines, the posterior dorsal fin contains only rays. Another single fin, called the **anal fin,** grows along the midline on the ventral side of the fish. Like the dorsal fins, the anal fin helps the fish keep its balance.

Powerful muscles occupy the region of the trunk above the spinal column. A thinner muscle layer lies along the body wall on the sides of the trunk. The tail region is nearly solid muscle.

34-7 | A fish's spines are often a good defense. This catfish has spines that provide protection. *(Allan Roberts)*

Organ Systems of Fishes

Fishes have the same systems typical of vertebrate bodies. These are outlined in Chapter 33. Fishes, however, have many specialized organs and structures that are adapted to their aquatic environment. In the following discussions of organ systems, the yellow perch will be used as a typical example of all bony fishes.

The Digestive System If you've ever gone fishing, you may have used the earthworm for bait. Carnivorous fish may also eat frogs, other fish, insects, crayfish, and other invertebrates.

Most fishes have large mouths at the anterior end. Car-

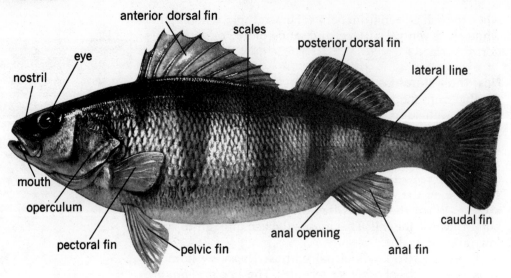

anterior dorsal fin

scales

posterior dorsal fin

eye

nostril

lateral line

mouth

operculum

pectoral fin

pelvic fin

anal opening

anal fin

caudal fin

34–8 | The external structure of a bony fish, the yellow perch.

nivorous fishes, like the yellow perch, have many small, sharp teeth. These grow from the jawbones and the roof of the mouth. The teeth slant backward. This makes it easy for the fish to swallow, but hard for its victim to escape. The tongue is fastened to the floor of the mouth. It cannot move as human tongues can. Specialized sensory structures called taste buds are on the tongue, line the mouth, and are even on the surface of the head. They give the fish its sense of taste and enable it to detect chemicals in the water.

The perch, and many other fish, have a special hinge on their mouths that moves forward as the mouth opens. This feature greatly increases the size of prey a perch can swallow.

The *pharynx*, or throat cavity, leads to the short *esophagus*. The esophagus, in turn, joins the upper end of the *stomach*. The stomach is in a straight line with the esophagus. This allows a fish to swallow food almost as big as itself. Sometimes the prey's tail will hang from the fish's mouth while the head is being digested in the stomach. Close to the stomach lies a well-developed *liver*. The *pancreas* is near the stomach, but it is difficult to find in a fish dissection.

A rather short *intestine* leads from the lower end of the stomach. At this junction, short fingerlike tubes extend from the intestine. These tubes are called *pyloric caeca* (pie-LORE-ick SEEK-uh). Considerable digestion and absorption of food occurs in the pyloric caeca. Digestion continues as food passes along the short loops of the intestine. Digested food is absorbed through the intestine wall. Undigested material leaves through the *anus*, on the lower side.

THE ANATOMY OF THE FROG
DIGESTIVE SYSTEM

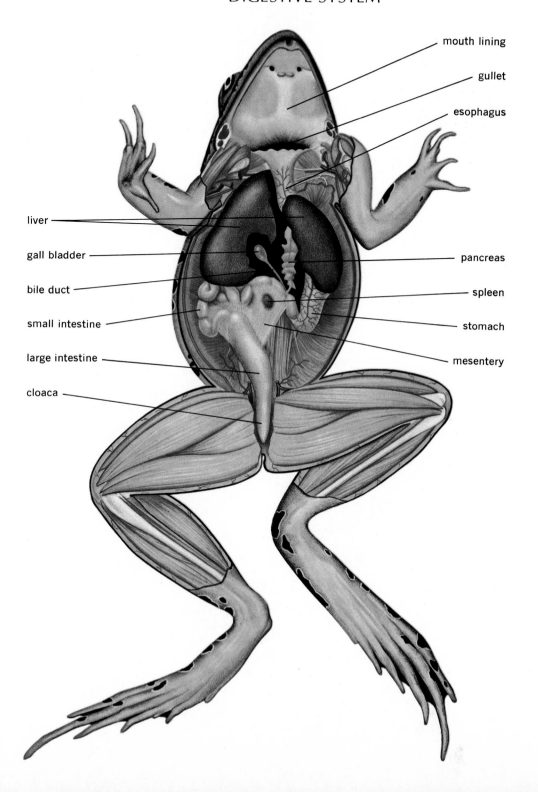

mouth lining

gullet

esophagus

liver

gall bladder

bile duct

small intestine

large intestine

cloaca

pancreas

spleen

stomach

mesentery

CIRCULATORY AND EXCRETORY SYSTEMS

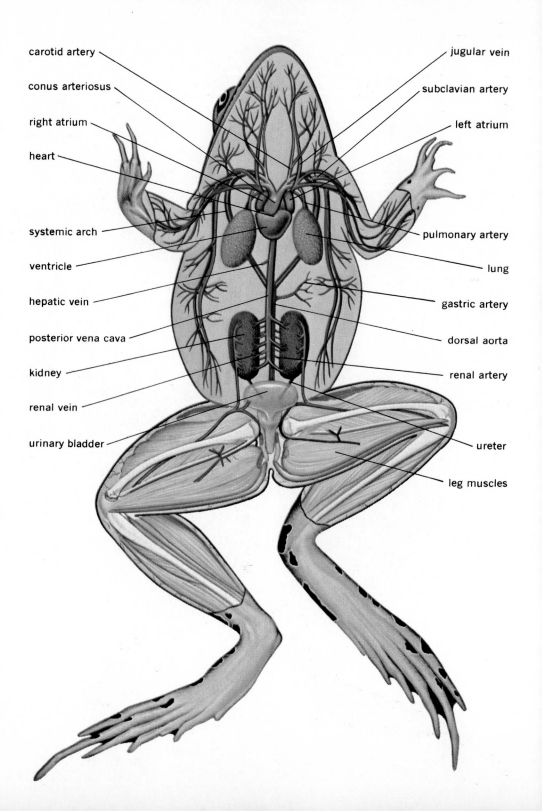

carotid artery

conus arteriosus

right atrium

heart

systemic arch

ventricle

hepatic vein

posterior vena cava

kidney

renal vein

urinary bladder

jugular vein

subclavian artery

left atrium

pulmonary artery

lung

gastric artery

dorsal aorta

renal artery

ureter

leg muscles

BACK BODY WALL AND NERVOUS SYSTEM

internal nostril openings

eye sockets

brain

Eustachian tube

spinal cord

dorsal wall of cloaca

vomerine teeth

teeth of upper jaw

spinal nerves

femoral vein

femur

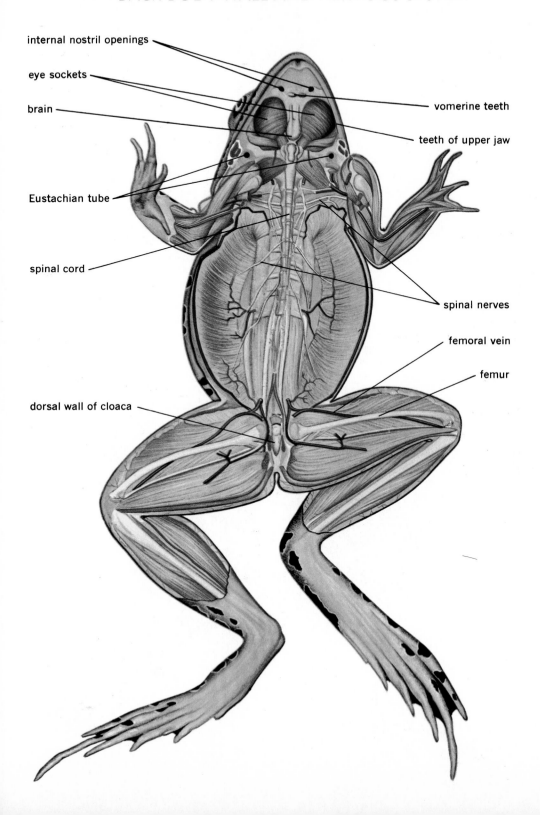

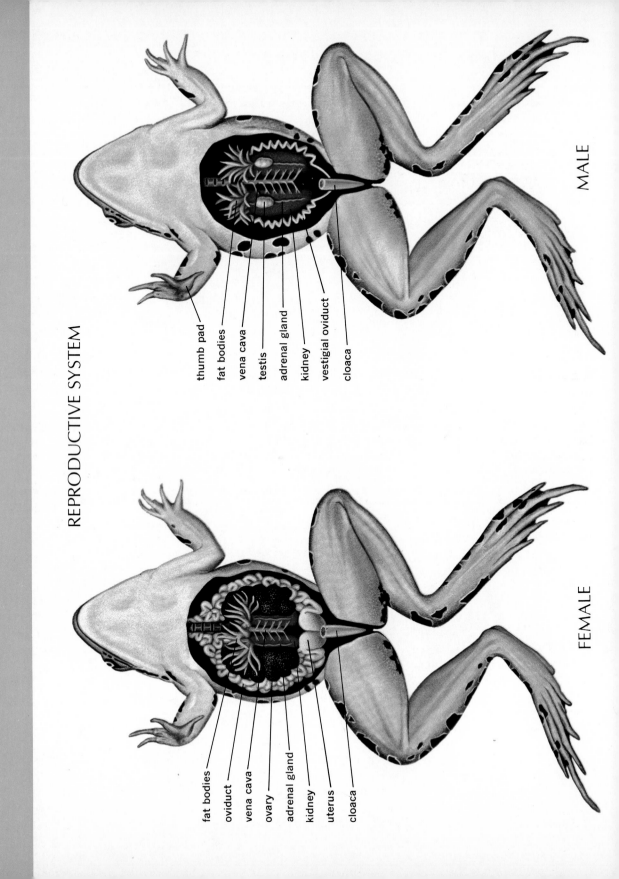

REPRODUCTIVE SYSTEM

MALE

thumb pad
fat bodies
vena cava
testis
adrenal gland
kidney
vestigial oviduct
cloaca

FEMALE

fat bodies
oviduct
vena cava
ovary
adrenal gland
kidney
uterus
cloaca

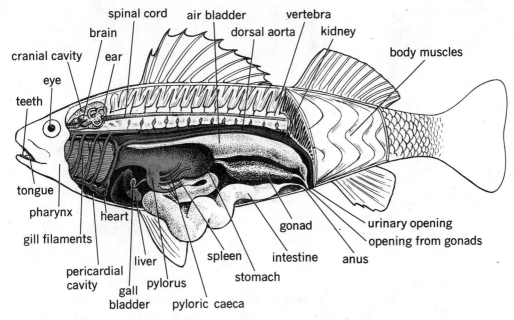

spinal cord air bladder vertebra
brain dorsal aorta kidney
cranial cavity ear body muscles
eye
teeth
tongue
pharynx heart
gill filaments
pericardial liver gonad urinary opening
cavity pylorus spleen intestine opening from gonads
gall stomach anus
bladder pyloric caeca

34-9 | The internal structure of a yellow perch.

The Circulatory System   **The purpose of blood circulation in fish is the same as in other organisms. Blood delivers oxygen and nutrients to the body tissues and removes carbon dioxide and other wastes from the tissues.** The blood of fish is similar to that of other vertebrates. It contains both red and white blood cells. As the blood circulates through the body of the fish, it goes through three different types of blood vessels: *arteries, capillaries,* and *veins.* It is through the thin membranes of the tiny capillaries that gases like oxygen and carbon dioxide are exchanged. The heart is the organ that pumps the blood through the blood vessels.

Blood pumped from the heart is carried through arteries to the capillaries of the gills. There the blood picks up oxygen gas that is dissolved in the water and gives off carbon dioxide. On leaving the gills, the oxygenated blood enters the dorsal aorta. This artery and its branches carry blood to all parts of the body. As the blood passes through the capillaries of various organs, it gives up its oxygen and takes up carbon dioxide and other wastes. When passing through the capillaries of the digestive organs, the blood picks up nutrients. When passing through the kidneys, the blood gives up various cell waste products, mainly nitrogen compounds.

When the blood leaves the capillaries, it enters the veins. The large cardinal veins and the veins from the liver return the blood to the heart. The cardinal veins expand into a thin-walled sac when the blood reaches the heart. This sac is the *sinus venosus.* It leads to the first chamber of the heart, called the **atrium.** From the atrium, blood flows

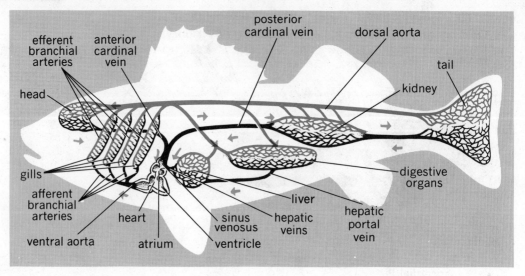

efferent branchial arteries

anterior cardinal vein

posterior cardinal vein

dorsal aorta

tail

head

kidney

gills

afferent branchial arteries

heart

ventral aorta

atrium

sinus venosus

ventricle

hepatic veins

liver

digestive organs

hepatic portal vein

34–10 | The circulatory system of a fish. Note that the blood flows in a single circuit—from the heart to the gills to the body and to the heart again.

into the **ventricle.** The ventricle is the muscular, thick-walled pumping chamber of the heart. Because the heart has one atrium and one ventricle, we say that the fish has a two-chambered heart.

The ventricle pumps the blood with great power through the *ventral aorta.* This artery begins with a muscular bulb-shaped structure called the *bulbus arteriosus.* This structure is very noticeable in the fish heart. The ventral aorta branches to carry the blood to the two sets of gills. Then it branches again into *branchial* (BRONG-kee-uhl) *arteries* that lead to the four gills on each side of the head.

The Gills and Respiration Bony fish, such as the yellow perch, have four gills in each of two gill chambers. There is one gill chamber on each side of the head. Each *gill* consists of an arch of bone or cartilage fringed with a double row of thin-walled projections. These projections are called *gill filaments.* **These gill filaments have many capillaries. This brings the blood in close contact with the water and its dissolved oxygen over a large surface.** On the throat side, the gill arches have hard, fingerlike projections. These are called *gill rakers.* The gill rakers prevent food and debris from getting to the gill filaments. This is necessary to insure that water moves freely over the gills.

Fish need a constant flow of water over their gills. Water is drawn through the open mouth as the cavity of the pharynx enlarges. The pharynx enlarges when the gill arches expand. As water is drawn in, the edge of the operculum is pressed against the body. Then the mouth closes, the gill arches contract, and the rear edge of the operculum opens. This forces water over the gill filaments, and out of the gill chamber around the raised edge of the operculum. The forward motion of a swimming fish aids in this process.

The Air Bladder: A Pressure Organ

A thin-walled sac, the *air bladder,* lies in the upper part of the body cavity of a fish. Some fishes swallow air. An example is the lungfish. In these fish the air bladder is connected with the pharynx by a tube. In other fish, the bladder is inflated by gases that pass into it from the blood. The gases are oxygen, nitrogen, and carbon dioxide.

The bladder acts as a float. It allows the fish to remain at any water depth without much effort. By adjusting the amount of gas in the air bladder, the fish can move to different levels in the water.

Fishes live at different depths at different times of year. The air bladder adjusts by losing gas to the blood or receiving more gas. When a fish that is adjusted to a great depth is caught and quickly brought to surface, the air bladder expands. This can push the esophagus and stomach up into the fish's mouth.

Some bony fish, such as the mackerel and darter, have no air bladder. These fish sink to the bottom, as do sharks, whenever they stop swimming.

The Excretory System

The excretory system of fishes is adapted to their aquatic environment. Wastes are eliminated through the gills by diffusion. They also have kidneys to filter wastes from the blood. Ducts transport wastes to a urinary bladder where they can be stored for a time, to be excreted later. The kidneys are important to maintain a water balance with the environment. In marine fishes, kidneys are also important in keeping a salt balance.

The Nervous System

The fish nervous system includes the brain, spinal cord, and many nerves that lead to all parts of the body. The brain lies in a small bony cavity in the head. This is called the *cranial cavity.* The brain has five different parts. (See also page 503.)

- At the anterior end are the *olfactory lobes.* From here, nerves sensitive to chemical changes in the environment extend to the nostrils.
- The two lobes of the *cerebrum* lie behind the olfactory lobes. The function of the fish cerebrum is not entirely clear. Much of it has to do with olfactory functions. Some motor impulses that control certain muscles may originate in the cerebrum.

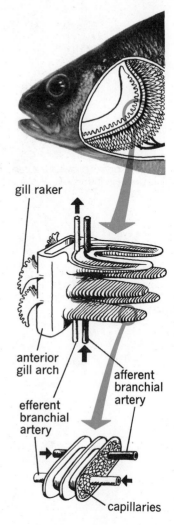

gill raker

anterior gill arch

efferent branchial artery

afferent branchial artery

capillaries

34–11 | The afferent branchial artery brings blood to the base of the gill arches. The oxygenated blood flows to the top of each gill through the efferent branchial artery.

olfactus = **to smell**

34–12 | A swim bladder allows this trumpetfish to adjust its depth in the water. *(A. Myshin; © Animals Animals)*

optic = of the eye

- Next are the **optic lobes.** These are the largest lobes of a fish's brain. The optic lobes receive sensory information not only from the eyes but from other sense organs as well. These lobes function as the main integrative center of the brain. After various sensations have been interpreted, nerve impulses are sent to other areas of the brain or along motor pathways that cause muscle contraction and movement.
- The **cerebellum** is behind the optic lobes. It coordinates muscle activities.
- Finally, at the back of the brain, is the **medulla oblongata.** This part of the brain helps control the activities of the internal organs.

The *spinal cord* passes back from the medulla. The spinal cord is encased in the vertebral column. **Cranial nerves** extend from the brain to the sense organs and head structures. **Spinal nerves** connect the spinal cord to the various areas of the body.

The fish's brain is not as well developed as those of the higher vertebrates, but the same basic regions are present. Compare the brains of other vertebrates to the fish brain. As vertebrates become more highly developed, the cerebrum is larger in proportion to the rest of the brain. With this increase comes an increase in nervous activity on higher levels. This includes emotional responses, memory, and intellectual activity.

The Sensations of Fishes   Fish have relatively large optic lobes. This might lead us to think that fish have a well developed sense of sight. However, sight is not the most important sense in fish. In fact, fish are known to be nearsighted. Also, the amount of light is reduced underwater. Fish probably cannot see very clearly for more than a half

34–13 | Although fish have large eyes, this red snapper can probably not see very far. How else do fish sense what is going on in their environment? *(William E. Ferguson)*

meter (1.6 ft).

The eyes of most fish are large; most fish can move their eyes. There are no eyelids. The transparent cornea that covers the eye is flattened. The pupils are large compared to those of other vertebrates. They let in as much light as possible. The lens is shaped almost like a ball. It moves backward or forward as the eye focuses, just as you focus a camera.

It was thought that fish lived in a world of black, white, and gray. Now, however, studies show that some fish may have color vision.

Unlike higher vertebrates, fish lack eardrums and middle ears. **Sound vibrations are probably transmitted through the body and skull bones.**

Closely associated with the sense of hearing is the lateral line. As in the shark, the lateral line on bony fishes is formed by a single row of pitted scales running along each side of the fish. The pits, or holes, in the scales lead into a canal, or tube, under the scales. The tube extends from head to tail. Sensory cells within the tube detect very low frequency vibrations in the water. This sense may be important in interpreting the environment. For example, it might help detect an insect struggling on the surface of a pond or in detecting a slight change in current.

The fish's olfactory sense is probably its keenest sense. Fish are very sensitive to dissolved substances in the water. This is similar to the sense of smell in air-breathing animals. Experiments show that fish are able to tell the difference between "smells" of different kinds of water plants. They can even detect the chemicals of hands washed in a stream. Scientists now believe that fish can locate food by this chemical sense.

Reproduction in Fishes The *gonads* (reproductive organs) of fish lie in the body cavity above the digestive

Facts & Figures

The South American *Anableps* has two pairs of eyes. It can see in the water and in the air at the same time.

organs. The opening from the gonads is just behind the anal opening.

The reproductive organs of the female fish are *ovaries.* In many fish, including the yellow perch, paired ovaries fuse into a single ovary during embryonic growth. When the female is mature, the ovary or ovaries produce eggs over a period of several months. As the eggs grow, the ovaries swell and may bulge the sides of the fish.

In male fish the sex organs are the *testes.* These develop sperm cells. When the female lays the eggs, or **spawns,** the male swims over them. The male discharges **milt** onto the eggs. Milt is a fluid containing the sperms. The sperms swim to the eggs and fertilize them. This is external fertilization.

Fertilized eggs begin to develop into embryos. This may take from a couple of days to many weeks, depending on the species and the water temperature. As the embryo develops, it is nourished by special food in the egg. This food is called **yolk.** The yolk is a large amount of nonliving material held in the egg. A *yolk sac* remains attached to a baby fish for a short time after it hatches.

In most fishes, spawning is not very efficient. Many eggs are never fertilized. Therefore, they never develop. Also, many fertilized eggs are eaten by predators before hatching. Those baby fish that do hatch are in constant danger of being eaten by bigger fish and other water animals. How does a fish species continue to survive under these harsh conditions? **The species survives because of the large number of eggs that are laid.** A female fish spawns anywhere from 500 to seven million eggs, depending upon the species.

Some fishes bear their young alive. The female keeps the eggs in her body. The female receives sperms from the male during mating. The young fish develop within the female's body. These kinds of fish are called *live-bearers.* Guppies, mollies, platys, and swordtails are examples of live-bearers.

The Spawning Habits of Various Fishes

The spawning habits of fishes vary greatly. Usually, freshwater fish spawn in the waters where they normally live. Often they swim to shallower water to spawn. Shallow waters give them both greater protection and a warmer temperature. The yellow perch moves from deep lake water to spawn in shallow water near the shore. In the spring, thousands of eggs are laid in ribbonlike masses.

Some fishes make nests in which eggs are deposited. The male stickleback, for example, builds a nest from bits of plants and other rubble. Then the male drives the female

34-14 | A salmon migrating upstream to the spawning areas. *(Stouffer, Animals Animals)*

into it for spawning. Later, he drives her away from the nest. The male takes charge of the nest and eggs. Channel catfish spawn in holes in banks or channel bottoms. They may even spawn in rusty cans they find on the bottom.

Some fishes travel long distances to their spawning areas. The eel has an interesting spawning migration. This long, slender fish lives in the rivers and streams of the Atlantic and Gulf coast regions. A few are found further inland. Adult eels live in fresh water for 5 to 10 years, depending on the climate and the food supply. When they are sexually mature, they go on a final journey downstream to the Atlantic Ocean. They travel to the spawning grounds where they began life. For some strange reason, they keep going until they reach the same special place just north of the West Indies and south of Bermuda. Scientists think that the eels follow warm water currents, but the exact route and depth at which they swim remain a mystery. Once there, each female lays a couple of million eggs. After spawning, all of the adults die.

The eel larvae hatch in the spawning grounds in the spring. By the autumn of the first year, the larvae arrive at the coast of North America. During the winter, they change into tiny adult eels. The next spring they enter the mouths of rivers and streams in droves. Males travel only a short distance. Females go much farther, sometimes thousands of kilometers.

European eels spawn in an area near the grounds of American eels. They are farther east, near the Sargasso Sea. These eels migrate almost 5,000 kilometers (3,000 miles) through the Atlantic. The return trip of the baby eels takes several years. American eels and European eels always go back to their own continents.

Part of this strange homing instinct can be explained by the fact that the American eels develop faster and are ready to enter fresh water when they find themselves off our coast. The European eels develop more slowly and are not ready to enter fresh water for a couple of years more. By that time they have been carried to the coast of Europe by the Gulf Stream.

Of all the migrating fish, the Pacific salmon have the strongest homing instinct. Generation after generation, the Pacific salmon leave the deep ocean waters where they live. They somehow find their way to the very same rivers in which their parents spawned three or four years earlier. Salmon migrations start in the late spring and early fall, depending on the specific species and the distance to be covered. The king salmon goes as much as 1,600 kilometers (960 miles) upstream to the cold fast-flowing streams.

When they finally reach their spawning areas, female Pacific Salmon lay three to five thousand eggs in a few days. The males discharge milt onto the eggs. Soon after this, the adults die. The eggs hatch after 30 or 40 days, and the young salmon head to sea. There they live until they are mature. Then they return home to spawn and die.

Summary

Type of Life	Aquatic—freshwater, marine
Systems	
Integumentary	scales Chondrichtyes—placoid scales Pelvic and pectoral girdle as fins with rays and spines
Skeletal	Chondrichthyes—cartilage Osteichthyes—bony
Respiratory	gills for gas exchange
Circulatory	one way system; arteries, capillaries, veins heart with two chambers—atrium, ventricle
Excretory	gills; kidney to filter wastes, also important in salt balance; urinary bladder
Nervous	(lateral line—sensory cells) central nervous system brain with five parts in a cranial cavity—large optic lobes
Reproductive	external fertilization—males discharge milt over eggs; large number of eggs
Digestive	pharynx, esophagus, stomach, intestine with pyloric caeca, anus
Development	external—lay eggs; bear live young eggs with yolk in yolk sac

gill
lateral line
operculum
chromatophore
pectoral fin
pelvic fin
caudal fin
anal fin
atrium
ventricle
air bladder

cranial cavity
olfactory lobe
cerebrum
optic lobe
cerebellum
medulla oblongata
cranial nerve
spinal nerve
spawn
milt
yolk

Biologically Speaking

Questions for Review

1. What characteristic of the head of a cyclostome distinguishes it from other fish?
2. List several characteristics that distinguish sharks from other fish.
3. Describe the body covering of bony fishes.
4. What is countershading? How does it camouflage a fish?
5. Locate and describe the sense organs of the fish.
6. Name and locate the fins of a yellow perch.
7. In the order in which food passes through them, name the parts of the fish digestive system.
8. Describe the structure of the fish heart.
9. What is the function of the air bladder?
10. Name the regions of the fish brain and state the function of each.
11. Describe external fertilization in most fish.

Applying Concepts

1. Why does a fish die in air, even though the atmosphere contains more oxygen than the water?
2. Fish lay large numbers of eggs. Of what important adaptive value is this?
3. Discuss the homing instinct of fish. Use the eel and the salmon as examples.
4. Trace the path of a drop of blood from the ventral aorta through the circulatory system of the fish. Describe the changes in the blood as it passes through the gills.

35

The Amphibians

A **LIST** the characteristics of amphibians.

B **NAME** the orders of amphibians.

C **DESCRIBE** salamanders.

D **DESCRIBE** reproduction in frogs.

E **DESCRIBE** the anatomy and physiology of the frog.

F **DESCRIBE** metamorphosis in amphibians.

G **DISTINGUISH** hibernation from estivation.

35–1 | A primitive fish thought to have been the ancestor of amphibians. (Courtesy of The American Museum of Natural History)

The Arrival of Amphibians

Amphibians are neither completely water animals nor completely land animals. They are interesting because they indicated how water animals may have adapted to a life on land. Amphibians alive today never completely adjusted to a land environment. Except for some woodland salamanders, all these animals return to water to reproduce.

Biologists believe that animals lived only in watery environments for millions of years. What environmental conditions would lead to a change that would cause animals to be able to live on land? Why should such land life evolve? Studies of rocks and fossils have led geologists to conclude that the Devonian period, the so-called Age of Fishes, had periodic droughts. It was a time when many different kinds of fishes existed. With frequent droughts in certain areas, only those fish that could withstand drought conditions could survive. For example, some fish could live in wet mud for a time. Some had finlike structures with which they could dig deeper into the drying pond. Some could scurry, slip, and slide from one water hole to another. Many fish that did not have these abilities died during droughts. The ones that had one or another of these adaptations survived and multiplied.

Evidence for this type of fish exists today in the lungfish. Lungfish have lunglike structures in addition to gills. They live in Australia, Africa, and South America in areas of seasonal drought. Their lunglike structures allow them to respire in air as well as water. When the area dries up or the water becomes stagnant, lungfish breathe air and survive. In times of drought, the lungfish burrows into the bottom of the pool. It curls up in its burrow in an inactive state until the rains bring water. However, there is no evidence that these may have been ancestors of amphibians.

Another type of fish with lunglike structures that *is* thought to have been the ancestor of amphibians are the lobe-finned fishes. Until the 1930's it was thought that lobe-finned fishes had died off in the Mesozoic era. Their fossil traces have been found in rocks of the late Paleozoic and Mesozoic eras; there is no trace of them in the Cenozoic rocks. This led biologists to believe that they had become extinct 70 million years ago.

In 1938, however, a South African fisherman caught a strange type of fish. It was about 1.5 meters (4.95 feet) long. It was covered with large bluish scales. He gave the strange fish to a local museum. It was stuffed and mounted. Finally Dr. J. L. B. Smith of Rhodes University saw it and recognized it as a lobe-finned fish called a *coelacanth* (SEE-luh-KANTH). Since then, many of these coelacanths have been caught in the waters between Madagascar and Mozambique.

Characteristics of Amphibians

Young amphibians are similar to fish. They can only live in water. As they mature, they move onto land to live. To become adults, amphibians go through a series of changes. They undergo a metamorphosis, a marked and drastic change of form and structure. They change from a water form to a land form. Many strange combinations of gills, lungs, fins, and legs occur. Gills can be found on creatures that have legs. Fins are sometimes found on animals with lungs.

Generally, amphibians differ from other vertebrate animals in the following ways.

- The skin is smooth, thin, and usually moist. There are no scales, fur, or feathers.
- The feet, if present, are often webbed.

- The toes are soft and lack claws.
- The immature or larval forms are usually vegetarian. Adults are usually carnivorous.
- Respiration is by gills, lungs, and skin.
- The heart is two-chambered in the larvae. Adults have three-chambered hearts with well-developed circulation.
- The eggs are generally laid in water. Eggs are fertilized externally as soon as they are laid.
- There is a metamorphosis from an aquatic larval stage of the adult form.

Orders of Amphibians

a = without
poda = feet

uro = tail (one of the meanings)

- Apoda: The order *Apoda* contains the few surviving legless amphibians of the tropics. These are strange wormlike creatures.
- Urodela: A second order, *Urodela*, or *Caudata*, includes amphibians that have tails throughout life. The salamanders and newts are in this order.
- Anura: The most familiar amphibians are the frogs and toads. These are members of the order *Anura*. Frogs and toads lack tails in the adult stage. This makes them different from other amphibians.

The Salamanders: Amphibians with Tails

Today's salamanders in general are smaller and far less numerous than their ancient ancestors. During the Carboniferous period, the Age of Amphibians, some salamander-like amphibians grew three meters (9.9 feet) or more in length. They also had a more bony skeleton. Salamanders are similar to lizards in appearance. They both have long bodies, long tails, and short legs. However, salamanders have soft, moist skin and no claws. Lizards, on the other hand, have bodies covered with scales and claws on their toes. These characteristics of reptiles are almost never found among amphibians.

Salamanders have little protection from enemies. A few have skin glands that secrete bad-tasting substances. Others have colored pigments that change in different surroundings. This helps to camouflage them. Salamanders cannot survive in dry areas. Thus, they are usually found under damp logs and stones. They may also be found swimming in the water.

Salamanders range from a few centimeters to about a meter in length. In the United States, the giant salaman-

Facts & Figures

The largest amphibian was a salamander found in China. It was approximately 1.7 meters (5.6 feet) long.

ders are represented by the *American hellbender*. It can grow to 60 centimeters (24 inches) in length. This creature has loose gray or red-brown skin. It lives in the streams of the eastern United States. A Japanese relative of this salamander grows to one and a half meters (5 feet) in length. It is the largest living amphibian.

The *mud puppy* is another large salamander. It lives in the American Midwest. Many fishermen have been startled when they pull up one of these slimy salamanders from a mud-bottom stream. Mud puppies can grow to as long as 60 centimeters (2 feet). They have flat, rectangular heads, small eyes, a flattened tail, and two pairs of short legs. Their most striking body feature is three pairs of dark red, bushy external gills. These are attached at the base of the head just above the front legs. The presence of gills is a larval trait kept throughout the life of this salamander.

The tiger salamander is also found in the United States. It sometimes grows to 25 centimeters (10 inches) in length. The tiger salamander's colors give it its name. It has bright yellow bars and blotches on dark brown skin. The tiger salamander lives as an aquatic, gill-breathing larva for about three months. It then leaves the water and lives on land. Its lungs and thin, moist skin function in respiration during its land-living stage.

Some tiger salamanders and their close relatives remain aquatic for their whole lives. These salamanders reproduce while still in the larval stage. Larval salamanders called *axolotls* (ack-suh-LOT'lz) are found in Mexico and the southwestern United States. Once biologists thought they were actually a separate species because they produced eggs or sperms in the larval stage. But when they were fed thyroid gland hormones, they changed into land-living adults. This showed that axolotls were larval forms of the tiger salamanders and some of their relatives. Research revealed that the waters in which axolotls live do not have enough iodine. Iodine is essential for the production of a thyroid hormone needed for metamorphosis. Thus, axolotls remain larvae because of a thyroid deficiency.

Newts are very small land-living salamanders. The *crimson-spotted newt* is particularly interesting because of its "triple life." This salamander hatches in May as a gill-breathing aquatic larva. After about two months, it changes into a land-dwelling form with lungs. At this stage, it is a coral-red color, and it is called a *red eft*. After a couple of years its color changes to green with red spots.

35-2 | (top) mud puppy; aquatic throughout its life. (middle) red eft, a juvenile form; terrestrial. (bottom) spotted newt, an adult form; aquatic. *(top: Z. Leszczynski, © Animals Animals; middle: E. R. Degginger, Bruce Coleman; bottom: Allan Roberts)*

Toads and Frogs: Amphibians Without Tails
Of all amphibians, frogs and toads are probably most familiar. Their croaking mating calls at night are known to

35-3 | (top) An adult tiger salamander; (bottom) an axolotl. *(both: Allan Roberts)*

35-4 | (top) a toad and (bottom) a leopard frog. The skin of the toad is somewhat rough and warty, whereas that of the frog is smooth. *(top: Walter Dawn; bottom: Breck P. Kent, © Animals Animals)*

most people who live near a stream or pond. The oldest fossils of these amphibians date back to the Jurassic period, 155 million years ago. At that time they had long bodies with short tails. The changes that led to the present body type occurred rather rapidly. The most obvious change was the disappearance of the tail in the adult. Other changes increased the ability of this animal to jump.

Toads Frogs and toads are similar, but they differ in some ways. The toad is better adapted to life on land. Like the frog, the toad starts life as an egg, fertilized in the water. The egg hatches as a small black tadpole. The tadpole soon grows legs and resorbs its tails. Early in life it hops onto land as a small, brown creature with warty dry skin. Though the toad lives in very humid areas, it returns to water only to lay its eggs. Adults of the common toad, *Bufo* (BOO-foe), are usually red-brown on top and gray-yellow underneath.

Toads often live in areas that have loose, moist soil. They dig in and hide from enemies and summer heat. They can dig quickly with their hind legs. If a toad is unable to bury itself when disturbed, it may crouch low to the ground and remain still. The color and texture of its skin provide good camouflage but poison glands in the skin are a toad's best defense. These glands secrete an irritating, bad-tasting substance. This causes most animals to leave the toad alone. However, this defense does not keep snakes from eating the toads. Snakes are the toad's major enemy.

The toad has been called the "gardener's friend." Toads feed upon insects, worms, and other animals harmful to plants. It is probably the moist loose garden soil that attracts toads to gardens.

Frogs Unlike toads, frogs usually live very near water. You often see them around ponds. The most common frog in the United States is the *leopard frog*. These frogs live in almost every pond, marsh, and roadside ditch. They often travel a long way from water. Sometimes they can be seen hopping through grassy meadows. They are grayish-green with large dark spots surrounded by yellow or white rings. This coloration gives them their name. The soft underbelly of the leopard frog is creamy white. This makes it hard to see the frog when it is in the water. Its back color blends in with a grassy pond, and its belly blends with the sky when seen from below.

The *bullfrog* is named for its loud bellowing sound. It is the most aquatic of frogs. It seldom leaves the water except to sit on the bank of a lake at night. The color of bullfrogs ranges from green to nearly yellow. Most of them are greenish-brown. The underbelly is gray-white with dark splotches. Bullfrogs are excellent swimmers because of their large, webbed hind feet. Their legs are strong and well developed. Their legs can be 25 centimeters (10 inches) long. Bullfrogs eat insects, worms, crayfish, and small fishes. Big bullfrogs will sometimes even eat a small duckling.

A major part of a frog's diet is insects. This makes frogs valuable because they help control the insect population. Many states have laws to regulate frog hunting for this reason. These laws forbid the capture of frogs during the breeding season.

Anatomy of the Frog

Frogs are a favorite in biology labs as specimens for dissection. The frog's internal organs have the same basic arrangement as a human's. Thus, dissecting frogs is an excellent introduction to human anatomy. The leopard frog will be used as a typical example of all amphibians in the following discussions.

The External Structure

The frog's body is short, broad, and angular. It lacks the streamlined shape of fishes. For this reason frogs do not swim as well as fish do. The frog's hopping is not as graceful as the movement of most land animals but the frog is able to move about in both of these environments.

Frog skin is thin, moist, and loose. It is richly supplied with blood vessels. Glands in the skin secrete mucus. This reaches the skin's surface through tiny tubes. This skin slime makes frogs hard to hold. Frog skin lacks protective growths such as the scales of fishes and reptiles.

Adaptations of the Frog's Legs

The frog's front legs are short and well adapted to taking the shock of landing from a jump. Each front foot has four inturned toes with soft, rounded tips. These feet are not webbed and are not used for swimming. Instead, the front legs are used to prop up the body when on land. The inner toes, or thumbs, are enlarged on male frogs. These *thumb pads* become even larger during the breeding season as they are used to expel eggs from the female.

The frog's hind legs are well developed and strong. They are adapted for swimming and jumping. The thigh and calf muscles are very powerful. The bones of the lower hind legs are fused. The ankle bones and toes are long and form a foot which is longer than the lower leg. A flexible

Facts & Figures

The oldest North American bullfrog was recorded as 16 years old.

35-5 | What features of this bullfrog are adaptations to its aquatic life? *(William E. Ferguson)*

web membrane connects the five long toes. This webbing makes each foot a very efficient swimming organ. When a frog rests on land, its hind legs fold against its body. In this position a frog is ready to jump very quickly.

The Head

Frog eyes are very noticeable because they bulge up above the head. The colored iris surrounds an elongated black pupil opening. Muscles attached to the eyeball rotate the eye in its socket. The eyes can be pulled into the sockets and pressed against the roof of the mouth. This helps hold food in the mouth. When a frog's eyes are pulled down, the upper and lower eyelids close.

The frog can float just below the water's surface with only its bulging eyes showing. This allows the frog to see the surface when hiding in the water. The frog has a third eyelid called the **nictitating** (NICK-tuh-TAY-ting) **membrane.** This joins the lower lid. This thin covering keeps the eyeball moist when a frog is on land. It also protects the eye when the frog is under water.

nictare = to wink

The nostrils are forward, near the top of the head. This allows the frog to breathe air when all but the top of its head is under water.

Frogs have no external ears, but they do have eardrums, or **tympanic** (tim-PAN-ick) **membranes.** These are located on the body surface just behind the eyes. The cavity of the middle ear lies just below the tympanic membrane. A canal connects each middle ear with the mouth cavity. These canals are called the **Eustachian** (yoo-STAY-shun) **tubes.** Their function is to allow air from the mouth cavity to enter the chamber behind the eardrums. Thus the air pressure is the same on both sides of the eardrum. The inner ear functions in hearing and in balance. It is embedded in the skull.

tympanum = drum

The Mouth: An Insect Trap The frog's thick tongue is attached to the floor of its mouth at the front. This sticky tongue has two projections at its free end.

To catch an insect, a frog opens its mouth wide and flips its tongue over and outward. If the aim is good, the insect is caught on the tongue surface and is instantly drawn into the mouth. The mouth snaps shut quickly. Then the frog swallows the insect. This all happens so quickly, it is hard to see. Two teeth project from bones in the roof of the mouth. They are called *vomerine teeth*. They aid in holding the prey. Small, cone-shaped *maxillary teeth* project from the upper jaw. These also help hold on to prey. Frogs have no teeth on their lower jaws.

There are various openings inside the frog's mouth.

35-6 | Compare the legs and feet of this tree frog with that of the bullfrog. *(Z. Leszczynski, © Animals Animals)*

Internal nostril openings are located in the roof on either side of the vomerine teeth. Far back on the sides of the roof are the openings of the *Eustachian tubes*. Openings to the *vocal sacs* are located at the back of the floor of the mouth of the male frog. When a male frog croaks, air is forced down these openings into the vocal sacs. This air forces the sacs to expand between the frog's ears and shoulders. This action makes the croak louder and more powerful. When a frog croaks under water, air is forced from the lungs, over the vocal cords, into the mouth, and then back to the lungs. The throat has two openings. The large *gullet opening* leads to the stomach. Below the gullet opening is the slitlike *glottis*. The glottis leads to the lungs.

Organ Systems

Amphibians have some organ systems adapted for an aquatic environment and others adapted to a terrestrial environment. As previously mentioned, almost all amphibians return to the water to reproduce. The respiratory and excretory systems are basically terrestrial. That is, they do not depend on a watery environment as the same systems do in fishes. Many adaptations in the frog, such as moist skin, help amphibians conserve body water, a problem with all terrestrial animals.

The Digestive System **Adult leopard frogs usually feed on insects and worms.** However, they can swallow even larger meals because of their large, elastic *gullet*. The short gullet leads to a long *stomach*, an enlargement of the food tube. The upper end of the stomach is large, and it tapers at the lower end. At a point called the *pylorus*, the stomach links up with the coiled, slender small intestine. At the lower end of the stomach, there is a muscle called the *pyloric valve*. This valve controls the movement of food from the stomach into the small intestine.

The *small intestine* is looped several times. It is supported by a fanlike membrane called the **mesentery.** The anterior area of the small intestine, which curves from the pylorus, is the *duodenum*. The middle portion is the coiled *ileum*. The lower end of the small intestine leads into a short, broad *colon*. The colon is also called the *large intestine*. The colon opens into a cavity called the **cloaca** (kloe-AY-kuh). Tubes from the kidneys, the urinary bladder, and the sex organs also open into the cloaca. Waste materials and eggs or sperms pass out the cloaca through the *cloacal opening*.

Tiny *gastric glands* in the stomach walls secrete gastric fluid. Gastric fluid chemically digests some of the food. A large, three-lobed *liver* partially covers the stomach. The

35–7 | The frog's tongue is well adapted for catching insects in that it is both flexible and sticky. Note how it is attached at the front of the mouth.

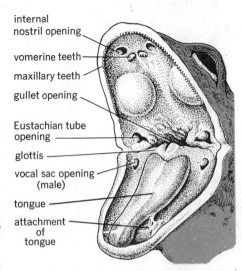

internal nostril opening

vomerine teeth

maxillary teeth

gullet opening

Eustachian tube opening

glottis

vocal sac opening (male)

tongue

attachment of tongue

35–8 | The frog's mouth. Its relatively large size is an adaptation for obtaining food.

liver stores sugar in the form of *glycogen*. The glycogen is converted back to glucose when it is needed by the cells. The *liver* also produces bile which is collected and stored in the *gall bladder*. From the gall bladder the bile runs through the *bile duct* into the upper part of the *small intestine*. In the intestine it *emulsifies*, or breaks up, fat into small globules that can be digested more easily.

A second digestive gland, the *pancreas*, lies close to the stomach. Pancreatic fluid leaves the pancreas through the *pancreatic duct*, which joins with the bile duct. The fluid enters the small intestine. Pancreatic fluid contains *digestive enzymes*. *Digestive glands* that line the intestine also produce digestive enzymes. *Mucus glands* produce *mucus*. The mucus lubricates the food passing through the digestive tube. **Basically, the frog's digestive system is like those of other vertebrates. It is a long food tube, generally called the *alimentary canal*. This canal has special regions for digestion and absorption of digested food.** Increased length of the alimentary canal increases the general efficiency of these processes.

The Respiratory System Adult frogs are air-breathers. Have you ever wondered how they can stay under water for a long time? Also, during the winter, a frog will hibernate buried in the mud on the bottom of a pond. The skin of the frog is thin, and it has a lot of blood vessels. **Thus, the frog's skin directly absorbs dissolved oxygen from the water.** It also gives off carbon dioxide. As long as a frog stays quiet, this type of respiration is enough to keep it alive. When a frog is active and swimming, however, it needs more oxygen. The frog then comes to the surface and breathes air.

Humans inhale and exhale air by increasing and decreasing the size of their chest cavities. This is done by moving the ribs and diaphragm. The *diaphragm* is a muscular partition at the bottom of the chest cavity. The frog lacks a rib cage. It has no diaphragm, and thus no chest cavity. **Frogs inhale by changing the volume and pressure of air in their mouths.** When a frog lowers the floor of its closed mouth, it causes a partial vacuum. Air rushes in through the open nostrils. Then, when the floor of the mouth springs up, air passes out through the nostrils.

The lining of the mouth also is adapted for respiration. It is thin and moist and has many blood vessels. **Frogs can perform both mouth breathing and lung breathing.** They may pump air in and out of their mouths for some time without using their lungs. When the lungs are used, the nostrils are closed by skin flaps as the floor of the mouth rises. Air from the mouth cavity is forced through a slit called the **glottis** in the back of the throat. The air then passes through the *larynx*, or voice box. Two short branches called *bronchi* lead directly from the larynx into the lungs.

When exhaling air from the lungs, the frog closes its nostrils, and the floor of the mouth is lowered. Air then rushes from the lungs into the partial vacuum in the mouth. By moving the floor of the mouth up and down, the frog can exchange air between mouth and lungs several times. The frog can then open its nostrils and, with a sharp rise of the floor of the mouth, expel the air.

Frogs use their lungs only to assist mouthbreathing. As you might expect, frog lungs are small compared to lungs of higher vertebrates. Frog lungs have thin-walled sacs that lack the spongy tissue our lungs have.

The Circulatory System
The circulatory system of the frog is a step more complex than that of the fish. One of these advances is the heart. Recall that the fish has a two-chambered heart. One chamber pumps blood through the body, and the other receives it from the body. It is a single-circuit system—from heart to body and back to heart.

The frog has a three-chambered heart and two separate circulations: lung circulation and general body circulation. The *left atrium* receives blood from the lungs. The *right atrium* receives blood from the rest of the body. This blood in the right atrium is not entirely unoxygenated venous blood. It includes oxygenated blood returning from the skin, where some gas exchange has occurred. When the frog is under water, this blood from the skin is its only source of oxygen.

The single *ventricle* pumps blood both to the lungs and through the rest of the body. Both atria contract at the same time. This forces blood into the ventricle. The ventricle then contracts and pumps blood out of the heart. The blood leaves through a large vessel that lies against the front side of the heart. This is called the *conus arteriosus*. This large vessel immediately divides into two branches, the right and left *truncus anteriosus*. Each of these again branches into three arches. The anterior pair are the *carotid arches*. These carry blood to the head. The middle pair are the *aortic arches*. They transport blood around the right and left sides of the heart. They join below the liver to form the *dorsal aorta*. This great artery carries blood to muscles, the digestive organs, and other parts of the body. The posterior pair of arches are called the *pulmocutaneous arches*. They carry blood to the lungs, skin, and mouth.

The blood that returns to the frog's heart, after a trip through the body, has lost most of its oxygen. This blood is loaded with carbon dioxide and other cell wastes. Three

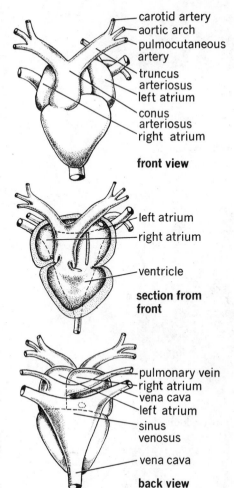

carotid artery
aortic arch
pulmocutaneous artery
truncus arteriosus
left atrium
conus arteriosus
right atrium

front view

left atrium
right atrium

ventricle

section from front

pulmonary vein
right atrium
vena cava
left atrium
sinus venosus

vena cava

back view

35-9 | The frog's heart. Note that three branches of the vena cava lead to the right atrium. The pulmonary veins lead from the lungs to the left atrium. Blood from both these chambers passes through the conus arteriosus. In the back view, you can see where the vena cava enter the sinus venosus.

large veins carry blood back to the heart. These are called the *venae cavae*. They join a triangle-shaped, thin-walled sac, called the *sinus venosus*, at the back of the heart. This empties into the right atrium.

Part of the blood, returning from lower parts of the body, flows through the vessels of the digestive system. There it absorbs digested food. This blood then flows through the *hepatic portal vein* which carries it to the liver. The liver picks up some of the food substances carried by this blood and screens out some of the wastes. From the liver, this blood moves on to the right atrium.

Pulmonary veins carry blood from the lungs to the left atrium. This blood is oxygenated when the frog is using its blood in air-breathing.

The Excretory System **Frog skin is a vital excretory organ. Most of the carbon dioxide leaving the blood passes through the frog's skin rather than through the mouth or lungs.** The liver, too, removes certain wastes. The liver eliminates these wastes with bile, or changes them chemically so the kidneys can remove them. The large intestine eliminates undigested food and other wastes. **The *kidneys* are the main excretory organs.**

The kidneys are large, dark red organs. They lie on either side of the spine against the back body wall. Blood flows into the kidneys, through the *renal arteries* and out through the *renal veins*. The kidneys filter nitrogen-containing wastes from cell activity and collect it as urine. The urine then flows to the cloaca through tiny tubes, called **urinary ducts.** Urine may be excreted immediately, but frogs are also able to force urine from the cloaca through a small opening that leads to the *urinary bladder*. Urine may be stored here for a while before being excreted.

The Nervous System **The frog brain is more highly developed than the fish brain.** *Olfactory lobes* lie at the anterior end of the brain. The long lobes of the *cerebrum* are proportionally larger than those of the fish. Next are the *optic lobes*. Behind the optic lobes is the *cerebellum*. This is a small band of tissue lying at right angles to the long axis of the brain. The *medulla oblongata* lies at the back of the frog brain. It joins the short, thick *spinal cord*. The spinal cord extends down the frog's back. The spinal cord is encased in bony vertebrae. As in the fish, *spinal nerves* branch from the cord to various parts of the body. Ten pairs of *cranial nerves* extend from the brain. (See also page 503.)

The Reproductive System In both sexes, the frog's sex organs are internal. Thus it is difficult to differentiate

hepatic = liver

renal = kidney

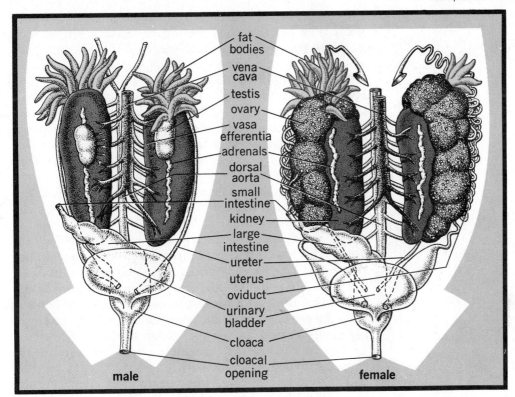

fat
bodies
vena
cava
testis
ovary
vasa
efferentia
adrenals
dorsal
aorta
small
intestine
kidney
large
intestine
ureter
uterus
oviduct
urinary
bladder
cloaca
cloacal
opening

male

female

35–10 | The urogenital organs of a male frog and a female frog.

between the sexes, except during the breeding season. At this time the thumbs of the males are enlarged.

The male reproductive organs are two bean-shaped testes. The testes are a creamy-white or yellow color. They lie in the back, one on each side of the spine, in the anterior region of the kidneys. Sperm cells develop in the testes. The sperms then pass through tubes, the *vasa efferentia*, into the kidneys. When the sperms are discharged, they pass through the *urinary ducts* into the *cloaca*. Some frog species have an enlargement, the *seminal vesicle*, at the base of each urinary duct. The seminal vesicles store sperms. When mating occurs, the sperms are discharged through the cloaca opening to fertilize the eggs.

In the female frog, the eggs develop in a pair of large lobed ovaries. The ovaries lie along the back above the kidneys. During the breeding season, the eggs enlarge and burst through the thin ovary walls. This frees the eggs into the body cavity. The abdominal muscles work the eggs toward the anterior. Here funnellike openings to the *oviducts* gather the eggs. Oviducts are long and coiled, and are lined with ciliated cells. The cilia fan the eggs into the oviduct openings. Oviducts lead into the cloaca. Near the openings to the cloaca, the walls of the oviduct secrete a

ova = egg

jellylike substance. This substance surrounds each egg. There is an **ovisac** at the base of each oviduct. The eggs are stored in the *ovisacs* until they are laid.

Frog Development

Fertilization and Development of the Eggs

The female leopard frog lays up to 200 eggs between early April and mid-May. When the eggs are to be laid, the male clasps the female. The male uses its large thumb pads to press down on the female. This is called **amplexus.** It helps the female expel the eggs. As the eggs pass from the female's cloaca into the water, the male spreads sperm over them. The sperm cells reach most of the eggs with this *direct fertilization.*

The jellylike coat that surrounds each egg swells in the water. This binds the eggs together in a round mass. In this clump, the eggs look like small beads covered by transparent jelly. **The jellylike coat protects the eggs from injury and makes it difficult for fish to eat them. It also helps to keep the eggs at a constant temperature. Later, the covering serves as food for the young tadpoles.**

The yolk is heavier than the embryo. This causes the frog eggs to float with the dark side up. The eggs are difficult for predators to see from below because the lighter lower half blends in with light from the sky. The yolk is used as food for the developing embryo. After about 8 to 20 days, depending on the weather and temperature, the free-swimming tadpoles hatch.

35–11 | Male and female chorus frogs mating. The mass of eggs in the water indicates external fertilization. *(Allan Roberts)*

The Metamorphosis of the Frog: From Tadpole to Adult The hatched tadpole is a tiny, short-bodied creature. It has a little round mouth. It clings to the egg mass or to a plant. Yolk stored in the body nourishes the tadpole until it starts to feed. Soon the body grows longer and three pairs of gills develop at the outside of the head. The tail grows longer and develops a caudal fin. Then the tadpole's mouth opens, and it begins to scrape the leaves of water plants with its rough lips.

Not long after the tadpole starts to swim around, its rough lips disappear. A long, coiled digestive tract develops and the tadpole starts to eat the scum of water plants. Then a flap of skin grows over the gills, leaving only a small opening on its left side. This allows water to pass out of the gill chambers. At this stage, the tadpole is like a fish. It has a lateral line, a fin, a two-chambered heart, and a one-circuit circulation.

The change to an adult frog is amazing. First, hind legs appear on the tadpole's fishlike body. The front legs start to form at about the same time. However, they remain hidden under the tadpole's fishlike operculum for a while. When

35–12 | The life history of the frog. The length of time for metamorphosis varies in different species of frogs.

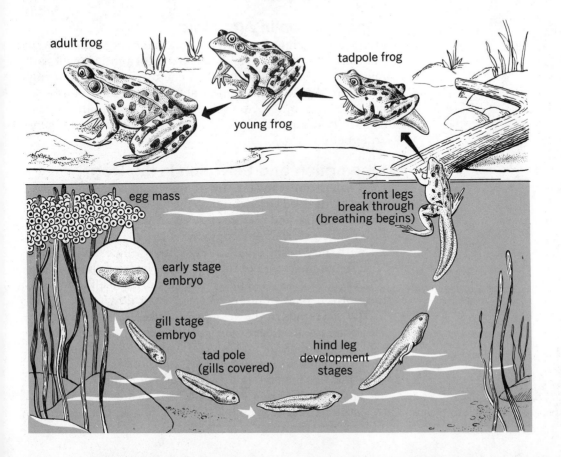

the front legs do appear, the tadpole starts resorbing its tail.

Near the end of the metamorphosis, the mouth broadens and teeth develop. As these external changes happen, internal changes also occur. A saclike chamber, resembling the swim bladder of a fish, forms behind the tadpole's throat. This divides into two sacs, which become the lungs. The heart develops three chambers. The gill arteries change into the carotids, aortic arches, and pulmocutaneous arteries. Soon the gills stop functioning and the tadpole starts swimming to the water's surface to gulp air. At this time, the tadpole's thin skin and broad, flat tail still play important roles in respiration.

Even before the tail is completely resorbed, the tadpole starts moving out on the land. From this point, the tadpole is considered a young frog. The young frog usually takes about a month to become a full-grown frog.

The metamorphosis of the leopard frog takes from two to three months. Adult leopard frogs usually appear around the beginning of July. Bullfrogs usually spend two winters as tadpoles, and it may be three years before the adult bullfrog is fully formed.

Regeneration in Amphibia

Many amphibians, especially salamanders, can regrow injured or lost body parts. A foot, a part of a limb, or the tail may be lost in escaping from an enemy. Regeneration can occur rapidly. In their tadpole stages, frogs and toads also have this capability. However, as the tadpole matures, the capability disappears. Adult frogs and toads cannot regenerate body parts.

Hibernation and Estivation in the Frog

Like fishes and reptiles, frogs are "cold-blooded" vertebrates. This does not mean that the blood is always cold. It means that the body temperature varies with the temperature of the external environment.

With the coming of fall, a frog's body temperature drops with the temperature of the air. Soon the frog's body is too cold to remain active. This is when it buries itself in mud at the bottom of a pond. Its heart slows down and blood hardly circulates in the vessels. Because it is so inactive at this time, the frog needs very little oxygen. Enough can be supplied through the moist skin. Body tissues stay alive by the slow oxidation of stored food. The food is stored in the liver and in the **fat bodies** above the kidneys. Nervous activity stops almost completely. The frog lies in its burrow in a stupor. This is the condition of the frog during **hibernation.** Hibernation is a winter rest.

hiber = winter

With the coming of spring, the water gradually warms. The frog's body activities speed up, and soon the frog wakes from its winter sleep. After a while, it begins the activities of a normal life again.

The hot summer months bring other problems for the frog. Lacking a way to cool its body, the frog must escape from excessive heat. It may lie quietly in cool, deep water. In tropical or subtropical climates frogs have to survive extremely high temperatures and dry seasons. Under these conditions the frog may bury itself in mud at the bottom of a pond. This inactivity is called **estivation.** Cool weather eventually returns, and ponds fill with water again. The frog comes out of estivation and continues normal activity until hibernation.

estas = summer

Summary

Type of Life	Aquatic—freshwater Aquatic—terrestrial
Integumentary System	thin, moist skin
Skeletal System	bone and cartilage pelvic and pectoral girdle
Digestive System	gullet, stomach, small intestine, large intestine (colon), cloaca, stomach with gastric glands, intestine with digestive glands
Respiratory System	skin absorbs oxygen from the water; mouth-breathing, lung-breathing, gills in tadpole stage
Circulatory System	circulation to and from body and lungs three chambered heart—right atrium, left atrium, ventricle
Excretory System	kidneys; urinary bladder skin as an important excretory organ
Nervous System	central nervous system brain with 5 parts
Reproductive System	external fertilization—male discharges sperm through cloaca
Development	external eggs with jellylike coating; metamorphosis—tadpole to adult

Biologically Speaking

nictitating membrane	urinary duct
tympanic membrane	oviduct
Eustachian tube	ovisac
mesentery	amplexus
cloaca	fat body
alimentary canal	hibernation
glottis	estivation
kidney	

Questions for Review

1. Why do biologists believe that the early lobe-finned lungfishes were amphibian ancestors?
2. What characteristics of amphibians distinguish them from other living vertebrates?
3. Explain why the axolotl does not undergo metamorphosis.
4. Describe how a frog catches a flying insect.
5. In the order in which they receive food, name the organs forming the alimentary canal of the frog.
6. How is the frog, an air-breather, able to stay under water for long periods of time?
7. In what way is the frog's heart more developed than the fish's heart?
8. Describe the structures used when the frog excretes waste from the blood.
9. Name and describe the type of fertilization exhibited by frogs.
10. List, in order of occurrence, the changes during the metamorphosis of the frog.
11. Describe the changes that occur in a frog's body during hibernation.
12. List and describe the orders of amphibians.

Applying Concepts

1. Although amphibians became terrestrial, discuss why they were never completely successful on land.
2. Describe the structures of the frog that enable it to adapt to its life in water. List the structures that enable it to adapt to its life on land.
3. How is the direct fertilization of the frog's eggs more efficient than spawning in fishes?
4. Explain how the frog shows a relationship to the fish in the frog's early development.

The Reptiles

A **DESCRIBE** the characteristics of some ancient reptiles.

B **EXPLAIN** the evolutionary importance of the amniote egg.

C **DESCRIBE** the characteristics of modern reptiles.

D **NAME** and **DESCRIBE** examples of each order of reptiles.

E **DESCRIBE** structural adaptations of the snake as a predator.

F **COMPARE** oviparous and ovoviviparous snakes.

36–1 | A komodo dragon, the largest living lizard. *(Bruce Coleman)*

The Rise of Reptiles

People of ancient Egypt honored such reptiles as the cobra and crocodile in their religion and art. Biologists look at reptiles with interest because they represent the first true land animals. Unlike the amphibians they do not have to return to water to reproduce. As the first true land animals they are believed to be the ancient ancestors of all other land vertebrates.

At the close of the Paleozoic Era great land masses were uplifted. Mountain-building processes created the Appalachian Mountains of the eastern United States. These and other geologic changes produced many different types of land environments with a variety of climate and vegetation. Biologists know that reptiles existed at this time, because fossils have been found from the Paleozoic Era. This fossil evidence suggests that as the environment changed, reptiles also changed in many different ways.

With the beginning of the Mesozoic Era, 225 million years ago, the Age of Reptiles began. During this period reptiles dominated all other forms of life. The Mesozoic Era lasted about 155 million years. It is best known for the

giant reptiles called *dinosaurs*. It is well to remember that other important forms, ancestors of forms still present today, also appeared during the Age of Reptiles. These included other reptiles such as snakes, turtles, lizards, and some mammal forms.

With the formation of the Rocky Mountains, the Mesozoic Era came to an end, about 70 million years ago. Some forms of reptiles survived and gave rise to our present-day reptiles. The dinosaurs perished. One theory, however, maintains that one direct descendant of dinosaurs remains on the planet—birds.

The Dinosaurs

Dinosaurs have been extinct for millions of years. All that remains of the once great dinosaurs are the eggs and footprints preserved in rock, and fossilized bones. This evidence has been gathered in many parts of the world. A great deal of knowledge and skill have been used by paleontologists to piece together a history of dinosaur life.

The word *dinosaur* means *terrible lizard*. Some dinosaurs were no larger than today's large lizards, but some were giants that would dwarf an elephant. **It is thought that dinosaurs developed from a "stock," or basic group, of early reptiles called Thecodonts.** These were relatively small animals that walked on their hind legs. The *Thecodonts* may have evolved into other groups of reptiles including the flying reptiles, crocodiles, and, some believe, birds.

Other hypotheses are suggested. Some believe dinosaurs were warm-blooded, like mammals, and some be-

36–2 | Certain groups of early reptiles, called Thecodonts, were thought to be the first animals to walk erectly. These reptiles lived during the early Mesozoic era and are believed to be the ancestors of dinosaurs.

lieve they were cold-blooded, like today's snakes and lizards. Scientists who believe dinosaurs were warm-blooded think that the proof is in the microscopic structure of dinosaur fossil bones. This is because the structure resembled that of warm-blooded animals. They point out that the large plates and fanlike structures on the backs of some dinosaurs might have been used for cooling the blood as well as for defense. They claim that present-day birds, which are warm-blooded, are the direct descendants of a certain group of dinosaurs.

Brontosaurus   The best-known dinosaurs were the largest. The *Brontosaurus,* or thunder lizard, was probably the largest. It was about 25 meters (82 feet) long and 5 meters (16.4 feet) high, and it weighed over 15,000 kilograms (33,069 pounds). Recent evidence suggests that *Brontosaurus* may have led a giraffelike life on open land rather than inhabiting the swamps or shallow lakes as thought previously. Its long neck was balanced by an equally long and heavy tail.

Stegosaurus   The *Stegosaurus* was one of the most heavily armored dinosaurs. It was about 10 meters (33 feet) long and ate plants. This giant lizard had a double row of plates rising almost a meter (3.3 feet) from its back. It had two pairs of sharp spikes on its tail. This was probably used as a weapon against its enemies. The Stegosaurus had a very small head and cranial cavity. Its brain was no larger than the brain of a small dog. This small brain was aided by a mass of nerve tissue near the spinal cord in the hip region. This second "brain" was 20 times larger than the true brain. It is thought that this second "brain" controlled the two-meter-long (6.6 feet long) hind legs and large tail.

Tyrannosaurus   The *Tyrannosaurus,* or tyrant lizard, was the most ferocious of the dinosaurs. It walked erect on its powerful hind legs. The Tyrannosaurus balanced its heavy body with its long tail, much as a kangaroo does. This meat eater was nearly 17 meters (56 feet) long and stood over 6 meters (19.8 feet) high. It had powerful jaws armed with double-edged teeth that were as long as 15 centimeters (1 foot). These teeth could rip the hide of even an armored victim. Certainly Tyrannosaurus was one of the most terrifying creatures ever to roam the earth!

Pteranodon   During the Jurassic period, there were flying reptiles called *pterosaurs* (TEH-ruh-soarz). One of the best known was a pterodactyl, the *Pteranodon.* It had a body about the size of a turkey, but it had a wing spread of more

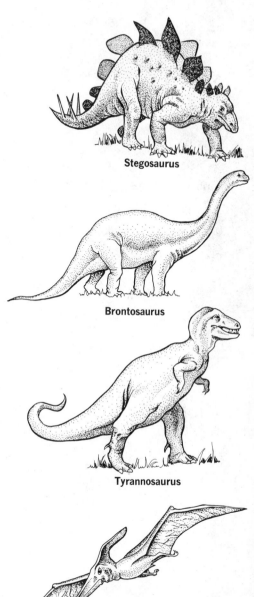

Stegosaurus

Brontosaurus

Tyrannosaurus

Pteranodon

36–3 | Some reptiles of the Mesozoic era.

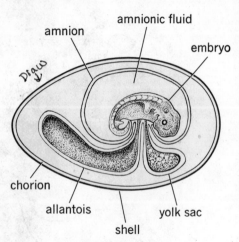

amnion

amnionic fluid

embryo

Draw

chorion

allantois

shell

yolk sac

36-4 | A cross section of an amniote egg.

than eight meters (26.4 feet). Its wings were made of membranes that stretched from very long wrist bones. Its skull was almost a meter (3.3 feet) long and turned into a crest at the back. The jaws came forward into a toothless beak. The Pteranodon could fly and soar gracefully, but it must have been very awkward on land. Scientists believe that it fed by swooping down to catch fish swimming close to the surface of lakes.

As strange as some of these dinosaurs seem, they are like modern reptiles in some basic ways. Both the dinosaurs and modern reptiles have some advantages over the amphibians. That is why the development of reptiles is considered a step forward in vertebrate development.

The Amniote Egg: Key to the Rise of Reptiles

Reptiles were the first land vertebrates that did not depend on water for a stage in their development or for reproduction. **What was the key to the success of reptiles on land? The answer is the *amniote egg.*** The *amniote* egg is an egg that has a membrane enclosing the developing embryo. It is believed to have appeared first among the reptiles.

You learned that all amphibians are bound to water. Their eggs lack protective structures to stop them from drying out. Reptilian eggs do not have this limitation. The amniote egg is enclosed in a porous *shell*. The shell prevents rapid water loss and protects the internal structures.

The amniote egg also contains four **embryonic membranes** which are very important to the survival of the embryo. These are the **chorion,** the **allantois,** the **amnion,** and the **yolk sac membrane.**

The *chorion* lines the inside of the shell. It is the outermost embryonic membrane. This membrane, like the shell, allows gases such as carbon dioxide and oxygen to diffuse through it.

The *allantois* is a membrane that develops from the embryo and expands to fuse, or join, with the chorion. The allantois has many blood vessels, and it also serves in respiration. Carbon dioxide diffuses out of the developing bloodstream while oxygen is absorbed into the bloodstream. It is also important in excretion of the nitrogenous wastes.

The *amnion* is the innermost membrane enclosing the embryo. The cavity formed by the amnion fills with a salty fluid surrounding the embryo. Thus the embryo floats and develops in its own private "sea."

The *yolk sac membrane* does not enclose the embryo but rather forms a sac that contains stored food. This yolk supplies the embryo with food for a longer time than does the amphibian egg yolk. This longer period of embryonic development eliminates the larval stage. The embryo develops directly into the adult reptile.

Another reproductive advance occurred with the development of the amniote egg. This important feature is called **internal fertilization.** Internal fertilization occurs when, **during mating, sperm cells are placed into the oviducts of females.** Fertilization takes place before the development of the protective egg shell. Some reptiles lay the fertilized egg when the shell has formed. Others keep the fertilized egg in their bodies until the young reptile hatches internally and is brought forth alive. This allows reptiles to be independent of water. Another important aspect is that fewer eggs need to be developed because fertilization of an egg is more certain.

Characteristics of Reptiles

The amniote egg and internal fertilization allowed reptiles to reproduce outside of a water medium. Changes in body structures also allowed reptiles to maintain life in land environments.

The reptilian characteristics are summarized here.

- A body covering of horny scales or plates that protects against physical damage and loss of water. The scales are similar in origin to the fingernails of humans. They are formed of surface cells (epithelium) filled with a protein called *keratin*. They are very different from the bonelike fish scales.

- Limbs, if present, with claws on the toes that are good for climbing, digging, and moving on land.

- Well-developed air-breathing lungs, eliminating the need for skin or mouth respiration.

- A partial division of the heart ventricle. This results in further separation of oxygenated blood from the lungs and deoxygenated blood from the body tissues. The separation increases the oxygen supply to tissue.

- A body temperature that varies with that of the environment. A reptile's temperature will fall to the cool environmental temperature at night. However, the term "cold blooded," when applied to reptiles, is misleading because in the daytime the reptile's body temperature will be higher than at night. Reptiles control their internal temperatures by their behavior. They can seek the sun or the shade during the day.

Classification of Modern Reptiles

There are about 6,000 species in the class *Reptilia* today. This may seem like a great many, but it is only a small fraction of the number that inhabited the earth during the Age of Reptiles. Once there were 16 orders of reptiles. Only four orders of reptiles exist today. One of these orders is represented by a single species that is nearing extinction.

Some of today's reptiles are very much like their prehistoric ancestors. Others, called modern reptiles, have become very different. Reptiles are most numerous in the tropics. Some reptiles, however, have migrated to more temperate climates. In fact, reptiles are even found in colder parts of the earth. However, there are no reptile populations in icy regions, high mountains, and the ocean depths. There are about 275 reptile species in the United States.

rhyncho = snout
cephalic = head

squama = scale

chele = claw

- *Rhynchocephalia* consists of one species, nearing extinction; *Sphenodon* (tuatara).
- *Squamata* includes reptiles with horny epidermal scales; lizards and snakes.
- *Chelonia* (Testudinata) have bodies with two bony shells; turtles and tortoises.
- *Crocodilia* are large reptiles with elongated skulls the most prominent feature; alligators, crocodiles, gavials, and caimans.

The Sphenodon: Holdover from the Past

One of the rarest animals on the earth today is a species of reptile. This is the sole surviving species of the order Rhynchocephalia. This ancient reptile, even older than the dinosaurs, is *Sphenodon punctatus* or *tuatara* (Too-ah-TAH-rah). Its closest relatives became extinct early in the Mesozoic era. They probably could not compete with more adaptable lizards and, later, with various mammals. The tuatara escaped extinction in New Zealand and its neighboring islands; here there were no mammals with which to compete. Once English settlers brought in their rats, pigs, cats, and weasels, however, the tuatara became extinct on the mainland. Today the last few tuatara live on a few small islands off the coast of New Zealand. The New Zealand government now protects them. Because the creatures live well in captivity, it may be possible to preserve this species.

The tuatara reaches a length of 60 centimeters (2 feet). It looks like a large lizard. One of the tuatara's most unusual characteristics is a third eye on the top of its head called a **parietal** (puh-RY-ut'l) **eye.** Although covered by thin, small scales and skin, the parietal eye senses when the lizard may be exposed to too much of the sun's radiation. When the eye is artificially blocked or covered, the lizard no longer shows the behavioral patterns that protect it from excess heat.

36–5 | *Sphenodon punctatus,* the tuatara of the islands off the coast of New Zealand, is the only surviving species of a once-flourishing order. *(Allan Roberts)*

Tuatara come out at night to feed on insects, worms, and other small animals. The eggs are buried in a shallow depression in the ground. It is almost a year before they hatch. The female tuatara usually lays 12 to 14 eggs.

The Lizards: Strange and Beautiful Reptiles

Today there are more than 2,500 species of lizards. These are thought to have come from ancestors of the Mesozoic era. Because they look like dragons and dinosaurs, they are feared by many people. Only two species of lizards are poisonous. Most lizards are shy and harmless creatures.

Lizards live mostly in tropical regions, though a few live in colder areas. Lizards have developed many adaptations for different environments.

Iguanas *Iguanas* (i-GWAH-nahz) are thought to be the most primitive lizards. In this family is the so-called *horned toad*. This "toad" has a series of horny spines on its head and back for protection. It lives in the dry plains of the western United States. The spiny skin, which conserves water, is an excellent adaptation for dry areas. This small lizard survives because its color blends with the sand and spiny cacti of its environment.

The best-known iguana is the 12-centimeter-long (4.8 inches) *Anolis carolinensis*. Members of this species are often called *chameleons* (kuh-MEEL-ynz) because, like the true chameleons, they can change color from green to brown. They may be green on a leaf and brown on a rock. The true chameleons, however, are of a different family. They are of the genus *Camaeles* and live in Africa, Madagascar, and India. Color changes in chameleons, both the true chameleons and the iguanas commonly called chameleons, may be caused by light, temperature, or even their own state of excitement.

Geckos Geckos are a group of highly specialized lizards. Their toes are expanded into clinging pads. They use these pads to climb up vertical surfaces and even to walk on ceilings. They are the only lizards that can make loud noises. Since they eat insects, they are also welcome in homes throughout the tropics.

Skinks *Skinks* are known for their shiny cylindrical bodies and weak legs. They live in the forests of Africa and the East Indies, where they are the most abundant reptiles; they are also common in the United States. Skinks are not often seen because they are shy animals. If you grab a skink, anole, or gecko by the tail, it can snap off and the lizard will escape. This is a protective adaptation because they can easily grow new tails.

36–6 | An American "chameleon" *(Anolis)* shedding its skin. Like many other lizards, the *Anolis* eats the shed skin. *(Allan Roberts)*

36-7 | Examples of lizards: (top) Gila monster; (middle top) horned toad; (middle bottom) skink; (bottom) fence lizard. *(top: K. Bobrowsky, Monkmeyer Press; middle top: Dr. E. R. Degginger; middle bottom and bottom: Z. Leszczynski, © Animals Animals)*

Gila Monsters and Beaded Lizards *Gila* (HEE-luh) *monsters* and their cousins, the *beaded lizards*, are the only poisonous lizards. Gilas live in the southwestern United States and Mexico. Beaded lizards live only in Mexico. A large Gila monster is less than 60 centimeters (2 feet) long. Poison glands are located in the rear of their lower jaws. Grooved teeth are found in both jaws. The Gila holds its victim in its mouth and shakes its head from side to side. This action releases the venom. Neurotoxins in the venom affect the nerves that control the victim's breathing. Few humans die from their bites, but Gila monsters should be avoided.

Monitor Lizards Monitor lizards are the largest lizards in the world. They are thought to be related closely to snakes because they have several adaptations that are also found in snakes. The largest of the monitors is the Komodo dragon. This monster can grow to be three meters long (almost 10 feet) and sometimes weighs over 140 kilograms (308 pounds). It lives on Komodo Island in the East Indies. Except for their inability to breathe fire, monitor lizards look like mythical dragons.

The Crocodilians: Crocodiles, Alligators, and Their Relatives

The crocodilians and their extinct relatives had their supremacy in the late Mesozoic era. They were found in many types of environments, but they thrived only in water. Crocodilians like modern alligators and crocodiles first appeared in the Triassic period, the earliest period of the Mesozoic era. They have remained relatively unchanged for the last 225 million years. They are very well adapted to their shallow water environment. For example, they have a way of breathing while being nearly hidden in the water.

They breathe through their raised nostrils. These nostrils are connected to the lungs by an air passage in the skull. At the back of the mouth is a fleshy valve that prevents water from entering the lungs when the mouth is open. With this ability, crocodilians can lie in the water, with only their nostrils and eyes above the surface. Unwary animals do not notice the crocodilian until it is too late.

Of the many crocodilian species that once lived, only a few still exist. Currently, there are 25 species of alligators, caimans (KAY-manz), crocodiles, and gavials in the order *Crocodilia*. They all live in tropical and subtropical zones. Their few differences are in length and width of snout, and arrangement of scales and teeth. The best known crocodilians are alligators and crocodiles. Crocodiles are more aquatic than alligators. Crocodiles have triangular heads

and pointed snouts. On each side of the lower jaw there is a tooth that fits into notches in the upper jaw. This distinguishes crocodiles from alligators.

The Turtles: Reptiles with Shells

Turtles that live on land are called **tortoises.** They have hard shells and are slow-moving. They have strong feet and claws for walking on land and digging. Most tortoises are vegetarians. They live on a variety of plant foods. **Terrapins** are hard-shelled, freshwater turtles. These turtles are used as food in many parts of the country. Sea turtles are large, marine animals. Their limbs are in the form of flippers. These animals are well adapted to swimming in the ocean. For convenience, we shall refer to all of these forms as turtles.

There are only 335 species of turtles. They are found in most parts of the world except the Arctic and Antarctic. Some land turtles are on remote islands like the Galapagos, which are far from any mainland. They are thought to have drifted to these islands on mats of trees and vegetation that drifted out to sea.

Turtles have not changed much in the last 200 million years. Giant sea turtles very similar to present-day turtles existed in the Cretaceous period. The turtle's unusual armor is probably a major factor in its ability to survive unchanged for so many years.

It is possible that the first turtles were land reptiles. Some of these may have become adapted to life in water. This seems to be the reverse of the usual trend of vertebrates to adapt from a water to a land environment. However, it would explain why all turtles return to the land to lay their eggs.

The most apparent feature of the turtle is its shell. Most turtle shells consist of symmetrical plates. These plates are called *scutes*. Their number and arrangement vary from species to species. They are made of hard, horny material

36–8 | What difference do you see between (left) the alligator and (right) the crocodile? *(right: Allan Roberts; left: Stevenson, Animals Animals)*

Facts & Figures

Crocodiles may live to be 50 years old or more.

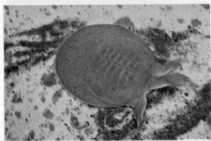

36-9 | Various turtles: (top) common snapping turtle; (middle top) Eastern soft-shelled turtle; (middle bottom) desert tortoise; (bottom) Eastern box turtle. *(top and middle top: John H. Gerard, L. L. Rue III, National Audobon Society; middle botom: Stephen J. Krasemann,© Peter Arnold; bottom: Z. Leszczynski, © Animals Animals)*

that overlies a deeper bony layer that usually includes the vertebrae and ribs. The dorsal, or upper, shell is called the **carapace.** The ventral, or belly, shell is called the **plastron.** It is connected to the carapace by side scutes.

The shell of soft-shelled turtles is covered by a leathery skin rather than scutes. The bony layer is rather soft. These are freshwater turtles. Turtles have long necks which aid them in capturing prey.

The heads, legs, and tails of some turtles, such as the box turtle, can be withdrawn completely into the shell. Other species, such as the snapping turtle, cannot completely withdraw their long necks. Picking up a snapping turtle can be a foolish act. Its jaws are extremely powerful, and it is an aggressive reptile.

The skin that covers the turtle's head, tail, and legs is covered with scales. The head is usually triangular. The mouth is a horny toothless beak that can cut and crush either meat or plants. Turtles have *tympanic membranes* on either side of their heads. Sound waves stimulate these membranes and enable turtles to hear sounds. Like frogs, turtles have a transparent *nictitating membrane* that serves to protect the eyes.

Most turtle legs are short and heavy with horny claws. The legs of sea turtles are adapted for flippers which make them excellent swimmers.

Snakes: The Most Widespread Reptiles

Snakes are relative newcomers among reptiles. There is no good fossil record of these creatures. They could have descended from reptiles with legs. In fact, pythons and boas still have vestigial hind legs. Snakes evolved rapidly during the Tertiary period, about 70 million years ago. This is the same time that rodents and other small mammals, which some snakes eat, were developing.

Snakes are the most numerous of today's reptiles. They are also distributed most widely. Snakes are found in water, on rocks, under the ground, and in trees. They are most abundant in tropical regions. There are fewer of them in cooler climates. There are 126 species in the United States and 22 species in Canada.

Only a few of the more than 2,000 species of snakes are poisonous. The harm caused people by the few dangerous snakes is far outweighed by the valuable service snakes render by killing insects and rodents.

Nonpoisonous Snakes Among the many nonpoisonous snakes, you may be familiar with the harmless *garter snake,* *black snake,* and *racer.* The common garter snake feeds primarily on amphibians. Many other nonpoisonous snakes feed on mice and rats and are therefore very helpful to humans. The king snake is a valuable snake because it eats other snakes as well as rodents. It is immune to rattlesnake poison. The constrictors of South America, Africa, and Asia are also nonpoisonous snakes.

Poisonous Snakes **All poisonous snakes have specialized teeth, or fangs, for injecting venom.** They are grouped into four families. The *cobras* live mostly in the tropics of Asia and Africa. All members of the cobra family are deadly to human beings. The king cobra of Thailand is the largest of all poisonous snakes. Some species of cobra spit venom at their enemies in a fine spray. This spray can travel about a meter (3.3 feet) with amazing accuracy. This venom can cause temporary or permanent blindness if it enters an eye. The coral snakes of North America are in the same family as the cobras. They are small, but they have very beautiful coloration. Their venom is very potent, but they do not kill many humans. Their fangs are located at the back of their mouths as hollow short teeth. Their fangs cannot penetrate heavy clothes or shoes, but a bite on the hand or bare foot can be fatal.

Sea snakes are related to the cobra, but they are placed in another family. They live in the shallow waters of the East Indies and in the South Pacific.

The third group of venomous snakes is the *vipers*. They include all the poisonous snakes of Europe, Africa, and most of Asia that are not cobras. The most common viper is the European viper. In England, it is called the adder. The largest number of viper species live in Africa.

The fourth family of poisonous snakes is called *pit vipers*. Pit vipers are different from true vipers in that they have heat-sensitive organs. These organs are pits located in front of their eyes. Biologists have discovered that these pits sense infrared rays. This helps pit vipers strike accurately at any prey that produces heat. Pit vipers usually prey upon warm-blooded animals. Some of these snakes live in southern Asia, but most are found in North and South America.

Rattlesnakes are the most widespread poisonous snakes in the United States. Of the more than 19 species found in the United States, at least 12 live in the Southwest. The largest North American species is the diamondback. This snake lives in marshy areas in the Southeast. It can grow to be over two meters (6.6 feet) long. Other species include the prairie rattlesnake, western diamondback, and sidewinder. The timber rattlesnake is found in most of the eastern United States.

Snake Venom The toxin part of snake venom is made of complex protein substances. The two types of snake venom

Facts & Figures

Anaconda snakes may grow to about 11 meters (37 feet) long. Pythons may grow to about 10 meters (33 feet) long.

are *neurotoxins* and *hemotoxins.* Neurotoxins affect the parts of the nervous system that control breathing and heart action. Hemotoxins destroy red blood cells and break down the walls of small blood vessels. All poisonous snakes have both types, but the proportions vary with the species. The venom of cobras, coral snakes, and sea snakes contains mostly neurotoxin. That of vipers and pit vipers tends to be mostly hemotoxin.

The danger of any snakebite depends on a number of factors. The amount of venom injected and the concentration of toxin are both critical. Another important factor is where the venom enters. It can enter the main circulatory system rapidly through a blood vessel or slowly through muscle or fatty tissue.

Anatomy of the Snake

As the first vertebrates fully adapted to a terrestrial environment, reptiles have few adaptations not a part of the amphibian anatomy. The main adaptation, already discussed, is the amniotic egg. The main difference in anatomy is the reproductive system; a difference in the circulatory system is that reptiles have a four-chambered heart. Reptilian scales minimize water loss.

The snake will be discussed in this section as the representative of the class Reptilia. Since the differences between amphibians and reptiles is not great, each system will not be discussed in this chapter. However, the manner in which snakes eat and how they move will be discussed as unique characteristics.

Body Structure

Snake bodies are long and thin. A close look will show you that they have three separate areas. These areas are the head; the trunk containing the body cavity; and the tail, which extends beyond the anus. As in all reptiles, snake bodies are covered with scales. On the back and sides, the scales are small and ovoid. On the lower side, they form broad plates, the scutes.

Several times a year, snakes shed their outer layer of scales. The process is called *molting.* The thin outer layer loosens. Then the snake usually hooks a piece of the loose covering to a sharp object and works its way out. The newly exposed scales are brighter than the old ones.

Sense Organs

Snakes have a very acute sense of smell. Olfactory nerve endings lie in the nasal cavities. These cavities open as

36–10 | Three venomous snakes found in the United States. (top) Copperhead; (middle) water moccasin; (bottom) coral snake. *(top: Allan Roberts; middle: Walter Dawn; bottom: Z. Leszczynski,* © *Animals Animals)*

paired nostrils near the front of the head. The sense of smell is aided by a forked tongue. This tongue rests in a sheath on the floor of the mouth. It flicks out through a small opening that is left when the jaws are closed. The tongue picks up dust and odor-bearing particles from the air. It transfers them to tiny pits in the front of the roof of the mouth. These pits are called *Jacobson's organs.* They contain nerve endings that are very sensitive to odors.

Unlike other reptiles, snakes have no lids on their eyes. Instead, a transparent scale covers each eye. Just before molting, this scale becomes cloudy. This makes vision difficult for a time. The eyes can turn in their sockets.

The Feeding Habits of Snakes

All snakes eat animals. No vegetarian snakes are known to exist. Snakes are classified into three groups according to feeding habits. Many snakes, including most of the nonpoisonous species, simply seize an animal in their mouth and *swallow it alive.* Most of these snakes feed on insects, frogs, toads, lizards, fishes, and other small animals.

Some of the larger snakes, including the python, boa, king snake, and bull snake use a special method of food-getting. They squeeze their prey to death. These snakes seize the prey, usually by its head, and coil themselves around it. The prey is killed by *constriction.* The snake's muscular body squeezes the victim so hard that the chest is compressed and breathing is stopped. This great pressure also cuts off the victim's circulation and stops the heart. The shock kills the prey, often without breaking a bone. If the snake feels a pulse in its victim, it will squeeze again. These snakes begin to swallow their prey as soon as it is killed. Biologists have found that warm-blooded animals are killed more quickly by constriction than cold-blooded animals.

A relatively few snakes *poison their prey.* Poisonous snakes kill their prey with toxic venom before swallowing the victim. They produce this venom in salivary glands at the side of their heads. The poisonous snake strikes by thrusting its head directly at the prey. It embeds its paired fangs into the prey. Venom flows from poison glands through ducts inside the fangs. The hollow fangs are like hypodermic needles. The amount of venom injected varies with the species and the size of snake, but the smaller species and the young of larger species have more concentrated venom. They can be just as dangerous as the larger poisonous snakes.

Adaptations for Swallowing
Snakes do not eat often. They may go for weeks, sometimes even a year under some conditions, without eating. It is amazing to watch a snake

when it does eat. A snake can swallow an animal four or five times larger in diameter than its own body. This is possible because of the structure of the snake's jaws. The lower jaw can drop down due to the many hinges that permit a very wide mouth opening. Also, the two halves of the lower jaw are fastened by ligaments that can stretch. This allows each half to work independently of the other. Numerous slanting teeth hold the prey firmly while it is being swallowed.

During swallowing, one side of the lower jaw pulls the prey into the snake's mouth. The other side pushes forward for a new grip. With this seesaw action, the prey is pulled slowly down the snake's throat. It is similar to pulling a rope, hand over hand. The snake actually crawls forward around its prey. Swallowing takes quite a long time, so the snake needs special adaptations for breathing while it has a large prey in its throat. The trachea extending into the lower jaw allows the snake to breathe.

How Snakes Move

Snakes move in several different ways. When they are crawling quickly or swimming in water, they use a method called *lateral undulatory movement*. The body winds from side to side in broad curving motions, and the entire body follows the same track. Little bumps and irregularities in the ground give the snake a grip.

When snakes crawl slowly in a straight line, they use a motion called *caterpillar movement*. The snake pushes its scutes forward in several body sections. The rear edge of each scute grips the ground. The body is pulled forward by wavelike muscular contractions.

The third method of snake movement is called *sidewinding*. This movement is used by snakes of sandy desert areas. The snake twists its body into S-shaped loops. Except for two or three points of contact, it raises itself off the ground. The sidewinder "walks" across the sand on these loops.

Even with these special adaptations, snakes cannot move very quickly. Most travel at less than a kilometer (0.6 miles) per hour. Even the fastest snakes do not exceed five kilometers per hour. You can easily walk at this speed, and most people can run short distances at 15 to 30 kilometers per hour (9 to 18 miles per hour).

The Internal Organs of a Snake

A snake's spine may have over 300 pairs of ribs attached to the vertebrae. Most have about 200 pairs of ribs. These ribs are set in muscle and are flexible. This allows for movement and swallowing of large prey. The flexible ribs also allow the body wall to expand for breathing. The right lung is well developed, but the left lung is small or missing

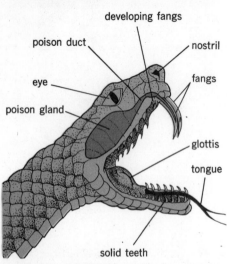

36–11 | The head of a poisonous snake is well suited for poisoning prey and swallowing it whole. *(William M. Partington, National Audubon Society)*

entirely. The large heart has a *septum*. This wall partially separates the ventricle into two chambers.

Development in Snakes

Most snakes are *oviparous* (oh-VIP-uh-rus). This means that they lay eggs. Their eggs resemble those of other reptiles. Each egg is enclosed in a tough white shell. This egg contains stored food to nourish the young snake during development. The female snake gives the eggs no care after she lays them. The only incubation warmth the eggs receive is from the sun.

A smaller group of snakes bring forth their young alive. The eggs are not laid. They remain in the uterus until they develop into young snakes, but the mother's body provides no food for the embryos. Animals that bring forth their young already hatched are classed *ovoviviparous* (oe-voe-vie-VIP-uh-rus). On the other hand, **mammals that bring forth and nourish their young during development are called** *viviparous* (vie-VIP-uh-rus).

ovi = egg
vivus = alive
parous = to bring forth

36–12 | (top) Baby pilot snakes hatching from eggs and (bottom) a mother garter snake with newly born young. Which snake is oviparous and which is ovoviviparous? *(top: Allan Roberts; bottom: Phil A. Dotson, DPI)*

Summary

Type of Life	terrestrial water dwelling
Integumentary System	scales skin scutes; carapace, plastron
Skeletal System	bones and cartilage snakes apodal and have spines with over 100 pairs of ribs in most snakes; other reptiles have pectoral and pelvic girdles with limbs.
Digestive System	gullet, stomach, small intestine, large intestine and rectum (colon), cloaca. snakes with organs adapted to swallowing prey whole.
Respiratory System	lungs well developed
Circulatory System	3-chambered heart, one ventricle with septum
Excretory System	kidneys; urinary bladder
Nervous System	enlarged cerebrum in comparison to amphibians
Reproductive System	internal fertilization females produce fewer eggs in comparison to amphibians
Development	oviviparous, ovoparous external development

Biologically Speaking

amniote egg
embryonic membrane
chorion
allantois
amnion
yolk sac membrane
internal fertilization
parietal eye
tortoise
terrapin

carapace
plastron
neurotoxin
hemotoxin
molting
Jacobson's organ
oviparous
ovovivparous
viviparous

1. Name and describe a plant-eating dinosaur, a flesh-eating dinosaur, and a flying reptile.
2. Describe the functions of the shell, chorion, amnion, allantois, and yolk sac of an amniote egg.
3. List six characteristics of reptiles that enabled them to live on land.
4. Give examples of each of the four orders of reptiles.
5. In what respect is Sphenodon a reptile of special interest to the biologist?
6. List three methods used by various snakes to capture prey.
7. What characteristics of the snake's mouth allow it to swallow large prey?
8. Contrast oviparous and ovoviviparous.
9. Describe the action on the victim of each of the two types of toxin found in snake venom.
10. What are the differences between alligators and crocodiles?
11. What adaptations have enabled the turtle to survive through the ages?
12. Discuss the theory of warm-blooded dinosaurs.

1. Discuss the amniote egg as the key to the development of land-dwelling vertebrates.
2. In what respect is cold-bloodedness a limiting factor in the distribution of reptiles?
3. Discuss several body structures of a reptile that represent a survival advantage over the amphibians.

37

The Birds

A **DESCRIBE** the evolutionary origin of birds.

B **NAME** the characteristics of birds.

C **EXPLAIN** the structure and function of feathers.

D **DESCRIBE** the systems of birds and their functions.

E **EXPLAIN** reproduction in birds.

F **DESCRIBE** how birds are adapted to flight.

37–1 | Can you see why some people call birds "glorified reptiles"? *(DPI)*

The Origin of Birds

Many people buy books each year to identify some of the many species of birds that either stay in their area all year or pass through on their annual migrations. The study of birds is called *ornithology*. Birds delight us with their mating songs, their grace in flight, their nesting habits, and their colors.

Birds have been called "glorified reptiles." The next chance you have, take a close look at any bird. Which of its features are similar to a reptile's? Notice its horny, toothless beak, claws, and the scales on its legs. They are similar in structure and origin to those structures on certain reptiles. The amniotic egg is also similar.

Like the dinosaurs, birds are thought to have developed from lizards called *Thecodonts*, which were discussed in Chapter 36. The thecodonts are thought to have given rise to various groups, one of which was birds, the other dinosaurs.

Archaeopteryx: A Very Important Fossil

Although modern birds have one or two of the characteris-

ornitho = birds
ology = study of

tics of flying reptiles such as the Pteranodons, birds are thought to have developed along different lines.

The earliest fossil birds that link birds to reptiles were found in the late 1880's in Bavaria, Germany. The fossil was called *Archaeopteryx* (ark-ee-OP-tuh-ricks). Three such fossil birds have been discovered. All were found in Jurassic rock, and were more than 135 million years old. Not only the skeletons but impressions of both flight and tail feathers were clear. Without the feathers, the fossil bird would probably have been classified as a reptile. Many of its characteristics were more like those of a small dinosaur than those of a bird.

archeo = ancient
pteryx = wing

Modern Birds

The biological success of a group of organisms is measured by the number of species and individuals, their adaptation to a variety of environments, and their distribution throughout the world. If we accept these standards for success, birds are among the most successful vertebrates.

There are over 8,500 species of birds. Birds range in size from tiny hummingbirds to ostriches. Birds' diets vary from seeds, nectar, insects, small animals, to even rotten flesh. The structure of their beaks often indicates what they eat. For example, some beaks are modified for grasping seeds or insects, others for tearing meat. Some birds are masters of the air. Others, like ostriches and penguins, cannot fly. Some birds never leave their home environment. Others go on migrations that span the globe. Birds' nests are varied also. A nest can be a woven bag, a pile of sticks, or a hole in a tree or the ground.

Flying birds have an advantage over all other vertebrates. They can travel long distances and avoid unfavorable seasonal changes. Many follow the food supply as it changes with the seasons. Ducks, geese, and other water birds are at home on the land, at sea, and in the air. This is a distinction not shared by any other vertebrates.

The Order of Birds

So far, scientists have catalogued over 8,500 species of birds. These are grouped into 27 orders. The better-known birds of North America represent 17 of these orders. Classification of this large number of species into orders, family, and genera is a difficult task for biologists.

Biologists have settled on several different bird characteristics for classifying birds in orders. Among these structures are the feet and beaks. Modifications in feet and beaks usually relate closely to the life habits and diets. Foot struc-

37–2 | Archeopteryx. Observation of fossils of the reptilelike bird, such as that above, led to the artist's representation at the bottom. *(Courtesy of the American Museum of Natural History)*

Columbiformes
(mourning dove)

Charadriiformes
(gull)

Cuculiformes
(yellow-billed cuckoo)

Strigiformes
(owl)

Apodiformes
(hummingbird)

Caprimulgiformes
(whipporwill)

Coraciiformes
(kingfisher)

Piciformes
(sapsucker)

Passeriformes
(robin)

37-3 | Some examples of common orders of North American birds.

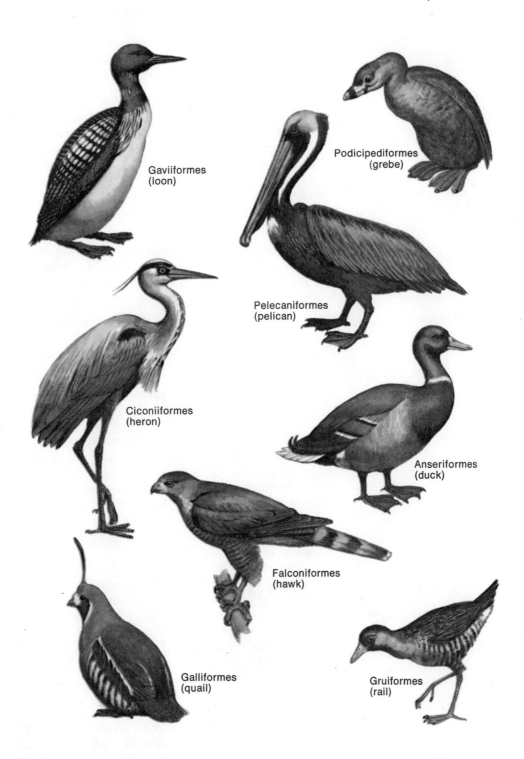

Gaviiformes
(loon)

Podicipediformes
(grebe)

Pelecaniformes
(pelican)

Ciconiiformes
(heron)

Anseriformes
(duck)

Falconiformes
(hawk)

Galliformes
(quail)

Gruiformes
(rail)

ture adapts some birds for diving and others for swimming, wading, perching, running, or carrying prey. Beak modifications determine if some birds are insect eaters, seed eaters, flesh eaters, mud probers, or wood borers.

Characteristics of Birds

Birds differ in size, color, diet, and other adaptations, but they all have similar body structure and characteristics. The characteristics of the vertebrate class *Aves*, which includes all birds are:

- Body covering of feathers.
- Bones that are very light. They have larger cavities and are thinner than mammal bones.
- Forelimbs specialized as wings. These are used for flight in most birds. They are never used for grasping.
- Body supported by two hind limbs.
- Mouth in the form of a toothless, horny beak.
- A four-chambered heart; a well-developed circulatory system, with a right aortic arch only.
- A constant body temperature (warm-blooded).
- An amniote egg encased in a lime-containing shell.
- The egg usually is incubated in the nest.

Feathers Feathers are actually modified scales similar in origin to reptile scales. Rather than lie flat against the skin as a reptile scale does, the epidermal scale of a bird forms a *cylinder*. As the cylinder forms, its base sinks deeper into the skin, forming a **follicle** (a sac). The follicles that hold the feathers lie in rows in certain skin areas. The cylinder, or **quill**, sticks out of the follicle and gives rise to one of various types of feathers.

The soft feathers seen on newly hatched birds are called *down feathers*. In older birds, especially waterfowl, down feathers lie close to the skin and serve as insulation. Each down feather is made of a fluffy tuft at the end of a short quill. They reduce heat loss very efficiently. These feathers allow ducks and geese to fly through very cold air and still maintain a body temperature of over 38°C (100.4°F). The slender, hairlike feathers with tufts on the ends are known as *filoplumes*.

Contour feathers round out a bird's body, helping to make it streamlined. They also protect against injury and provide coloration. The males are usually the brightly colored individuals of the species. The color is used to attract females during the mating season. Also, since the female usually sits on the nest, her less striking colors are good protection. They allow her to blend with the natural background while predators can be led away by the more noticeable male.

Quill feathers are large contour feathers growing in the wing and tail. These large feathers help provide lift and balance needed for flying and steering. The quill feather has a fairly complex structure. The hollow quill extends into a central axis called a *rachis* (RAY-kiss). Spreading from the rachis is the broad, flat *vane*. The vane is composed of many small rays called *barbs*. If you magnify a barb, it looks like a tiny feather with many projections, called *barbules*. Tiny hooks hold the barbules together. This structure makes the vane strong. Yet it is still light and elastic. The rachis is grooved, and the quill is hollow. This gives the feather more strength with the least possible weight. If a vane is split, a bird can shake itself to put it together again. Have you ever seen a bird draw a single feather through its beak? It's repairing the split vane by rehooking the barbules.

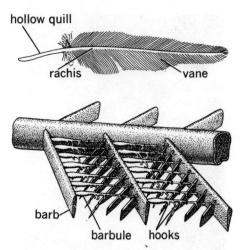

37–4 | The structure of a quill feather. The enlargement shows a portion of the rachis and vane as seen through a microscope.

Many birds oil their feathers after they get wet. Closely watch ducks on a pond. You will eventually see one rub its tail with its beak, then rub its beak on its body feathers. The duck is spreading oil from its *tail gland*. This makes the surface of the feathers waterproof. **The larger oily tail gland is an adaptation for water birds.** Oil on the feathers is crucial to most swimming and diving birds. It prevents water from getting through the feathers to the skin. This oil also prevents birds from chilling and helps them stay afloat. Ducks, geese, swans, loons, and grebes all need to oil their feathers.

Molting The process of feather replacement is called *molting.* A bird sheds its feathers and grows new ones at least once a year. This usually happens in late summer, before the fall migration. A partial molt may occur in the spring, before the mating season. This molt results in the bright breeding plumage of many birds.

Molting is a gradual process in birds. Some feathers are being replaced while others are being lost, so the bird's skin is never bare. The wing feathers of most species are shed in pairs. This allows the bird balanced flight during a molt. Ducks and many water birds molt by losing groups of feathers from the wings. They are unable to fly for a time. This occurs when the birds are nesting and caring for their young. They grow new flight feathers as the young birds are getting their plumage.

The ptarmigan of the far north molts twice a year. The early summer molt provides brown plumage to blend in with rocks and soil. The fall molt provides a white plumage to blend in with the winter snow.

37–5 | Two seasonal molts occur in the ptarmigan. The early summer molt and the fall molt provide seasonal camouflage. *(Krasemann, Peter Arnold)*

Facts & Figures

There are more bones in the neck of any bird than in the neck of a giraffe.

Head and Senses The bird's *skull* is made of thin bones. These bones fuse together early in the bird's life. The cranium is rounded and encases the brain. The upper jaw is called the *maxilla,* and the lower jaw, the *mandible.* These project forward as the toothless beak.

The *tongue* is small and is used mostly as an organ of touch. Birds have a poor sense of taste, but they are known to reject bad-tasting food. Paired nostrils, or *nares,* open through the beak. The nares admit air into the mouth cavity. Birds also have a poor sense of smell.

Bird's *eyes* are large and set in deep sockets. Unlike their senses of smell and taste, birds' sense of sight is very keen. It is said that many birds have vision that is 8 to 10 times as keen as human vision. They can judge distance accurately both at close and at far range. Birds' eyes can shift focus rapidly. Owls and other birds that are active at night have excellent vision in reduced light. Eyes are protected by an upper and lower eyelid, plus a thin *nictitating membrane.* The nictitating membrane is transparent. It can be drawn across the eyeball from the front corner of the eye socket. The nictitating membrane protects the eye and keeps it moist.

Ear canals open on either side of the head just behind the eyes. These canals are covered by protective tufts of feathers. They lead to the *tympanic membrane,* or eardrum. *Eustachian tubes* run from the middle-ear cavities to a single opening in the upper wall of the throat. They serve to equalize the air pressure on both sides of the eardrum. Birds can hear very well. The ears are especially sensitive to high-pitched sounds.

Neck and Trunk A bird's neck is long and flexible. It has vertebrae that slide easily on one another. This provides the freedom of movement needed to look in all directions. Birds are unable to use their forelimbs for grasping, so they need flexibility in order to use their beaks to feed easily, preen, and build nests.

Tail vertebrae are also flexible. This allows a bird to move its tail feathers freely. This is needed for balance and steering during flight. The trunk bones, on the other hand, are fused together solidly. This provides needed body support during flight.

The breast bone, or *sternum,* is enlarged. It covers much of the bird's ventral surface. Ribs are attached to the dorsal part of the sternum. The ventral part forms a deep ridge, called a *keel.* This provides a broad surface where the powerful breast muscles used in flying can attach.

Shoulders and Wings The shoulders, or pectoral girdle, are made of three pairs of bones. The *scapulae,* or shoulder

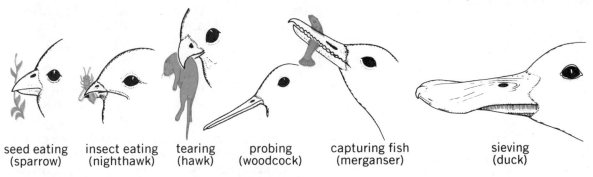

seed eating (sparrow)   insect eating (nighthawk)   tearing (hawk)   probing (woodcock)   capturing fish (merganser)   sieving (duck)

blades, lie on either side of the spine above the ribs. They are imbedded in the back muscles. The *coracoid* bone extends from each scapula to the sternum. Further support of the girdle is provided by the two *clavicles*. These form the V-shaped wishbone. When certain muscles are contracted, this girdle of bones aids in lifting the wings.

The structure of a bird's wing has the same structure, so is *homologous* to, your own arm. The upper portion of a bird's wing contains a large, single bone, the *humerus*. The head of the humerus fits into a socket at the shoulder. Powerful breast muscles connect the humerus to the broad keel of the sternum. When these muscles contract, they supply the downward power stroke when the bird is in flight.

When a bird flies, it does more than move its wings up and down. The wings go down and back, then up and forward. The downward stroke is the power stroke. The upward stroke returns the wings for the next power stroke. Each movement uses a different set of muscles.

Pelvic Girdle and Legs The *pelvic girdle* is made of three pairs of bones. These are fused together firmly, and are united with the lower spine. The legs are attached at the hip joint, high on the pelvic girdle. This structure provides excellent balance. Such balance is very important to birds when they move on land. Birds must balance on only two legs when walking, running, or hopping.

The upper leg contains a large, single bone, the *femur*. The upper end of the femur joins the pelvic girdle in a ball-and-socket joint. The lower leg contains two bones. The large bone is the *tibia*, or "drumstick." A second bone, the *fibula*, is reduced to a slender spine that lies alongside the tibia. Bones of the ankle and foot are fused. They are elongated and often confused with the leg. The bird walks on its toes. In most birds, the first toe is shorter and is turned backward. The second, third, and fourth toes are directed forward. All of the toes end in claws.

Birds that Do Not Fly

Some birds have lost the ability to fly. These birds inhabit

37–6 | The beaks of birds often indicate what they eat.

Facts & Figures

The maximum wingspan of the albatross is 3.6 meters (12 feet).

Facts & Figures

A peregrine falcon can fly between 104 and 120 kilometers per hour (65 and 75 miles per hour).

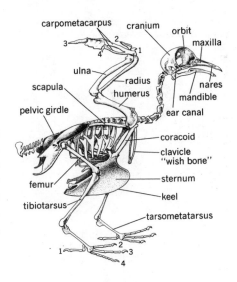

37–7 | A bird's skeleton.

many parts of the world. The best known are the ostriches of Africa, rheas of South America, kiwis of New Zealand, and cassowaries of Australia. The various penguins of the southern hemisphere are also flightless birds.

Many flightless birds have survived only because they live in areas free of predators. However, human beings have caused the extinction of several flightless birds. The giant elephant bird of Madagascar died off only after humans arrived with their domestic animals. The extinction of the dodo of the Mascarene Islands and the moas of New Zealand occurred only after the arrival of people to these islands.

In most flightless birds interesting adaptations have developed. The ostriches, the rheas, and the cassowaries are able to survive among predators. This is possible because of their adaptations to life on land. These birds have very strong legs. They can run fast and kick very hard. They also have very keen vision. Penguins have interesting adaptations to their flightless life. Their wings are well developed, but they are used for swimming through water. Their feet are webbed. These webbed feet serve as rudders. Penguins have the keeled breast that most flightless birds lack: This serves as attachment for the muscles used in swimming.

Birds' feet vary greatly in structure from species to species. Feet are used for locomotion, getting food, building nests, and other activities. The feet of most ground birds are adapted for scratching the ground in search of food. Swimming and diving birds have webbed or lobed feet. The legs of these birds are set far back on the body. This position is good for paddling in the water. Wading birds have long legs and long toes. Birds of prey usually have strong feet with long, sharp claws or talons. Hawks and eagles have feet like this. Woodpeckers have two toes turned to the back and two turned forward. This helps them cling to the sides of trees. Most birds have only one backward toe.

Organ Systems

Many structural adaptations are necessary for birds to fly. They have a streamlined body to reduce air resistance. Their flight muscles are strong. Weight is sacrificed without reducing strength. Their digestive system is efficient. Birds eat large amounts of food to get the tremendous energy needed by the flight muscles.

The body temperature of a bird is higher than that of most animals. It averages from 38°C to 45°C (100.4°F to 113°F). Release of this heat energy requires a high metabolic rate. To support this cellular activity birds have highly developed respiratory, circulatory, and excretory

37–8 | The ostrich (top) and (bottom) the penguins are flightless birds. *(top: Rue III, National Audubon Society; bottom: Roger T. Peterson, Photo Researchers)*

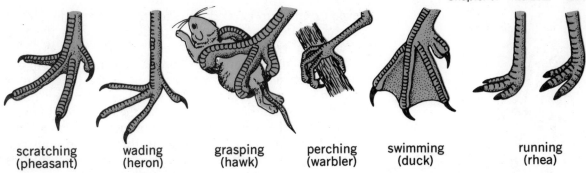

scratching (pheasant) wading (heron) grasping (hawk) perching (warbler) swimming (duck) running (rhea)

37-9 | Diversity in the structure of bird's feet allows for adaptation.

systems. Finally, they have a large brain in proportion to their body to control all this activity. Birds are vertebrate "powerhouses." That is why they are most likely eating or looking for something to eat when you see them.

Digestive System You may have noticed that birds always seem to hurry when they feed. Besides the competition for food, there is another reason for this hurry. When birds are feeding, predators can attack them more easily. Birds eat quickly. They usually swallow food, especially seeds, whole. At the base of the bird's neck the long esophagus enlarges into a *crop.* The crop is a sac that stores and moistens the food. It is largest in seed-eating birds. After filling the crop, the bird can fly to some safe place and digest the food.

From the crop the food passes into the *proventriculus*, the first division of the stomach. The proventriculus has thick glandular walls. These walls secrete gastric fluid, which mixes with the food. Then the food passes into the second stomach area, called the *gizzard*. This often contains small stones. With the aid of these stones, the muscular wall of the gizzard grinds up the food. This ground-up mass of food and juices then passes through the *pyloric valve* into the slender, coiled *intestine*. The lower end of the intestine joins the *rectum*. The short rectum leads to the *cloaca*. Waste products leave the body through the cloacal opening. Also opening into the cloaca are ducts from the kidneys and genital organs.

Birds have a large two-lobed liver. Some species of birds have a *gall bladder* on the lower side of the liver. Bile pours into the small intestine through two ducts. Another digestive organ, the *pancreas*, lies along the U-shaped part of the intestine. The pancreas pours its secretions into the intestine through three ducts.

Respiratory System Birds have a respiratory system adapted to their great need for oxygen during flight. Their lungs are connected to a system of **air sacs.** The air sacs

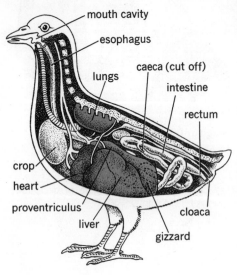

mouth cavity
esophagus
caeca (cut off)
lungs
intestine
rectum
crop
heart
proventriculus
cloaca
liver
gizzard

37–10 | The internal organs of a bird.

even extend into parts of the skeleton. Unlike other vertebrates, gas exchange in birds takes place when the bird breathes out (exhales).

The abdominal and rib muscles, and the sternum are involved in moving air into and out of the lungs. Air is drawn in through the nostrils in the beak. It passes down the trachea and through the **syrinx,** the bird's song box. It then enters the two bronchi. Each bronchus enters a lung. Each main bronchus goes directly through the lung and connects to the posterior air sac. Most of the air enters this posterior air sac. Air then flows from the posterior air sac through small tubes in the lung. Here gas exchange occurs. The air then enters the anterior sacs and then is exhaled. Other sacs located on the sides also serve in respiration and in making the bird lighter in weight.

The efficiency of this respiratory system maintains the rapid oxidation of nutrients and the high body temperature of birds. It also explains how some birds can fly at such high altitudes, where oxygen is scarce.

Circulatory System A bird's *heart* is large, powerful, and very efficient. **It has four chambers. The bird's heart is superior to any vertebrate hearts you have learned about thus far.** It consists of two thin-walled atria and two muscular ventricles. The right side of the four-chambered heart receives blood from the body and pumps it to the lungs. The left side receives blood from the lungs and pumps it to the body. The bird's heart, unlike those of amphibians and reptiles, has only a *right aortic arch.* In birds, this continues as the aorta.

A bird's heart beats at very high rates. Depending upon the bird's activity, the rate can be anywhere from 135 to 570 beats a minute for the mourning dove. The heart of the English sparrow may beat from 350 to 500 times per minute, and the chickadee's heart may beat as fast as 1,000 beats per minute.

Excretory System A pair of dark brown, three-lobed *kidneys* lies along the back. They filter *uric acid* from the blood. Uric acid is a nitrogenous waste product of cell metabolism. Very little water is needed for its excretion. The kidneys then excrete this acid through ureters into the cloaca. Here it is eliminated along with intestinal waste. **Birds have no urinary bladder for the temporary storage of uric acid. This is considered an adaptation that saves on weight.**

Nervous System The brain of the bird is large and broad. It fills the cranial cavity completely. The *olfactory lobes* are relatively small, indicating a poor sense of smell. The *cere-*

brum on the other hand, is the largest of any animal discussed so far. The highly developed instincts of birds are centered here, as is the control of their voluntary muscles.

The *optic lobes* are also large, indicating excellent vision. The large *cerebellum* explains why birds have such good muscle coordination. The *medulla oblongata* joins the *spinal cord.* The spinal cord extends down the back; it is encased in vertebrae. (See also page 503.)

Reproductive System The oval *testes* of the male bird lie in its back above the kidneys. Small tubes, the *vas deferentia,* lead from the testes to openings in the cloaca. In some birds these are enlarged at the lower ends to form sacs called *seminal vesicles.* Sperms travel from the testes through the vas deferentia. They are stored in the seminal vesicles until mating takes place. During mating, sperms are transferred from the cloaca of the male to the cloaca of the female bird.

In most birds, the female reproductive system is greatly reduced. There is only a single left *ovary.* All of the eggs develop in this one ovary. A long coiled oviduct leads from this ovary to the cloaca. **The disappearance of the right ovary and oviduct early in life decreases the weight of the bird. Again this is an adaptation for flight.**

An egg is made up of a *yolk,* a *nucleus,* and *cytoplasm.* The **yolk** stores food. As the egg matures, the yolk increases in size and pushes the nucleus and the cytoplasm to the egg's surface. When the yolk is full-sized, the egg cell breaks loose from the ovary. It is moved into the upper end of the oviduct by waving cilia. After mating, sperm travels up the oviduct from the cloaca. Fertilization takes place at the upper end of the oviduct. Fertilization occurs before any more egg structures form around the egg cell.

Once fertilized, the egg begins a journey down the oviduct. It is surrounded by layers of **albumen.** Albumen is the egg white. The egg cell hangs in the albumen by strands of **chalaza.** The chalaza extends into the albumen toward the ends of the egg. Soon, a **shell membrane** forms around the albumen. Finally, these membranes are surrounded by the *shell.* The shell is secreted by *lime-producing glands* in the lower part of the oviduct. The egg is laid soon after the shell forms, usually about 40 hours after the egg is fertilized.**The only living part of an egg is the egg cell.** This egg cell gradually develops into the young bird. The rest of the egg nourishes and protects the developing embryo. Both the albumen and the yolk are stored food. The albumen is mostly protein, while the yolk is protein and lipid. The shell and shell membranes serve as protection against injury and water loss. However, these must be porous enough to admit air for respiration. Respiration supplies energy for

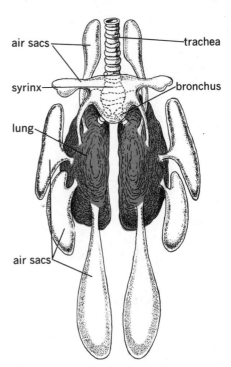

37-11 | The respiratory system of a bird. The air sacs also extend into cavities of larger bones such as the humerus.

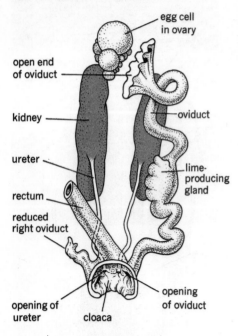

37-12 | The reproductive system of a hen. Note the immature eggs in the ovary.

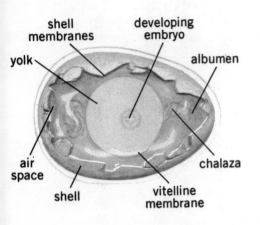

37-13 | A chicken egg; fertile, newly laid.

growth and survival during incubation. However, the pores are large enough to let in bacteria. This is why eggs may rot during warm weather. Fertilization of the egg cell is not necessary for the formation and laying of the eggs.

The Embryo's Incubation and Development

Development of the embryo begins soon after fertilization. It continues after the egg is laid only if the egg is *incubated,* or kept warm. The female usually sits on the eggs. In some species her mate shares in this responsibility. The egg incubation temperature of most birds is about 38°C (100.4°F). In addition to providing body warmth, the nesting bird turns the eggs with her beak at intervals. The time of incubation varies. In smaller birds, it may be 13 to 15 days. It may be as long as 40 to 50 days in larger birds. The chicken's egg is incubated for 21 days; duck eggs require 28 days.

Once the egg is fertilized, cell division begins in the nucleus. Soon a plate of cells forms on the surface of the yolk. This embryonic bird grows gradually larger. It starts to develop various organs. As growth continues, a membrane grows out of the embryo's digestive tract. This membrane surrounds the yolk. It is called the *yolk sac.* The yolk sac contains a network of blood vessels, and it produces digestive enzymes. These enzymes transform the food in the yolk into a soluble form. This food is carried through the blood vessels of the yolk sac to the growing embryo. As the embryo gets larger, the yolk gets smaller. By hatching time, the yolk is entirely absorbed.

As with the reptiles, another membrane grows from the embryo's body wall and encloses the embryo. This is the *amnion.* It fills with amniotic fluid, which surrounds the embryo.

A third membrane, the *allantois,* grows from the embryonic digestive tract. This forms a saclike, vascular organ. The allantois functions in respiration. It also receives waste products from the embryo. The allantois comes in contact with the *chorion.* The chorion is another embryonic membrane. It lies against the double shell membrane. **Thus, the development of the bird is like that of the reptile.** In fact, it has been said that "the reptiles invented the amniotic egg and the birds inherited it."

When the embryo is fully developed, hatching begins. The baby bird has a sharp structure on the tip of its bill called the *egg tooth.* The egg tooth is used to cut through the shell. The baby bird pecks a small hole in the shell. The hole is enlarged and finally cuts the shell nearly in two. The young bird pushes the halves of the shell apart and works its way out. The egg tooth is lost a few days after hatching.

37–14 | Stages in the development of a chicken.
*(Oxford Scientific Films, © Animals Animals; d,
e, h: Allan Roberts)*

Egg and Parental Care in Birds   Birds of different species lay different numbers of eggs. The young of different species are developed to different degrees when they hatch. Therefore, **the type of parental care given a young bird differs for different species.**

Precocial birds, including ducks, geese, quail, grouse, turkeys, and other fowl, lay between 10 and 20 eggs. Precocial birds, except the wood duck, nest on or near the ground. Incubation does not begin until the last egg is laid. Their incubation period is longer than that of most smaller birds, but the young are almost fully developed when they hatch. They all hatch within a few hours of one another. They soon are able to leave their nests. At this stage they can already follow their parents and feed themselves. The young birds often cluster under the wings of the mother for warmth and protection.

Altricial birds include robins, thrushes, sparrows, and warblers. They usually lay fewer than six eggs. Again, incubation begins only when the last egg is laid. However, their incubation period is shorter—usually less than two weeks. The young birds hatch at about the same time, but they are weak, helpless, and nearly featherless. Therefore, they are kept warm and fed in the nest. They remain in the nest until they are feathered and ready to fly. This means that either one or both parents are constantly busy with these tasks. However, all this attention increases the chances of the young birds' survival. This protection helps to insure the survival of the smaller number of young.

Most birds defend their eggs and their young when they are threatened. They use many different methods. Many birds that nest on the ground sit on the nest, trying to conceal it when another animal approaches. But the ground-nesting killdeer bird has a different method. It tries to lure the intruder away from its nest. The killdeer bird slowly moves away from the nest while pretending to have a broken wing. Even birds that are normally shy become brave when they are defending their offspring. Many will swoop down on an intruder, trying to divert its attention from the nest. At the other extreme is the cowbird. The cowbird lays its eggs in the nests of other birds. It then depends on the "foster parents" to incubate the eggs.

37–15 | Which of the above are altricial and which are precocial? *(top: C. Lockwood, © Animals Animals; bottom: David C. Fritts, © Animals Animals)*

Type of Life	terrestrial
Integumentary System	feathers
Skeletal System	bones and cartilage long bones hollow as an adaptation for flight; pectoral girdle modified into wings
Digestive System	same as reptiles except: crop, proventriculus, gizzard. Rectum ends in cloaca.
Respiratory System	lungs with air sacs, an adaptation for flight
Circulatory System	4-chambered heart, 2 atria, 2 ventricles
Excretory System	kidneys; *no* urinary bladder
Nervous System	cerebrum enlarged in comparison to reptiles; olfactory lobes reduced
Reproductive System	females with only one ovary internal fertilization
Development	external development oviparous

Biologically Speaking

follicle	syrinx	incubate
quill	yolk	yolk sac
molting	albumen	egg tooth
crop	chalaza	precocial
air sac	shell membrane	altricial

Questions for Review

1. What characteristics of modern birds show evidence of a reptile ancestry?
2. List eight characteristics that distinguish birds from other vertebrates.
3. Name the different kinds of feathers forming a bird's plumage.
4. Rate the following senses of a bird as good or poor: smell, taste, sight, and hearing.
5. Why is a flexible neck important to a bird?

6. Of what importance is the bird's greatly enlarged sternum?
7. List the organs of the alimentary canal in the order in which food passes through them.
8. What is the function of the air sacs extending from the lungs of the birds?
9. What advancement can be seen in the structure of the bird heart?
10. Why is the excretion of uric acid rather than urine considered an adaptation for flight?
11. Describe the embryonic membranes of a bird egg.
12. Distinguish precocial from atricial birds.
13. Describe how the wing is used in flight.

Applying Concepts

1. Discuss the structural characteristics of birds that are adaptations for flight.
2. What structural advances are associated with warm-bloodedness in birds?
3. Explain the limited distribution of flightless birds.
4. In terms of what you learned about mutation, variation, and survival, relate the various forms of beaks and feet to the diet of birds.

The Mammals

A **LIST** the characteristics of mammals.

B **DESCRIBE** the various types of mammals, both past and present.

C **LIST** several structural adaptations of mammals.

D **DESCRIBE** the development of the circulatory, respiratory, and nervous systems of mammals.

E **DESCRIBE** reproduction and parental care of mammals.

38–1 | The mammary glands give mammals their class name. *(Jen and Des Bartlett, Bruce Coleman)*

Rise of Mammals

The houses, roads, towns, and cities that are accepted as a normal environment are the effects of recent events. Less than 400 years ago North America was wilderness. In the preceding chapters great spans of time have been discussed. Changes were slow enough that hundreds of millions of years could be identified by the fossil remains of the kinds of animals that dominated the earth during that time. The Age of Mammals has now lasted 70 million years. The vast changes in North America during the past 400 years have been caused by just one of those dominant mammals, *Homo sapiens*, the human.

    The Age of Reptiles, the Mesozoic Era, came to an end when great mountain-forming forces changed the surface of the earth. The Rocky Mountains were formed. Once again land and climate changed. Climatic zones evolved. Warm, tropical lands began to have seasonally cold periods. What was humid swamp became rolling hills and open, grassy plains. Many animals, including dinosaurs, perished. Among those animals that survived, multiplied, and flourished were the mammals. The climate and land

sapiens = wise

499

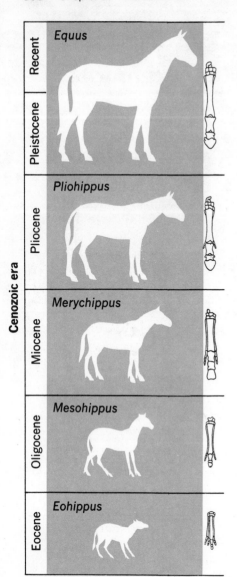

Cenozoic era

Recent	*Equus*
Pleistocene	
Pliocene	*Pliohippus*
Miocene	*Merychippus*
Oligocene	*Mesohippus*
Eocene	*Eohippus*

38–2 | Evolution of the horse. Our knowledge of the history of horses is based on fossil records. *Eohippus,* or "dawn horse," is believed to have developed from an ancestor with five toes on each foot.

favored them. We call the present Age of Mammals the Cenozoic Era.

How Mammals Evolved

Some mammals already were present when dinosaurs walked the earth. Fossils indicate that these mammals most likely evolved from some mammallike reptile group. They were not a dominant group, however, until their rapid spread and their gradual evolution during the Cenozoic Era.

The evolution of the horse is a good example of how an animal evolves. Its history is well documented by fossil evidence. During the earliest period of the Cenozoic Era the ancient horse, called *Eohippus*, had four toes and was about the size of a fox terrier. During the Oligocene epoch, beginning about 35 million years ago, the horse developed into a three-toed mammal. It grew to the size of a sheep. During the following Miocene and Pliocene epochs, horses grew to almost the size they are today. At the end of these epochs, about one million years ago, they still had three toes on each foot. They could run rapidly over the grasslands on which they grazed. It is most probable that these variations allowed horses to be selected by environmental changes. Those horses that had the favorable adaptation survived and reproduced. Horses developed a single-toed foot during the following early Pleistocene epoch, or Ice Age. Although the horse first developed in North America, it became extinct there several thousand years ago. By that time the horse had migrated to Asia, Africa, and Europe. Early Spanish explorers were the first to bring horses back to North America.

Many other early mammals have become extinct. These include the woolly rhinoceros, the ancient camel without a hump, the straight-horned bison, and the large wild pig. Flesh-eating mammals that are now extinct include the great bear dogs, the giant short-faced bears, and the sabertooth tigers. During the million years of the Ice Age, mastodons and mammoths migrated to Africa from North America, Europe, and Asia. These early elephants have long been extinct, but their descendants are still found in Asia and Africa.

The Characteristics of Mammals

There are over 4,000 different species of mammals. They vary in size from a tiny mouselike shrew to the giant whale. Animals of the class *Mammalia* have the following general characteristics:

- Body covered with hair.
- Viviparous; young nourished during development in the uterus of the mother.
- Young nourished after birth with milk secreted by the **mammary glands** of the mother. This is the characteristic for which the class is named.
- Lung-breathing throughout life.
- A **diaphragm** (breathing muscle) separating the thoracic (chest) cavity and abdominal cavity.
- Heart is four-chambered, with left aortic arch only.
- Warm-blooded.
- Seven cervical (neck) vertebrae in most species.
- Two pairs of limbs for locomotion in most species (pelvic and pectoral girdles).
- Cerebrum and cerebellum of brain highly developed.

woolly mammoth

Organ Systems

The rate at which the body respires, the heart beat rate, and the rate of chemical processes are among the factors that determine *metabolic rate*. Thermoregulation, ability to regulate body temperature, requires a higher rate of metabolism. Fish, amphibians, and reptiles are cold-blooded. Birds and mammals are warm-blooded, which means they can maintain a constant body temperature. A higher rate of metabolism produces more heat, which maintains the body temperature. The mammalian heart is more efficient, helping to maintain the higher rate of metabolism.

woolly rhinoceros

Mammals have the most highly developed organ system. Notably they have the most complex nervous system in regard to development of parts of the brain that govern intelligence. Since the human organ systems will be discussed in detail in the next unit, only those systems that are basically different than other vertebrates will be discussed here.

saber-toothed cat

38–3 | Some mammals of the Pliocene epoch that have become extinct as conditions changed.

The Heart of a Mammal The heart of a mammal is the most highly advanced and complex of all animal hearts. A brief review of vertebrate heart structure will show its increasing complexity as animals adapted to new environments. The heart of each animal is well adapted to the life the animal leads.

Recall the heart of a fish. It is strong enough to force blood through the circulatory system. One ventricle gives enough pressure to pump blood from the body to the gills and then through the vessels of the body. The one ventricle provides the circulation a fish needs to pump blood from the body. The metabolic rate of a fish is much below that of higher vertebrates, and it varies with water temperature.

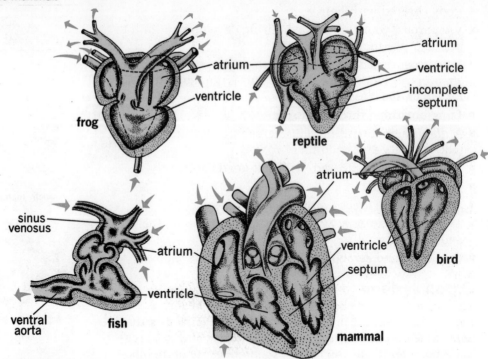

38–4 | Heart structures characteristic of the vertebrate classes. Trace the increasing complexity and number of chambers, from the two-chambered heart of the fish to the human four-chambered heart.

The life of the amphibian presents environmental problems not faced by the fish. Many amphibians, such as frogs, carry on respiration through their skin as well as through their lungs. The single ventricle receives blood from both atria. The absence of a partition separating the ventricle into two chambers is related to skin respiration. The single ventricle enables blood to bypass functionless lungs when the amphibian is under water.

The reptile does not have skin respiration. Its ventricle is partially divided into two chambers by a *septum*, or wall. This arrangement enables blood to be pumped continually to the body and lungs.

The warm-blooded birds and mammals lead a far more active life than the cold-blooded reptiles. The structure of the heart is an adaptation for higher oxygen needs. **The mammalian heart, like that of a bird, prevents mixing of unoxygenated and oxygenated blood.** The mammalian heart has a complete septum forming two separate ventricles. Thus it is really a double pump. The right side receives the deoxygenated blood from the body and pumps it to the lungs. The left side receives oxygenated blood from the lungs and forces it throughout the entire body.

The Mammalian Nervous System The development of the mammalian brain is a remarkable adaptation. Intelligence enabled humans to grow their own crops, invent machines, develop language and art, and to create civilization.

The part of the brain that makes humans intelligent is the *cerebrum.* When we compare the brains in various vertebrates, the relative size of the cerebrum increases in the more complex animals. The cerebrum, consisting of two cerebral hemispheres, is relatively small in the fish. It becomes more prominent in the amphibian and reptile. The cerebrum is largest in the bird and mammal.

In the fish and amphibian the cerebrum is concerned mostly with the sense of detecting chemicals in the environment. It receives nerve impulses from the olfactory lobes. These lobes in turn receive nerve impulses from receptors in the nasal cavities.

In reptiles, birds, and mammals the cerebrum is enlarged and more complex. It is an area that analyzes various senses, including smell. With analysis, the animal can respond. In mammals the cerebrum has reached its highest level of development. It has become a complex organ of response, learning, and memory.

The *cerebellum* is a part of the brain that coordinates muscle movement. The amphibian has a relatively small cerebellum. The bird is a very active, complex animal; it has a large cerebellum. In the mammal, the cerebellum is very well developed. You have only to watch the muscular

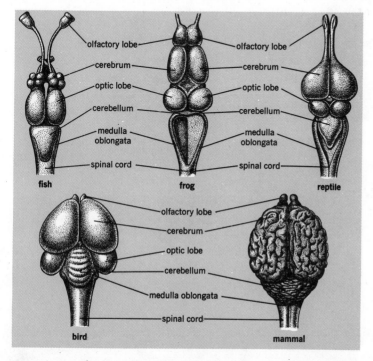

38–5 | Compare the size of the cerebrum in the mammalian brain with that of the brains characteristic of the other vertebrate classes.

Monotremata
(duckbilled platypus)

Marsupialia
(koala bear)

Insectivora
(mole)

Chiroptera
(bat)

Edentata
(armadillo)

Rodentia
(beaver)

Lagomorpha
(rabbit)

Cetacea
(whale)

38–6 | Examples of some of the better-known orders of mammals.

Sirenia
(sea cow)

Proboscidea
(elephant)

Carnivora
(mountain lion)

Perissodactyla
(horse)

Artiodactyla
(bison)

Primates
(monkey)

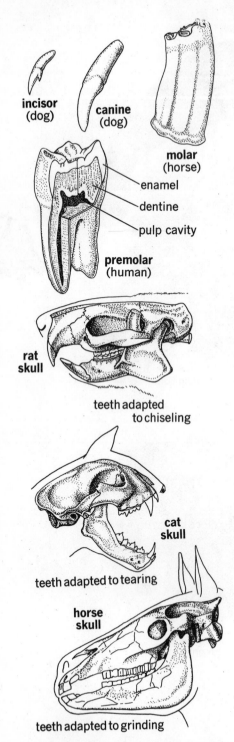

incisor
(dog)

canine
(dog)

molar
(horse)

enamel

dentine

pulp cavity

premolar
(human)

rat
skull

teeth adapted
to chiseling

cat
skull

teeth adapted to tearing

horse
skull

teeth adapted to grinding

38–7 | Four types of mammalian teeth. Notice how these types are adapted for different functions in the rat, cat, and horse.

coordination of an Olympic gymnast to appreciate the finely tuned functions of the human cerebellum.

The short *medulla oblongata* controls vital body processes. It lies below the cerebrum and extends to the spinal cord. Cranial nerves extend from the brain to the sense organs and other head structures. The spinal nerves extend from the spinal cord to and from all body regions.

Mammalian Reproduction and Parental Care As vertebrates become more complex, there generally has been an increase in the efficiency of reproduction. There is also a decrease in the number of young. In fish, fertilization is external. The male swims over the eggs and discharges milt over them. This is inefficient. Many eggs are never fertilized, and many are eaten before they hatch. In most fishes, there is little or no parental care. Fish produce a huge number of eggs.

Amphibians lay a smaller number of eggs. These are fertilized directly as they are laid. This insures fertilization and the development of a greater proportion of the eggs. However, like fish, amphibians must lay their eggs in water, because the eggs have no protection against drying out.

Reptiles were the first vertebrates to lay eggs on land. This requires internal fertilization. It also requires the enclosure of the egg in a protective shell. Similar eggs are produced by birds. With this greater protection, reptiles and birds need not produce as many eggs to insure survival of the young. Parental care, especially in birds, also reduces the loss of many young.

Like reptiles and birds, mammals have internal fertilization. However, the eggs are kept and protected within the body of the female. Here they develop until birth. Fewer eggs are produced and parental care is greater than in less complex animals. After birth all young mammals depend upon their mothers' milk for nutrition. An adaptation to parental care is a small number of offspring. Mice, rabbits, and other small mammals mature rapidly. Several litters of at least 10 babies per litter are born each season. This number is not great compared to the eggs produced by a fish or amphibian. Black bears have only one or two cubs during the winter, and the mother takes care of the cubs for a long while.

The Orders of Mammals

An elephant, a horse, a bat, and a beaver all have the characteristics discussed previously. These animals also differ in many ways. Because there is a wide variety of structural differences, mammals are classified in 18 different orders. Structural differences show how these animals are adapted to various ways of life.

For example, some are classified according to their teeth. Mammalian teeth differ in number and shape, depending on the species and the kind of food that species eats. The *incisor* teeth of lions, for example, are adapted for tearing flesh. *Premolars* and *molars* are adapted for grinding.

Foot structure also varies among mammals. The entire soles of the feet of some mammals rest on the ground. The human has such a foot. Many mammals walk on their toes with the heel raised. These include cats and dogs. The horse walks on one toe with the entire foot raised.

The fingers and toes of mammals also vary. Some toes and fingers have *nails*, such as those of the human. Many mammals, such as cats and dogs, have *claws*. Still others, such as the horse, cow, and deer, have hooves.

Differences in the way mammalian offspring develop also are used to classify mammals. *Monotremes*, or egg-laying mammals, and *marsupials*, or pouched mammals, form two different lines of mammalian development. All other mammals are *placental* mammals.

The Monotremes: Egg-Laying Mammals

The order *Monotremata* is made up of the most primitive mammals. Like their reptilian ancestors, monotremes lay eggs, have a cloaca into which the intestine and urogenital system empty, and lack external ears.

The *duckbilled platypus* and the *spiny anteater* are the only monotremes still in existence. They live in remote areas of Australia and New Guinea. Here they were isolated

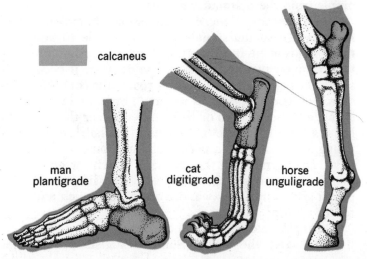

calcaneus

man
plantigrade

cat
digitigrade

horse
unguligrade

38-8 | Mammalian foot modification. Note the relationship of the calcaneous in each foot.

from large predators. If it were not for this isolation, monotremes may have become extinct ages ago. The platypus is about 40 centimeters (16 inches) long. It has waterproof fur, a ducklike bill, and webbed feet. It burrows into stream banks and builds grass-filled nests. The platypus uses its beak to probe for worms and grubs in the mud on the stream beds. The platypus usually lays two or three eggs. The eggs are kept in the body of the female for some time before they are laid in the nest. After laying the eggs, the mother curls herself around them to incubate them. After hatching, the young are nourished on milk secreted by a type of sweat gland. These sweat glands are similar to mammary glands of other mammals. The platypus has no nipples. Instead of suckling, the babies lick milk from their mother's body hair.

Spiny anteaters are well protected by a coat of sharp spines. Their long toothless jaws form a snout well adapted for probing into ant hills. Spiny anteaters lay two eggs at a time. These eggs are incubated in a *brood pouch*. This pouch is on the lower side of the mother. The eggs remain in the pouch for several weeks before hatching.

The Marsupials: Pouched Mammals

Marsupialia is another order of primitive mammals. They are represented by a relatively small number of species. **Marsupials differ from other mammals in the way they care for their young.** The marsupial egg does not contain enough yolk to feed the fetus for the entire period of its development. Thus, marsupials are born before their development is complete. After they are born, the young use their front legs to pull themselves into the mother's pouch. The pouch contains mammary glands. Each baby attaches to a nipple with its mouth. Milk is pumped through the nipple from the mammary glands.

The opossum is the only marsupial found in North America. These marsupials have been able to adapt to many kinds of environments, including suburban areas. It is a common mammal, but you seldom see it because it sleeps during the day. At night it roams the countryside in search of food. Oppossums eat small birds and mammals, eggs, and insects. Two or three times a year the opossum bears a litter of from 6 to 20 young. The hairless, helpless young are born after a period of development of only 13 days. They remain in the mother's pouch for about two months. The young opossums adjust to life outside the pouch gradually. They wander out of the pouch and then return to it for a while.

During the early epochs of the Cenozoic era, marsupials lived all over the world. Some biologists believe that

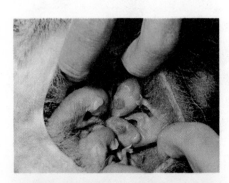

38-9 | Oppossums. After birth, the helpless young find their way into the mother's pouch where they continue to develop. Later, they are carried on her back. *(Allan Roberts)*

almost every placental mammal had a marsupial counterpart. Some were bearlike, while others resembled dogs. One marsupial of the Pliocene epoch was a large flesh-eater that bore a striking resemblance to the saber-toothed cat. Other marsupials resembled modern moles, mice, and groundhogs. Marsupials and placentals lived in similar areas and ate the same foods. Because placentals were better adapted, they gradually became more numerous. Today, marsupials abound only in those few places that were not accessible to placental mammals. Marsupials are found mostly in Australia and New Guinea.

In Australia, the *kangaroos* and the *wallabies* live in the grasslands. They resemble the deer and antelope in head structure and grazing habits. The *koala bear* lives in the forests of Australia. It feeds only on the leaves of the eucalyptus tree. Other modern marsupials of Australia include the *wombat* and the *phalanger*. On the island of Tasmania, south of Australia, two flesh-eating marsupials are found. The *Tasmanian devil* resembles a raccoon. The *Tasmanian wolf* resembles a wild dog.

Placental Mammals: The Most Successful Mammals

About 95 percent of the mammals alive today are *placental mammals*. These differ from monotremes and marsupials in the way they nourish the young before birth. Early in its development, the embryo of a placental mammal becomes embedded in the wall of the uterus. Then the embryonic membranes begin to develop. The chorion grows from the embryo. It spreads over the wall of the uterus. The chorion plus nearby uterine tissue make up the **placenta. The placenta receives oxygen and nutrients from the blood of the mother. These are then transferred to the blood of the fetus** (the developing offspring). Embryonic development in placental mammals will be discussed more fully in Chapter 47.

Placental mammals have an advantage over marsupials. The newly born of placental mammals are more developed than those of marsupials. This is because of a longer period of development within the mother. Even the most helpless newborn placental mammals, for example, mice, rabbits, kittens, and puppies, are far more advanced than newborn marsupials. Within a week or two these mammals are ready to move about with their parents. Hooved mammals, including cows, horses, deer, sheep, and pigs, are born in a still more advanced condition. These mammals are able to walk within a few hours after birth. The whale is even more advanced; a newborn whale is able to swim immediately at birth.

38-10 | A shrew's long nose aids in rooting out worms. (© Animals Animals, Stouffer Productions Ltd.)

The period of development in the uterus is called the **gestation period.** The length of gestation, or *pregnancy*, varies in placental mammals. Generally, the longer the gestation period, the more advanced and larger the newborn mammal is at birth.

Placental mammals have adapted to a wide variety of environments. These adaptations are expressed in their physical development and their life style. Let's look now at some of the different placental mammals.

Insect-Eating Mammals Members of the order *Insectivora* were probably the first placental mammals. All of today's higher mammals probably developed from this order. These are represented today by *shrews* and *moles*. They never became very large. They have small brains and primitive teeth. The shrew is the smallest of all mammals. It looks like both a mole and a mouse. It has a high metabolic rate and a ravenous appetite. It eats a lot of insects, mice, and even other shrews. Shrews are hard to find because they burrow in the grass and hide under leaves. Moles are well adapted to underground life. They have strong claws for digging. Their small eyes are covered with flaps of skin. Their long noses are good at rooting out grubs and worms.

Flying Mammals **Bats are the only mammals that have developed structures for flight.** Most bats eat insects, but they are classified in a different order from insectivores. There are more than 600 kinds of bats in the order *Chiroptera*. Bats' wings are formed by the lengthened bones of the last four fingers and a membrane that extends between them. The thumb is free of the wing and is used for grasping. Bats fly during twilight hours and at night when there are many insects in the air. They spend the days hanging in caves or hollow trees. Most are helpless on the ground because of their weak hind legs and their long wings. Bats are able to find their way in the dark because of their highly developed hearing. In fact, they usually find their way by listening to the bouncing echoes of their own squeaks.

Vampire bats live in tropical America. They live on the blood of other mammals, including horses and cattle. The front teeth of the vampire bat cut the skin and the bat laps up the oozing blood.

Gnawing Mammals The order *Rodentia* outnumbers all other orders of mammals combined. They are found in almost every area of the world. Most are terrestrial, tree-living, or burrowing. The *beaver* and the *muskrat* live a semiaquatic life. The flying squirrel can even glide from tree to tree. Rats and mice are the most common rodents.

Some others are squirrels, woodchucks, prairie dogs, chip-munks, and gophers. The beaver is the largest North American rodent.

Why have rodents been successful? Most of them are small. This allows them to live in environments not suitable to larger animals. They have a rapid rate of reproduction. There is very little specialization in the body build. All have strong, chisel-shaped teeth called *incisors*. The front edge of the incisors is harder than the back edge, causing the biting surface to wear at an angle. So the sharp edges become even sharper with use. The forelimbs of rodents are adapted for running, climbing, and getting food.

Rodentlike Mammals Like rodents, the *Lagomorphs*, rabbits, hares, and pikas have sharp, chisellike teeth. The main difference between animals of this order and rodents is that the lagomorphs have four upper incisors instead of two. Two of these teeth are very small and are set behind the two larger ones in front. The animals grind plants with a sideways motion of the lower jaw.

lagos = hare
morph = shape

The *cottontail rabbit* is the most widely hunted mammal of the United States. Even though they are preyed upon by people, predatory birds, and other animals, these rabbits have been able to hold their own in most localities. The *jack rabbit* is common in the broad expanses of the western prairies and plains. It reaches a length of nearly 75 centimeters (30 inches) and has characteristic long ears and large, powerful hind legs. Both its sight and hearing are especially keen, enabling it to escape from its enemies.

Toothless Mammals The mammals of the order *Edentata* are mostly toothless. The order is composed of armadillos, sloths, and great anteaters. They have small brains. Some have nine cervical vertebrae instead of the usual seven found in mammals. They have large claws. Armadillos have survived since the Tertiary period probably because of their protective armor. They eat bugs, dead flesh, bird eggs, grubs, birds, and small animals. Various species live in the southwestern United States, Mexico, and South America. The North American armadillo hides in a burrow during the day and digs for food at night.

e = without
dens = tooth

Tree sloths live in the jungles of Central and South America. They spend most of their time hanging upside down from tree branches. They hang by their long limbs with two or three hooked claws. They eat leaves from the trees. The hair of some sloth species is green from the algae that live in it.

Anteaters probably evolved from the same ancestors as tree sloths. Anteater skulls are long, ending in thin, long snouts. Inside the snout is a sticky tongue that is used to

38-11 | What are the differences between this flying mammal and birds? *(Hans Pfletschinger,© Peter Arnold)*

catch termites. The feet have large, curved claws for digging up termite nests. These claws make walking and running difficult. Anteaters walk mostly on the knuckles of their front feet.

Aquatic Mammals The order *Cetacea* includes whales, dolphins, and porpoises. They probably evolved from some land mammal during the Tertiary period. They developed adaptations to life in the ocean. They have torpedo-shaped bodies, and fishlike tails and flippers. They breathe air. They are able to hold their breath for a long time. The young of these animals can swim at birth. Just after birth the mother pushes them to the surface for their first breaths of air.

Dolphins are usually under 4.2 meters (14 feet) long. They are found in seas throughout the world. They are very intelligent. Scientists are trying to figure out how these marine mammals communicate. Porpoises are from a different family than dolphins. They are usually smaller than dolphins and have a blunt rounded head. They travel in herds and catch fish with their toothlined jaws.

Sirenia is another order of aquatic mammal. This order includes the *sea cow*, or manatee. They have blunt, wrinkled faces covered with coarse hair. The body is streamlined and the hind limbs are lacking. The forelimbs are modified to form flippers. They are found along the Atlantic coast of Africa, the Gulf of Mexico, and the east coast of South America. They inhabit rivers where they feed on aquatic plants.

Trunk-Nosed Mammals There are only two species of elephants still alive to represent the order *Proboscidea*. During glacial and preglacial times there were over 30 species of elephantlike mammals. They lived in Asia, Europe, Africa, and North America. No one knows why most of these elephants became extinct.

Elephants are the largest land dwellers alive today. They can weigh more than six metric tons (6.6 tons). The *Asiatic elephant* is the one you usually see in the circus. It is used as a beast of burden in many parts of the world. The *African elephant* is taller and more slender with larger ears. African elephants are not as easily domesticated as their Asian relatives.

Flesh-Eating Mammals Mammals of the order *Carnivora* probably evolved from insectivores during the Tertiary period. Carnivores are flesh-eating mammals. They all have strong jaws and enlarged canine teeth. All of their major characteristics help them prey on other animals. Carnivores have intelligence, keen sight and smell, strong

Facts & Figures

The *blue whale* is the largest animal alive today. It may be the largest animal that ever lived. Blue whales may grow longer than 30 meters (99 feet) and may weigh as much as 130 metric tons (143 tons).

carni = flesh
ivore = voracious eater

bodies, and limbs with claws.

There are many families of carnivores, most of which are probably familiar to you. There are several members of the dog and cat families. The *mountain lion* was found over most of North America at one time. However, civilization has driven it to the remote regions of the southwest. The chief harm it does is the killing of livestock, especially young horses. Both the *bay lynx* (links), or bobcat, and the *Canadian lynx* live in deep forests and seldom are seen. The *jaguars* of South America, the *lions* of Africa, and the *tigers* of Asia are all members of the cat family.

The *gray wolf*, or timber wolf, is most frequently found in the northern forests. It may be dangerous to humans during the winter, when it runs in packs. The *coyote* (KY-ote), a prairie wolf, has been more successful than its larger cousin in surviving the effects of civilization. It is still abundant on the western plains. However, in some regions, too many have been destroyed and their natural prey, including rodents and jack rabbits, have become pests. Therefore, it has been necessary to import coyotes into these regions.

The *raccoon* has a black mask and long, ringed tail. Young raccoons have sometimes been captured and kept as pets. The raccoon prefers fish and clams as its food, but it will eat other things if these are unavailable. It has a habit of "washing" its food before eating. This is probably to moisten the food rather than to clean it.

The weasel family includes some of the most bloodthirsty carnivores. It also includes some of the most valuable fur-bearing mammals. The *mink* especially is prized for its fur. These long-bodied, short-legged animals live along streams. The *ermine* is an Arctic weasel that grows a coat of white fur (except for a black-tipped tail) in winter. It is brown in summer.

The *bears* were the last carnivores to evolve. They have changed little since Pleistocene times more than 150,000 years ago. Bears have teeth that are specialized for eating plant substances as well as meat.

Sea lions, *walruses*, and *seals* are waterliving carnivores. Their bodies are streamlined for swimming. They do not have the finlike appendages of whales. They have webbed feet. The front feet serve for balance and stability, and the rear feet provide an efficient means of propulsion. Walruses probably evolved from sea-lion ancestors. Their canine teeth have become long tusks. They have developed broad molars to facilitate crushing and grinding the oysters and other mollusks on which they feed.

Hoofed Mammals People have depended on hoofed mammals since prehistoric times. Hoofed mammals are

38–12 | Manatees were sometimes called mermaids by sailors, probably because manatees looked like they might be mermaids from a distance. *(Jeff Foott, Bruce Coleman)*

38-13 | Once raccoons only lived in the wild. Lately they have been invading the suburbs where they live on garbage. *(Charles E. Summers, Jr. AMWEST)*

ungula = hoof

called **ungulates.** We use the *ungulates* as beasts of burden and as food. The ungulates include goats, horses, camels, oxen, llamas, cows, pigs, sheep, deer, elk, caribou, moose, and antelopes. In all, there are about 16 families.

Ungulates are all herbivores, or plant eaters. Their teeth are adapted to cropping and grinding grasses or browsing on leafy trees and bushes. Some of the hoofed animals have long limbs and feet that help them run rapidly over hard ground. They walk on the tips of their toes. Hooves are modified toenails. They help absorb the shock of running.

Some ungulates, including cows, sheep, and antelopes, are called **ruminants.** They have specialized digestive systems. Their stomachs have four chambers. While grazing, they eat large amounts of food. They store it in the first stomach division, the *rumen.* The fluid in the rumen contains large populations of bacteria and other microorganisms. These single-celled organisms produce digestive enzymes which break down the plant cellulose. Some products of this digestion are absorbed by the single-celled organisms, but most are absorbed by the ruminant. These cellulose-digesting bacteria are necessary since vertebrates do not produce cellulose-digesting enzymes.

Later the partially digested vegetation is forced back into the mouth. It is then chewed as a cud. After it is thoroughly chewed, it is swallowed and passes through the other three chambers of the stomach. Only the last chamber contains glands that secrete digestive enzymes as our stomachs do. The *bison, goat, camel, llama, giraffe, deer, elk, caribou*, and *moose* are all ruminants. In nonruminants, such as horses, rabbits, and rodents, bacteria also aid in cellulose digestion. This digestion, however, takes place in a blind-ended digestive tube called the *caecum*.

Primates: Tree-Dwelling Mammals The order of **primates includes** those animals that have the best-developed brains. Most of the species are tree-dwelling. They include lemurs, tarsiers, monkeys, apes, and humans.

Most species of primates have brains so well developed that the cerebral hemispheres cover other parts of the brain. As a group they generally have five *digits* (fingers or toes) on each limb, and usually have nails rather than claws.

The eyes of most primates are arranged in a forward position on a flattened face. Both eyes can then be focused on a single point. This gives these animals three-dimensional, or stereoscopic, vision. Can you guess why such vision might be an advantage for life in trees? If you ever watch monkeys in a zoo you will seldom see one miss a branch or a bar when swinging from one place to another.

Lemurs and *tarsiers* are of interest because they represent the most primitive, least developed primates. The lemur looks more like a squirrel than a primate. It has a long tail and a long snout or muzzle. Its eyes are more forward than a squirrel's or a rabbit's. Also, except for a claw on their second toe, lemurs have flat nails rather than claws. They are tree dwellers and are primarily found in Madagascar.

The tarsier of southeast Asia is a monkeylike animal. Its face has flat features similar to those of advanced primates. The two large eyes give this animal excellent stereoscopic vision. Tarsiers also have independently movable fingers and toes. Each digit ends in a pad that aids in gripping branches.

Monkeys are classified in two groups. These are the *Old World monkeys* of Africa and Asia and the *New World monkeys* of South and Central America. The Old World monkeys do not have prehensile tails. That is, their tails cannot be used for gripping and climbing. They also have cheek pouches for storing food. The New World monkeys use their prehensile tails for climbing and hanging. They have wide noses.

Apes differ from monkeys in that they lack tails and cheek pouches. The apes include *gorillas, orangutans, gibbons*, and *chimpanzees*. Gorillas are essentially land dwellers but usually retreat to trees for sleeping. They lean

38–14 | Tarsier. This animal shows the basic characteristics of the primate. Notice the frontal eyes and the flexible fingers. *(M. P. L. Fogden, Bruce Coleman)*

forward on their knuckles when walking. They can walk erectly only for short distances. The orangutan, as well as the chimpanzee, is at home in trees but spends much time on the ground. The graceful long-armed gibbon spends almost its entire life in trees and is very awkward on land.

The apes and monkeys all have brains with well-developed cerebrums. Almost all types live in groups or colonies that have very complex social structures. Except for humans, they seem to be more capable of learning than any other animals.

Summary

Type of Life	terrestrial water dwelling
Integumentary System	skin hair or fur scales on some (pangolin, beaver tails, etc.)
Digestive System	glottis, esophagus, stomach, duodenum, small intestine, large intestine and rectum (colon); *no* cloaca; ruminants with 3 chambered stomachs
Respiratory System	lungs; diaphragm
Circulatory System	4-chambered heart, 2 atria, 2 ventricles, well-developed septums
Excretory System	kidneys; bladder
Nervous System	cerebrum most highly developed of the vertebrates
Reproductive System	internal fertilization females with glands for suckling young
Development	internal development (except monotremes) viviparous (except monotremes)

Biologically Speaking

mammary gland	placenta
diaphragm	gestation period
cerebrum	ungulate
cerebellum	ruminant
medulla oblongata	primate

1. Name several extinct mammals.
2. List 10 characteristics of mammals that distinguish them from other vertebrates.
3. Describe several characteristics used to classify mammals into different orders.
4. What evidence of reptilian ancestry is shown in the monotremes?
5. Distinguish a marsupial mammal from a placental mammal. Give an example of each.
6. In what way is the order Chiroptera unique among the mammals?
7. Rodents vary greatly in size. What characteristics do they have in common?
8. Why are rabbits placed in a separate order from the rodents?
9. Describe how cetaceans are adapted for life in the water.
10. On what basis might we consider primates the most highly developed mammals?
11. List several structural adaptations of mammals that make them adaptable to diverse environments.
12. Trace the increasing number of heart chambers of vertebrates from fish to mammals.
13. Describe how the mammalian brain is more developed than the brains of other animals.
14. What are the advantage of mammalian reproduction compared to other vertebrates?

1. Discuss several environmental changes during the Cenozoic era that probably favored the survival of mammals and caused the decline of reptiles.
2. Discuss three ways mammalian embryos develop, and explain the supremacy of placental mammals today.
3. Organisms that undergo internal development usually produce and fertilize fewer eggs than do organisms that undergo external development. Explain.

UNIT 6

Activities

1. Collect frog or salamander eggs and place them in a well-aerated aquarium. Use a magnifying glass and examine the eggs every day. Record all changes, and make drawings of those changes. Submit a report of your findings.

2. Visit your local pet shop and list the imported species of reptiles for sale. Then submit a written or oral report on the effects of this trade on reptile populations in foreign countries. Cite at least two references in your report.

3. Build a bird feeder and place it outside a window or in a yard. Use library books to identify the birds that visit the feeder. Carefully observe the feeding behavior around the feeder. Is competition greatest between birds of the same species or between different species? Do the birds actually hurt one another when competing? Give a report on these and other observations.

4. Keep a record of birds observed during the various seasons. Report observed changes in bird populations.

5. How much of human activity relates to the characteristics of mammals, and particularly of primates? For example, do the living habits of humans correspond to those of other primates? What about territorial rights, choosing a mate, courtship, gathering food, creating art, or using tools? Report on which human activities are uniquely human and which are not.

Related Reading

Books

Boorer, Michael, *Mammals of the World*. Grosset and Dunlap, Inc., New York. 1967. Presents a concise survey of evolution, overall structure and classification of mammals.

Burgess, Robert F., *The Sharks*. Doubleday & Co., Inc., Garden City, NY 1970. Relates the history of people's fear of sharks and the myths invented about these fish, and how these fears are gradually being overcome.

Ewer, R. F., *The Carnivores*. Cornell University Press, Ithaca, NY 1973. Selected observations on the systematics, anatomy, behavior, reproduction, and fossil relatives of the carnivores.

Flanagan, Geraldine Lux, *Window into an Egg*. William R. Scott, Inc., New York. 1969. Using excellent photographs, this book probes the day-by-day development of a chicken.

Minton, Sherman A., *Giant Reptiles*. Charles Scribner's Sons, New York. 1973. An informative source on both the factual and mythical areas of reptile evolution and behavior.

Parker, H. W., and A. G. Grandison, *Snakes—A Natural History*. Cornell University Press, 1977. A well-organized guide dealing with snakes, their habits and characteristics.

Riedman, Sarah R., and Elton T. Gustafson, *Home is the Sea for Whales*. Abelard-Schuman, Ltd., New York 1971. An excellent scientifically accurate study of Cetaceans; traces the evolution of the whales.

Robbins, Chandler S., Bertel Bruun, and Herbert S. Zim, *Birds of North America*. Western Publishing Company, New York, 1966. Featuring excellently colored illustrations, this paperback is recommended for bird identification.

Stephen, David, ed., *Dolphins, Seals, and other Sea Mammals*. G. P. Putnam's Sons, New York. 1973. Excellent descriptions and beautiful color photographs of the various sea mammals, with their classifications and maps showing their habitats.

Articles

Bakker, Robert T., "Dinosaur Renaissance," *Scientific American*, April, 1975. This article discussed dinosaurs as being warm-blooded, and the ancestors of birds.

Bertram, Brian C. R., "The Social System of Lions," *Scientific American*, May, 1975. A fascinating account of the organization of the social system of lions, and how the behavior of the lions reflects their adaptation to the environment.

Thomson, Keith S., "Secrets of the Coelacanth," *Natural History*, February, 1973. An interesting study on the natural history of the little-known coelacanth.

Zahl, Paul A., "Shadowy World of Salamanders," *National Geographic*, July, 1972. A close-up look at some of our more interesting salamanders.

Phyla	Ichthyes	Amphibia	Reptilia	Aves	Mammalia
Type of Life	aquatic: fresh water, marine	freshwater, terrestrial	terrestrial, water dwelling	terrestrial	terrestrial, water dwelling
Integumentary System	scales	moist skin	scales; scutes; some with 2-piece shells	feathers	skin; hair or fur; few with scales on their bodies
Skeletal System	Chondrichthyes: cartilage; Osteichthyes: bones; appendages as fins	bones and cartilage	bones and cartilage; snakes without appendages	bones and cartilage; long hollow bones	bones and cartilage; some with appendages as flippers
Digestive System	alimentary canal (intestine not divided into small and large)	alimentary canal (small and large intestine)	alimentary canal; small intestine more coiled (increases absorption area)	alimentary canal with crop, proventriculus, gizzard	alimentary canal with large absorptive area
Respiratory System	gills for gas exchange	moist membranes especially in skin; gills in larval stage; lungs in adult	well-developed lungs	lungs with air sacs	lungs; diaphragm
Circulatory System	2-chambered heart: atrium and ventricle not divided	3-chambered heart: ventricle, right and left atria	3-chambered heart: ventricle with a partial septum	4-chambered heart: 2 atria, 2 ventricles	4-chambered heart
Excretory System	gills; a kidney in most groups	kidneys; urinary bladder	kidneys; urinary bladder	kidneys; no urinary bladder	kidneys; urinary bladder
Nervous System	cerebrum small, olfactory center large	similar to Ichthyes	enlarged cerebrum in comparison to Amphibia	enlarged cerebrum in comparison to Reptilia	cerebrum most highly-developed
Reproductive System	external fertilization; large number of eggs	external fertilization; large number of eggs	internal fertilization; fewer eggs produced	internal fertilization	internal fertilization
Development	oviparous; ovoviviparous	oviparous; metamorphosis	oviparous, a few ovoviviparous and viviparous	oviparous; parents incubate eggs	viviparous (monotremes-oviparous)

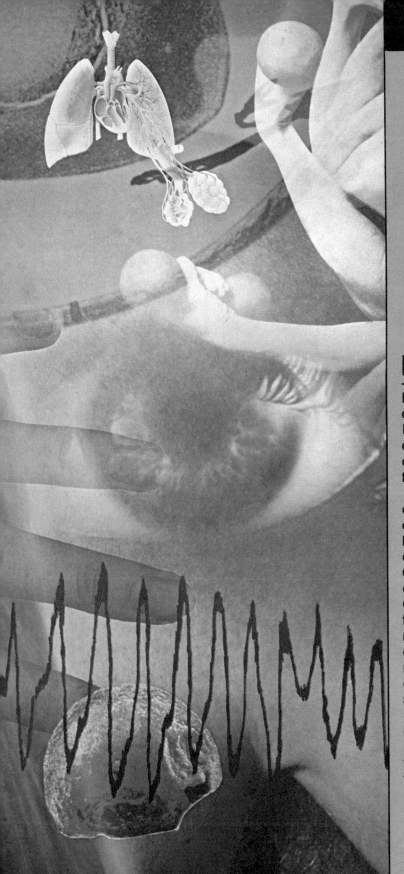

Human Biology

Humans are vertebrates of the class *Mammalia.* Humans are born, grow, reach maturity, decline, and die, as do other animals. What sets humans apart from the rest of the animals?

Perhaps the greatest difference between humans and other animals is that only humans adapt their environments to suit themselves. Other mammals live where they are suited to their environment. Certain characteristics enable us to mold our environments to our needs. These include our highly developed brains, our ability to make and use tools, and our ability to develop a written and spoken language.

In this unit you will learn what makes you human, what you are like structurally, and how you function.

Human History

A **LIST** the characteristics that separate humans from other mammals.

B **EXPLAIN** how fossils are dated.

C **DESCRIBE** some early hominids.

D **DESCRIBE** some of the early forms of the genus *Homo*.

39–1 | Art work of early humans. Cave drawings in France. (Mazomowicz, Monkmeyer Press Photo)

Clues Left from the Past

Geological evidence supports the idea that there have been changes in the earth over the ages. Fossil evidence supports the idea that there have been changes in organisms that live on the earth. The intelligence and curiosity of humans have led many to question our own history. What was life like for prehistoric humans? What were early humans like? There is a special branch of science that deals with these very questions, called **anthropology.**

Anthropologists study all primates and present human cultures in hopes of finding clues to the past. They also gather information from fossils. The fossils may be imprints, preserved remains of humans that once lived, or actual bones. Often bones are broken and only small pieces can be found. Clues from many such pieces can give an idea of what the total picture could have been.

Characteristics of Humans

Anthropologists face an important problem as they study history: What distinguishes humans from other mammals, especially from humanlike apes?

There are physical and cultural traits of humans that make them unique. Physical factors include an upright posture; a larger brain size and greater anatomical complexity of the brain; the structure of teeth and shape of jaw are distinctive. Classically, cultural factors have included use of tools and language. However, use of tools and use of an abstract language has been demonstrated in chimpanzees. However, actual construction of tools and development of a language continue to rank among our unique traits.

Upright Posture By measuring the depression of the imprint and the distance between the steps, an anthropologist can hypothesize about the size and weight of early humans. Shape of the foot and length of toes can indicate if the foot that made the imprint was adapted for walking upright. For example, the arch of the foot is unique to humans.

The bone structure of the human pelvis makes it possible for humans to walk erectly. In figure 39–2 you can see that the human pelvis is broader than that of the chimpanzee. The wider pelvis gives better support to the internal organs in a standing position. Notice that the human pelvis also has a large posterior section. This makes the pelvis strong and acts as a place for the attachment of the large muscles used in walking.

Use of Tools A study of the environment of primitive people gives clues to human development. The kind of food early people ate tells anthropologists something about the climate and the natural surroundings in which they lived.

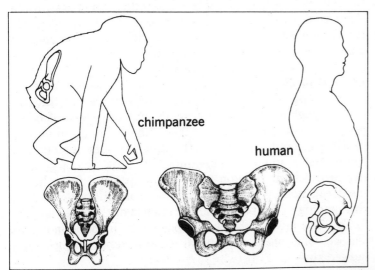

chimpanzee

human

39–2 | Compare the human pelvis to that of a chimpanzee. Structural differences allow humans to walk upright.

39-3 | Human hands are suitable for the manipulation of tools. Compare the human hands pictured to those of the ape. *(above: © James Sugar, Woodfin Camp and Associates; below: Matthew Stettler)*

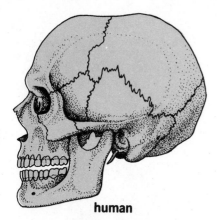

human

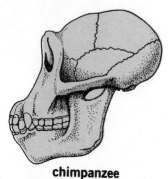

chimpanzee

39-4 | Comparison of the skulls of a human and a chimpanzee.

Anthropologists also look for animal fossils when they find a place where early humans lived. These animals may have been used for food. Charred bones in the area may be a clue that the humans living there knew how to use fire to cook meat.

Humans are the only animals that make and use a variety of tools. When tools are found they may give clues as to how highly developed early people were. Evidence of simple stone tools would show that the people were primitive. Complicated tools made from metal would show that the early people were more developed. Sometimes, similar tools are found over a large area. This suggests that the people who used them communicated with each other as to how tools were made.

Structural characteristics permit the human to use tools. Pick up a book and then look at your hand. Notice that your thumb and fingers are adapted for grasping the book. You have what is known as an "opposable thumb." That is, your thumb is opposite your fingers. Try to pick up the same book while keeping your thumb and fingers on the same side. You will find this very awkward. Primates other than humans have opposable thumbs, but humans are best adapted for use of more complex tools.

Brain Capacity Anthropologists have ways of finding out about the development of the human brain. They compare skulls of modern humans and apes to the fossil skulls of early humans. Look at the drawings of the human and chimpanzee skulls in figure 39-4. You will see that the skull is larger compared to the size of the body in humans.

Intelligence has to do with brain capacity and the internal anatomy of the brain. This evidence is lost in fossils but the shape of the fossil skull can also indicate a greater intelligence. For example, humans have comparatively short faces. This is thought to be due to various factors including greater development of the front part of the brain.

Teeth and Jaws Fossil teeth and jaws also give clues to anthropologists. **There are major differences in the size and arrangement of human teeth and the teeth of other primates.** Notice in figure 39-5 that the chimpanzee, human, and baboon all have the same number of teeth, but the shapes of some teeth are quite different. The large tearing teeth of the baboon show an adaptation for a heavy meat-eating diet. Another difference you will notice is that the spacing of the teeth and the shapes of the jaws are different. The jaws of the chimpanzee and the baboon are U-shaped. The jaw of the human shows teeth arranged in a curved row.

Similarities of Mammals

As you can see, humans differ from other mammals in many important ways. However, mammals have many things in common. The organs and systems of their bodies are quite similar. Internal structures of the heart and blood vessels, the digestive and excretory organs, the lungs and the glands are much alike in humans and the other primates.

The chemical secretions of humans and other mammals are similar. For example, the insulin that is used to save the lives of diabetics can be obtained from the pancreas of a cow or pig.

The History of Human Development

In the late 1800s several scientific papers were written on the possible origin of humans. One of the most well known was Charles Darwin's *The Descent of Man*, published in 1871. Each book, including Darwin's, explored the question of a human's "place in nature." **The general consensus was that humans and other primates evolved from some very early common ancestor.**

This idea may become clearer if you think about the evolution from general to specialized forms. As you recall, biologists believe that the less-specialized primitive forms can move most easily into new environments. Therefore they are most likely to evolve into new species. The apes of today are highly specialized forms. Most likely they evolved from less-specialized primitive forms. Human beings are also a highly specialized form. Scientists in the late 1800s suggested that humans may also have evolved from less specialized ancestors.

What would you find if you could trace the history of primates back ten million years? You might find that both modern humans and modern apes have evolved from the same early primate. However, most biologists think that the two lines of evolution separated a very long time ago. Today they are specialized in quite different ways.

In the later 1800s no remains of early humans had been found. Today, hundreds of bones have been found, dated, and studied, but this evidence still does not give us a complete picture of the history of human development. However, these fossils can help anthropologists hypothesize. For example, a fossil skull can show us the size of the brain, the shape of the head, and the age at death.

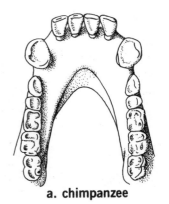

a. chimpanzee

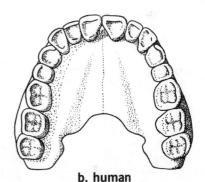

b. human

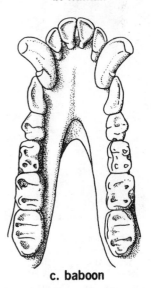

c. baboon

39–5 | The difference in the teeth of a chimpanzee, a human, and a baboon.

Dating Fossils

As you may remember from Chapter 3, the basic element in life is carbon. Carbon normally has an atomic weight (proton plus neutron number) of 12. It is referred to as C^{12}.

In 1930 an isotope of carbon with an atomic weight of 14 was discovered. That is, it has six protons but eight neutrons. It is a radioactive isotope in that it gives off radiation at a steady rate. It eventually will become C^{12}, the stable form of carbon. The time it takes half the radioactive isotope to reach its stable form of C^{12} is called its **half-life.** The half-life of C^{14} is 5,568 years. This means that in 5,568 years half the C^{14} will become C^{12}.

In living organisms, there is about one C^{14} atom to one trillion C^{12} atoms. As long as an organism is alive, it adds carbon compounds to its body by ingesting food. At death, the addition of carbon stops.

By measuring the amount of C^{14} in a fossil, its age can be determined, the assumption being that the amount of C^{14} taken in by an organism has remained at a constant level throughout the ages. This means that if a piece of bone has half the amount of C^{14} as living organisms today, its age would be about 5,568 years. The C^{14} method or **radiocarbon method** for determining the age of fossils is very good for dating materials as old as 50,000 years.

Other radioactive dating methods such as the potassium-argon method have been used to determine the age of rock sample. These methods also are helpful in determining age of fossils over 50,000 years. When this and other rock sample methods are used, it is necessary to find a rock that was formed about the same time the organism was living. Using these methods, some very valuable information has been obtained about primitive people.

Humanoid Fossils

In 1924, a small fossilized skull was found in a South African quarry. It was given to a South African medical school. There, Professor Raymond Dart noticed that it looked like a human skull. He named it *Australopithecus* (aw-STRAY-lo-pith-EE-kuss) *africanus.* The name means "southern ape from Africa." Since then, other bones of this primate have been found. Fossils of *Australopithecus* have been dated from 4.5 to 1.5 million years ago.

The famous anthropologist family, the Leakeys, have been digging up fossils and studying them for more than 40 years. Much of their work has been in the Olduvai Gorge in Tanzania. In 1959 they were digging in an area believed to have been a campsite of some ancient humans. Mary and Louis Leakey found bones from skulls, a foot, fingers, and a

39–6 | These fossil footprints were discovered in Tanzania by Mary Leakey. They are believed to have been made by a humanlike creature more than 3.5 million years ago. From fossil footprints like these, anthropologists can tell that these creatures walked upright. (John Reader © National Geographic Society)

lower jaw. Using the potassium-argon method, scientists say this Olduvai Gorge man is 1,750,000 years old.

Most recently, findings have shown that a walking hominid has been on the earth for as long as 3.75 million years. In 1977 Mary Leakey announced the discovery of fossil footprints dated at least 3,600,000 years old. Fossilized bones have been found in the area. This humanlike creature has been named the Laetoli man. What do these footprints indicate? According to Mary Leakey, they demonstrate that nearly four million years ago, the modern human's direct ancestor walked upright. Further, the form of the foot was exactly the same as it is today. This and other discoveries led to the support of a theory that an earlier form could have produced as many as three lines with a common ancestory, one of which led to modern humans.

Early Human Forms

In 1891, part of a skull, a piece of jaw, and an upper leg bone were discovered on the island of Java. Similar bones were also found there in 1937. These bones belonged to what was called Java man. Since it is believed to have walked upright, it is now called *Homo erectus*. This hominid probably lived from 1.5 to nearly 2 million years ago. It lived on the earth for a period of about 1.5 million years. Similar forms of *Homo erectus* have been found in caves near Peking.

Anthropologists believe that *Homo erectus* lived in groups that hunted animals, used bone and stone tools, and cooked their meat. Charred bones of bats, rodents, bear, deer, and even elephants have been found at their campsites. *Homo erectus* had a slanting forehead and heavy brow ridges. The size of the skull shows that its brain was only half the size of the modern human brain, but the brain of *Homo erectus* was more than a third larger than that of the present day gorilla. It is believed that they may have communicated by speech.

The Neanderthal More is known about the *Neanderthal* (nee-AN-der-thawl) form of human than other forms because there is more fossil evidence for them. They are believed to have lived on earth approximately 50,000 years ago. Their remains have been found in Europe, Asia Minor, Siberia, and North Africa. They might have lived as long ago as 100,000 years. Scientists think Neanderthals disappeared about 25,000 years ago. Almost 100 Neanderthal skeletons have been found and studied. The average Neanderthal was probably about 1½ meters (about 5 feet) tall. Bone structure shows that they were powerful. Their facial features were similar to *Homo erectus*. The forehead sloped

39-7 | Summary of a theory about human ancestry.

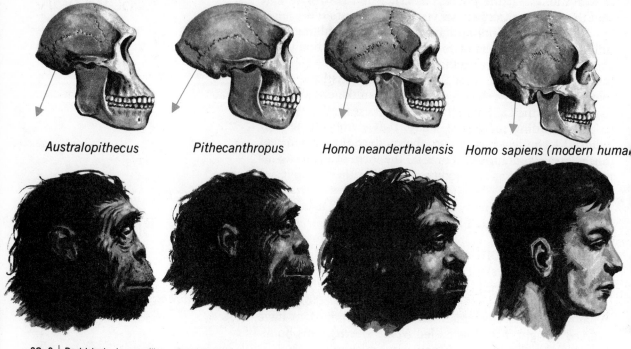

Australopithecus   *Pithecanthropus*   *Homo neanderthalensis*   *Homo sapiens (modern huma*

39–8 | Prehistoric humanlike primates and a modern human. In what ways do their skulls differ? In what ways are they similar? The arrows show how erect the postures probably were compared to the erect stature of the human.

backward from heavy brow ridges. The mouth was large, with a small chin.

Neanderthals lived in caves. They were hunters of the hairy mammoth, saber-toothed cat, and wooly rhinoceros. Their brains were as large or larger than the modern human brain. Neanderthals had stone tools and weapons. They used fire, buried their dead, and lived in family groups.

There is some disagreement, but Neanderthals are considered by most anthropologists to be in the same genus and species as modern humans, *Homo sapiens* (HOE-moe SAPE-ee-enz).

The Cro-Magnon Anthropologists also put the *Cro-Magnon* in the same species as modern humans. Cro-Magnons lived in Europe about 50,000 years ago. These primitive humans had high foreheads and well-developed chins. They did not have heavy brow ridges like most of the more primitive hominids. Cro-Magnon skeletons have been found in caves along the coast of southern France along with their weapons of stone and bone. The walls of these caves have beautiful drawings, mostly of animals and hunting scenes.

Cro-Magnons may have killed the Neanderthals. It is also possible that the two groups interbred and the Neanderthals lost their identity.

Summary

It is not known exactly when humans first inhabited the earth, but many clues help the anthropologists as they form hypotheses. Footprints and fossil bones are studied carefully. Charred remains of campsites provide information about the distribution and food of early humans. Upright posture, use of tools, a larger brain than that of an ape, teeth, and jaw structures are characteristics used to identify early humans. These characteristics adapt the human to a variety of environments and diets. The brain is believed to be one of the most important characteristics that allows *Homo sapiens* to dominate the biological world today.

Biologically Speaking

anthropology
radiocarbon method

Questions for Review

1. What features separate humans from other animals?
2. What features are used to distinguish true humans from apelike primates?
3. How are fossils dated?
4. Why is the finding of an old skull important?
5. What can be learned from a study of the lower jaw and teeth?
6. How can a type of environment that existed thousands of years ago in a given area be determined?
7. How can anthropologists determine the diet of primitive humans?
8. Why do anthropologists study the primitive human in a modern world?

Applying Concepts

1. How can the intelligence of the primitive human be judged from fossil evidence?
2. Compare the skull of the modern human with the skulls of *Homo erectus*, Neanderthal, and Cro-Magnon.
3. Discuss similarities and differences between the teeth of a chimpanzee, a human, and a baboon.

40

The Organization of the Human Body

40-1 | The specialization of the human body allows the power behind the pitch. *(HRW photo by Ken Karp)*

Cell Specialization

Homo sapiens is a multicellular organism. The human body is made up of cells and cell products. As in all multicellular organisms, life begins as a single cell, the zygote. Many cell divisions soon form the *germ layers*. These germ layers are the ectoderm, the mesoderm, and the endoderm. During further cell division and growth, the cells become different from one another and form the many tissues of the human body. A *tissue* is a group of cells with similar structures and functions. The tissues of the human body can be divided into four groups.

Connective tissues bind together and support other structures. Different kinds of connective tissue have different properties so they can perform their own special tasks. Some give strength and firmness to softer tissues. Fibers in organ walls, and the bones themselves, are some of the forms of connective tissue. Connective tissue is formed from the cells of the *mesoderm*.

Muscle tissues function in movement. They move the bones, cause the heart to beat, and cause food to be moved through the alimentary system. Muscle tissue is also formed from the cells of the *mesoderm*.

Nervous tissues form the communication system of our bodies. They coordinate the moving parts. They inform us about our environment. The brain, spinal cord, and nerves are examples of this tissue. They are formed from the *ectoderm*.

Epithelial tissues secrete or absorb material as well as protect the body surfaces, both externally and internally. For example, one type lines the blood vessels and the heart. It is formed from *mesoderm*. Another type covers the body organs and lines the coelom. This is also formed from the *mesoderm*. Some epithelial cells line the alimentary tract and secrete mucus and enzymes. These are formed from *endoderm*. The ciliated lining of the trachea and the lining of the tubes in the lungs are other examples of epithelial tissue formed from *endoderm*. The epidermis of the skin, and the linings of the mouth, anus, and nostrils are more examples of epithelial tissue. These, however, develop from the *ectoderm*. As you can see, the various types of epithelial tissue are formed from *all three* germ layers.

epi = on, upon

derma = skin, leather

Organs and Systems

Different tissues grouped together to perform a function as a unit are an organ. You are familiar with some organs of the human body. These include the arms, legs, ears, eyes, heart, liver, lungs, and so on. Each of these organs is specialized. Each has its own job to do and each organ is made of several different tissues. **Organs working together to do a specific job make up a system.**

The Human Body Plan

Our body form is similar to that of other vertebrates. Humans have limbs (arms and legs), a head, neck, and trunk. The trunk has a cavity surrounding the body organs. This cavity is a true coelom. It has a lining of specialized cells that were formed from the mesoderm. The lining also covers the body organs and forms a double membrane that suspends the alimentary canal. A dome-shaped muscular partition, called the **diaphragm,** divides the body cavity into two parts. The **thoracic cavity** is surrounded by the ribs, breastbone, and spine. It contains the lungs, trachea, heart, and esophagus. The **abdominal cavity** is surrounded by the lower spine, pelvis, and muscles of the abdomen. It contains the stomach, liver, pancreas, intestines, kidneys, and spleen. The abdominal cavity of the female also contains the ovaries.

Another cavity is formed by the bones of the skull and

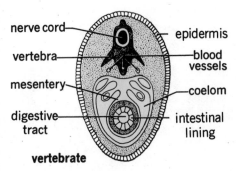

vertebrate

40–2 | The general body plan of a vertebrate.

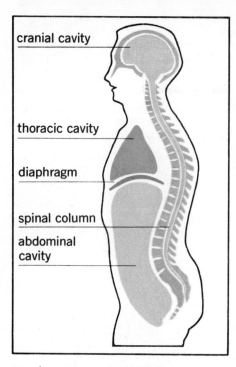

cranial cavity

thoracic cavity

diaphragm

spinal column

abdominal cavity

40–3 | The body cavities of the human.

encloses the brain. This the **cranial cavity.** The head contains many of our sense organs. These organs are near the brain and send impulses to it.

Skeletal System

Vertebrates have a strong supporting structure. This is their internal skeleton, or **endoskeleton.** Recall that arthropods have external skeletons, or *exoskeletons.*

The bones that make up our framework, or skeleton, are very efficient. They give the greatest support with the least weight, and allow us to move freely. However, there is one disadvantage to having an internal skeleton. It does not offer protection against injury as does an exoskeleton. Many soft parts of the body are exposed. **An organism with an endoskeleton must rely on its nervous system and sense organs for protection.**

The Functions of the Skeleton

The bones in your body function in several ways. 1) They provide support and form. For example, the vertebral column, the shoulder and hip girdles, and the arm and leg bones support the body. In addition, the vertebral column also gives the body its shape. 2) They provide a surface to which the muscles attach, forming a leverage system. These bones have muscles attached to them that supply the force enabling us to walk, lift, and sit. 3) They protect delicate organs. Some bones, such as those in the cranium, enclose and protect the brain; other bones form protection for the heart and lungs. 4) They store minerals that supply calcium and phosphorous to the blood. 5) Marrow is found within the skeleton bones. It has an important function in producing red blood cells. Throughout life the function of the skeleton provides us with support, protects the internal systems, and allows movement.

How Bone Develops

Bone can develop in two main ways. It can be formed from **cartilage,** or from *membrane layers.* Let's look at cartilage first. Some vertebrates, such as sharks, have skeletons made entirely of cartilage. This cartilage skeleton lasts all through their lives. Cartilage cells are spread out through a tough and flexible substance. In the early development of a human, the skeleton is made almost entirely of cartilage. After about two months of development, some cartilage cells are replaced by bone cells. Bone cells remove calcium phosphate and calcium carbonate from the blood. These substances are used to form the bone structure. The process of forming bone is called **ossification** (oss-i-fi-KAY-shun). Ossification occurs throughout childhood. Some cartilage

40–4 | Cartilage cells allow for flexibility.

does not form bone. You have permanent cartilage in the end of your nose. Feel the tip of your nose and then the bridge of your nose. Do you notice a difference? Cartilage is also found in the earlobe and the walls of your voice box and trachea.

Not all bones come from cartilage. Flat bones, like those of the skull and sternum, are formed from membrane layers that undergo ossification. You may know that the skull bones of a newborn baby are not fused; the cranium is not solid. As babies develop, the edges of the bones come together. This forms irregular seams called *sutures.* Both processes of bone formation involve the deposit of calcium compounds between bone cells.

Milk is the natural food of all young mammals. It is an excellent source of calcium compounds, but the minerals alone are not enough. Certain vitamins, especially vitamin D, are also needed for the normal growth of bone. Supplied with the minerals and vitamins, bone cells deposit calcium phosphate and calcium carbonate.

osteon or *os* = bone

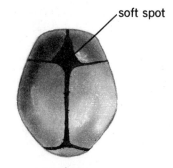

soft spot

newborn

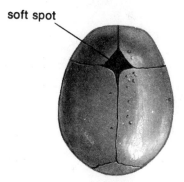

soft spot

1-year old

Bone Structure

Bone seems so solid. How do minerals get to the bone cells? Let's look at the structure of a long bone, such as the thigh bone. If this bone is cut lengthwise, several parts can be seen. A tough membrane covers the bone and also serves as an attachment for muscles. Beneath the covering, the bone itself varies in hardness. The outer part of the shaft of the long bone is made of extremely hard material. This forms a solid bony layer. A central cavity runs through the length of the long bone. At the ends of the long bone, the solid layer becomes very thin. Most of the material forming the ends of long bones is porous and spongy. Many channels form a network running through the bony layer. These channels are called *Haversian canals.* They carry food to the living cells of the bony layer through blood vessels that come from the surface of the bone.

Many bones are hollow. These cavities contain a soft tissue called marrow. Nerves and blood vessels are in the *marrow.* Two types of marrow are found in bones. *Red marrow* is found in flat bones, such as the ribs and sternum. It is also found in the ends of long bones and vertebrae. Red marrow forms the red corpuscles and most of the white corpuscles of the blood. *Yellow marrow* fills the central cavity of long bones. It extends into the Haversian canals of the bony layer. Yellow marrow is made up mostly of fat cells. Yellow marrow may produce corpuscles in an emergency. This may happen if a great deal of blood is lost or in certain blood diseases.

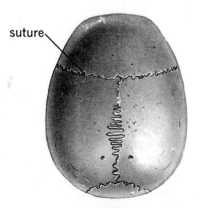

suture

adult

40–5 | The skull develops from a membrane that forms separate plates of bone. By the time adulthood is reached, the margins of these bony plates have joined.

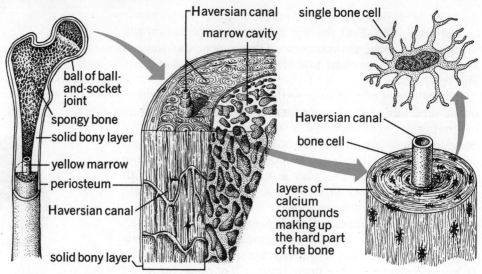

40-6 | The structure of the human femur shown at increasingly greater magnification.

The Bones Form Joints

The area where two bones meet is called a *joint*. The bones in the human body are connected by several different kinds of joints. These linkages are designed in a certain way to fulfill a particular function. Some joints, such as those between the bony plates of the skull, do not move at all. Other joints have a large range of power and movement. For example, at the elbow and knee, *hinge joints* combine strength and mobility. This joint is designed for only bend-stretch movements.

When you throw a ball, another type of joint is used. The *ball-and-socket joint* of your shoulder allows you to "wind up" for a good throw. If you have watched a pitcher during a baseball game, you have observed that his whole body is used to produce the force to throw the ball. His leg is able to swing up and over because of another ball-and-socket joint in the hip. This joins the thigh bone, or *femur*, to the socket in the hip bone, the *pelvis*.

The wrist bones are connected by *angular joints*. These can supply a twisting and a flicking motion to give a baseball a fast thrusting motion. The ankle bones also have angular joints. The vertebrae are connected by *gliding joints*. A slight motion is possible with the vertebrae also. You can twist your head to look around you because of the *pivot joint* connecting your head to your spine.

Some joints are only *partially movable*. The joints attaching your ribs to the vertebrae in your backbone are examples of partially movable joints. Some of the ribs are attached to the breastbone, or *sternum*, by long strands of

Facts & Figures

Cartilage forms the skeleton of less complex vertebrates such as the cyclostomes and elasmobranchs.

THE HUMAN BODY

SKELETAL SYSTEM

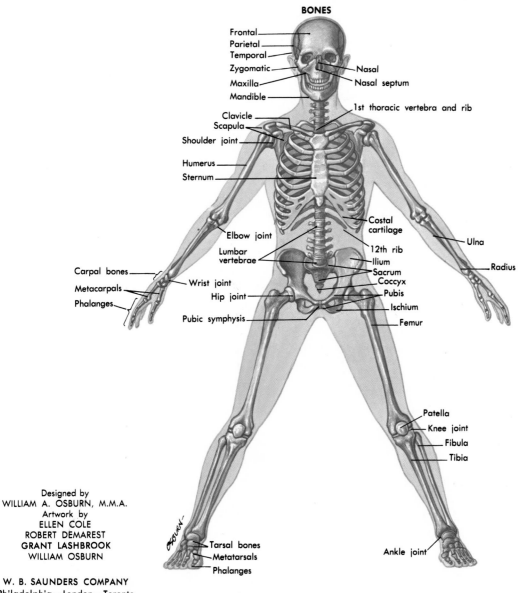

BONES

Frontal
Parietal
Temporal
Zygomatic — Nasal
Maxilla — Nasal septum
Mandible
Clavicle
Scapula
Shoulder joint
Humerus
Sternum
Elbow joint
Lumbar vertebrae
Carpal bones
Metacarpals
Phalanges
Wrist joint
Hip joint
Pubic symphysis

1st thoracic vertebra and rib

Costal cartilage
12th rib
Ilium
Sacrum
Coccyx
Pubis
Ischium
Femur

Ulna
Radius

Patella
Knee joint
Fibula
Tibia

Tarsal bones
Metatarsals
Phalanges

Ankle joint

Designed by
WILLIAM A. OSBURN, M.M.A.
Artwork by
ELLEN COLE
ROBERT DEMAREST
GRANT LASHBROOK
WILLIAM OSBURN

W. B. SAUNDERS COMPANY
Philadelphia — London — Toronto

SKELETAL MUSCLES

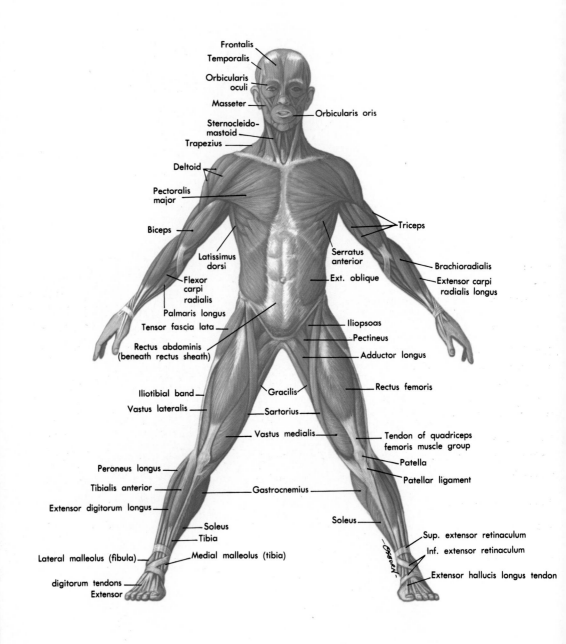

Frontalis
Temporalis
Orbicularis oculi
Masseter
Sternocleido-mastoid
Trapezius
Deltoid
Pectoralis major
Biceps
Latissimus dorsi
Flexor carpi radialis
Palmaris longus
Tensor fascia lata
Rectus abdominis (beneath rectus sheath)
Iliotibial band
Vastus lateralis
Peroneus longus
Tibialis anterior
Extensor digitorum longus
Lateral malleolus (fibula)
digitorum tendons
Extensor

Orbicularis oris
Triceps
Serratus anterior
Brachioradialis
Ext. oblique
Extensor carpi radialis longus
Iliopsoas
Pectineus
Adductor longus
Rectus femoris
Gracilis
Sartorius
Vastus medialis
Tendon of quadriceps femoris muscle group
Patella
Patellar ligament
Gastrocnemius
Soleus
Soleus
Tibia
Medial malleolus (tibia)
Sup. extensor retinaculum
Inf. extensor retinaculum
Extensor hallucis longus tendon

RESPIRATION AND THE HEART

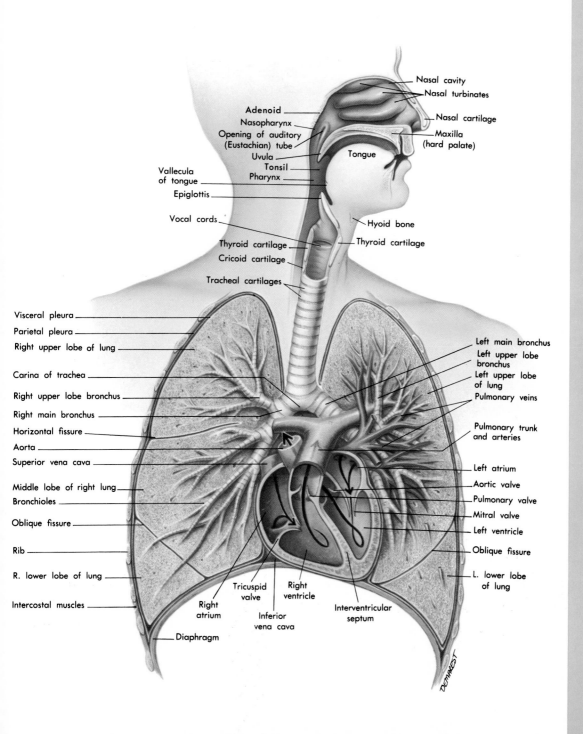

Nasal cavity
Nasal turbinates
Adenoid
Nasopharynx
Nasal cartilage
Opening of auditory
(Eustachian) tube
Maxilla
(hard palate)
Uvula
Tongue
Tonsil
Vallecula
of tongue
Tonsil
Pharynx
Epiglottis
Hyoid bone
Vocal cords
Thyroid cartilage
Thyroid cartilage
Cricoid cartilage
Tracheal cartilages

Visceral pleura
Parietal pleura
Right upper lobe of lung
Left main bronchus
Left upper lobe
bronchus
Carina of trachea
Left upper lobe
of lung
Right upper lobe bronchus
Pulmonary veins
Right main bronchus
Horizontal fissure
Pulmonary trunk
and arteries
Aorta
Superior vena cava
Left atrium
Aortic valve
Middle lobe of right lung
Pulmonary valve
Bronchioles
Mitral valve
Oblique fissure
Left ventricle
Rib
Oblique fissure
R. lower lobe of lung
L. lower lobe
of lung
Intercostal muscles
Tricuspid
valve
Right
ventricle
Right
atrium
Inferior
vena cava
Interventricular
septum
Diaphragm

BLOOD VASCULAR SYSTEM

VEINS

STRUCTURE

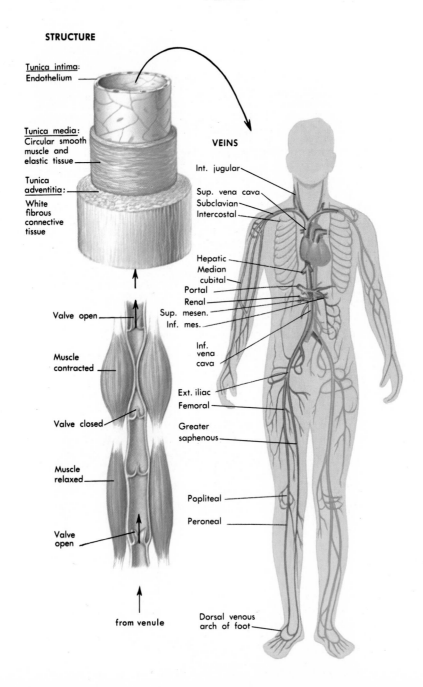

Tunica intima:
Endothelium

Tunica media:
Circular smooth
muscle and
elastic tissue

Tunica
adventitia:

White
fibrous
connective
tissue

VEINS

Int. jugular

Sup. vena cava
Subclavian
Intercostal

Valve open

Muscle
contracted

Valve closed

Muscle
relaxed

Valve
open

from venule

Hepatic
Median
cubital
Portal
Renal
Sup. mesen.
Inf. mes.

Inf.
vena
cava

Ext. iliac
Femoral

Greater
saphenous

Popliteal

Peroneal

Dorsal venous
arch of foot

ARTERIES

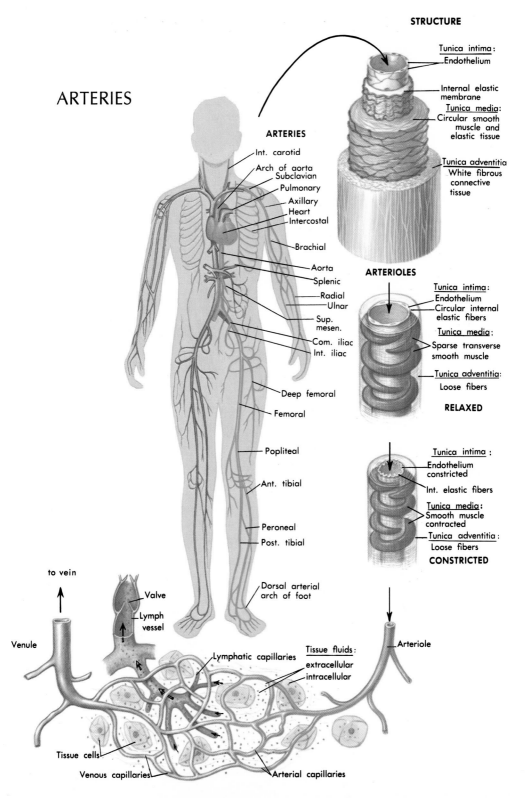

STRUCTURE

Tunica intima:
Endothelium

Internal elastic membrane

Tunica media:
Circular smooth muscle and elastic tissue

Tunica adventitia
White fibrous connective tissue

ARTERIES

Int. carotid
Arch of aorta
Subclavian
Pulmonary
Axillary
Heart
Intercostal
Brachial
Aorta
Splenic
Radial
Ulnar
Sup. mesen.
Com. iliac
Int. iliac
Deep femoral
Femoral
Popliteal
Ant. tibial
Peroneal
Post. tibial
Dorsal arterial arch of foot

ARTERIOLES

Tunica intima:
Endothelium
Circular internal elastic fibers

Tunica media:
Sparse transverse smooth muscle

Tunica adventitia:
Loose fibers

RELAXED

Tunica intima:
Endothelium constricted

Int. elastic fibers

Tunica media:
Smooth muscle contracted

Tunica adventitia:
Loose fibers

CONSTRICTED

to vein

Valve
Lymph vessel

Venule

Lymphatic capillaries

Tissue fluids:
extracellular
intracellular

Arteriole

Tissue cells

Venous capillaries

Arterial capillaries

A CAPILLARY BED

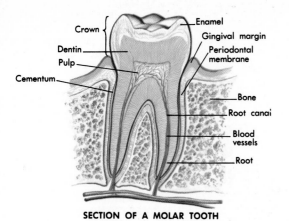

Crown
Enamel
Dentin
Gingival margin
Pulp
Periodontal membrane
Cementum
Bone
Root canal
Blood vessels
Root

SECTION OF A MOLAR TOOTH

DIGESTIVE SYSTEM

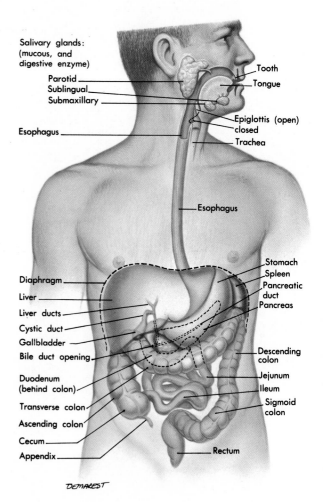

Salivary glands:
(mucous, and
digestive enzyme)

Parotid
Sublingual
Submaxillary

Tooth
Tongue

Esophagus

Epiglottis (open)
closed
Trachea

Esophagus

Diaphragm
Liver
Liver ducts
Cystic duct
Gallbladder
Bile duct opening
Duodenum
(behind colon)
Transverse colon
Ascending colon
Cecum
Appendix

Stomach
Spleen
Pancreatic duct
Pancreas

Descending colon
Jejunum
Ileum
Sigmoid colon

Rectum

DEMAREST

BRAIN AND SPINAL NERVES

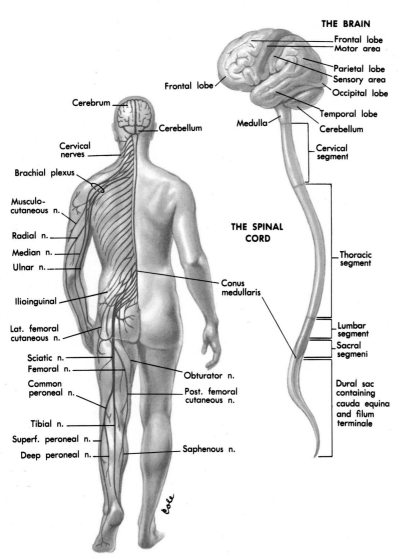

THE BRAIN

Frontal lobe
Motor area
Parietal lobe
Sensory area
Occipital lobe
Temporal lobe
Cerebellum

Frontal lobe

Medulla

Cervical
segment

**THE SPINAL
CORD**

Cerebrum
Cerebellum

Cervical
nerves

Brachial plexus

Musculo-
cutaneous n.

Radial n.

Median n.

Ulnar n.

Ilioinguinal

Lat. femoral
cutaneous n.

Sciatic n.

Femoral n.

Common
peroneal n.

Tibial n.

Superf. peroneal n.

Deep peroneal n.

Conus
medullaris

Obturator n.

Post. femoral
cutaneous n.

Saphenous n.

Thoracic
segment

Lumbar
segment
Sacral
segment

Dural sac
containing
cauda equina
and filum
terminale

THE MAJOR SPINAL NERVES

ORGANS OF SPECIAL SENSE

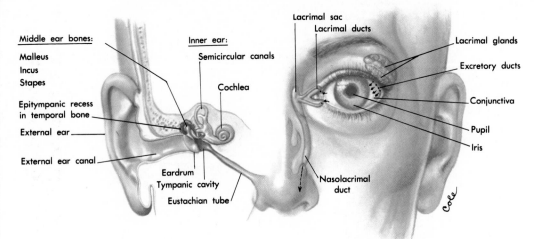

Middle ear bones:

Malleus
Incus
Stapes

Epitympanic recess
in temporal bone

External ear

External ear canal

Inner ear:
Semicircular canals

Cochlea

Eardrum
Tympanic cavity
Eustachian tube

Lacrimal sac
Lacrimal ducts

Lacrimal glands
Excretory ducts
Conjunctiva
Pupil
Iris

Nasolacrimal
duct

Cole

THE ORGAN OF HEARING

THE LACRIMAL APPARATUS AND THE EYE

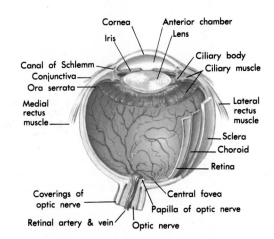

HORIZONTAL SECTION OF THE EYE

Cornea
Iris

Anterior chamber
Lens

Canal of Schlemm
Conjunctiva
Ora serrata

Medial
rectus
muscle

Ciliary body
Ciliary muscle

Lateral
rectus
muscle

Sclera
Choroid
Retina

Coverings of
optic nerve

Retinal artery & vein

Central fovea
Papilla of optic nerve

Optic nerve

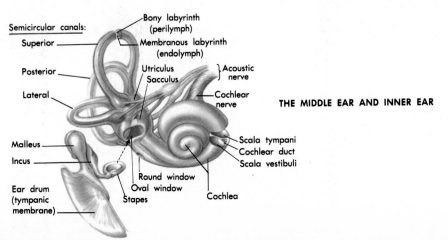

Semicircular canals:

Superior

Posterior

Lateral

Malleus

Incus

Ear drum
(tympanic
membrane)

Bony labyrinth
(perilymph)
Membranous labyrinth
(endolymph)

Utriculus
Sacculus

} Acoustic
nerve

Cochlear
nerve

Scala tympani
Cochlear duct
Scala vestibuli

Round window
Oval window
Stapes

Cochlea

THE MIDDLE EAR AND INNER EAR

cartilage. Partially movable joints of the ribs allow your chest to expand and contract when you breathe.

Movable joints are held in position by tough strands of connective tissue, called **ligaments.** The ligaments can be stretched by exercise. This loosens the joints and allows you to move more easily.

The inside surfaces of your joints are covered with layers of cartilage. A secretion lubricates the joints. The fluid makes the cartilage surfaces slippery so they can slide freely. In some joints, such as your knee and shoulder, a sac acts as a cushion between the bones. Such a sac is called a *bursa*. Sometimes stress on a joint causes the bursa to produce more fluid, which results in inflammation, pain, and stiffness. This condition is known as *bursitis*.

Muscle Systems

Bones form the framework of your body. Wherever one bone meets another in the human body a joint is formed, but the bones do not have the ability to move by themselves. The *biceps* is the muscle that moves the forearm by bending the elbow joint.

Muscle is a tissue made of specialized cells that are able to shorten, or contract. When muscle cells are grouped in bundles and they all contract at once, bones can then move with great force. This is what happens when you throw a baseball. Muscle contraction also causes your heart to beat. Food is moved through your digestive system by the contraction of muscle cells. About 400 different muscles are in your body. They make up about half your body weight.

Let's consider the biceps muscle that moves the forearm. The long, slender cells are called muscle *fibers*. Each fiber contains fine threads called *myofibrils*. These myofibrils lie parallel and run lengthwise in the cell. When these myofibrils are examined with an electron microscope, many details can be seen. The myofibrils are actually bundles of two kinds of protein filaments. They are the thick *myosin filaments*, and thin *actin filaments*. Figure 40–8 shows that they are arranged in a definite pattern.

Muscle cells contract when they are supplied with energy from ATP and activated by a nerve impulse. The exact action that causes muscles to contract still is not clear. Many scientists think that the thick and thin protein filaments slide over one another. This would cause the myofibrils to shorten.

You can throw a ball or lift an object by causing your biceps to contract whenever you wish. Therefore, the muscle cells of the biceps must have nerve connections. Microscopic studies show that each nerve cell that carries impulses to the muscle has branches. Each of these

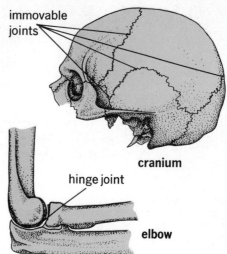

immovable joints

cranium

hinge joint

elbow

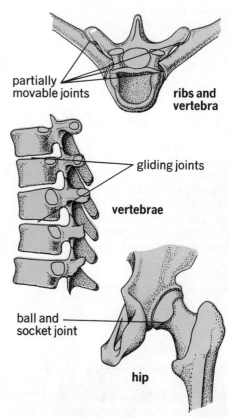

partially movable joints

ribs and vertebra

gliding joints

vertebrae

ball and socket joint

hip

40–7 | Five types of joints.

myos = muscle
fibra = fiber or filament

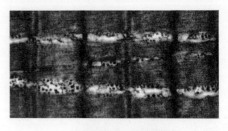

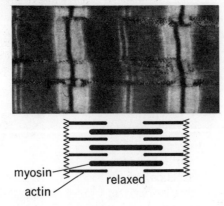

myosin — relaxed

actin

contracted

40-8 | A representation of the current concept of muscle contraction. (left) Compare the relaxed muscle tissue with (right) the contracted muscle tissue. *(Lewis Koster)*

branches stimulates a few muscle fibers. The combination of nerve cell and muscle fibers is called a *motor unit.* When stimulated, *each* fiber contracts as tightly as possible. The strength of each fiber contraction is always the same. The strength of the movement depends on how many motor units are called into action. **The more units that contract, the greater the movement.** As a result, our movements can be very precise or very forceful. A ball can be pitched very forcefully toward a batter in a game, or can be tossed gently to a child.

Types of Muscle Cells

There are three types of vertebrate muscle cells: *smooth muscle,* *skeletal muscle,* and *cardiac muscle.* Each *smooth muscle* cell is a long spindle with one nucleus, usually near its center. The stomach and intestinal walls are layered with smooth muscles. They contract in waves to churn food or to pass it along the digestive tract. Artery walls are also layered with smooth muscle. Impulses from the nervous system can make these walls tighten. This raises your blood pressure during times of danger or emotional upset. **All smooth muscle action is carried out by parts of the nervous system over which you have no conscious control.** This is why smooth muscle is called *involuntary muscle.*

The skeletal muscles are voluntary muscles. Your biceps is a voluntary muscle. You can control it at will. Each fiber is a long cylinder with tapering ends; each has many nuclei. These nuclei are located along the inside edges throughout the length of the cells. Most skeletal muscle fibers do not stretch from one end of a muscle to the other. Instead, they are bound in small bundles by strips of connective tissue. These bundles are held together by heavier strips that cover the entire muscle. This structure gives most voluntary muscles a spindle shape.

Facts & Figures

Invertebrates also have smooth muscles and skeletal muscles, but their skeleton is external. Giant barnacles and the Alaskan king crab have the thickest muscle fibers known. They may be 3 mm (.12 inches) in diameter and 6 cm (2.4 inches) long. These fibers can be seen with the naked eye.

40-9 | A motor unit. *(Courtesy of General Biological Supply House, Inc.)*

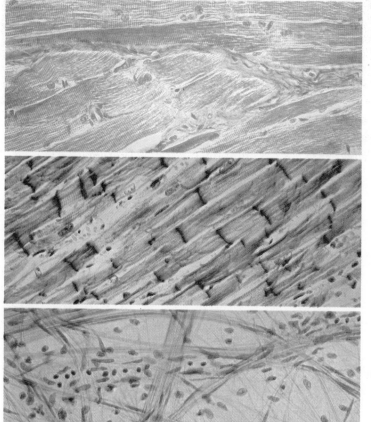

40-10 | Three types of muscle cells. (a) striated cells (b) cardiac cells (400X) (c) smooth cells (350X). *(Manfred Kage, © Peter Arnold Inc.)*

Facts & Figures

Muscles form about 40 percent of the body's weight.

ex = out
tendere = to stretch
flexus = bent, turned, curved

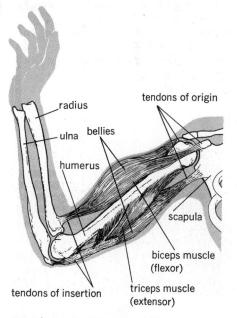

40-11 | The biceps and the triceps, two opposing muscles.

Some skeletal muscles attach directly to the protective covering of the bones. Some attach to other muscles. Some skeletal muscles have **tendons** that act as linking cables and join the covering where it is attached to the bone. Tendons are thick bands of connective tissue that are not elastic.

Muscles must attach at two points for movement to occur. The attachment to the stationary part is called the **origin.** The attachment to the movable part is called the **insertion.** Look at the biceps in figure 40–11. As you know, when this muscle contracts, the hinge joint of the elbow bends, bringing up the forearm. What is the origin and the insertion of the biceps?

The skeletal muscles that move the trunk and limbs are always in pairs. The muscles of these pairs oppose each other. Muscles that bend joints are called *flexors.* The biceps is a flexor because it causes the elbow to bend. Muscles that straighten joints are called *extensors.*

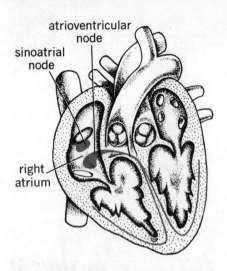

atrioventricular
node

sinoatrial
node

right
atrium

40-12 | The conducting pathways in the heart. The impulse for the heartbeat originates in the sinotrial node. It is carried through the muscle to the atrioventricular node. It is then relayed through the muscles of the lower chambers.

Facts & Figures

Muscles can exert a powerful force. More than 6,000 pounds is the greatest weight ever raised by a human.

Can you locate the extensor muscle that opposes the biceps? To do so, bend your right elbow with the flexor. Now, with your left hand, grasp the back side of your upper arm. This is the extensor muscle called the *triceps*. Repeat this process and you will notice how the triceps contracts and the biceps relaxes. The action of the triceps and the biceps oppose one another. Even when you are not moving your joints, flexor and extensor muscles are slightly contracted. This is called *tone*. The more you use your muscles, the larger they get and the more tone they have. When you do not use them at all, muscles become weak and flabby. They get smaller and lose their tone. This is called *disuse atrophy*.

Cardiac muscle is the involuntary muscle found in the heart. It is made of a third kind of contracting cell. It was once thought that cardiac muscle cells contained many nuclei. However, the electron microscope shows us that this is not true. These cells are separated by plasma membranes. The cells form a branching, woven network. Thus, when cardiac muscle fibers contract, the chambers of the heart are squeezed. This action forces blood out through the vessels.

Heart muscle does not act like any other muscle. The beat begins in a small mass of tissue called the **sinoatrial** (SIE-noe-AY-tree-uhl) **node.** This tissue is located in the wall of the right atrium of the heart. From this *pacemaker*, the beat is carried through the muscle of the upper chambers to another node, the **atrioventricular** (AY-tree-oe-ven-TRICK-yoo-ler) **node.** From there it is relayed through the muscles of the lower chambers. The beat is conducted from cell to cell through the heart muscle. This results in the rhythmic wave of contraction that is known as the heartbeat.

Summary

Cells of connective tissue, muscle tissue, nervous tissue, and epithelial tissue are specialized in the functions each performs.

The human skeleton gives our bodies form, serves as levers for muscles to move, protects delicate organs, serves as a storehouse for minerals, and manufactures blood cells.

Skeletal muscles are voluntary and cause the bones to move. Smooth muscles are involuntary and form layers in the walls of internal organs. Cardiac muscles control the action of the heart and are also involuntary.

Biologically Speaking

connective tissue
muscle tissue
nervous tissue
epithelial tissue
diaphragm
thoracic cavity
abdominal cavity
cranial cavity
endoskeleton
cartilage
ossification
suture
Haversian canal

red marrow
yellow marrow
joint
ligament
motor unit
smooth muscle
skeletal muscle
cardiac muscle
tendon
origin
insertion
sinoatrial node
atrioventricular node

Questions for Review

1. How do the tissues, organs, and systems of the human body show division of labor?
2. Name the three body cavities. By what structures are they enclosed? Name the organs found in each.
3. What are the main functions of bones? Give an example of a bone serving each purpose.
4. What are some important functions of the Haversian canals?
5. Describe some of the tissues surrounding a joint. What are their functions?
6. Describe the kinds of joints found in the body.
7. Describe a theory of muscle contraction.
8. Classify the three types of muscle tissues.
9. Why are muscles often found in opposing pairs in the body?

Applying Concepts

1. Explain the importance of a highly developed nervous system in an organism with an internal skeleton.
2. Proper diet does not insure good teeth and healthy bones. What other factors do you think are involved?
3. Why is it possible that hearts removed from some less complex animals and placed in nutrient solutions keep beating?

41

Nutrition

A DEFINE food.
B EXPLAIN the body's use of water.
C LIST the food substances, their functions, and their sources.
D NAME and **DESCRIBE** the organic nutrients.
E IDENTIFY the importance of carbohydrates, fats, and proteins.
F DESCRIBE the anatomy and physiology of the organs that form the alimentary canal.

41-1 | Eating nutritious food is vital to our health. *(HRW photo by Russell Dian)*

Characteristics of Food

Perhaps you have heard the expression, "you are what you eat." Can you get the proper nutrition eating potato chips, soft drinks, and candy bars? These items are sometimes called "junk foods." These are foods containing the energy equivalent of many calories but do not provide the essential nutrients for a balanced diet. You would not feel hungry but over a period of time, such poor nutrition would endanger your health. Heredity together with environment makes you what you are. Heredity plays a role in determining the size to which you may grow. Environment, including food taken into your body, also will influence your growth. What you eat also will influence how you feel. Perhaps you have had the experience of waking up too late to eat breakfast. By noon you felt tired and hungry. What is a balanced diet? What does your body do with the food you eat?

A *food* is any substance taken into an organism to be used for work, or repair, and maintenance of life processes. Food provides the fuel for energy, the raw materials for growth and the essential ingredients to maintain your body. Water, minerals, and vitamins, by this definition, can be considered food. So are carbohydrates, fats, and proteins. You may want to review Chapter 3 in which the chemical structure and importance of carbohydrates, fats, and proteins are discussed.

The Importance of Water

Water is an inorganic substance that is essential to the body tissues. If you weigh 50 kilograms (110 pounds), your body contains 30 to 35 kilograms (66 to 77 pounds) of water. In the digestive tract, water is the solvent in which the enzymes work. The digested foods are dissolved in water as they move into the blood. The fluid part of blood is 91 to 92 percent water. Wastes are also dissolved in water and are carried from body tissues. Every day, 1 to 2.5 liters (2.1 to 5.25 pints) of water pass out of the body in the urine. This water must be replaced.

Water also helps regulate your body temperature. *Evaporation*, or the change from liquid to gas, requires heat. Heat is lost when perspiration evaporates from your skin.

The water lost from our bodies through the kidneys and the skin must be balanced by the water we take in. We take in this needed water in three ways: 1) From the food we eat; 2) as a by-product of oxidation reactions and dehydration synthesis in our cells; and 3) from drinking water.

What happens if you do not drink enough water? First, you lose water from the intercellular spaces. Then you lose water from the cells themselves. When this happens the protoplasm becomes more concentrated. Finally, the cell cannot function and it dies. This water loss is part of the process called *dehydration*.

Mineral Salts

Minerals are important to the body in many ways. We get minerals from dissolved salts such as *sodium chloride*, or table salt. The dissolved minerals are in the form of ions such as sodium, potassium, calcium, and cloride ions. Salts are lost from the body through perspiration and through the kidneys. People exposed to considerable heat for a long period of time should take in more salt as well as water in the form of salt solutions.

Our bodies also need *calcium* and *phosphorous*. Calcium is needed for proper functioning of plasma membranes and for the clotting of blood. Together with *magnesium*, calcium is essential to nerve and muscle action. Phosphorus is a component of ATP, DNA, and RNA. Calcium phosphate is needed to form bones and teeth. In fact, calcium and phosphorus make up about five percent of animal tissue when

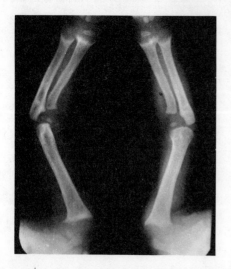

41-2 | X-rays of the arms of a child with rickets. This is a deficiency disease due to a lack of vitamin D in the diet. *(Henry Ford Hospital, Detroit)*

they combine with the other elements in proteins. Milk, whole-grain cereals, meat, and fish are good sources of calcium and phosphorus.

Potassium compounds are needed for growth. In order to form red blood corpuscles, you must have *iron compounds.* You can get this iron from eating meat, green vegetables, and fruits such as plums, prunes, and raisins. *Iodine salts* are needed to form the thyroid gland's secretion. You can get iodine from drinking water, or by eating seafoods. Iodine is also added to table salt. Most likely the container of table salt you use will have "Iodized" on the label.

These minerals must be replaced as the body uses them, or excretes them in perspiration or through the kidneys. A balanced diet provides these required mineral salts. Perhaps now you are beginning to understand why a diet of "junk foods" will not provide nutrition for a healthy body.

Vitamins

In 1911, Dr. Casimir Funk discovered some substances in foods that were not ordinary nutrients. These substances seemed to be necessary to body growth and activity. They also were needed to prevent certain **deficiency diseases.** These substances are called **vitamins.** Deficiency diseases result when the body does not have the required amount of vitamins. At first each vitamin discovered was identified by a letter—A, B, C, and so on. Scientists discovered that some of them were made of many different substances. The vitamin-B complex is a good example. When its different parts were discovered, they were labeled B_1, B_2, and so on. Today, vitamins have names that describe the chemicals in them, but the letters are still used for easy identification. Vitamins are organic substances essential to life, but not required as energy sources. Look at Table 41-1 for more information on the better-known vitamins.

Your body can store some vitamins, but others must be supplied constantly because the excess is excreted in the urine. Vitamin D can be produced in the skin. Other vitamins must be obtained from the food you eat or from extracts, such as vitamin pills. As with other body requirements, the best way to get your vitamins is from a balanced diet.

Synthetic Vitamins You can get most vitamins in synthetic form. Vitamin pills can be taken in addition to the natural vitamins in your diet, if you need them. Your doctor can tell you if you have a vitamin deficiency. He or she can prescribe concentrated vitamins if you seem to need them. But if you eat properly, these additional vitamins are probably unnecessary for the average person.

Table 41-1 FUNCTIONS AND IMPORTANT SOURCES OF VITAMINS

VITAMINS	BEST SOURCES	ESSENTIAL FOR	DEFICIENCY SYMPTOMS
vitamin A (oil soluble)	fish-liver oils liver and kidney green and yellow vegetables yellow fruit tomatoes butter egg yolk	growth health of the eyes structure and functions of the cells of the skin and mucous membranes	retarded growth night blindness susceptibility to infections changes in skin and membranes defective tooth formation
thiamin (B_1) (water soluble)	seafood meat soybeans milk whole grain green vegetables fowl	growth carbohydrate metabolism functioning of the heart, nerves, and muscles	retarded growth loss of appetite and weight nerve disorders less resistance to fatigue faulty digestion (beriberi)
riboflavin (B_2 or G) (water soluble)	meat soybeans milk green vegetables eggs fowl yeast	growth health of the skin and mouth carbohydrate metabolism functioning of the eyes	retarded growth dimness of vision inflammation of the tongue premature aging intolerance to light
niacin (water soluble)	meat fowl fish peanut butter potatoes whole grain tomatoes leafy vegetables	growth carbohydrate metabolism functioning of the stomach and intestines functioning of the nervous system	smoothness of the tongue skin eruptions digestive disturbances mental disorders (pellagra)
vitamin B_{12} (water soluble)	green vegetables liver	preventing pernicious anemia	a reduction in number of red blood cells
ascorbic acid (C) (water soluble)	citrus fruit other fruit tomatoes leafy vegetables	growth maintaining strength of the blood vessels development of teeth gum health	sore gums hemorrhages around the bones tendency to bruise easily (scurvy)
vitamin D (oil soluble)	fish-liver oil liver fortified milk eggs irradiated foods	growth regulating calcium and phosphorus metabolism building and maintaining bones, teeth	soft bones poor development of teeth dental decay (rickets)
tocopherol (E) (oil soluble)	wheat germ oil leafy vegetables milk butter	normal reproduction	(undetermined)
vitamin K (oil soluble)	green vegetables soybean oil tomatoes	normal clotting of the blood normal liver functions	hemorrhages

Organic Nutrients

Carbohydrates, fats, and proteins are *organic nutrients.* They are formed by living cells and contain the element *carbon.* Carbohydrates and fats supply energy. The tissue-building value of foods can only be measured by observing growth of animals when they are fed. The energy value of foods are most commonly measured in heat units. These called called **food Calories.** One food Calorie is the amount of heat needed to raise by one centigrade degree the temperature of one kilogram of water. One food Calorie equals one kilocalorie (1 kcal).

If you are dieting, you may be "counting calories." In fact, however, you are counting kilocalories. For example, a piece of pie that is said to have 310 "calories" really has 310 food Calories or kilocalories. This is a lot of energy. It is about as much as the energy in 500 grams of coal or one sixth cup of gasoline.

The amount of calories you need depends on your size and build, your age, and what you do.

Carbohydrates

The bread in the sandwich and sugars in the fruit you eat are *carbohydrates.* More than half of what you eat is carbohydrate food. Carbohydrates are primarily fuel foods. They are oxidized very rapidly and supply the energy your body needs. Some carbohydrates are digested easily. Others have to be broken down before the cells can use them. Some carbohydrates, such as the cellulose in the lettuce of a sandwich, are not digested at all. All digestible carbohydrates reach our body cells as *glucose* (or *dextrose*).

There are many simple sugars in your food. These include glucose, fructose, and galactose. They are *monosaccharides.* These simple sugars are made of single hexose molecules with the chemical formula $C_6H_{12}O_6$. They are quick-energy sources and require almost no chemical change before the blood can absorb them.

Disaccharides are made of two hexose units. Disaccharides include *sucrose* (cane sugar), *lactose* (milk sugar), and *maltose* (malt sugar). These double sugars undergo hydrolysis. As you learned in Chapter 3, this process breaks them into simple sugar molecules.

Starches, or *polysaccharides,* make up a large part of the carbohydrates in most diets. There is much starch in potatoes and cereal grains.

Starches are made of large chains of glucose units. Each unit has the formula $C_6H_{10}O_6$. Digestion occurs when a water molecule (H_2O) is added to a glucose unit. In this

41-3 | Examples of organic nutrients. *(Courtesy of the American Dental Association)*

process, starch is reduced first to maltose. This double sugar then is broken down into glucose. Glucose is absorbed by the blood and carried to the body tissues.

Much of the glucose that goes into the blood is changed temporarily into animal starch, or glycogen, by the liver. As cells oxidize glucose, glycogen is changed back to glucose (or dextrose) in the liver. The glucose is released into the bloodstream. This maintains the level of blood sugar. If the liver did not do this, we would constantly have to eat small amounts of carbohydrates to supply the body's energy needs.

Celluloses are complex carbohydrates. They are found in the cell walls of vegetables. **Humans cannot digest celluloses.** Even so, the bulkiness of celluloses is important to the digestive system. Celluloses cause the intestines to expand as they move through them. This *roughage* also stimulates muscle contractions in the intestine walls causing movement of the food. This muscular activity is necessary for normal digestion to take place.

Fats

Fats and oils yield more than twice as much energy as carbohydrates. Common sources of fats or oils include butter, cream, cheese, margarine, shortening, vegetable oils, and meat fats.

Fats can be absorbed directly into the bloodstream. During digestion, enzymes slowly hydrolyze fats. That is, there is a decomposition of molecules by the action of water. This happens in a series of chemical reactions. The enzymes cause three water molecules to combine with each fat molecule. The result is one molecule of *glycerol* and three molecules of *fatty acids*.

The absorbed fat is either oxidized or stored in the body until needed. Most body fat is stored in tissue spaces under the skin, and around the kidneys and liver. Excess carbohydrates are converted into body fats. You should control the amount of carbohydrate and fat you eat. Too much body fat causes a strain on the heart and on the muscles that function to move the body.

Proteins

As you learned in Chapter 3, *proteins* are complex molecules. They are made of many units called *amino acids*. The

Table 41–2 FOOD SUBSTANCES

SUBSTANCE	ESSENTIAL FOR	SOURCE
A. Inorganic compound Water	composition of protoplasm, tissue fluid, and blood; dissolving substances	all foods (released during oxidation)
B. Mineral salts sodium compounds calcium compounds	blood and other body tissues deposition in bones and teeth, heart and nerve action, clotting of blood	table salt, vegetables milk, whole-grain cereals, vegetables, meats
phosphorus compounds	deposition in bones and teeth; formation of ATP, nucleic acids	milk, whole-grain cereals, vegetables, meats
magnesium potassium compounds	muscle and nerve action blood and cell activities, growth	vegetables vegetables
iron compounds	formation of red blood corpuscles	leafy vegetables, liver, meats, raisins, prunes
iodine	secretion by thyroid gland	seafoods, water, iodized salt
C. Complex organic substances Vitamins	regulation of body processes, prevention of deficiency diseases	various foods, especially milk, butter, lean meats, fruits, leafy vegetables; also made synthetically
D. Organic nutrients carbohydrates	energy (stored as fat or glycogen) bulk in diet	cereals, bread, pastries, tapioca, fruits, vegetables
fats	energy (stored as fat or glycogen)	butter, cream, lard, oils, cheese, oleomargarine, nuts, meats
proteins	growth, maintenance, and repair of protoplasm	lean meats, eggs, milk, wheat, beans, peas, cheese

proteins you eat are foreign to your body and cannot be used by your cells as they are. During digestion the proteins are broken down to individual amino acids or small groups of amino acids. Then your body cells combine the amino acids to synthesize your own protein molecules. Protein is very important in your diet for both the growth and repair of your body. Amino acids are also required for the synthesis of proteins that serve as enzymes.

Not all the amino acid molecules absorbed by the blood are used in protein synthesis. Some are broken into two parts by the liver. This chemical action is called *deamination*. One part contains carbon and is sent to the tissues as glucose. The other part contains nitrogen. It combines with carbon dioxide to form urea, a waste product. Urea is transported by the blood to the kidneys. There it is excreted in the urine.

The Digestive System

Why can't your body tissues use most foods in the forms in which you eat them? There are two reasons. First, many foods will not dissolve in water. This means that they could not get through cell membranes even if they could reach them. Second, the foods you eat are chemically complex. Tissues cannot use them either in oxidation or in protein synthesis. Digestion solves both these problems. In **digestion, complex foods are broken down into small water-soluble molecules.** These molecules can be absorbed and used by your cells.

Digestion occurs in two phases. The first is *mechanical.* You chew the food. Then the muscular movement of the wall of the digestive system churns and mixes it with various juices. This aids the second phase of digestion, which is *chemical.* In this phase, digestive enzymes, secreted by the digestive glands, complete the job.

The digestive system includes the organs that form the **alimentary canal,** or food tube. Other organs in the digestive system do not receive undigested food. Instead, they deliver secretions into the alimentary canal through ducts. Ducts are tubes that go from certain glands into the organs where food is being digested.

The Mouth: The Beginning of Digestion

The mouth is an organ of sensation and speech, but its chief job is to get food ready for digestion. Move the tip of your tongue from your teeth up to the roof of your mouth. You can feel the **hard palate.** This bony structure covered with membranes forms the roof of the chewing area. By moving

Facts & Figures

The human digestive tube is about nine meters (about 30 feet) long.

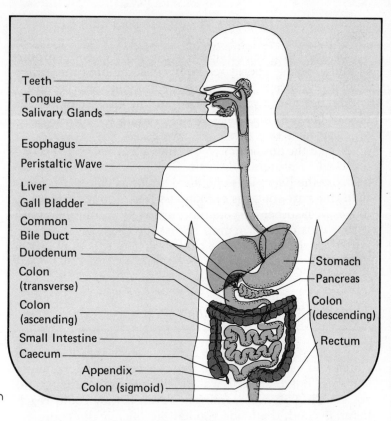

41-4 | The organs of the digestive system in the human body.

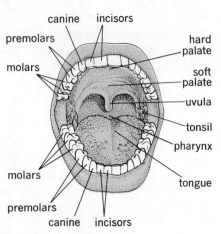

41-5 | Digestion begins in the mouth.

the tip of your tongue still further back, notice a soft area. This is the **soft palate.** This part of the mouth is made of folded membranes. These membranes extend from the rear of the hard palate to the top of the throat. If you open your mouth and look in a mirror, you can see a knob at the end of the soft palate. This is the *uvula* (YOO-vyuh-luh).

The back of the mouth opens into a muscular cavity called the **pharynx** (FA-ringks). The nasal cavity also opens into the pharynx. The soft palate partly separates the mouth cavity from the nasal cavity. The inside of the cheeks are the side walls of the mouth cavity. The cheek linings are mucous membranes. They contain many mucous glands. **Mucus** is a lubricating solution that mixes with food in the mouth. It softens the food and helps you to chew and swallow. The front of the cheek lining turns outward to form the lips.

The Salivary Glands In addition to the mucous glands in the cheek linings, your mouth also has pairs of **salivary glands.** The *parotid glands* are the largest of the salivary glands. There is a parotid gland on each side of the face, situated in front of the ears. These glands secrete saliva into the mouth through ducts. These ducts are located opposite your second upper molars. When you have the mumps, the parotid glands are infected and cause pain. The *submaxillary glands* are in the angles of the lower jaws. The *sublingual glands* are located in the floor of your mouth under the tongue. Ducts from these two glands open in the floor of the mouth, under the tongue. When your mouth "waters" these glands are secreting saliva. This happens when you taste and chew food. The salivary glands may also be stimulated simply by the smell, sight, or thought of food.

The Tongue and Its Functions   The tongue lies along the floor of the mouth, but it begins in the throat. This muscular organ has several important functions.

- *It acts as an organ of taste*. Notice that the surface of your tongue is covered with tiny bumps. These bumps hold **taste buds,** which have nerve endings at their bases. When you eat, the food in your mouth touches these bumps. This stimulates the nerve endings to send "taste" messages to your brain.

- *It helps you chew*. The movement of your tongue keeps food between your teeth.

- *Your tongue helps you swallow*. As you swallow, your tongue moves food toward the back of your mouth. The tongue is then jerked downward. This lodges the food in the pharynx and passes it into the esophagus opening. While this is happening, the pressure of your tongue closes off the trachea. Each time you swallow your breathing stops for a moment.

- *Your tongue keeps the inner surface of your teeth clean*. This happens because, though you may not be aware of it, you often roll your tongue around the inside of your mouth.

- *The tongue is essential to speech*. Your tongue works with your lips, teeth, and hard palate to form the sounds into words. Without this interaction, sounds could not be formed into words.

The Structure of Teeth   The permanent teeth are arranged in the same way in upper and lower jaws. The two flat front teeth are called *incisors*. They have sharp edges for cutting food. Next to the incisors, at the corner of your lips on either side, is a large cone-shaped tooth. This tooth is called the *canine*. Behind the canine tooth are the *premolars*. There are two on either side. Next are the *molars*. You have three molars on either side if you have cut your wisdom teeth; if not, you have two. Premolars and molars have flat surfaces which are good for grinding and crushing. Many jaws are too small to hold the third molars, or wisdom teeth. In these jaws, wisdom teeth often grow in crooked or

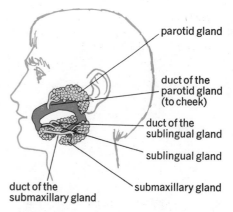

41–6 | A section of the head showing the location of the three pairs of salivary glands.

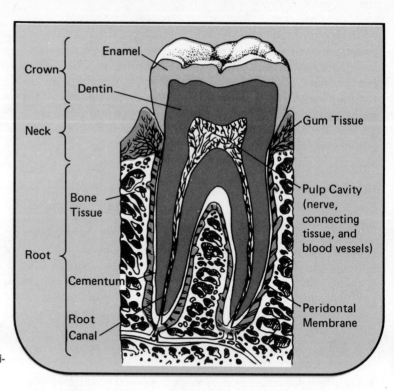

Enamel

Crown

Dentin

Neck

Gum Tissue

Bone
Tissue

Pulp Cavity
(nerve,
connecting
tissue, and
blood vessels)

Root

Cementum

Root
Canal

Peridontal
Membrane

41-7 | Diagram of a typical molar, longitudinal section.

grow into the second molars. Sometimes the wisdom teeth remain embedded, or impacted.

A tooth has three general areas. The part above the gum is called the *crown*. A narrow part at the gum line is called the *neck*. The *root* is the part beneath the surface. The root is held in a socket in the jaw bone. A fibrous *periodontal membrane* anchors it firmly in the jaw socket. Different kinds of teeth have differently shaped roots. Some are long and single. Some have two, three, or four projections. The covering of the root is called *cementum*. It holds the tooth firmly together. The crown has a hard white covering called *enamel*.

If a tooth is cut lengthwise, you can see the *dentine* beneath the enamel and cementum. Dentine is very hard, but somewhat softer than the enamel and cementum. It forms the bulk of the tooth. The *pulp cavity* is in the center of the tooth. The pulp cavity contains blood vessels and nerve fibers.

The Esophagus and Stomach

When food is swallowed it passes into the **esophagus.** This is a tube about 30 centimeters (1 foot) long. It connects the mouth to the stomach. Layers of smooth muscle line the wall of the esophagus. One layer is circular and squeezes in. The other layer runs lengthwise. The circular muscle contracts in a wave that travels downward. The food is pushed ahead of the contraction.

The **stomach** is in the upper part of the abdominal cavity. It lies just below the diaphragm. The stomach walls have three layers of smooth muscle. One layer is circular, another layer extends the length of the stomach, and the third layer is arranged on an angle. This arrangement of muscle fibers enables the stomach to twist and churn.

The stomach lining is a thick, wrinkled membrane. It contains three different types of *gastric glands*. One kind secretes an enzyme. Another secretes hydrochloric acid. The third secretes mucus. Each gland is a tiny tube that opens into the stomach. The gland walls are lined with secretory cells. The mixture of the secretions from these three kinds of glands is called **gastric fluid.**

Food usually remains in the stomach two to three hours. Rhythmic muscle contractions churn the food back and forth in a circular path. This churning separates food particles and mixes them thoroughly with the gastric fluid. When the stomach finishes its digesting, a valve at its intestinal end opens and closes several times. This is the **pyloric valve.** Each time the pyloric valve opens, food moves into the small intestine. When the stomach is finally empty, it rests for a while. However, after several hours without food, the stomach starts contracting again. These contractions are what make you say your stomach is "growling."

The Small Intestine

When food leaves the stomach, it enters the **small intestine.** This is a narrow tube about three centimeters (1.2 inches) in diameter and seven meters (23.1 feet) long. The small intestine has three sections. The first 25 centimeters (10 inches) is called the *duodenum* (doo-uh-DEE-num). The duodenum curves upward, then backward to the right, beneath the liver. The next section of the small intestine is the *jejunum* (ji-JOO-num). The jejunum is about two meters (6.6 ft) long. The lower part of the small intestine is the *ileum* (ILL-ee-um). This section is about five meters (16.5 feet) long and coils through the abdominal cavity. The end of the ileum joins the large intestine.

Several important digestive processes occur in the small intestine. The mucous lining of the small intestine has many tiny *intestinal glands*. These glands secrete *intestinal fluid* into the small intestine. The fluid contains some of the enzymes used in digestion. Secretions from the liver and the pancreas add other enzymes to the contents of the small intestine.

carbohydrates

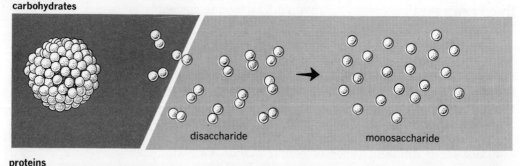

disaccharide   monosaccharide

proteins

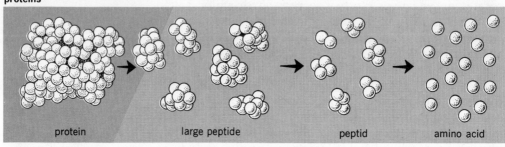

protein   large peptide   peptid   amino acid

fats

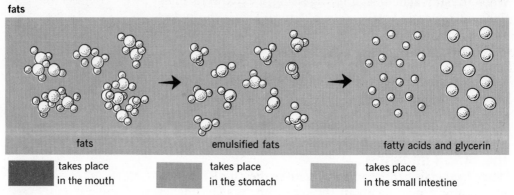

fats   emulsified fats   fatty acids and glycerin

takes place in the mouth

takes place in the stomach

takes place in the small intestine

41-8 | Phases in the digestion of carbohydrates, proteins, and fats. Why can they not be used by the tissues of the body in the form in which they are eaten?

The Liver: The Chemical-Processing Plant

The *liver* weighs about 1.5 kilograms (3.3 lbs) and lies in the upper right area of your abdomenal cavity. **The liver secretes *bile*, a brownish-green fluid.** Bile passes from the liver through a series of *bile ducts*. The bile ducts join in a Y-shape. The secreted bile travels down one branch of the Y and up the other to the *gall bladder* where it is stored. In the gall bladder some water is removed, thus concentrating the bile. The base of the Y is the *common bile duct*. It carries bile from the gall bladder to the duodenum. Sometimes the common bile duct becomes clogged by a gallstone or a plug of mucus. This causes the bile to enter the bloodstream and produce a *jaundice* condition. Jaundice causes the eyes and skin to turn a yellowish color.

The Pancreas

The *pancreas* lies behind the stomach and the upper end of the small intestine against the back wall of the abdominal cavity. The pancreas is long and white and has many lobes. It looks much like a salivary gland. The pancreas performs two very different functions. It secretes digestive enzymes. The secretion is called **pancreatic fluid.** The pancreatic duct carries the pancreatic fluid and joins the common bile duct as it enters the duodenum. The second function of the pancreas is to produce *insulin.* Insulin is required for glucose to enter a cell.

The Large Intestine, or Colon

The large intestine is also called the **colon.** It begins in the lower right part of the abdominal cavity. At this point where the small intestine joins it, the colon forms a blind sac called the *caecum*, commonly known as the appendix. Sometimes infection makes the appendix become painfully inflamed. This condition is known as *appendicitis.*

The colon is shorter and wider than the small intestine. It is about seven centimeters in diameter and one and a half meters long. The colon forms an upside-down U in the abdominal cavity. The lower end of the colon is called the *sigmoid colon.* At the end of the large intestine is a large muscular cavity called the **rectum.** The lower end of the rectum forms the *anal opening.* A valvelike muscle in the lower end of the rectum controls elimination of the remains of the intestinal contents.

The Chemical Breakdown of Food

As foods move along the digestive tract, they undergo a series of chemical changes. At each step, a specific enzyme is secreted. **Digestive enzymes are hydrolytic enzymes.** Each causes a chemical change in which water molecules interact with food molecules. Each enzyme splits specific kinds of molecules. Enzymatic action in the digestive tract takes place *outside* the cells. Most other enzymes in your body act *within* cells.

Digestion in the Mouth

Chemical action on food begins in the mouth. Here a salivary enzyme begins the hydrolysis of starch. As you know, saliva is secreted by the salivary glands. Saliva is more than 95 percent water. It also contains mineral salts, lubricating mucus, and the enzyme *salivary amylase* (AM-i-lace).

Facts & Figures

Digestive enzymes are only a few of the thousands of enzymes that regulate all body processes.

The amylase changes cooked starch into the disaccharide maltose. Starchy foods, like potatoes, should be cooked before eating. This bursts their cellulose cell walls and allows amylase to reach the starch grains. Food is only in the mouth for a short time, so starch digestion is seldom finished when food is swallowed. However, amylase continues to act for a while in the stomach.

Digestion in the Stomach

The main enzyme in gastric fluid is *pepsin*. Pepsin splits the complex protein molecules into simpler groups of amino acids called *peptides*. **This splitting is the first in a series of chemical changes involved in protein digestion.**

Pepsin is sometimes called *gastric protease*. This enzyme splits complex protein molecules into simpler groups of amino acids. These are known as *peptones* and proteoses. **This splitting is the first in a series of chemical changes involved in protein digestion.**

Hydrochloric acid helps pepsin. This acid also dissolves minerals and kills many of the bacteria that enter the stomach with food. In addition, it regulates the action of the pyloric valve. You may remember that this valve opens when digestion is complete and lets the food into the small intestine.

What does the food that passes from the stomach to the small intestine contain? It contains 1) fats, unchanged; 2) sugars, unchanged; 3) maltose, formed by amylase acting on starch; 4) any starches not changed by amylase; 5) coagulated milk casein; 6) peptides formed by pepsin acting on protein; and 7) any proteins not changed by pepsin.

The Liver and Bile

The liver has several vital functions. It takes glucose from the blood and changes it to glycogen. Thus, it acts as a chemical factory. The liver is also a storehouse. It holds reserve carbohydrates as glycogen. The liver also synthesizes urea from amino groups and CO_2. The urea enters the bloodstream and is excreted by the kidneys.

The liver is an excretory organ also. It removes bile pigments which are sent to the intestine through the bile duct. Bile contains material from dead red blood corpuscles filtered from the bloodstream by the liver.

In the small intestine bile has another important function. *Lipase*, made by the pancreas, is a water soluble enzyme. It can only attack fat globules at the surface. Bile causes the fat globules to break into smaller particles. Lipase, then, can split more molecules of fat. **Bile, itself, is not a digestive secretion.** It merely breaks the globules of fat into smaller droplets called an *emulsion*. Bile also activates lipase.

Facts & Figures

The human body does not produce the enzyme cellulase to break down plant cell walls.

Careers

Dieticians work in hospitals, schools, and other institutions. They also work in industry research organizations. They provide nutritional information especially in relation to health. A four-year college program is a minimum requirement for some jobs. However, more education and an internship are usually required.

41-9 | A dietician instructs a hospital patient in what foods she has selected for him and why. (*HRW Photo by Russell Dian*)

The Role of the Pancreas in Digestion

Pancreatic fluid acts on all three kinds of organic nutrients. It contains three enzymes: *trypsin, amylase,* and *lipase.* Trypsin continues the breakdown of proteins that began in the stomach. It splits groups of amino acids into *peptides.* Trypsin can also act on proteins that were not split during stomach digestion. Peptides are not the final product of protein digestion. Other enzymes split peptides into individual amino acids.

Like the amylase in saliva, pancreatic amylase changes starch into maltose. This is how the potatoes not acted upon by salivary amylase are changed into sugar. Lipase splits fats into fatty acids and glycerol. Both these substances can be absorbed by your body cells.

Digestion in the Small Intestine

The fluid secreted by the intestinal glands is highly alkaline. This neutralizes the stomach acid. It contains four main enzymes. They are peptidase, maltase, lactase, and sucrase. *Peptidase* completes protein digestion. It splits the peptides, formed by pancreatic fluid, into amino acids. *Maltase* splits the disaccharide maltose into monosaccharide glucose. This is the final product of carbohydrate digestion. *Lactase* has a similar action on *lactose,* or milk sugar. It changes lactose into glucose and galactose. *Sucrase* splits sucrose into glucose and fructose.

Bile, pancreatic fluid, and intestinal fluid together complete the digestion of all three classes of food. Carbohydrates, fats, and proteins become soluble substances. They leave the digestive system in the form of simple sugars, fatty acids, glycerol, and amino acids. They also enter the blood and lymph.

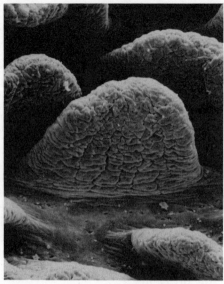

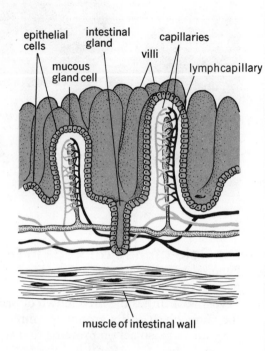

epithelial cells
intestinal gland
capillaries
mucous gland cell
villi
lymphcapillary

muscle of intestinal wall

41–10 | Villi create an enormous surface area that absorbs the end products of digestion. (left) Scanning electron micrograph of villi (265X) *(Richard G. Kessell, Randy H. Kardon,© W. H. Freeman and Company)* (right) Diagram of villi, sideview.

Absorption in the Small Intestine

The small intestine has many fingerlike projections in its irregular lining. These projections are called *villi.* There are so many villi that they give the intestinal wall a velvety appearance. There are blood vessels and branching lymph vessels inside the villi. The villi bring blood and lymph close to the digested food. Because of their form, they enormously increase the absorption surface of the intestine. Absorption is also increased by a constant swaying motion of the villi through the intestinal contents.

Glycerol and fatty acids enter the villi and are carried away by the lymph. Eventually they reach the general circulation and travel to the tissues. Monosaccharides and amino acids enter the blood vessels of the villi. From there they are carried directly to the liver through the portal vein.

Water Absorption in the Large Intestine

The large intestine receives watery masses of undigestible food bulk from the small intestine. **As these masses move through the colon, much of the water is absorbed** and is taken into the tissues. The remaining intestinal content is called *feces* (FEE-seez). It becomes more solid as the water is absorbed. The feces pass into the rectum. From there, they are eventually eliminated through the anal opening.

Summary

PLACE OF DIGESTION	GLANDS	SECRETION	ENZYMES	DIGESTIVE ACTIVITY
mouth	salivary	saliva	amylase	changes starch to maltose; lubricates
	mucous	mucus		lubricates
esophagus	mucous	mucus		lubricates
stomach	gastric	gastric fluid	pepsin	changes proteins to peptides
		hydrochloric acid		activates pepsin; dissolves minerals; kills bacteria
	mucous	mucus		lubricates
small intestine	liver	bile		emulsifies fats; activates lipase
	pancreas	pancreatic fluid	trypsin	changes proteins to peptides
			amylase	changes starch to maltose
			lipase	changes fats to fatty acids and glycerol
	intestinal glands	intestinal fluid	peptidase	changes peptides to amino acids
			maltase	changes maltose to glucose
			lactase	changes lactose to glucose and galactose
			sucrase	changes sucrose to glucose and fructose
	mucous	mucus		lubricates
large intestine (colon)	mucous	mucus		lubricates

Biologically Speaking

food	esophagus
deficiency disease	stomach
vitamin	gastric fluid
organic nutrient	pyloric valve
food Calorie	small intestine
roughage	liver
digestion	bile
alimentary canal	gall bladder
hard palate	pancreas
soft palate	pancreatic fluid
pharynx	colon
mucus	rectum
salivary gland	villi
taste buds	feces

Questions for Review

1. What are the functions of foods?
2. Why must the body have water?
3. In what two general ways must food be changed during digestion?
4. What are organic nutrients?
5. Why are carbohydrates an important food?
6. List, in order, the divisions of the digestive tract. What digestive processes occur in each?
7. Name the parts of a tooth.
8. Why is it especially important that you chew bread and potatoes thoroughly?
9. Suppose that you had a glass of milk and a sandwich made of bread, butter, and ham. Tell what would happen to each of these foods as it was digested in the (a) mouth, (b) stomach, and (c) small intestine.
10. Name two important functions of the large intestine.

Applying Concepts

1. Explain how a vitamin deficiency is possible even if an adequate amount of vitamins is taken daily.
2. Why is food acid in the stomach and alkaline in the small intestine?
3. Explain how interference with the rhythmic waves of the walls of the large intestine may cause either constipation or diarrhea.
4. Why is it easier to digest sour milk than fresh milk?

42

Transport and Excretion

A **DEFINE** blood.
B **LIST** and **DESCRIBE** the function of each part of the blood.
C **EXPLAIN** how blood clots.
D **EXPLAIN** how the Rh factor may affect childbirth.
E **TRACE** the circulation of blood through the body.
F **IDENTIFY** the parts and functions of the kidney.

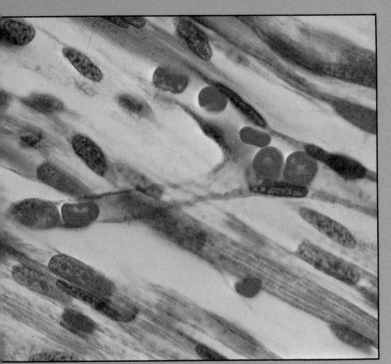

42–1 | Capillaries seen through a microscope. *(© Lennart Nilsson from Behold Man, Little Brown and Co., Boston)*

The Transport System

The production of a car involves a number of stages. An assembly line transports the various automobile parts along a moving belt. These parts then are assembled into the final product, a car. Your body does a similar thing with the food you eat. The food you eat is first broken down into simple molecules. Then these smaller molecules are absorbed into the bloodstream and carried to the cells of your body. In the cells, the parts are put together and used.

Nutritive fluids, waste materials, and water flow through the bodies of living organisms. The movement of these substances through organisms is called **circulation.** The system is called the *circulatory system*, or *transport system*. Many lower organisms transport fluids in different ways. Sponges, for example, literally pump the ocean into their bodies! Seawater supplies each cell with needed oxygen. The seawater also washes away wastes. The solution that bathes human cells is called *tissue fluid*. It contains salts but is much less salty than seawater.

Humans have a more complex circulatory system than

invertebrates. The food you eat provides the raw materials used to make your own "seawater." Other vital substances are also added to it. This fluid is piped through our bodies and circulated by a pump. The pump is the human heart. If your heart stops working, your cells can no longer obtain oxygen and nutrients or eliminate waste products and would die quickly.

Composition of Blood

The fluid that carries all of your body substances is called *blood.* The average person has about six liters (12 pints) of blood. This is about nine percent of your body weight. Blood is a rather special type of connective tissue. Whole blood consists partly of a solid part, the blood cells. There are three types of blood cells. They are **red corpuscles** (red blood cells, or erythrocytes), **white corpuscles** (white blood cells, or leucocytes), and **platelets** (thrombocytes). **The blood cells are scattered within the nonliving fluid part, called *plasma.***

corpus = body

Plasma is a sticky, straw-colored liquid. Plasma is about 90 percent water. There are many different kinds of proteins in the blood plasma. One of the plasma proteins is *fibrinogen* (fy-BRIN-uh-jin). Fibrinogen is necessary to blood clotting. *Serum albumin* is another plasma protein. It is necessary to the normal blood-tissue relationships during absorption of water. The third is *serum globulins*. These proteins include the antibodies that make you immune to various diseases.

Three other materials are also in plasma.

- *Inorganic minerals,* dissolved in water. These compounds give plasma a salt content of about one percent. The salt content of seawater is about three percent. These compounds include carbonates, chlorides, and phosphates of the elements calcium, sodium, magnesium, and potassium. They are necessary to your blood and for normal functioning of your body tissues. Without calcium compounds, for example, your blood would not clot in a wound.

- *Digested foods* in the form of glucose, fatty acids, glycerol, and amino acids. These are transported to body tissues. They also are carried to the liver and other storage places.

- *Nitrogenous* (ny-TROJ-uh-nus) *wastes,* from protein metabolism in the tissues. One of these wastes, urea, is produced largely in the liver during the breakdown of amino acids. These nitrogenous wastes travel in the plasma to the organs of excretion.

42-2 | (left) Fresh blood in a test tube. (right) Blood in a test tube after the clot has formed. What is the clear fluid called? *(HRW photo by Ken Karp)*

Red Corpuscles

The *red corpuscles* are shaped like discs. They do not have nuclei. Both sides of these discs are concave, or curved inward. Sometimes they travel in the blood in rows that look like stacks of coins. They may also separate and float alone. Red cells are very small. Ten million of them can be spread out in about six square centimeters (.5 square inches), and you have many of them in your body. A normal person has about 25 trillion (25×10^{12}) red blood cells. If you laid the cells side by side, there would be enough to go around the earth four times at the equator. The red pigment in red corpuscles is called **hemoglobin**. Hemoglobin is a protein substance essential to life.

Red corpuscles are produced in red marrow. Red marrow is found at the ends of such bones as the ribs, vertebrae, and skull. In children, even the ends of long bones can make these cells. Developing erythrocytes are large, colorless, and have large nuclei. Usually, they have lost the nuclei by the time they enter the bloodstream. They also have synthesized hemoglobin by this time. Red corpuscles live from 20 to 120 days. When they die, they are removed by the liver or the spleen. At this time these organs release certain valuable compounds into the bloodstream to make new red blood cells.

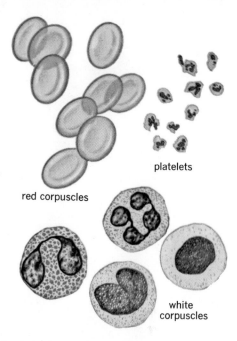

platelets

red corpuscles

white corpuscles

42–3 | The solid components of blood include red corpuscles, white corpuscles, and platelets. The red corpuscles are 7.2 microns in diameter.

Function of Erythrocytes

The erythrocytes circulate throughout the body in the bloodstream. **The red color of your blood is due to the pigment hemoglobin in the cytoplasm of the red blood cells.** Hemoglobin is a complex protein containing iron. In your lungs the iron in hemoglobin combines loosely with oxygen. The erythrocytes now become bright red. Then, in the tiny blood vessels of your body tissues, the hemoglobin gives up its oxygen. Here, part of the carbon dioxide formed in the tissues combines with the hemoglobin. The erythrocytes now become a very dark red color. In this way some of the carbon dioxide is carried to your lungs where it is released. The cycle then is repeated.

When the iron in hemoglobin is combined with oxygen it is said to be *oxygenated*. This is quite different from when an iron object turns red with rust. Rust is produced when iron is *oxidized*. This means that iron forms a strong chemical bond with oxygen from the air. Rusting iron does not give up its oxygen. Oxygenated hemoglobin, though, does release the oxygen for use by your body's cells. Hemoglobin, therefore, is a very special molecule.

The White Blood Cells

Most *white corpuscles* are larger than red corpuscles, and they differ from them in three ways.

Facts & Figures

Red blood cells of humans and other mammals do not have nuclei. Red blood cells of other vertebrates are nucleated.

- White corpuscles have nuclei.
- White corpuscles have no hemoglobin and are colorless.
- Some white corpuscles are capable of ameboid movement.

There are fewer white blood cells than there are red blood cells. The ratio is about one white cell to every 600 red cells. White corpuscles are formed in red marrow and in the lymph glands. Normally, you have about 8,000 white corpuscles in a cubic millimeter of blood. There are about 4.5 to 5 million red corpuscles in the same amount of blood.

Some white blood cells move about on their own. They can ooze through capillary walls into the tissue spaces. Here they engulf solid materials, including bacteria. Thus, **white blood cells are important in defending your body against infection.** Whenever you develop an infection, your white-cell count goes up. It may rise from 8,000 to more than 25,000 per cubic millimeter. These corpuscles collect in the infected area. Then they ingest and destroy bacteria. You have seen the pus that sometimes forms on infections. The remains of dead bacteria, white corpuscles, and tissue fluid is known as *pus*.

The Platelets *Platelets* are much smaller than red corpuscles. Platelets are shaped irregularly and are colorless. They are formed in the red marrow. Platelets are not able to move on their own; they float along in the bloodstream. **Platelets are important for forming blood clots.**

Table 42-1 SUMMARY OF COMPOSITION OF BLOOD

PLASMA	SOLID COMPONENTS
water	red corpuscles
proteins	white corpuscles
fibrinogen	platelets
serum albumin,	
globulin	
digested foods	
mineral salts	
organic nutrients	
cell wastes	

The Clotting of Blood

When you cut small blood vessels in a minor wound, blood oozes out. Most of us are not alarmed by such cuts. We know a clot will form and the blood flow will stop. **Clotting results from chemical and physical changes in the blood.** When a blood vessel is cut, platelets disintegrate in the

42-4 | The microscopic changes that occur during the clotting of blood. (a) Before clotting begins, (b) formation of threads of fibrin, (c) shortening of the fibrin threads and trapping of blood cells.

blood that is leaving the vessel. Platelets probably are destroyed by tissue fluids at the wound site. In the process, they release *thromboplastin*. Plasma contains an enzyme called *prothrombin*. Prothrombin is produced in the liver in the presence of vitamin K. Thromboplastin reacts with *prothrombin* in the presence of *calcium* to form *thrombin*. Thrombin changes *fibrinogen*, a soluble blood protein, to insoluble *fibrin*. Fibrin is made of tiny threads. These threads form a network that traps blood cells. When this happens, a clot is formed that stops any more blood from escaping. These trapped corpuscles dry and form a scab. Then the edges of the wound grow toward the center until it is healed. Clotting can be summarized as:

1. thromboplastin $\xrightarrow[\text{prothrombin}]{\text{calcium}}$ thrombin

2. fibrinogen $\xrightarrow{\text{thrombin}}$ fibrin

If any of these substances mentioned in this process is missing, blood will not clot.

When you fall you can sometimes damage blood vessels. When this happens, clotting results. The discolored area is known as a *bruise*. The clotted blood is gradually absorbed as the bruise heals. As this happens, the color of the bruise changes, and finally disappears.

42–5 | (a) The mixing of blood types shows no clumping (20X). (b) Agglutination results from the action of certain antigens and agglutinins (28X). *(Runk, Schoenberger, Grant Heilman)*

Blood Types

The four blood types are A, B, AB, and O. Differences in blood type are due to the **antigens** on the surface of the red cells. Antigens are proteins that stimulate antibody production. Type A blood contains A antigen and type B blood contains B antigen. Type AB blood has both A and B antigen. Type O blood has neither antigen. (See Table 42–2.)

Certain conditions in the body require blood transfusions. These include hemorrhage, wound shock, severe burns, and a variety of illnesses. If whole blood is used, patients get both plasma and blood cells. The blood plasma

Table 42-2 BLOOD TYPES

TYPE	ANTIGEN (in the RBC)	ANTIBODIES (in plasma/serum)	CAN GET BLOOD FROM	CAN GIVE BLOOD TO
A	A	anti-B	O, A	A, AB
B	B	anti-A	O, B	B, AB
AB	AB	none	A, B, AB, O	AB
O	none	anti-B, anti–A	O	A, B, AB, O

of type A blood contains anti-B antibody. The antibody attacks type B antigen. Type B blood has anti-A antibody and will attack type A antigens. If type A blood is injected into a person with type B blood, the red cells will clump together. The reverse is also true. The clumping of red blood cells is called *agglutination*. When agglutination occurs, the red corpuscles cannot carry oxygen and carbon dioxide. The result is fatal.

Type AB blood has neither anti-A nor anti-B antibodies. People with type AB blood (universal recipient) could receive any blood type because no clumping will occur. People with type O blood (universal donor) have no antigens and therefore the blood cells will not be attacked by agglutinins.

Transfusion of incorrect blood types results in agglutination. It is important that the blood of the donor and the recipient be cross-matched. Sometimes patients need only an increase in the *amount* of liquid in the bloodstream. They do not really need red blood cells. The erythrocytes form quickly if the blood volume is high enough. This condition is called *shock*. If you are in shock, plasma may be transfused instead of whole blood.

Blood Banks   During World War II, countries desperately needed blood. Dr. Charles R. Drew, a famous American, helped save countless lives of servicemen because of his experiments in preserving blood plasma. A blood bank that was established at the Columbia Medical Center under his supervision in 1938 resulted in his discovering that blood plasma could replace whole blood in transfusions.

The Rh Factor in Blood   The blood type antigens are made of one type of protein in blood. The **Rh factor** is another kind of protein found in the red blood cells. Rh is named for the rhesus (REE-sus) monkey. This factor was discovered from tests done on these monkeys. About 85 percent of the people in the United States have the Rh factor in their blood. Their blood is called Rh positive. The other 15 percent without the factor are Rh negative. Like blood types, the Rh factor is inherited. It is actually one of the six antigens.

If Rh-negative patients receive Rh-positive blood, they produce antibodies against this factor. These antibodies cause the corpuscles of the Rh-positive blood to agglutinate and dissolve. There is little danger during the first transfusion. This is because the antibody is not present when the Rh-positive blood is added. However, a second transfusion can be serious, even fatal. Why? Because the patient has already formed antibodies against the Rh-positive blood.

anti = against
gen = to be produced

The Rh Factor and Childbirth   **The Rh factor may cause a problem in childbearing.** This problem occurs in about one in three or four hundred mothers. It may happen when the mother is Rh negative and the father is Rh positive. The child may inherit the Rh-positive factor from the father. During prenatal development, Rh-positive blood may seep from the child into the mother's circulation. It can go through tiny ruptures in the membranes that normally keep the two circulations apart. The mother's blood can also seep into the child in the same way. The seepage usually occurs from a few days before birth to the time during birth.

This seepage does not happen very often. Therefore, many Rh-negative mothers bear normal Rh-positive children. Usually the situation becomes serious with second Rh-positive children. In that case, the mother has already produced antibodies from her first pregnancy. When the mother's antibodies pass into the second child's circulation, these antibodies cause serious damage. Sometimes the child dies before birth. Sometimes the damage is not so serious. A transfusion immediately after birth may save the child's life. The child's blood may be almost entirely replaced by transfused Rh-negative blood. This blood does not contain the antibody.

A method is now used to avoid the Rh problem in future pregnancies. The Rh-negative mother is given an injection around the time of the child's birth. This injection contains Rh antibodies. These antibodies circulate in the mother's blood for several weeks. They destroy all the Rh-positive factor from the baby. Thus, the mother's system does not develop its own antibodies against Rh factor. The mother should not have Rh problems with future babies.

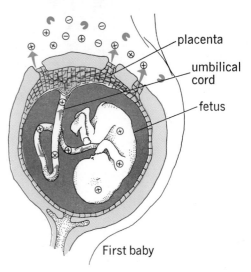

placenta

umbilical cord

fetus

First baby

⊖ mother's Rh-negative blood
⊕ baby's Rh-positive blood
⋒ mother's antibodies

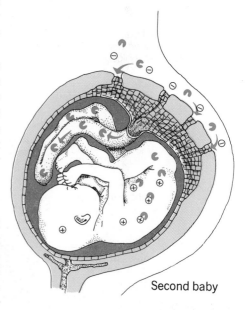

Second baby

42–6 | If an Rh-negative mother produces Rh-positive antibodies as a result of an earlier Rh-positive fetus, a problem may arise in a future Rh-positive fetus.

The Design of the Heart

The heart is a cone-shaped, muscular organ. It is located under your breastbone and between your lungs. The heart is enclosed in a sac called the *pericardium* (per-ri-KAHR-dee-um). The heart is usually a little to the left of the midline of your chest cavity. The tip of the heart points downward and to the left between the fifth and sixth ribs. Your heartbeat is strongest near this tip. That is why many people have the mistaken idea that their hearts are entirely on the left side.

Your heart has two sides, right and left. These two halves are separated by a wall called the *septum*. Each half has two chambers. There is a thin-walled chamber called the **atrium,** and there is a thick, muscular **ventricle.** The two atria are reservoirs for the blood that enters the heart. They contract at the same time. This contraction forces blood into the two ventricles. Next, the muscular walls of the ventricles contract forcing the blood through the arteries.

The heart has two sets of one-way valves. They control the flow of blood into and out of the ventricles. They also maintain pressure in the arteries between heartbeats. The valves between the atria and ventricles are called the *atrioventricular valves*, or a-v valves. These valves are small sections of tissues that are anchored to the floor of the ventricles by tendonlike strands. Blood passes freely through a-v valves into the ventricles. However, the a-v valves cannot be opened from the lower side because the tendons anchor them. The result is that blood cannot flow backward into the atria when the ventricles contract. The other set of valves are called *semilunar valves*, or s-l valves. These cuplike valves are located at the openings of the arteries. The force of blood passing from the ventricles into the arteries opens the s-l valves. The semilunar valves then prevent blood from backing up into the ventricles.

Circulation Through the Heart

One of the best ways to study the parts of the heart is to trace the path of blood through it. (Refer to figure 42–7 as you read the following description.) The blood first enters the right atrium of the heart from two different directions.

42–7 | The human heart. Note the location of the valves to the heart chambers and blood vessels. The arrows indicate the direction of blood flow.

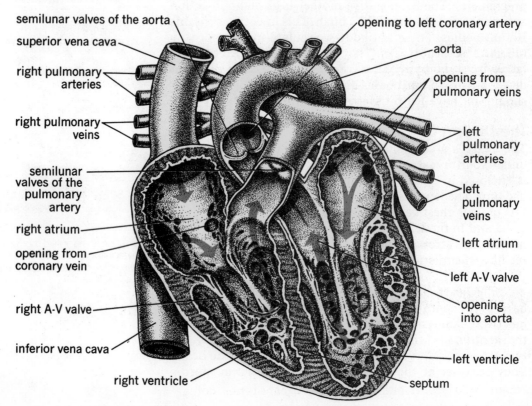

semilunar valves of the aorta

superior vena cava

right pulmonary arteries

right pulmonary veins

semilunar valves of the pulmonary artery

right atrium

opening from coronary vein

right A-V valve

inferior vena cava

right ventricle

opening to left coronary artery

aorta

opening from pulmonary veins

left pulmonary arteries

left pulmonary veins

left atrium

left A-V valve

opening into aorta

left ventricle

septum

Blood enters through the *superior vena cava* (VAY-nuh KAH-nuh) and the *inferior vena cava*. The superior vena cava carries blood from the head and upper parts of the body. The inferior vena cava returns blood from the lower parts. From the right atrium, blood goes through the right a-v valve into the right ventricle. Then the right ventricle contracts. This forces blood through a set of s-l valves into the *pulmonary arteries*. These arteries carry the blood to the lungs. The blood passes through the lung and into the right and left *pulmonary veins*. These vessels return blood to the heart and open into the left atrium. From there, the blood passes through the left a-v valve into the left ventricle. Finally, blood passes out the **aorta** (ay-OAR-tuh) and goes to all parts of the body.

pulmo = a lung

Of course, the heart is filled with blood, but its muscle layers are too thick to be nourished by this blood. Instead, the heart muscle cells are nourished by special arteries called *coronary arteries*. The aorta is largest just as it leaves the heart. This is called the *aortic sinus*. The right and left coronary arteries branch off from here. They curve downward around each side of the heart. Each sends off smaller vessels that penetrate the heart muscle.

Facts & Figures

Arteries are found in all parts of the body except in the hairs, nails, epidermis, cartilage, and cornea.

The Heart, A Highly Effective Pump A complete cycle of heart activity is called a beat. A beat has two phases. In the first phase, or **systole,** the ventricles contract and force blood into the arteries. In the second phase, or **diastole,** the ventricles relax and receive blood from the atria.

systaltikos = contractile
diastole = an expanding; dilation

Have you ever listened to your heart in a stethoscope? A normal heart sounds like the syllables "lub" and "dup" repeated over and over. They are in perfect rhythm. The "lub" is the systole phase. It is the sound of the contraction of the a-v valve. The "dup" is the diastole. This is the sound of the closing of the semilunar valves at the base of the arteries.

The heart of an average adult beats about 70 times per minute. This is when the person is resting. During hard work or exercise, the heart rate may be as high as 180 beats per minute.

The Blood Vessels

Blood moves in a system of tubes or vessels of different sizes. **Arteries** and **arterioles** carry blood away from the heart. **Veins** and **venules** carry blood toward the heart. **Capillaries** are very small thin-walled vessels.

The aorta branches into several large arteries. These arteries further branch and become arterioles. The arterioles branch into capillaries. The tiny capillaries pass through tissues and organs. Then the capillaries come

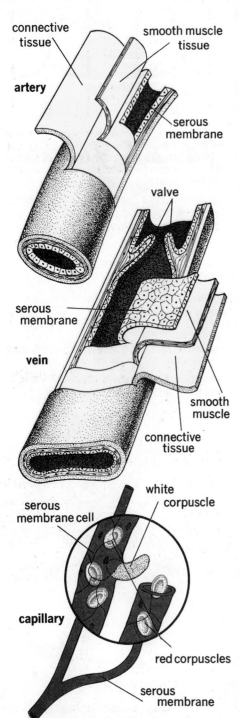

connective tissue

smooth muscle tissue

artery

serous membrane

valve

serous membrane

vein

smooth muscle

connective tissue

white corpuscle

serous membrane cell

capillary

red corpuscles

serous membrane

42–8 Three types of blood vessels.

together to form venules. The venules join to become veins. The veins take blood toward either the inferior or superior vena cava. These large veins lead into the right atrium of the heart.

Arteries *Arteries* have muscular walls with smooth linings. These walls have many elastic fibers. This allows arteries to expand and absorb great pressure. The pressure is created when the ventricles contract at systole. Place the fingers of one hand on the wrist of your other hand until you can feel your **pulse.** The pulse you feel is caused by *systolic pressure* in an artery. It has the same rhythm as your heartbeat. The elastic walls also maintain pressure in the arteries when the ventricles relax. This is called *diastolic pressure.* The pressure in the aorta leading from the left ventricle is greater than that in the pulmonary artery pumped by the smaller right ventricle. This greater pressure aids in pushing blood out through the aorta to the rest of the body.

Capillaries Arterioles penetrate the tissues where they branch into **capillaries.** The walls of capillaries are thinner than the walls of the other vessels. **Capillary walls are only one-cell thick.** Also, capillaries are barely larger in diameter than red corpuscles. These red corpuscles pass through the capillaries in single file.

Veins and arteries are important for carrying blood through our bodies. **All the vital relationships between blood and tissues occur through the capillaries.** Dissolved foods, waste products, and gases pass freely through the thin walls of the capillaries and in and out of the tissue spaces. White corpuscles squeeze between the membranes of the cells that make up the capillary walls. This is how white corpuscles leave the bloodstream and enter the tissue spaces. Some of the plasma diffuses from the blood through the capillary walls. This filtered plasma becomes tissue fluid.

Vein Structure and Function Arterioles branch into capillaries upon entering organ tissues. As capillaries leave an organ, they unite to form veins. Most veins carry dark red blood. This blood has given up some of its oxygen to the tissues. You can see some veins through your skin. The veins appear to be blue. *A yellow pigment in the skin makes the dark red blood in them look bluish.*

The walls of veins are much thinner and less muscular than those of arteries. So the *internal* diameter of a vein is greater. Many of the larger veins have cuplike valves. These valves keep blood from flowing backwards.

Circulation in the Body

Your four-chambered heart is really a double pump. Its two sides work in unison. Each side pumps blood through a major division of your circulatory system. The right side pumps blood through the lungs. The left side pumps blood to all the other body tissues.

When blood enters the right side of your heart, the blood is deoxygenated. This dark red blood leaves the heart through the arteries of the **pulmonary circulation.** The pulmonary artery carries the blood from the right ventricle. It then branches into two smaller arteries, each branch going to a lung. Within the lungs, each branches into a great many arterioles and then into capillaries. In the lungs, blood releases carbon dioxide and water. Capillaries join to form veins in the lungs. Oxygenated blood is then carried to the left atrium through the pulmonary veins.

The oxygen-rich blood passes through the left chambers of the heart and out the aorta under great pressure. It must supply blood to all the body tissues except the lungs. This system is called the **systemic circulation.** The systemic circulation is much longer and more complicated than the pulmonary circulation. In the pulmonary circulation all the blood from the right side of the heart goes to the lungs. In the systemic circulation, all the blood does not go to the same organs before it returns to the venae cavae. Systemic circulation includes several shorter circulations. Each supplies or drains a special organ of the body. Three special circulations are: *coronary, renal,* and *portal.*

The **coronary circulation** supplies blood to the heart itself. This circulation was mentioned in the discussion of the heart muscle. The coronary circulation begins at the right atrium.

The **renal circulation** starts with two renal arteries branching from the aorta. One artery goes to each kidney. Within the kidneys the arteries branch into capillaries. The renal veins return blood from the kidneys to the inferior vena cava. Blood in the renal circulation nourishes the kidneys and removes waste products from the cells.

The **portal circulation** is a system of veins involving the digestive organs: stomach, pancreas, small pancreas, small intestines, colon, and the spleen. Blood coming from these digestive organs transports digested food and water. The large veins from these organs unite to form the *portal vein.* As the portal vein enters the liver, it branches into many capillaries. The thin capillary walls allow the exchange of substances between the blood and the liver cells. The capillaries then unite to form the *hepatic vein.* The hepatic vein empties into the inferior vena cava.

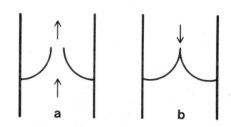

42–9 | The valves in veins maintain direction of blood flow. The valves prevent blood from flowing backwards in the veins as shown in the above diagram. Flow of blood is shown with arrows.

renes = the kidneys

hepatic = pertaining to the liver

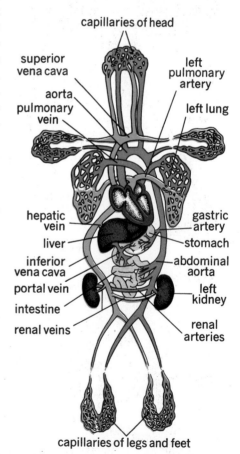

42–10 | A diagrammatic representation of the various circulations in the human body. Trace the pulmonary, systemic, renal, and portal circulations.

Table 42-3 BLOOD AS A TRANSPORTING MEDIUM

TRANSPORTA-TION OF	FROM	TO	FOR THE PURPOSE OF
digested food	digestive organs and liver	tissues	growth and repair of cells, supplying energy, and regulating life processes
cell wastes	active tissues	lungs, kidneys, and skin	excretion
water	digestive organs	kidneys, skin, and lungs	excretion and equalization of body fluids
oxygen heat	lungs tissues	tissues skin	oxidation equalization of the body temperature
secretions	ductless glands	various organs, glands	regulation of body activities

The Lymph

The tissue fluid carries nutrients and oxygen to each cell, and it carries away wastes and the products of cells. **Tissue fluid collects in tubes to be returned to the bloodstream.** This fluid is called *lymph* (limf). Tiny lymph vessels join to form larger ones. This is similar to the way capillaries join to form venules. Enlargements of lymph vessels form *lymph nodes*. They appear along the vessels like beads on a string. In each lymph node the tubes branch into many fine vessels. Certain white corpuscles collect here and destroy bacteria in the lymph. **The lymph nodes, or lymph glands, purify the lymph before returning it to the blood.** The greatest number of lymph nodes are in your neck, armpits, inner elbow, and groin. Perhaps you have had an infection in your arm or hand and noticed a swelling in your armpit. This can be very painful. *Tonsils* and *adenoids* are masses of lymphatic tissue in your throat. You may have had them become infected and swollen. Surgical removal of the tonsils is called a *tonsillectomy*.

One vessel in your body that returns lymph to the bloodstream is the *right lymphatic duct*. This vessel carries lymph from your right arm and the right side of your head and neck. The lymph is returned to your blood in the *right subclavian vein*. A larger vessel carries the lymph from the rest of your body. This is the *thoracic duct*. The thoracic duct empties into the *left subclavian vein.*

Large lymph vessels have valves in their walls. These valves are similar to those found in veins. The valves control the direction of flow of lymph. Activity increases the flow of lymph. In inactive tissues the lymph flows slowly or stops completely. The main difference between blood and tissue fluid of lymph is the presence of red blood corpuscles and the various proteins.

The Excretory System

When the body oxidizes foods involved in metabolism, it produces waste products as well. **You get rid of these metabolic wastes in a process called** *excretion.* Some waste products come from protein metabolism. The carbon and nitrogen parts in amino acids separate before the carbon is oxidized. The nitrogen parts are released as waste. These nonprotein nitrogenous wastes include *urea* and *uric acid.*

A buildup of wastes in the tissues is dangerous. It causes rapid tissue poisoning, starvation, and finally suffocation. This is especially true of nonprotein nitrogen wastes. **Tissues filled with wastes cannot absorb food or oxygen.** If this occurs the person suffers fever, convulsions, coma, and death.

One-celled organisms empty their wastes directly into a water environment. Animals such as the sponge and jellyfish also do this. The process is not as simple for many-celled organisms. In multicellular organisms each cell discharges its waste materials into the tissue fluid. This fluid flows to the bloodstream. Then the blood carries cell wastes to excretory organs to eliminate the wastes.

Kidneys: The Main Excretory Organs

The *kidneys* are bean-shaped organs. They are about the size of your clenched fist. The kidneys lie on either side of the spine, in the small of your back. Deep layers of fat cover and protect each kidney. If you cut a kidney lengthwise, you can see several different regions. The firm outer part is called the *cortex.* The cortex makes up about one third of the kidney tissue. The inner two thirds are called the *medulla.* The medulla is filled with cone-shaped projections called *pyramids,* which point into a saclike cavity. This cavity is the *pelvis* of the kidney. The pelvis leads into a long, narrow tube, the **ureter.** Two ureters, one from each kidney, empty into the **urinary bladder.**

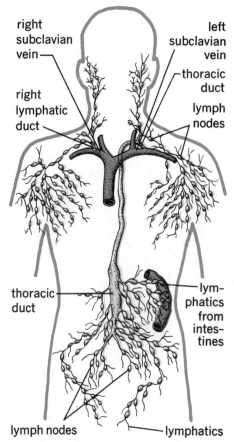

42–11 | The lymphatic system returns tissue fluid to the bloodstream.

Facts & Figures

About 2,000 liters (500 gallons) of blood pass through the two million nephrons of the kidneys every day.

nephros = the kidneys

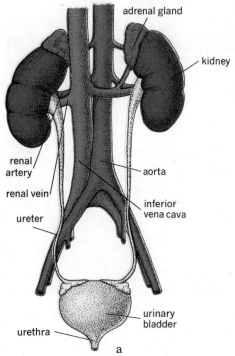

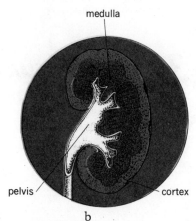

42–12 | (a) The excretory system. (b) Cross section of a kidney.

Each kidney has about 1,250,000 tiny filters. These filters are called **nephrons.** Nephrons control the chemical makeup of blood. Each nephron has a small cup-shaped structure called a *Bowman's capsule.* A tiny, winding *tubule* comes from each capsule. This tubule becomes very narrow as it straightens and goes toward the renal pelvis. The tubule widens again and forms a loop, called *Henle's loop.* Then the tubule goes back into the cortex. In the cortex, the tubule becomes coiled again. Then it enters a larger *collecting tubule.* The collecting tubule is a straight tube that receives the tubules of many nephrons. It carries fluid to the renal pelvis. If all these tubules were put end to end, they would reach more than 280 kilometers (168 miles).

The Nephron Blood enters each kidney through a large *renal artery.* The renal arteries branch directly from the aorta. In the kidneys, each artery branches and rebranches. This fills all areas of the cortex with tiny arterioles.

Each arteriole ends in a coiled knob of capillaries. This knob is called the *glomerulus* (glom-ERR-yuh-lus). Each glomerulus fills the cuplike part of a Bowman's capsule. **There are two stages to removing waste from the blood: 1) filtration and 2) reabsorption.** Filtration takes place in the glomeruli. The pressure of the blood is very high here. Remember, the heart pumps blood through the aorta directly into the renal arteries. Water, nitrogenous wastes, glucose, and mineral salts are forced by this pressure through the capillary walls of the glomerulus. These filtered materials move into the surrounding Bowman's capsule. This process is called *filtration.* The filtered solution is like blood plasma without blood proteins. However, too much of the blood content is filtered out of the blood. This is corrected in the second stage of the process, *reabsorption.*

After the fluid leaves the capsule through the tubules, it passes through a network of capillaries. This network reabsorbs many of the substances into the blood by *active transport.* Much water is reabsorbed by osmosis. Some recent studies indicate that for every 100 milliliters (3 fluid ounces) of fluid that pass from the blood into the capsules, 99 milliliters (2.97 fluid oz) are reabsorbed. What is left passes through the tubules of the pelvis of the kidney as *urine.* **Urine is made of nitrogenous wastes, excess water, and excess mineral salts.**

The urine passes from the pelvis of the kidney to the ureters. The ureters carry the urine to the urinary bladder. Cleansed blood leaves the kidneys through the renal veins. The blood returns to the general circulation by way of the inferior vena cava.

The urinary bladder is muscular. At intervals, these muscles contract. This pushes the urine out of the body through the **urethra** (yooh-REETH-ruh).

Your kidneys have tremendous reserve power. If one is removed, the other will grow bigger and take over the job.

Another Role of the Kidneys Kidneys do more than eliminate urea and wastes of protein metabolism from the body. They also excrete other substances. Sometimes your body builds up excess sugars, acids or bases, and water. The kidneys eliminate the excess of these from the blood. Kidneys also maintain just the right amount of salts in the body fluid. **If the kidneys are working properly, they keep the environment of your cells constant.** Do you remember studying the effect of changes in osmotic concentration in cells? If so, you know the importance of this constant environment, or *homeostasis*.

The Skin: Another Excretory Organ

The skin is also an excretory organ. It excretes some water, salts, and some urea. This excretion is in the form of *perspiration*. However, this fluid has a more important role than excretion. *Perspiration helps regulate your body temperature.* The evaporation of sweat acts as a cooling system. Heat is lost to the air as sweat evaporates from the surface of the skin. The skin is supplied with blood that contains body heat. As the body temperature rises, the skin becomes more flushed with blood. Heat is thus conducted to the surface. At the same time, secretion of sweat and rate of evaporation and the amount of heat loss increase.

The skin is made of two general layers. They are the epidermis, and the dermis. The epidermis is the outer portion of your skin. It is made up of many epithelial cells. The outer cells form the *horny layer*. These outer cells are flattened, dead, and scalelike. The inner cells form the *germinative layer*. These cells are larger and more active. The epidermis protects the more active tissues beneath. Epidermal cells are rubbed off constantly, but active cells in the lower layers replace epidermal cells as fast as they are lost. Friction and pressure on the epidermis stimulate cell division. This may produce a thickening of cells called a *callus*.

The **dermis** lies under the epidermis. It is a thick, active layer, made of tough, fibrous connective tissue. This tissue is filled with blood and lymph vessels, nerves, sweat glands, and oil glands.

Beneath the skin is a layer of fat cells which provide insulation for the body and serve as an energy store. This layer is called *subcutaneous tissue.*

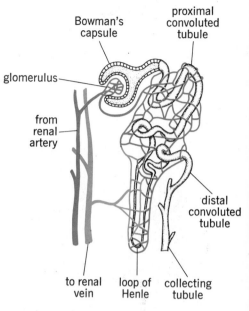

42-13 | The structure of a nephron. Note the relationship of the tubules and blood vessels by which materials are reabsorbed into the blood.

epi = upon
derma = skin, leather

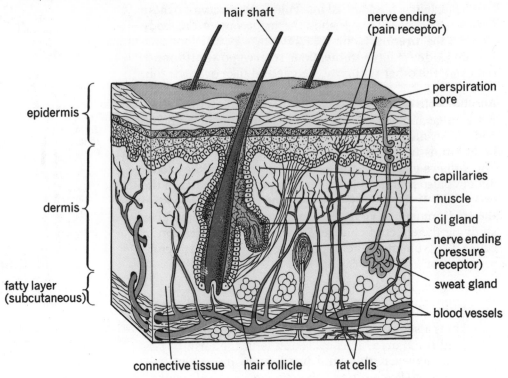

epidermis

dermis

fatty layer
(subcutaneous)

hair shaft

nerve ending
(pain receptor)

perspiration
pore

capillaries

muscle

oil gland

nerve ending
(pressure
receptor)

sweat gland

blood vessels

connective tissue   hair follicle   fat cells

42-14 | The structure of a highly magnified,
thin section of skin.

Functions of the Skin   Here are some of the major functions of the skin.

- It protects your body from mechanical injury and inva-
sion by bacteria.
- It keeps the inner tissues from becoming dry. Aided by oil
glands, it is nearly waterproof. Little water passes
through it, except out through the pores.
- It holds the *receptors* that respond to touch pressure,
pain, and temperature.
- It excretes some wastes in the form of perspiration.
- It controls the loss of body heat. This happens when perspiration evaporates on the surface of your skin.

Other Areas of Excretion   During expiration, your *lungs*
excrete carbon dioxide and water vapor. You will remember that the *liver* also has an excretory function. It forms
urea. The bile stored in your *gall bladder* also contains
waste.

The large intestine removes undigested food from your
body. Of course, this is not really cell excretion. The food
waste collected here was never absorbed into tissue cells.

Blood is made of liquid plasma and solid components. Plasma contains water, blood proteins, prothrombin, inorganic substances, digested foods, and cell wastes. Blood has three solid parts: red corpuscles, white corpuscles, and platelets. White corpuscles help fight disease bacteria. Platelets are important in the process of blood clotting. Arteries carry blood from the heart to the body tissues. Veins return it to the heart. The arterial and venous systems are connected by networks of tiny capillaries.

Wastes are removed from the body through the kidneys, skin, lungs, liver, and large intestine. The kidneys filter the nitrogenous wastes and regulate the water content of the body. The skin rids the body of excess water, salts, and some urea in perspiration.

Summary

circulation	systole	portal circulation
blood	diastole	lymph
red corpuscle	artery	excretion
white corpuscle	arteriole	kidney
platelet	vein	ureter
plasma	venule	urinary bladder
hemoglobin	pulse	nephron
Rh factor	capillary	urine
antigen	pulmonary circulation	urethra
atrium	systemic circulation	epidermis
ventricle	coronary circulation	dermis
aorta	renal circulation	

Biologically Speaking

1. What is blood?
2. Where are blood cells made in the body?
3. What conditions might cause the white blood cell count to go up?
4. What are the steps in the clotting of blood?
5. Why can you feel a pulse in arteries and not veins?
6. What is tissue fluid? How does it get back to the blood-stream?
7. How do the kidneys regulate blood content?

Questions for Review

1. What is the reason for saying that "we are as young as our arteries"?
2. Alcohol dilates the arteries in the skin. What would be its effect, then, on temperature control of the body?
3. In an Rh-negative patient, why might a second transfusion with Rh-positive blood be fatal, even though the first transfusion with Rh-positive blood caused no complications?

Applying Concepts

43

Respiration and Energy

A **EXPLAIN** breathing mechanics.

B **CONTRAST** the differences between external and internal respiration.

C **NAME** the structures of the respiratory system and **IDENTIFY** each of their functions.

D **EXPLAIN** gas exchange in the body.

E **DESCRIBE** the effects of oxygen debt.

F **DEFINE** basal metabolism.

G **EXPLAIN** the environmental influences on breathing and respiration.

43–1 | Humans must sometimes carry their air with them. *(Bill Wood, Bruce Coleman)*

re = back, again

Facts & Figures

Many aquatic organisms have gills. In air, gill filaments would stick together. Terrestrial invertebrates, such as snails, scorpions, and spiders, respire through membranes of larger air spaces. Highly vascularized cavities in lungs are adaptations of air-breathing vertebrates.

Respiration: Common to Living Things

All living cells need a constant supply of energy. Green plants change the sun's energy to chemical energy. In turn, the animal cells obtain nutrients from the plant's stored chemical energy. These cells then require oxygen to release the energy for their life processes. There are some anaerobic cells that can live without oxygen, but most cells would die without oxygen. Cellular respiration was discussed in Chapter 6. **Respiration is the intake of oxygen and the elimination of carbon dioxide, with the release of energy resulting from the oxidation of organic substances (food).** The exchange of gases between the atmosphere and the blood is *external respiration.* This process occurs in the lungs. The exchange of gases between the blood or tissue fluid and the cells themselves is *internal respiration.*

External Respiration

The organs involved in external respiration can be divided into two groups. One group includes the organs involved in the mechanics of breathing. They are the ribs, rib muscles, diaphragm, and abdominal muscles. The other group includes the passages though which air travels to get to the bloodstream. These are the nostrils, nasal passages, pharynx, trachea, bronchi, bronchial tubes, and air sacs.

The Nose and Nasal Passages   The air enters the nose in two streams through two nostrils. These nostrils are separated by the *septum*. From the nostrils, air enters the nasal passages. These passages lie above the mouth cavity. Before air enters the nasal passages, however, nostril hairs and moist mucous membranes filter out dirt and foreign particles. The length of nasal passages also warms and moistens the air before it enters the trachea. Both the filtering and warming advantages are lost when you breathe through your mouth.

The Trachea   From the nasal passages, air goes through the **pharynx** and down the windpipe, or **trachea.** The upper end of the trachea is protected by a flap of cartilage. This flap is called the **epiglottis.** When you swallow, the epiglottis closes over the trachea. This prevents food from getting into the lungs. The upper end of the trachea holds the voice box, or **larynx.** This forms a lump on the outside

epi = upon
glottis = mouth of the windpipe

43–2 | The organs involved in breathing and external respiration in humans.

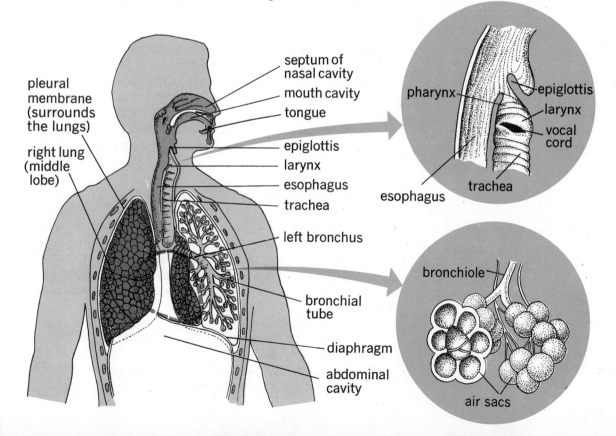

of the neck called the Adam's apple. *Vocal cords* are located inside the larynx. Our vocal cords are used to make sounds. Rings of cartilage support the trachea to keep it open for the passage of air.

The trachea and its branches are lined with tiny hairs called cilia. The cilia are constantly moving. They carry inhaled dirt and foreign particles upward toward the mouth. This dirt is removed when you cough, sneeze, or clear your throat.

bronchos = windpipe

The Bronchi and Air Sacs   The trachea divides at its lower end. It forms two branches called *bronchi.* One bronchus extends to each lung. Each bronchus divides and forms many small *bronchial tubes.* These divide again into even smaller *bronchioles.* The bronchioles end in *air sacs.* Each air sac is made of clusters of tiny sacs called *alveoli.* Lung tissue is made mostly of alveoli. The walls of the alveoli are very thin and elastic. Gases are exchanged through these thin walls and the air sacs. Capillaries in the alveolar walls carry blood which unloads carbon dioxide and picks up oxygen. **All the tiny alveoli provide the great amount of surface area needed for this exchange of gases.**

alveolus = a pit, a small hollow

The Mechanics of Breathing

Do you remember the last time you ran to catch a bus or train? By the time you took your seat you probably were breathing heavily. *Breathing* is the movement of the air into and out of the lungs.

The lungs are spongy, air-filled sacs in the chest cavity. **Breathing is caused by muscle action.** The muscles are those between the ribs, and in the diaphragm and abdomen.

The Movements of Breathing

The lungs fill much of the body cavity from under the shoulders down to the diaphragm. This cavity is called the *thoracic cavity.* The lungs are covered by a double membrane called the *pleural membrane.* One membrane is attached to the surface of the lungs. The other covers the inside of the thoracic cavity. These membranes secrete a lubricating mucus. This lets the lungs slide freely in the chest during breathing.

pleura = a rib, the side

Place your hands on the sides of your chest and take in a deep breath. This is called *inspiration.* Can you feel your chest cavity expand? **During inspiration, three things happen to expand your chest cavity:**

in = in
spiro = to breathe

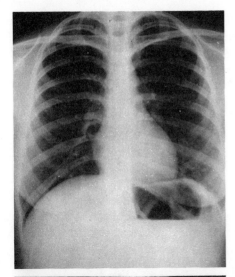

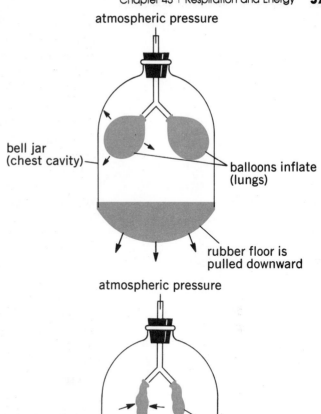

atmospheric pressure

bell jar
(chest cavity)

balloons inflate
(lungs)

rubber floor is
pulled downward

atmospheric pressure

bell jar
(chest cavity)

balloons deflate
(lungs)

rubber floor resumes
this position under
atmospheric pressure

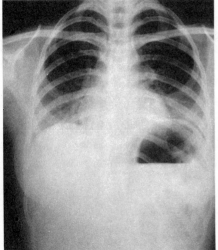

43-3 | These X rays show the chest during exaggerated breathing. (top) Inspiration, and (bottom) expiration. The schematic diagrams illustrate the mechanics of breathing.

1. The rib muscles contract, pulling the ribs up and out.
2. The muscles of the dome-shaped diaphragm contract. This straightens and lowers the diaphragm. This action enlarges the chest cavity from below.
3. The abdominal muscles relax. This allows compression of the abdominal contents when the diaphragm lowers.

When the chest cavity is expanded, air pressure inside the thorax decreases. Air rushes into the lungs to equalize the pressure.

Place your hands on your chest again and observe the changes when you force the air from your lungs. This is called *expiration*. **During expiration four things happen to reduce the size of your chest cavity.**

ex = out, out of

1. The rib muscles relax. This allows the ribs to spring back.
2. The diaphragm relaxes, rising to its original position.
3. The abdominal muscles contact. This pushes the abdominal organs up against the diaphragm.
4. Elastic fibers in your lungs shrink and help to force air out of the lungs.

At expiration, the decrease in size of the chest cavity increases the air pressure inside the cavity. Air rushes out of the lungs to equalize the pressure.

Control of Breathing Looking at another person, count the number of inspirations for one minute. This is the *respiration rate*. In humans, inspiration and expiration (the cycle) occur from 16 to 24 times a minute. The exact rate depends on physical activity, position, mood, and age. **Nerves and chemicals control your breathing and the respiration rate.**

Nerves from the lungs, diaphragm, and rib muscles lead to a respiratory control center. This center is located at the base of the brain. It controls the regular rhythm of breathing. The amount of carbon dioxide in the blood is detected directly by the breathing control center. If the carbon dioxide concentration is high, the brain signals the diaphragm and rib muscles. They increase the breathing rate. This increased rate forces more carbon dioxide out through the lungs and breathing settles back to a normal rate.

Air Capacity of the Lungs Each time you inhale and exhale, only about 500 milliliters (almost 1 pint) of air are exchanged. The maximum amount of air that you can move through your lungs is called the *vital capacity*. This is the total amount of air that moves through your lungs when you inhale and exhale as hard as you can. The vital capacity of the normal person is about 4,500 milliliters (8.4 pints). A well-trained athlete may have a vital capacity of 6,500 milliliters (12 pints).

Artificial Resuscitation Soon after a person stops breathing, the blood oxygen level drops below that needed for normal cell activity. If it is not raised quickly, cells will begin to die. **Artificial resuscitation** is simply a way of *forcing* air into and out of the lungs. The mouth-to-mouth method is recommended by the American Red Cross.

Internal Respiration
The major gases that make up air are nitrogen, oxygen, and carbon dioxide. These gases have properties that are vital

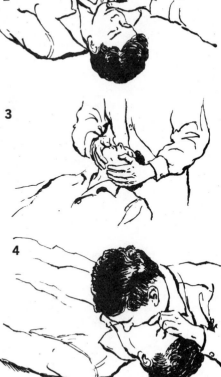

for life. These gases can diffuse through membranes. For instance, if there are different concentrations of oxygen on either side of a membrane, oxygen molecules will pass through the membrane until the oxygen concentration is the same on both sides.

Gases can also dissolve in liquids. This is why oxygen and carbon dioxide can be transported by the blood. The solubility of oxygen, carbon dioxide, and nitrogen varies. Temperature changes will also affect the amount of gas that can be dissolved in a liquid. Warm water will hold less dissolved gas than will cold water.

Gas Exchange in the Lungs   The *pulmonary artery* carries deoxygenated, dark red blood to the lungs. There it branches into an extensive network of small capillaries. These capillaries completely surround each alveolus. The air in the alveoli and the blood in the capillaries contain gases in different concentrations. Therefore, diffusion occurs through the thin, moist membranes of both the alveoli and capillaries. **Oxygen diffuses from the air into the blood, and carbon dioxide diffuses from the blood into the air.**

The Transport of Oxygen   Oxygen is not very soluble in the plasma of blood. It is even less soluble at our body temperature of 37°C (98.6°F). Oxygen would be more soluble at lower temperatures. Remember, the erythrocytes contain a substance called hemoglobin. Hemoglobin has a chemical attraction for oxygen. This is why blood can carry such a high concentration of oxygen. At sea level, blood leaving the lungs is about 97 percent saturated with oxygen.

43-4 | Mouth-to-mouth resuscitation. First, tilt the head back so the chin is pointing upward (1). Pull the jaw into a jutting-out position (2 and 3). Second, open your mouth wide and place it tightly over the victim's mouth. At the same time, pinch the victim's nostrils shut (4 and 5). Third, remove your mouth, turn your head to the side, and listen for the return rush of air that indicates air exchange. Fourth, if you are not getting air exchange recheck the head and jaw position.

Table 43-1 COMPOSITION OF NORMAL ATMOSPHERE

	Percentage of volume
Nitrogen	78.03
Oxygen	20.99
Argon	0.94
Carbon dioxide	0.03
Hydrogen, neon, helium	0.01

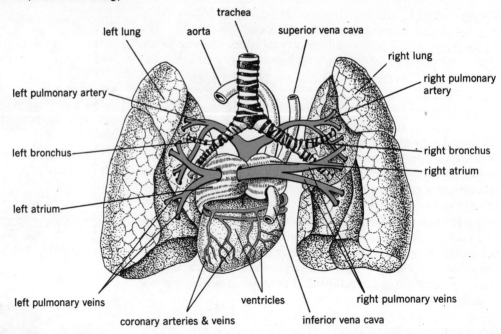

43-5 | This posterior view of the lungs and heart shows the branches of the pulmonary arteries and the pulmonary veins.

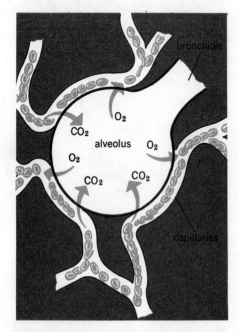

43-6 | The relationship between alveoli and capillaries. A cluster of alveoli make up each air sac at the end of a bronchiole.

When the blood reaches tissues with low concentrations of oxygen, the hemoglobin releases its oxygen. The oxygen diffuses into the tissue fluid; from there it reaches the cells.

Hemoglobin has another important characteristic. **The attraction of hemoglobin for oxygen decreases with an increase in acidity.** During exercise, lactic acid is produced by the active muscle cells. This causes the hemoglobin to release more of its oxygen than it would normally.

The Transport of Carbon Dioxide **Carbon dioxide is much more soluble than oxygen.** It passes through membranes quickly and goes into the bloodstream. In the blood, only about 10 percent of the carbon dioxide is dissolved in the plasma. Hemoglobin joins with about 20 percent of the carbon dioxide. How is the remaining 70 percent of the carbon dioxide carried to the lungs? It passes into the red blood cells, and an important enzyme joins it to water to form *carbonic acid.* Then the carbonic acid forms bicarbonate ions (HCO_3^-). When the blood reaches the lungs, the opposite occurs, and carbon dioxide diffuses from the erythrocyte. Then it passes through the capillary membranes, into the alveoli, and leaves your body in the expired air.

Oxygen Debt   During times of great muscular activity, the cells need more oxygen than the body can supply. The lungs cannot take in oxygen fast enough, nor can the blood deliver it fast enough. When this happens, the cells switch to anaerobic respiration. This means that oxygen is not used. Instead, pyruvic acid becomes the hydrogen acceptor in the process of energy exchange. For a short period, the cells have enough energy to function and survive. The anaerobic process produces *lactic acid*. This collects in the tissues, causing a feeling of fatigue. A buildup of lactic acid signals the brain's respiratory center to increase the breathing rate and supply the tissues with more oxygen.

If the heavy exercise continues, lactic acid keeps building up. This is called a state of *oxygen debt*. It continues until the heavy exercise ends. Then during a half-hour rest, some lactic acid is oxidized. Some is converted to glycogen. Carbon dioxide and excess water are excreted. The oxygen debt is paid. The body is ready for more exercise.

Basal Metabolism   The sum of all the processes occurring in a cell or an organism is called *metabolism*. Metabolism has two distinct phases. One phase is called *anabolism*. This phase involves carbohydrate fat and protein synthesis. The other phase is called *catabolism* and involves oxidation and energy release. The metabolic rate varies according to the body's activity.

Even when the body seems completely inactive, as during sleep, metabolism continues, but at a decreased rate. **The energy required to maintain basic life processes is called *basal metabolism.*** The rate at which such energy is used is called the *basal metabolic rate*, or BMR. The BMR may be calculated by measuring the amount of oxygen used up over a specific period of time. The subject must be resting, and can not have eaten recently. These factors would change the amount of oxygen needed by cells. Another way to measure BMR is to measure the amount of heat given off from the body surface. The BMR is low in a newborn infant but rises to a peak in the second year. It slowly falls until adolescence and remains constant into adulthood. It declines again in middle and old age.

Environmental Effects on Breathing and Respiration

The air's temperature, moisture, oxygen, and carbon dioxide content all influence the rate of breathing and respiration. Certain of these factors involve *ventilation*. If the air in a room is stuffy, it is likely to be too warm and moist. Very rarely is it caused by a build-up of carbon dioxide and lack of oxygen.

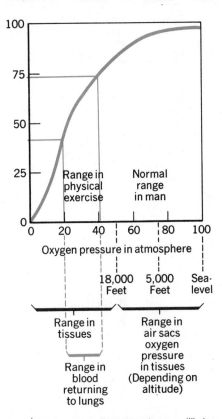

43-7 | When hemoglobin reaches equilibrium with the atmospheric oxygen in the air sacs, it is about 97 percent saturated. When blood reaches the tissues where the amount of oxygen is low, diffusion occurs and the hemoglobin gives up its oxygen.

Facts & Figures

The pressure of the air at sea level is around 760 mm Hg. Since oxygen makes up about 21 percent of air, the pressure of oxygen at sea level would be 21/100 X 760, or 160 mm Hg. You can figure out what it would be at a higher altitude where the pressure is 600 mm Hg.

hypo = under, less than usual

Facts & Figures

The greater the pressure of any gas in contact with a liquid, the greater will be the amount of a gas the liquid will dissolve. At sea level, more oxygen can be dissolved in the moist alveolar membrane than at a higher altitude.

Carbon Monoxide   Far too often you read of people who have died in a closed garage where an automobile engine was running. The cause of death is given as *carbon-monoxide poisoning.* Actually, the death is not caused by poisoning but by *tissue suffocation.* Carbon monoxide will not support life. Yet it combines with the hemoglobin of the blood 250 times more readily than does oxygen. As a result, the blood becomes loaded with carbon monoxide. Its oxygen-combining power decreases. The tissues suffer from oxygen starvation. The victim becomes light-headed. Soon paralysis sets in. Death follows from tissue suffocation.

High Altitudes   You live at the bottom of a large ocean of air. If you were to climb a high mountain, the air pressure would become less. At this height, the molecules of nitrogen, oxygen, and carbon dioxide are spread farther apart. You may have experienced your ears "popping" during an altitude change. Your middle ear must equalize the pressure.

Air and Space Travel   When an airplane approaches an altitude of 6,000 meters (1,650 feet), the pressure becomes so low that a pilot has difficulties in seeing and hearing. This condition is called **hypoxia.** It is the result of oxygen starvation of the cells. Passengers in modern airliners fly at high altitudes in pressurized cabins.

Diving   SCUBA divers are well aware of the problems of pressure and respiration. The weight of water causes an increase in pressure as a diver descends. The air that passes into the lungs must be under a greater pressure than that of the water. This pressure means that the molecules of nitrogen, oxygen, and carbon dioxide are closer together. The blood and tissues of a diver, then, dissolve more molecules of these gases than you have in your body now. If a diver returns too quickly to the surface, gas bubbles (mostly nitrogen) form in the tissues. These can cause pain and even death. This condition is commonly called the **bends.**

Summary

Respiration involves the exchange of gases between cells and their environment. Exchange of gases between the blood and the atmosphere is called external respiration. The cells of the body exchange gases with the blood and tissue fluid. This is internal respiration. The ribs, rib muscles, diaphragm, and abdominal muscles all act in the process of inspiration and expiration.

A vital property of gases is the ability to dissolve in fluids. Atmospheric pressure and the concentration of gases in the air are also important in the diffusion of gases through membranes. Metabolism involves respiration, oxidation, and the growth processes. The basal metabolic rate expresses the energy required to maintain life processes at rest.

respiration	vocal cord	pleural membrane
external respiration	bronchi	inspiration
internal respiration	bronchial tube	expiration
pharynx	bronchiole	artificial resuscitation
trachea	air sac	basal metabolism
epiglottis	alveoli	hypoxia
larynx	breathing	bends

1. How do pressure changes within the chest cavity cause inspiration and expiration?
2. What are the differences between respiration and breathing?
3. What properties of gases aid in respiration?
4. What is the purpose of artificial resusciation?
5. Describe gas exchange in the lungs and name the structures involved.
6. Why is hemoglobin vital to the respiratory processes of the cells in our bodies?
7. How is oxygen carried from lungs to tissues?
8. How is carbon dioxide carried in the blood from the tissues to the lungs?
9. How do you build up an oxygen debt?
10. Explain carbon-monoxide poisoning.
11. Compare respiration problems encountered on a high mountain to those in space travel.

1. If plants produce oxygen in photosynthesis, how do you explain the fact that they also respire?
2. What changes do you think would occur in the blood if you held your breath for a period of time? if you breathed rapidly and deeply for a period of time?
3. People who live in dry climates, such as the southwestern parts of our country, report that high temperatures there are easier to tolerate than the same temperatures in more humid areas. Why?
4. What differences would you find in the blood of a person living at high altitudes compared to a person living at sea level?

44

A **NAME** the two major parts of the human nervous system.

B **DESCRIBE** the structure and function of the neuron.

C **DESCRIBE** the functions of the parts of the brain.

D **IDENTIFY** the parts of the spinal cord.

E **LIST** the parts of the peripheral nervous system.

F **DESCRIBE** each of the body senses.

G **DESCRIBE** the anatomy of the eye and the ear.

44-1 | What is the difference in the acts of these two primates? *(left: HRW Photo by Russell Dian; right: Ringling Bros. Barnum and Bailey Circus)*

The Integration of the Nervous System

Compare the two photographs above. Your first conclusion may be that both chimps and humans can ride motorcycles. You are certainly correct. However, there are several important differences. The chimps are conditioned to sit quietly on their machine. Once the trainer starts the motor, these animals balance as they ride around in circles. The humans, however, will do many things besides ride in circles. They decide when to start and stop the machine. They decide where and when to turn. They observe traffic signals and try to stay out of the way of other drivers. At the end of the ride, they can tell their friends or family about their adventures. The behavior of the human is more complex than that of the chimpanzees.

The nervous system has reached its highest degree of development in the human body. The brain and spinal cord composes one part called the **central nervous system** (CNS). The cranial and spinal nerves make up the other division, the **peripheral nervous system.**

The Neurons

You have learned about many kinds of specialized cells. Muscle cells, bone cells, blood cells, and gland cells all have special structures that allow them to function in certain ways. The structural and functional unit of nervous tissue is the nerve cell, or **neuron.** Many neurons have star-shaped cell bodies. Notice in figure 44-2 that the nucleus and most of the cytoplasm are in the cell body. Threadlike projections, called *nerve fibers,* extend from the cell body. Messages, called *impulses,* travel through the nerve fibers. Perhaps you remember that in some animals, such as the sea anemone, impulses can travel in either direction. In human nerve fibers, impulses travel only in one direction. The fibers that carry impulses *toward a cell body* are called **dendrites.** Fibers that carry impulses away from a cell body are called **axons.** As many as 200 dendrites can carry impulses toward a single cell body, but there is only one axon leaving each cell body.

The dendrites carry sensory impulses to the central nervous system. When you stub your toe, an impulse travels *through a dendrite* to the nerve cell body in a ganglion, a group of nerve-cell bodies near your spinal cord. You probably wiggle your toe to be sure it is all right. Before this happens, impulses travel from a nerve cell body, *through the axon,* to a muscle in your toe. The neuron involved in the pain sensation is a *sensory neuron.* The *associative neuron* conveys the impulse to the motor neuron. Such neurons are also called *interneurons.* The one involved in causing your toe muscle to wiggle is a *motor neuron.* Cell bodies of neurons are located either in ganglia or in the brain or spinal cord. Nerve cell fibers can be quite long.

Bundles of Nerve Fibers Nerve cell fibers run together in bundles. These bundles are called **nerves.** A nerve is like an electrical cable, made of smaller wires bound together. There are three types of nerves in the peripheral nervous system. *Motor nerves* are made only of axons. These nerves carry impulses leaving the central nervous system and activate muscles or glands. *Sensory nerves* are made of dendrites only. They carry impulses toward the central nervous system. Many nerves of the peripheral nervous system contain both axons and dendrites. Such nerves are called *mixed nerves.*

Within a nerve, most axons are wrapped in a sheath of fatty cells. This sheath seems to protect the axon. It appears to act as an insulator. The connections between neurons are made in the central nervous system, or in ganglia. However, the fibers of one neuron never really touch those of another. A space lies between them. These spaces are called

Facts & Figures

The entire human nervous system develops from the ectodermal germ layer formed by the zygote.

dendron = a tree

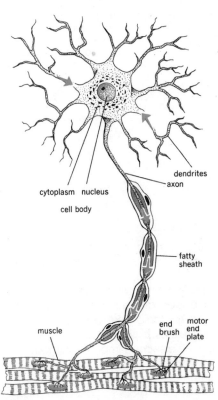

cytoplasm nucleus

cell body

dendrites
axon

fatty sheath

muscle

end brush

motor end plate

44-2 | The structure of a typical motor neuron.

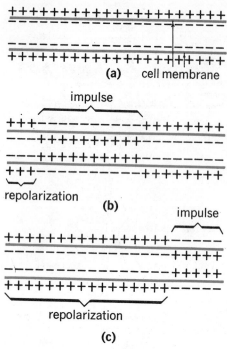

44-3 | The impulse travels along the neuron and can be measured as a change in electrical charge: (a) resting neuron; (b) impulse conducted as reverse of polarity; (c) original polarity restored.

Facts & Figures

There is a limit to the rate at which a nerve fiber can conduct impulses. This is because, for a brief period after the impulse has passed, the fiber will not transmit a second impulse. This **refractory** period is 1/1000 second or less in human nerves.

synapses (SIN-ap-seeze). Impulses must cross the synapses as they travel from one neuron to another. Furthermore, an impulse never travels from one motor neuron to another motor neuron. Nor do impulses travel from one sensory neuron to another sensory neuron. **Impulses are able to bridge the synapse with the help of fast-acting chemical reactions.**

The Nerve Impulse

Biologists have learned that an impulse travels along a nerve by a complex combination of chemicals and electricity. **A nerve impulse is not a flow of electricity.** Nerve impulses move much more slowly than electricity. They move at about 90 meters (297 feet) per second. Electricity moves at about 285,000 kilometers (171,000 miles) a second. Also, an impulse uses oxygen and gives off carbon dioxide as it travels along a nerve. This indicates that some chemical reaction is involved in its movement. This is why it is said that a *nerve impulse* is an *electrochemical* charge moving along a neuron.

A neuron that is not carrying an impulse has an electrical potential. That is, the outside of the cell membrane has an excess of sodium ions (Na^+) and the membrane becomes charged positively. The inside of the cell membrane contains a high concentration of potassium ions (K^+), chloride ions (Cl^-) and negative organic ions. This results in a negative charge within the nerve fiber. This resting neuron is said to be *polarized*. All this changes when an impulse moves along the neuron. The polarity reverses. The sodium ions rush inside the fiber until they are in excess, while the potassium ions move outside the membrane. This change in polarity sweeps along the neuron like a wave, carrying the impulse. After the impulse passes a given spot, the original polarity returns. The balance of sodium and potassium ions along the cell membrane affects this polarity change.

Biologists have also learned something about how a nerve impulse causes a muscle to contract. **As with the transmission of an impulse, muscle contraction is caused by an electrochemical reaction.** The impulse reaches to the end of a motor neuron. At the tip of the motor neuron are many *motor end plates*. Here, the impulse causes the release of a minute amount of a chemical called *acetylcholine* (uh-seet'l-KOE-leen). This substance transmits the impulse to the muscle fibers. Then the process of contraction begins. After a brief period of contraction, the nerve releases an enzyme, *cholinesterase* (kole-in-ESS-tuh-race). Cholinesterase splits the acetylcholine, and the muscle fibers relax. This whole process takes less than 0.1 second.

As mentioned before, chemical reactions at the ends of axons also transmit impulses across the synapses. Axon endings produce either acetylcholine or an adrenalin compound. These stimulate the dendrite of the next neuron to begin the impulse and carry it along.

The Brain and Spinal Cord: Central Nervous System

The brain is one of the most specialized organs in the human body. It weights about 1.4 kilograms (3 lbs), and it fills the cranial cavity. **The brain is made of soft nervous tissue. This is covered by three membranes.** These are called *meninges* (muh-NIN-jeez). The inner membrane is called the *pia mater*. It is well supplied with blood vessels that carry food and oxygen to the brain cells. The pia mater is very delicate. It closely adheres to the surface of the brain. It dips down into the many folds of the brain.

The middle membrane is called the *arachnoid* (uh-RACK-noid). It consists of fibrous and elastic tissue. This membrane does not follow the many grooves of the brain surface and the pia mater. The space between the pia mater and the arachnoid is filled with a clear liquid called *cerebrospinal fluid*. This fluid is also found around the spinal cord.

The outermost protective membrane is called the *dura mater*. This is a thick, strong, fibrous lining. It lines the inside of the cranium. All three meninges extend down the spinal column to protect the spinal cord.

Together, these meninges act as a cushion to protect the brain from bumps and bruises. Sometimes a bump on the head is so hard that it does damage the brain in spite of this protection. Such a bruise is called a *concussion*.

There are four spaces inside the brain. These spaces are called **ventricles.** The ventricles have openings connecting them to one another. The ventricles and the openings are filled with cerebrospinal fluid. Ciliated epithelium lines the ventricles. Action of the cilia circulates the cerebrospinal fluid. This brings nutrients to the brain tissue and removes wastes.

The Cerebrum

The largest region of the brain is the *cerebrum.* The cerebrum is proportionally larger in humans than in any other animal. It consists of two halves, or *hemispheres.* The hemispheres are joined by tough fibers and by nerve tracts. The

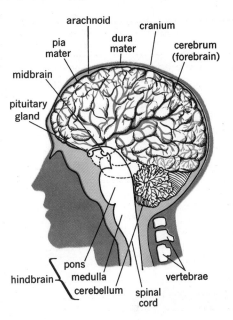

44-4 | A longitudinal section of the brain showing the regions and the meninges.

outer surface of the cerebrum is called the *cortex*. It is folded deeply in irregular wrinkles and furrows, called *convolutions*. The convolutions greatly increase the surface area of the cerebrum. The deeper grooves divide the cortex into lobes.

Countless numbers of neurons make up the cerebral cortex. This tissue is frequently called *gray matter* because of the color of the cells. The cerebrum below the cortex is called the *white matter*. It is formed by masses of fibers covered by fatty sheaths. These fibers extend from the neurons of the cortex to other parts of the body.

The Functions of the Cerebrum Specific regions of the cerebrum control specific activities. Some areas of the cerebral cortex are called *motor areas*. These centers control voluntary movement. Different motor areas of the *frontal lobe* control movements in particular body areas. Suppose you crossed your legs as you were reading. Can you find the control center in figure 44-5 that allowed you to do this?

Some areas of the cerebral cortex are *sensory areas*. This means that they interpret sensations. Different areas of the *parietal lobe* interpret sensations from particular body areas. For example, if you crossed your legs, you would be aware if you hit your shins on the rung of the table. However, you would be "aware" only when an impulse reached an area of the parietal lobe.

The sense of vision is interpreted in the *occipital lobes*. What do you think would happen if these lobes were

44-5 | The control areas of the cerebrum.

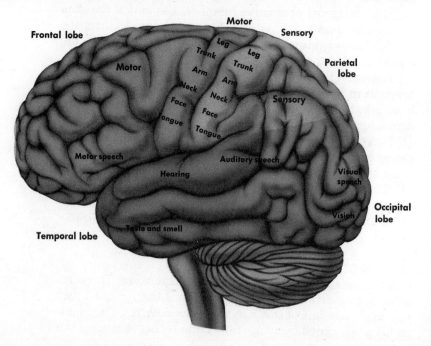

destroyed? You would not be able to see, even if your eyes were perfect. The sense of hearing is interpreted in the *temporal lobes*. The two frontal lobes are centers of emotion, judgment, will power, and self-control. These functions are also shared by other areas of the cerebral cortex.

It has been known for a long time that the right hemisphere controls the left side of the body, and the left hemisphere controls the right side of the body. Recently, scientists have learned that each hemisphere of the brain has different functions. The left hemisphere is specialized for language, learning, mathematical ability, and logical thinking. The right hemisphere is specialized for artistic, musical, intuitive, and perceptual abilities.

The Cerebellum

The *cerebellum* lies below the back of the cerebrum. Like the cerebrum, it has two hemispheres, but the cerebellum has shallower and more regular convolutions. The surface of the cerebellum is made of gray matter. Its inner part is mostly white matter. Bundles of nerve fibers connect the cerebellum with the rest of the nervous system.

The Functions of the Cerebellum **In a sense, the cerebellum assists the cerebrum in controlling muscular activity.** Nerve impulses do not originate in the cerebellum. You cannot control its activities. The cerebellum *coordinates* the motor impulses sent from the cerebrum. Without the help of the cerebellum, the cerebrum's impulses would produce uncoordinated motions. The cerebellum also reinforces impulses sent to the muscles.

Another function of the cerebellum involves the maintenance of balance. Impulses from the eyes and inner ears inform the cerebellum of your position in your surroundings. Then the cerebellum produces the muscular contractions necessary to maintain balance.

The cerebellum maintains tone in muscles. It causes muscles to remain in a state of partial contraction. You are not aware of this constant function. The cerebellum works below the level of consciousness.

The Brain Stem

The brain stem is an enlargement at the base of the brain. This is where nerve fibers from the cerebrum and the cerebellum collect before leaving the brain. The lowest portion of the stem is the *medulla oblongata* (muh-DULL-uh ob-long-GAH-tuh). It is located at the base of the skull. It protrudes from the skull and attaches to the spinal cord. The *pons* is another part of the brain stem. It receives stimuli from the facial area.

medulla = marrow, pith

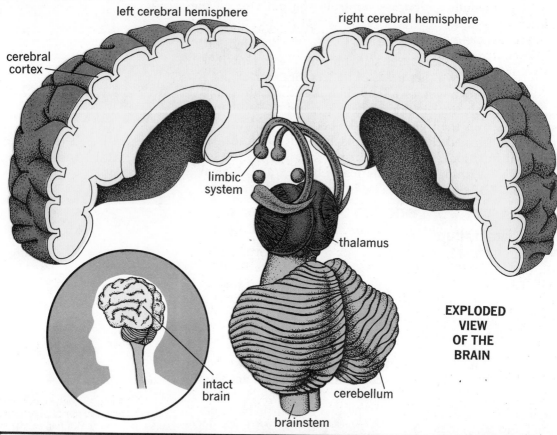

left cerebral hemisphere

right cerebral hemisphere

cerebral cortex

limbic system

thalamus

intact brain

EXPLODED VIEW OF THE BRAIN

cerebellum

brainstem

MUSCULAR COORDINATION

The cerebellum functions in coordination. It sends messages to the cerebral cortex for "awareness" and also to the various muscles of the body. The coordination required to ride a motorcycle is controlled by the cerebellum.

SENSE INTEGRATION

A mass of gray matter called the thalamus works with the cerebral cortex to integrate messages from the sense organs such as the eyes and ears.

Thus, the motorcycle rider is able to interpret what he sees and, if necessary, involve other centers to react to his environment.

THOUGHT AND MEMORY

The gray matter making up the cerebral cortex is the area of memory. Sensations are registered here and voluntary actions are begun. The cerebral cortex is involved when the young man is relating his experiences to his friends.

EMOTION

This area, buried deep within the brain is involved in emotional reactions and control. The sensation of fear, caused by the dog running in front of the motorcycle rider, involves this area of the brain.

44–6 | A color-coded diagram of the brain and some of its functions.

The medulla oblongata controls the activity of the internal organs. The respiratory control center, discussed in the last chapter, is located here. The medulla oblongata also controls heart action, muscular action in the digestive organs, glandular secretion, and other subconscious activities.

There are 12 pairs of **cranial nerves** connected to the brain. These are part of the peripheral nervous system. The cranial nerves connect with certain important organs of the body. One pair, for example, connects the eyes with the brain. Another cranial nerve connects the brain with the lungs, heart, and abdominal organs.

The Spinal Cord and the Spinal Nerves

The **spinal cord** extends down from the medulla oblongata. It passes through the bony protective arch of each vertebra, almost the whole length of the spine. The outer region of the spinal cord is white matter. It is composed of many nerve fibers covered by sheaths. The inner part of the spinal cord is gray matter. This is in a shape like that of a butterfly with outspread wings. The pointed tips of the wings of gray matter are called *horns*. The dorsal pair of horns point toward the back of the cord. The ventral pair point to the front of the cord.

The spinal cord has 31 pairs of **spinal nerves** that branch off from the cord. These pass out between the bones of the spine. The cranial nerves, the spinal nerves, and their branches make up the peripheral nervous system.

Each spinal nerve divides just outside the cord. The sensory fibers that carry impulses from the body to the cord go

44-7 | (a) A single vertebra seen from above. Note the sectioned spinal cord with its membranes and the spinal nerves. (b) shows the path of a spinal reflex involving a sensory neuron and motor neuron. The sensory and motor tracts to and from the brain are also shown.

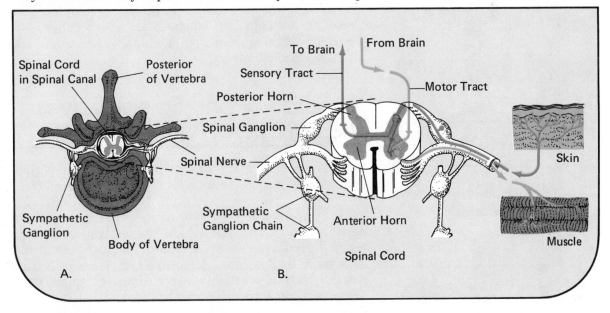

to the dorsal horns of the gray matter. This branch of each spinal nerve has a ganglion located near the point where it enters the cord. The sensory nerve cell bodies are found in the ganglia. The other branch at this junction comes from the ventral horns of the gray matter. The motor cell bodies are located in the gray matter. The motor fibers of this branch carry impulses from the spinal cord to the body.

If your spinal cord were cut, serious problems would result. All the parts of your body controlled by the nerves that leave the cord *below* the point of the cut would be paralyzed totally. In addition, you would lose all sense of feeling in many areas below the damaged spinal cord.

Reflex Reactions **There are several different kinds of nervous reactions. The simplest is called a *reflex action.*** This is an automatic reaction involving the spinal cord or the brain. The knee jerk is a good example of a simple reflex action. Sit on the edge of a table and let your knee swing freely. Then tap just below the kneecap with a narrow object. The lower part of your leg will jerk upward. The tap stimulates a sensory neuron in the tendon attached to the kneecap. An impulse travels along the dendrite to the spinal cord. Here the impulse travels to a central neuron. This, in turn, stimulates a motor neuron that extends to a muscle in the thigh, causing a jerk. The entire reflex takes only a split second.

These reflex actions serve a protective function. When you touch a hot object, your hand jerks away almost instantly. The reflex is complete even before your brain registers the pain. If the muscle response were delayed until the pain impulse was complete and interpreted, the burn would be much greater. Some other reflex actions are sneezing, coughing, blinking, laughing when tickled, and jumping when frightened.

The Cranial and Spinal Nerves: The Peripheral Nervous System

You have learned many things already about the peripheral nervous system. Actually, it is often considered to be two systems: *sensory* and *motor*. The **sensory system** is made of neurons that carry impulses toward the central nervous system. The dendrite and the cell body of the neuron in the reflex arc is a good example of this system. However, more than one neuron is involved. Axons pass from the cell body of a sensory neuron into the spinal cord. There, synapses are made with neurons that carry the impulses up to the cerebral cortex. In the cerebral cortex, the message is translated into being conscious of some stimulus.

The **motor system** is made of neurons that carry impulses away from the central nervous system. The motor system has two parts. The *somatic nervous system* is made of axons that cause contraction of muscle cells. The motor neuron in the knee-jerk reflex is part of this system. **All the nerve pathways outside the CNS that you use when you move any of your skeletal muscles are part of the somatic nervous system.**

The Autonomic Nervous System

Another part of the motor nervous system is the *autonomic nervous system.* **The autonomic nervous system is involuntary and automatic.** It is composed of two parts: the **sympathetic system** and the **parasympathetic system.** The sympathetic system includes two rows of nerve cords that lie on either side of the spinal column. Each cord has ganglia. These contain the cell bodies of the neurons. The largest sympathetic ganglion is located just below the diaphragm. It is called the *solar plexus.* Sympathetic ganglia are also located near the heart, the lower abdomen, and the neck. The sympathetic nervous system has a number of functions. It helps regulate the action of the heart, the secretion of the endocrine glands, the arterial blood supply, the action of the smooth muscles of the stomach and the intestines, and the activity of other internal organs.

The *parasympathetic system* opposes the action of the sympathetic system. The major nerve of the parasympathetic system is the *vagus nerve.* This cranial nerve extends from the medulla oblongata down through the neck to the chest and abdomen.

The whole autonomic nervous system serves as a system of checks and balances. For instance, the sympathetic system acts to speed up heart action, but stimulation by the vagus nerve slows down the heart rate.

The Senses

Special sense organs called **receptors** are located in the skin. Receptors are at the terminal branches of the dendrites of sensory neurons. Some receptors are composed of many cells. Others have one specialized cell. Some receptors are simply bare nerve endings. Each receptor is suited to receive only one type of stimulus. When a receptor is

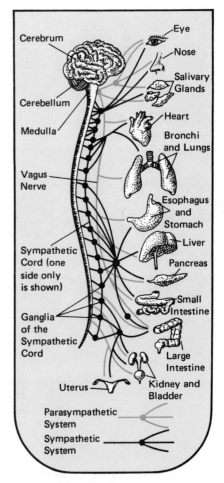

44-8 | The autonomic nervous system regulates the internal organs of the body. What are the functions of its two divisions?

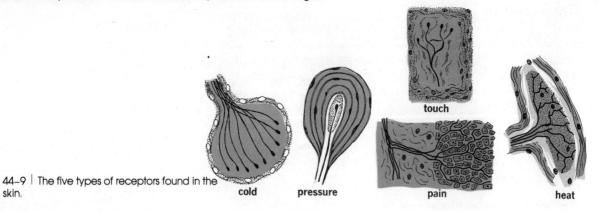

44–9 | The five types of receptors found in the skin.

cold   pressure   touch   pain   heat

stimulated, it starts an impulse along the dendrite to the central nervous system.

There are five distinct kinds of receptors. They are specialized to receive response to stimuli of either *touch, pressure, pain, heat,* or *cold.* The pain receptor, for example, is a bare dendrite. If the stimulus is strong enough, a pain receptor will react to mechanical, thermal, electrical, or chemical stimuli. The sensation of pain is a protective device. It signals a threat of injury to the body. Pain receptors are located throughout the skin.

The Senses of the Skin

The sensory nerves of the skin are distributed unevenly over the skin area and lie at different depths in the skin. For instance, if you move the point of your pencil very lightly over your skin, you stimulate only the nerves of *touch.* The receptors for touch are close to the surface of the skin. The fingertips, the forehead, and the tip of the tongue contain many receptors that respond to touch.

Receptors that respond to *pressure* lie deeper in the skin. If you press the pencil point against the skin, you feel both pressure and touch. Since the nerves are deeper, a pressure stimulus must be stronger than a touch stimulus. You may think that there is no difference between touch and pressure, but you can distinguish the mere touching of an object from a firm grip on it.

Heat and *cold* stimulate different receptors. This is an interesting protective adaptation of the body. Actually, cold is not an active condition. Cold results from a lowering in heat energy. If both great heat and intense cold stimulated a single receptor, you would be unable to tell the difference between the two. In turn, you would be unable to react to either. However, since some receptors are stimulated by heat and other by the absence of it, you can react to both conditions.

The Sense of Taste

Nearly all animals prefer some food substances to others. So they must be able to distinguish different chemical substances. **Like other senses, taste results from the stimulation of certain nerve endings.** In this case, the stimulation is chemical. In humans, the nerve endings for taste are located in *taste buds* on the tongue. Taste buds are shaped like little flasks. They lie on the front of the tongue, along its sides, and near the back. Food dissolved in saliva enters the taste buds through little pores at the tops. Once inside, they stimulate hairlike nerve endings. The message carried to the brain from these nerve endings is interpreted as a sense of taste.

Our sense of taste is not very well developed. **Only four common flavors can be tasted:** *sour, sweet, salty,* and *bitter.* The buds for each of these flavors are located in different areas of the tongue. Those sensitive to sweetness are on the tip of the tongue. That is why candy tastes sweeter when you lick it than when you chew it. Salt-sensitive buds are also on the tongue's tip. Those for sour flavors lie along the sides of the tongue, and those for bitterness lie on the back of the tongue. That is why, if you eat something both sweet and bitter, you taste the sweetness before the bitterness. Some foodstuffs, like pepper and other spices, have no distinct flavor. They taste the way they do because they irritate the entire tongue, causing a burning sensation.

The Sense of Smell

Like taste, smell results from chemical stimulation of certain nerve endings. The difference is that the chemical stimulator for smell is in the form of gas. The nasal passages are arranged in three layers of cavities. These are separated by bony layers called *turbinates.* The upper cavity contains the branched endings of a cranial nerve called the **olfactory nerve.**

Gases entering the nasal cavity dissolve in mucus. Then, they stimulate these nerve endings. This causes impulses to go to the central nervous system. These impulses are interpreted as smell. If smell receptors are exposed to a particular odor for a long time, they stop reacting to it, but they will still respond to other odors. If you ever go into a hospital, the iodoform odor will be obvious. However, the nurses who work there usually are not aware of the odor.

Hearing: The Structure of the Ear

Like all mammalian ears, human ears are very complex organs. The outer ear opens into the *auditory canal.* This canal is embedded in the bones of the skull. It is closed at its inner end by the *eardrum,* or *tympanic membrane.* The eardrum separates the auditory canal from the middle ear.

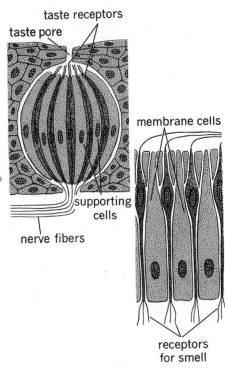

44–10 | (left) The receptor of taste; (right) the receptor of smell as they appear under a microscope.

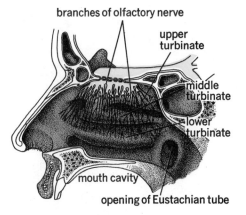

44–11 | The surface of the inner wall of the nose. What function does the Eustachian tube perform?

The *Eustachian* (yoo-STAY-shun) *tube* connects the middle ear with the throat. This connection equalizes pressure in the middle ear with that of the outer atmosphere. When the Eustachian tube becomes blocked by a cold, the inner and outer pressures do not equalize. If the pressure difference becomes great enough, the eardrum may burst.

In the middle ear, there are three tiny bones: the *hammer*, the *anvil*, and the *stirrup*. They form a chain across the middle ear. This chain extends inward from the inner face of the eardrum. At the inner end of the middle ear, the stirrup links with a membrane called the *oval window*. The oval window covers the opening to the inner ear.

The inner ear is composed of two general parts: the *cochlea* (KOCK-lee-uh) and the *semicircular canals*. The cochlea is a spiral passage that looks like a tiny snail shell. It is filled with fluid and its inner surface is lined with nerve endings. These nerve endings are highly sensitive to vibrations of the fluid. All these nerve endings join the **auditory nerve.** This nerve leads from the cochlea to the brain. The semicircular canals consist of three loop-shaped tubes. These tubes lie at right angles to one another. They function in keeping a sense of balance.

How You Hear   All noise is actually vibrations. When an object vibrates in the air, it mechanically moves the air molecules. The molecules are squeezed, or compressed together. Others are spread apart, or rarefied. The regular pattern that is produced by any vibrating object in the air, or any other medium, is called a *sound wave*. When sound

Facts & Figures

Loudness of a sound depends on how many cells are stimulated in the cochlea. The tone of a sound depends on which cells of the cochlea are stimulated.

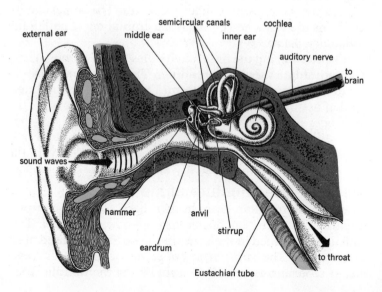

44-12 | The structure of the human ear.

waves reach the ear, they pass through the outer ear, down the auditory canal and to the eardrum. The sound waves start the eardrum vibrating in the same pattern as the particular wave. The vibrating eardrum then starts the hammer, the anvil, and the stirrup vibrating. These, in turn, cause the oval window to vibrate, and this sets up vibration in the fluid inside the cochlea. The vibrations of the fluid stimulate the nerve endings that line the cochlea. The nerve endings transmit impulses up the auditory nerve to the cerebrum. The specific pattern of the impulses is determined by the pattern of the sound wave that started the whole chain. The cerebrum picks up the impulses and translates them into a perception of sound. The whole process is a very sensitive chain reaction.

All the links in the chain are crucial to the process. If any link is destroyed, a person will either hear poorly or not at all. Vibrations are carried mechanically to nerve endings. These endings translate the vibrations into an electrochemical impulse that humans perceive as sound. If the auditory region of the cerebrum does not function, the person cannot hear. This is true even if all the ear mechanisms receive vibrations normally.

The Sense of Balance

The semicircular canals are the structures necessary to our sense of balance, or equilibrium. The canals lie at right angles to each other on three different planes. These canals contain many receptors. They also contain a fluid similar to the fluid inside the cochlea. When your head changes position, this fluid moves and stimulates the receptors. With this stimulation, the receptors start impulses that go through a branch of the auditory nerve to the cerebellum. The brain is then made aware of changes in head position. The canals lie in three planes so that *any* change in the head's position will move the fluid to the ends of the canals. A sensory conflict can cause a sensation of dizziness.

Vision: The Structure of the Eye

The normal eye is spherical, though slightly flattened from front to back. The wall of the eyeball is made of three distinct layers. The *sclerotic* (skluh-ROT-ick) *layer* is on the outside surface. It is tough and white and is normally called the "white of the eye." At its front, it bulges and is transparent. This section of the sclerotic layer is called the *cornea*.

The middle layer of the wall of the eye is called the *choroid layer*. This layer is supplied with many blood vessels. It surrounds the eye, except for the very front. The

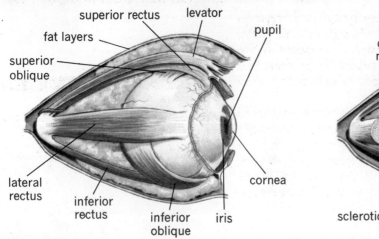

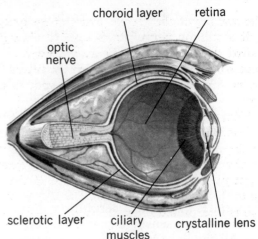

44–13 | The human eye. (right) The various internal structures; (left) the muscles and sockets

small opening at the front is called the *pupil*. The pupil lies directly behind the center of the cornea. The choroid layer contains pigmented cells around the pupil. These may be colored blue, brown, hazel, green, or combinations of these. This pigmented area is called the *iris*.

The pupil changes in size, depending on the intensity of light entering it. This adjustment is an automatic reflex. It is accomplished by muscles in the iris. In bright light, the pupil shrinks, or constricts. In dim light, it enlarges, or dilates.

Behind the pupil opening, there is a convex, *crystalline lens*. The lens is held in place by muscles that are attached to the choroid layer. These muscles are called *ciliary muscles*. When they contract, they change the shape of the lens. This allows you to focus on objects either close or far away. The space between the lens and the cornea is filled with a thin watery liquid called *aqueous humor*. Inside the eyeball, there is a thicker, transparent substance that keeps the eyeball firm. This fluid is called *vitreous humor*.

The Structure of the Retina   The innermost layer of the eye is the most complicated and delicate one. It is called the *retina*. Less than a millimeter (0.04 inches) thick, it is composed of several layers of cells: receptors, ganglia, and nerve fibers.

The function of all the structures of the eye is to focus light on the retina. The retina contains the receptors that are stimulated by light. These receptors are called **photoreceptors.** They are of two types: *cones* and *rods*. They lie deep in the retina. When they are stimulated they start impulses, through a series of short nerves, to ganglia near

photos = light

the surface of the retina. From these ganglia, more than half a million nerve fibers lead to a large cranial nerve called the **optic nerve.** There are no rods or cones at the spot where the optic nerve joins the retina. Thus, there can be no vision at this point. This spot is called the *blind spot.*

From the back of each eyeball, an optic nerve extends to the occipital lobe of the cerebrum. That is the vision center of the brain. Some of the fibers cross as they lead to the cerebrum. This means that some of the impulses from your right eye go to the left occipital lobe. Some from the left eye go to the right occipital lobe. Thus, what you see with each eye is interpreted in both lobes.

How You See Light rays pass through the cornea, aqueous humor, pupil, lens, and vitreous humor, and then strike the retina. The rays stimulate photoreceptors, which transmit impulses to the optic nerve. The lens focuses the rays mostly on a small portion of the retina called the *fovea.* The fovea has more cones than other parts of the retina. **Cones are more sensitive to bright light than are rods. Cones are responsible for color vision.** When light is focused on the fovea, we see an object clearly. Outside the fovea there are not as many cones. An image focused here is less distinct. Thus, if you focus your eyes directly on an object, you see it clearly, while surrounding objects tend to lack detail.

Facts & Figures

The retina of each human eye contains about 125 million rods and about 7 million cones.

44-14 | The structure of the back of the eye. The shapes and arrangement of the rods and cones are shown in greater detail in the enlargement.

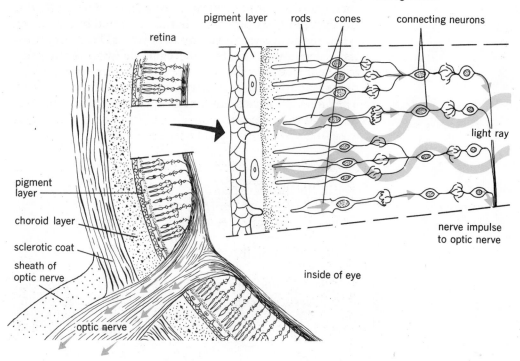

pigment layer rods cones connecting neurons

retina

light ray

pigment layer

choroid layer

sclerotic coat

sheath of optic nerve

nerve impulse to optic nerve

inside of eye

optic nerve

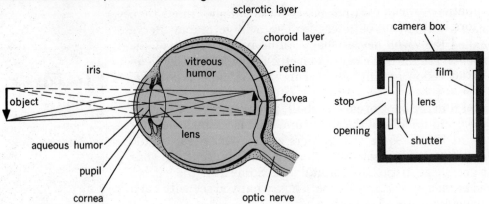

44–15 | How are the parts of the camera similar to those of the eye? How are the parts different? Why is the image reversed and inverted on the retina?

At night there is not enough light to stimulate the cones, but there is enough to stimulate the rods. However, rods cannot distinguish colors. Therefore, you do not see much color in dim light.

The fovea contains many cones, but no rods. The areas outside the fovea have more rods. Thus you can see things more clearly at night "out of the corner of your eye."

Eye Movement and Protection In its socket, the eyeball rests against protective cushions of fat. Pairs of muscles extend from the inside of the socket to the eyeball. These muscles move the eye. The sclerotic layer has pain receptors. So the brain is aware when a foreign object touches the eyeball. The eyeball further is protected by its recessed position in the socket, and by the eyelids. Tear glands keep its surface moist. Tears wash over the eye and then drain into tear ducts in the lower corners of the sockets. These ducts lead to the nasal cavity. Tears clear dirt from the eye. They also kill germs and bacteria because they contain an antibacterial enzyme.

Summary

The brain and spinal cord compose the central nervous system. The cerebrum controls most conscious activities and is the center of intelligence. Impulses from cerebral motor areas pass through the cerebellum. The medulla oblongata controls the activity of internal organs, including those of respiration.

The five different types of skin receptors respond to touch pressure, pain, heat, and cold. Smell receptors lie in the upper turbinate region of the nasal passages. Hearing receptors are located in the cochlea of the inner ear. Information on head position and balance is picked up by receptors in the semicircular canals of the inner ear.

The human eye receives light rays through the pupil and focuses them on the retina by means of the lens. Photoreceptors called rods and cones send impulses along the optic nerve.

central nervous system
peripheral nervous system
neuron
dendrite
axon
nerves
synapse
meninges
ventricle
cerebrum
cerebellum
medulla oblongata
pons
cranial nerve
spinal cord

spinal nerve
reflex action
sensory sytem
motor system
sympathetic ner-
 vous sytem
parasympathetic ner-
 vous system
receptor
olfactory nerve
Eustachian tube
auditory nerve
retina
photoreceptor
optic nerve

Biologically Speaking

1. Name the two main divisions of the nervous system and then state the functions of each.
2. How is a neuron specialized for its function?
3. What is a nerve impulse?
4. Name the parts of the brain and state the functions of each.
5. Describe the path of a reflex of arc.
6. List the parts of the peripheral nervous system.
7. In what way is the autonomic nervous system really two systems?
8. Describe how a sound wave in the air stimulates the receptors in the cochlea.

Questions for Review

1. What is intelligence?
2. Explain the activity that occurs after a chicken's head has been cut off.
3. Explain the fact that the sympathetic nervous system is sometimes called "the system for fight or flight."

Applying Concepts

45

Tobacco, Alcohol, and Drugs

A **DESCRIBE** the effects of smoking on the body.

B **EXPLAIN** the effects of alcohol on the body.

C **DEFINE** alcoholism as a disease.

D **LIST** and **DESCRIBE** drugs of abuse.

E **DISCUSS** some of the causes of drug addiction.

45-1 | Have we become a drug dependent society? *(HRW photo by Ken Karp)*

Substances in the Bloodstream

You probably have read reports about tragic deaths caused by drug overdoses, or of automobile or drowning accidents resulting from misuse of alcohol. At the same time you may read reports about "miracle drugs." In fact, many of us might not be living today if it were not for the development of antibiotics. However, the widespread use of antibiotics has created other problems. Chapter 17 presented the problem of a disease-producing organism becoming resistant to a particular antibiotic.

You are now familiar with the parts of the digestive tract and you know how nutritive substances are absorbed into the bloodstream. Mucous membranes in other parts of your body are very thin and richly supplied with capillaries. Small molecules can pass through these membranes into your bloodstream. When treating certain heart conditions a tiny tablet is placed under the tongue. Within seconds the medication is absorbed into the bloodstream through the membranes of the mouth. The medication relieves the pain. Other substances can also enter the blood through the lungs, where gases are exchanged.

Medications are often given as "shots." Penicillin, for example, may be injected into a muscle. Absorption by the bloodstream may be slow and continue for a period of time. Some medications may be injected directly into the bloodstream. Then they are rapidly carried to all parts of the body.

Substances such as tobacco, alcohol, and some drugs are not medicines. They can impair the body's activities. In this chapter you will learn about some of the effects of these substances on your body. You will then have the information to form your own opinions and make your own decisions about what is to enter your bloodstream.

Tobacco: The Smoking Habit

More than 70 million people in the United States use tobacco in some form. Most smoke cigarettes. Smokers have both a smoking habit and a tobacco habit. The first involves going through the motions of smoking. For example, many smokers automatically reach for a cigarette at regular intervals. Heavy smokers may even light a second cigarette before finishing the first one. Smokers also develop a physical desire for the nicotine in tobacco, which is the tobacco habit.

Many young people who smoke feel it makes them seem more mature. Yet, if people who have smoked for several years were asked their advice, it would be to not start smoking at all. Certainly, several things should be considered before deliberately starting the practice of smoking. Smoking is habit-forming and dangerous to your health.

The Effects of Smoking

Tobacco contains the substance *nicotine.* When chewed, the nicotine dissolves in mucus and is absorbed into the bloodstream. When smoked, it enters the nose, throat, trachea, bronchi, and lungs along with tar and smoke particles. In the smoker, gas and particles in tobacco smoke settle on the mucous membranes, causing irritation. The cilia of the epithelial cells are no longer effective in removing foreign substances. Sore throats and coughs are common complaints of smokers.

The nicotine passes through the membranes and enters the bloodstream. What does it do? For one thing, nicotine slows the digestive process. Smokers often complain of heartburn after a meal. This is because the acid in the stomach builds up enough to irritate the gastric lining.

Nicotine also affects the circulatory system. It constricts blood vessels. This causes an increase in blood pressure. The heart has to work harder. After smoking, the heartbeat may increase as much as 28 beats per minute. Just how risky is smoking for the cardiovascular system? The heart-attack rate among middle-aged men is twice as great for smokers as it is for nonsmokers. This rate also applies to blood vessel diseases, such as atherosclerosis.

Conclusions of Scientific Research

In 1964 the Public Health Service published a report on the effects of smoking. These findings were expanded and reinforced by another report in 1978. These reports were based on experiments with animals, clinical and autopsy studies in humans, and studies on the occurrence of disease. Some of the findings are as follows:

- Tissue damage. Lung tissue secretions from thousands of smokers were examined after the smokers' death. Abnormal cells were found in their lungs. This was true even of the individuals who did not die from cancer. Researchers also observed enlarged and ruptured alveoli and thickened arterioles. In the trachea and bronchii, the cilia and the protective cells of the mucosa were destroyed. These structures normally clean and lubricate the respiratory tract. They also help prevent infection.

- Higher death rate. Researchers compared the number of deaths among a large sample of nonsmokers with the number of deaths among a similar sample of smokers. These deaths were from many causes, but certain diseases stood out. There were 1,000 percent more deaths from lung cancer among the smokers, and there were 500 percent more from chronic bronchitis and emphysema. Bronchitis is an inflammation of the bronchus and bronchioles. Emphysema is a degenerative lung disease. These conditions greatly interfere with the exchange of gases in the lungs. Death rate of smokers is also much higher than for nonsmokers when other diseases are the cause. Other diseases include peptic ulcer, circulatory diseases, and cancer of the tongue, larynx, and esophagus.

- The greater the amount of smoking, the higher the death rate. In the sample population the death rate is about 40 percent higher for people who smoke less than 10 cigarettes a day than it is for nonsmokers. The death rate is 120 percent higher for people who smoke 40 or more cigarettes per day. The death rate rises the same way with the number of years of smoking. Obviously, smoking is a health hazard. Ninety-five percent of lung cancer victims are heavy smokers; one half of one percent are nonsmok-

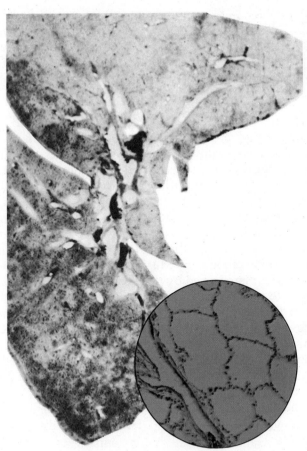
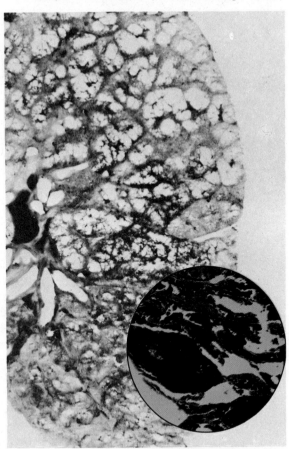

ers. Heart and circulatory diseases are the number one cause of death in the United States. The death rate from these diseases is 200 percent higher among smokers than nonsmokers.

45–2 | (left) Normal lung tissue. Air sacs are very small. (right) Lung tissue of a heavy smoker showing abundance of greatly enlarged air sacs. (Courtesy of American Cancer Society; inset left: Manfred P. Kage, Peter Arnold; inset right: Remy von Muchon/Medcom)

Changing Attitudes The research findings of 1964 and 1978 reinforced these major conclusions through years of scientific evidence. Today, three out of four people do not smoke and many smokers support nonsmoking policies. However, even with knowledge of the health hazard of smoking, tobacco sales have risen. Unfortunately, more young people are smoking. This increase has been greater among females.

In 1970 a law became effective that prohibited cigarette advertising on radio and television. The same law requires each cigarette package to have a warning: "The Surgeon General has determined that cigarette smoking is dangerous to your health." In 1975 about 70 percent of the smokers agreed that smoking cigarettes should be banned in more public places. Several states adopted laws that prohibit smoking in certain public areas.

The Facts about Alcohol

The alcohol in beverages is *ethyl alcohol*, or ethanol (C_2H_5OH). It is produced by the action of yeast on sugars. Most alcoholic drinks are made from the sugars in fruits or grains.

The alcohol molecule does not have to be changed to be absorbed. Alcohol enters your bloodstream within two minutes after it is swallowed. This time is even less if your stomach is empty. It rapidly diffuses into the tissue fluid and is absorbed by the cells. Alcohol is oxidized in the cells of the body at the rate of about one ounce in three hours.

When alcohol is oxidized it releases large amounts of heat. The excess heat raises the temperature of the blood. This, in turn, stimulates the heat-control center in the brain. The brain responds by causing increased circulation to the skin. Heat is released by the body. It is the increased circulation to the skin that causes a rosy skin tone. As you learned in the last chapter, the heat receptors are in the skin. The rush of blood to the skin gives a false impression of warmth. Actually, the internal organs are receiving a reduced supply of blood.

Not all the alcohol is oxidized. Part is released by the lungs as vapor. This causes an alcoholic breath odor. Some goes to the skin and is excreted with perspiration. Some passes through the kidneys and leaves the body in the urine.

Alcohol and its Effects on the Body

Alcohol is absorbed by all the body organs. The cells of some body organs seem to be affected more than others by alcohol. Alcohol oxidation produces water, but water is excreted by the skin in large quantities to control body temperature. The loss of water dries out the tissues. In the kidneys, much water is reabsorbed to make up for the skin water loss. This causes nitrogenous wastes to concentrate in the kidneys. Normal filtration, reabsorption, and secretion in the kidney are affected.

Vitamin-deficiency diseases are common among alcoholics. This is because they often eat very little during long periods of heavy use of alcohol. Also these fasts cause the liver to give up its stored food. The liver begins to swell as the carbohydrates are replaced by fats. This condition is known as *fatty liver*. It occurs in 75 percent of alcoholics. Over a long period of time, alcohol use can lead to a serious liver disease called **cirrhosis** (si-ROE-siss). Heavy alcohol use destroys normal tissues of the liver and replaces them with nonfunctioning scar tissue. This decreases the blood

---

Facts & Figures

Clay tablets record that people in Mesopotamia used alcohol 5,000 years ago.

flow and the functioning of the liver. Other conditions can cause cirrhosis, but it is most common among alcoholics.

Excessive use of alcohol can also affect the stomach. It causes an increase in stomach secretions. This can lead to **gastritis,** a painful swelling of the stomach lining.

Excessive drinking over a period of time can cause **alcohol psychosis.** This is a form of mental illness requiring hospitalization. The cause of alcohol psychosis is not fully understood. Part of the condition may be caused by the effect of alcohol on the brain. Another cause is a deficiency in the B-complex vitamins. These vitamins are necessary for normal nervous activity.

Alcohol psychotics become very confused. They may not be able to recognize members of their family. They may not even know who they are. They also have terrifying hallucinations. These usually involve visual horror and uncontrollable trembling. That is why this state is called *delirium tremens,* or the D.T.'s. Some alcohol psychotics suffer loss of memory of recent events. Alcohol psychosis is treated with psychotherapy, a controlled diet, and vitamin supplements.

Alcohol has an anesthetic, or numbing, effect on the nervous system. This makes people less concerned about their behavior. People mistake this feeling for a stimulant. However, the overall effect on the body is the opposite. Alcohol is a **depressant.** It diminishes the activity of the body functions.

The brain cortex shows the first effects of alcohol. Loss of judgment, will power, and self-control occur. Alcohol also affects the centers for emotion. This may lead to a feeling of joy, often shown by laughter. Others may feel sadness and weep. When alcohol reaches the vision and speech areas of the cerebrum, drinkers may experience blurred or double vision, and they will have difficulty judging distance. Their speech may become slurred.

Muscle coordination is affected when alcohol reaches the cerebrum. Drinkers become dizzy. They may stagger or may not be able to stand at all.

In the final stage of drunkeness, the brain cortex stops working. This can result in a state of unconsciousness. Heart action and digestive action slow down, as does respiration. The drinker becomes completely helpless.

Alcohol and Accidents Many experiments have tested thoroughly the relationship between drinking and driving a car. These tests were carried out under actual road conditions. Drivers were given measured amounts of alcohol, but not enough to make them drunk. All but one passed

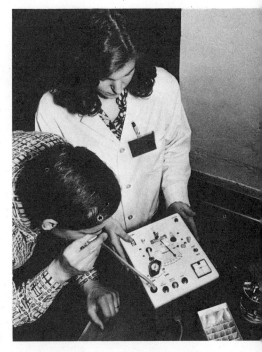

45–3 | An alchometer is used to determine the alcoholic content of the blood. *(HRW Photo by Russell Dian)*

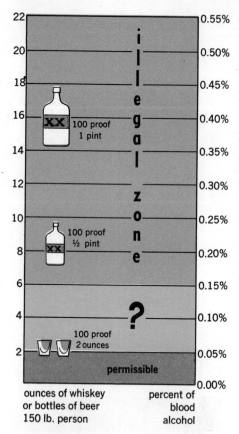

ounces of whiskey or bottles of beer 150 lb. person	percent of blood alcohol

45–4 | Drinking limits for drivers in the United States. Studies have shown that at 0.05 percent chances of highway accidents double.

the police sobriety tests. All the motorists made many errors that could lead to accidents. Most had a slower braking reaction time. They were also inaccurate in performance. Yet all the drivers thought they were doing well. *Judgment was found to be impaired after only one or two drinks.* Psychological tests proved this.

It is not surprising that alcohol is a factor in a large proportion of all fatal traffic accidents. In one-vehicle accidents, 70 percent of the drivers killed had been drinking. A drinking driver is killed in 50 percent of all multivehicle accidents. Alcohol was found to be partly responsible in more than 50 percent of pedestrian traffic deaths.

What are the effects of alcohol on the motorist?

- It increases reaction time. The driver takes longer to brake or to swerve to avoid collision.
- It impairs vision and distance judgment.
- It takes the driver's attention away from driving.
- It makes associating danger signals with danger more difficult. The driver pays less attention to stop lights, stop signs, and railroad flashers.
- It gives the driver a false sense of security. Most drunk drivers think they are good drivers.
- It makes the driver hostile.

The Alcoholism Complex *Alcoholism* **is a disease.** Alcoholics depend on alcohol continually. An individual may start with occasional social drinking. Alcoholics use drinking as an escape from problems. Drinking causes the loss of judgment and will power. The possibility of solving problems then becomes less likely. As the need for escape becomes greater, the alcoholic begins to drink when alone.

People who have studied alcoholism agree that some problem underlies the alcoholic's drinking. The first step in recovery is to recognize the problem. If the underlying problem is solved, the need for alcohol may disappear. Understanding and cooperation from family and friends help in overcoming alcoholism.

There may also be a biochemical reason why some people are alcoholics. Recent research suggests that a substance in the blood may be involved. This substance is *acetaldehyde.* Acetaldehyde is known to affect brain tissue. Alcoholics have more acetaldehyde in their blood than nonalcoholics. Alcohol is metabolized to acetaldehyde in the liver and other tissues. The acetaldehyde is then metabolized to acetic acid.

Whatever the cause of alcoholism, it is a problem of society. Most states have special agencies to deal with alcoholism. They carry on studies and research. They also give information to people who want to learn more about the disease. These agencies see the alcoholic as someone who needs help. This changing attitude is also seen in our courts. Many judges now recommend medical treatment or psychiatric counseling rather than punishment for the alcoholic lawbreaker.

There are many private organizations working on this problem. Perhaps the best known is Alcoholics Anonymous, or AA. This voluntary organization began in 1935. Since then, about one million alcoholics have stopped drinking with the help of AA.

Drugs: Proper Use vs. Abuse

When anything interferes with the normal functioning of your body's cells, you become ill. Your body has remarkable ways of healing wounds and defending itself against pathogenic organisms. Sometimes, however, a body's recovery may be aided with drugs. **A *drug* is any chemical substance that alters either the mind or the body.** Some drugs kill pathogenic organisms. Some speed healing. Others treat symptoms to make you feel better. When medical doctors prescribe a drug, they are familiar with its effects on the various tissues of your body. This is important because many drugs can have harmful effects, especially if they are taken for a long time or in large doses.

Medications that can be bought without a prescription are called over-the-counter drugs. Their labels give dosage and information on proper and improper use. It is a good idea to read these labels. Many substances thought to be harmless are actually drugs. Consider aspirin. Taken improperly, it can make you very ill, or even cause death. More than 100 children die each year from accidental aspirin overdoses. Vitamins, antacids, and cold remedies are just a few of the drugs many people take casually.

Descriptions of Drugs

Some drugs come from plants and are called *natural drugs.* Other drugs are made in laboratories and are called *synthetic drugs.* Sulfanilamide and some vitamins are examples of synthetic drugs.

There are natural drugs in coffee and tea. One of these drugs is *caffeine.* This substance is soluble in water and is removed from the tissues and excreted in the urine. Coffee,

Careers

Pharmacists dispense drugs and health products. They help people maintain their health by giving information, directing them to health services, and keeping individual patient profiles on the drugs prescribed.

Training includes completing a five- or six-year course in pharmacy. Passing a state licensing examination is required.

45–5 | A pharmacist can advise you in your choice of over-the-counter drugs. *(HRW photo by Russell Dian)*

tea, cocoa, and the kola nut, from which cola drinks are made, all contain natural drugs. However, these drinks prevent sleep and cause emotional excitement. Because of this, these drugs are classified among the **stimulating drugs.**

Narcotics *Narcotics* are potentially addictive drugs. Legally, narcotics are used in medicine as pain relievers or cough suppressors, and as remedies for various intestinal problems. These drugs depress the central nervous system and create a short-term sense of elation. They also induce drowsiness or sleep. Decreased physical activity and visual ability are also common. Opium, cocaine, and the drugs that are made from them are all narcotics. So are several synthetic compounds. Nonprescription sale of narcotics is illegal in the United States.

Opium comes from the juice of the white poppy. *Morphine* and *codeine* are both made from opium. *Heroin* is a synthetic compound made from morphine. Both morphine and codeine are used as pain killers. Codeine is also an ingredient in special kinds of medicine.

Barbiturates *Barbiturates* are synthetic drugs. They act as tranquilizers or sedatives. A sedative is a drug that causes you to sleep. It can also reduce emotional anxiety and relieve pain. Barbiturates are used habitually by hundreds of thousands of people in the United States. Barbiturates are not addictive in the same way as narcotics. However, people can come to depend on them psychologically.

If a heavy user is suddenly taken off barbiturates, withdrawal symptoms can occur.

Volatile Chemicals Some people have tried to escape reality by inhaling volatile chemicals. These include kerosene, paint thinner, model glue, gasoline, lighter fluid, and other solvents. They are not actually drugs, but inhalation of these volatile chemicals causes them to diffuse into the bloodstream. This reduces the amount of oxygen in the bloodstream. The user feels dizzy and loses coordination. Other reactions are slurred speech, blurred vision, loss of color vision, ringing in the ears, and nausea. Breathing these volatiles is very dangerous. It can cause unconsciousness and even death.

Marijuana Marijuana comes from the flowers, leaves, and seeds of *Cannabis sativa*, the scientific name for Indian hemp. This plant grows wild in many parts of the world and in parts of the midwestern United States. The leaves of the plant and flowers are crushed, chopped, or shredded. In powdered form the marijuana is sometimes sniffed or taken with food. Most frequently it is rolled into cigarettes or smoked in pipes.

The effects of marijuana vary with the user and the amount used. The effects also vary depending on the amount of *Tetra-Hydro Cannabinol (THC)* the marijuana contains. This drug produces a feeling of intoxication. When the drug starts acting on the nervous system, there is a distortion of time and space, loss of memory, and impaired judgment. This is why driving under the influence of marijuana is dangerous. Physical effects of marijuana include increased heart action and lowered body temperature.

Is marijuana dangerous? Research in humans and animals suggests that marijuana has harmful effects on vital bodily functions. Key scientists have agreed that marijuana is especially dangerous among persons in the middle-teens and younger, heart patients, pregnant women, persons with lung disease, and anyone who appears prone to emotional disturbances. The conclusions concerning cigarette smoking have caused similar fears of lung damage and possible cancer resulting from smoking marijuana. There have been reports that marijuana use may interfere with the body's immunological defense system, as well as having certain effects on hormone production, including the male sex hormone testosterone. Research continues to establish conclusive findings of the effects of marijuana. However, the risks of using marijuana should be considered seriously.

45-6 | Much of the marijuana entering the United States via Mexico has been found by health officials to be contaminated by paraquat, a deadly pesticide. *(Carolina Biological Supply Co.)*

Amphetamines *Amphetamines* (am-FET-uh-meenz) are stimulant drugs. They are used in *pep pills*. People may take them to stay awake. The pills impair judgment and vision and may even produce hallucinations. This is why they are dangerous to people who work machinery or who must drive.

Amphetamines are not necessarily physically addictive. However, habitual users may become emotionally dependent on them.

Hallucinogens *Hallucinogens* are chemical compounds that affect the mind. They change sensory perception, reaction to time and space, and the rate and content of thought. People using them often describe visions or hallucinations. The three most common types of hallucinatory drugs are *LSD, mescaline,* and *psilocybin.*

Physical reactions to LSD seem to vary. Heart rate and blood pressure may increase. The pupils of the eyes may dilate. The user may feel alternating periods of chill and fever. Trembling and nausea can also occur. Chromosomal changes resulting from LSD are well known in plants and animals. Medical investigators are still studying the effects of LSD on the human body.

PCP (angel dust) PCP is designated as a depressant under the Controlled Substances Act. However, it has been known to act as a stimulant, a hallucinogen, and an analgesic. Because of its dangerous side effects, it was banned for human use. PCP acts on the central nervous system. Its specific effects can range from feeling estranged to paranoid and violent behavior, depending on the dose.

Heroin Like alcoholism, drug abuse often seems to come from a desire to escape problems. For example, people who take heroin may feel better about their problems at first. They go into a dream world. However, the effects soon wear off. Another shot is needed to get that feeling back. Eventually, a tolerance develops to the drug.

Possession of heroin in the United States, even for medical purposes, is illegal. Therefore, the price to obtain it is high. An addict may require up to a hundred dollars' worth of heroin a day. The need for this kind of money may lead the addict to unwarranted actions.

Drug Addiction People who take a drug for a long time may come to depend on it. This is called *addiction.* There are two kinds of addiction. *Psychological addiction* is an emotional dependence on a drug. *Physical addiction* is a physiological dependence on a drug, which means that the body requires a continuing supply. Often, the two types of addiction go together. If the supply of an addictive drug is cut off, the addict will show *withdrawal symptoms*. The addict may be unable to sleep and may have difficulty breathing. Mental symptoms include depression and derangement.

Prevention and Treatment   There is no way of knowing the exact number of drug addicts in the United States, but the number of heroin addicts alone has been estimated at 56,000! Few addicts treated in hospitals are known to be able to avoid drugs when they are released. Many of these addicts are teenagers.

Methadone maintenance is regular supervision of heroin addicts. Methadone can be used medically to relieve pain or to reduce the withdrawal symptoms of morphine or heroin addiction. Patients in this program must first agree to stop taking heroin. Then they are given methadone regularly in prescribed doses. Over a period of several weeks or even months, the methadone dose is reduced. The person can overcome the physical dependence in this way. It takes longer to overcome the psychological dependence.

How can drug abuse be prevented? At one time heroin addicts were jailed for treatment. This practice was abandoned. Under state and federal law, stiff penalties are imposed for the illegal sale and possession of drugs. Under international agreements, strict control measures have been designed to stop illegal drug traffic. Yet despite these control measures, drug abuse is widespread.

45-7 | (top) Phencyclidine (PCP) rock crystal. (bottom) PCP added to parsley or other leaves in a cigarette. *(C. Gunther, Camera 5)*

Summary

Tobacco is not addicting in the same sense as narcotic drugs. The nicotine of tobacco enters the bloodstream and affects the heart, circulatory system, and stomach.

Alcohol is a depressant. Alcohol entering the bloodstream affects all body organs. It can produce organic diseases, and misuse can cause automobile accidents. Drug addiction can be psychological, physical, or both. People who take them habitually often do so in order to escape from problems. Narcotics are illegal except by prescription. Because of this, many addicts spend most of their time looking for ways to get the drug they need, and create more problems for them and for society as a whole.

Biologically Speaking

nicotine
cirrhosis
gastritis
alcohol psychosis
depressant
alcoholism

drug
stimulating drug
narcotic
barbiturate
sedative
amphetamine
hallucinogen
addiction

Questions for Review

1. What are some findings concerning the death rate among smokers?
2. What organs of the body are especially affected by alcohol?
3. Explain the progressive effects of alcohol on the nervous system.
4. Why is alcoholism considered a disease?
5. Name several drugs that fit the definition of a narcotic drug.
6. Why is it dangerous for a person who has consumed alcoholic beverages to take sleeping pills?
7. How could a person develop a mental dependence on both amphetamines and barbiturates? Can you suggest any alternatives to such a dependency?

Applying Concepts

1. Why is inhaling smoke from a cigarette injurious to your health?
2. Why is drinking alcohol on an empty stomach more injurious than drinking after eating?
3. Why does the presence of alcohol in the body give a person a feeling of warmth?

46-1 | What physical changes accompany emotions? *(HRW photo by Ken Karp)*

46

Body Regulators

A **EXPLAIN** the differences between an endocrine gland and an exocrine gland.
B **DESCRIBE** the anatomy of each endocrine gland.
C **EXPLAIN** the functions of each endocrine gland.
D **ILLUSTRATE** by examples the dynamic balance maintained by endocrine glands.

Endocrine Glands: Chemical Coordinators

Have you ever experienced the feeling of being frightened? Perhaps it involved a near-miss car accident, or unusual sounds in the middle of the night. Your heart was pounding and beating rapidly. Increased blood pressure caused your temples to throb, and there may have been a sensation of ringing in your ears. Your skin felt cold and clammy. If you looked into a mirror, you would have noticed that the pupils of your eyes were dilated. All these body changes were brought about by a small gland in your body.

The salivary glands of your mouth and the gastric glands of your stomach have ducts. Secretions from these glands enter the digestive tract. Such *duct* glands are called *exocrine* (EKS-oh-krin) *glands*. Secretions from a duct gland go directly into a specific organ. The gland responsible for your body's reaction to an emergency is quite different. It is a *ductless gland*. Secretions from ductless glands go directly into the bloodstream. The blood transports these secretions to all parts of the body. **Ductless glands are called *endocrine* (EN-doe-krin) *glands*.**

Like the nervous system, endocrine glands play a role in integrating and coordinating activities of the various body organs. The secretions of ductless glands are called **hormones.** Most hormones influence only specific organs. They regulate the activities of many body processes. The circulatory system is vital to the endocrine system. It supplies the raw materials and transports the finished product. The human body contains several endocrine glands. Some of these glands are in pairs and some occur singly. Figure 46–3 shows the location of the endocrine glands in the human body.

The Thyroid Gland

The *thyroid* gland is relatively large and lies close to the body surface. The thyroid gland is in the neck, near the lower part of the larynx where it joins the trachea. Figure 46–4 shows that the thyroid has two lobes connected by a narrow bridge, or isthmus. The lobes lie on each side of the trachea and extend up along the sides of the larynx. The isthmus crosses the front of the trachea.

The Function Of The Thyroid Gland
The thyroid gland is concerned primarily with the metabolism of the body. This gland produces a hormone called *thyroxine.* Thyroxine has the highest concentration of iodine found in any substance of the body. It regulates the energy-producing and the energy-releasing functions of the body. *Thyroid extract* is used for treating thyroid disorders in humans. It is purified from the thyroid glands of sheep. Thyroid extract is the least expensive of all commercial endocrine preparations.

Your body must have a normal level of the thyroid hormone to produce the energy needed for certain metabolic processes. A doctor can test the activity of a patient's thyroid gland by measuring the *basal metabolic rate* (BMR) of the patient. This indicates the minimum amount of energy required (heat production) for metabolism.

More accurate tests measure the rate at which iodine is taken into the gland. The amount of iodine in a blood sample might show this. However, many medical centers now use radioactive iodine. The patient takes a small amount of it by mouth. Later, a Geiger counter is placed over the thyroid gland. The counter shows the rate at which radioactive iodine concentrates in the thyroid tissue. This rate indicates activity of the gland.

Thyroid Disorders
If the thyroid gland is overactive, it produces a condition called **hyperthyroidism.** An excess of thyroxine is produced resulting in an increased rate of oxidation. As a result, the body temperature goes up. The heart

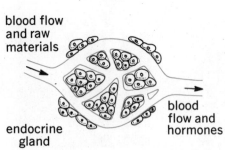

exocrine gland

product of gland

duct

capillary net

blood flow and raw materials

endocrine gland

blood flow and hormones

46–2 | Secretions from exocrine glands go directly into an organ. Secretions from endocrine glands go into the bloodstream.

hyper = above, beyond, over, more than usual

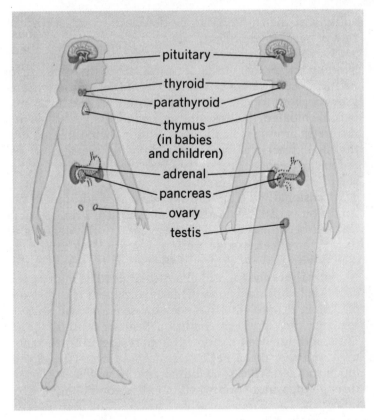

46-3 | The locations of the endocrine glands in the body.

also beats faster, and blood pressure goes up. Perspiring when the body should be cool is a common symptom. The hyperthyroid person gets very nervous and irritable. Some people's eyes bulge slightly, and they develop a staring expression.

Surgery used to be the only treatment for hyperthyroidism. However, an effective drug called *thiouracil* (thie-oe-YOOHR-uh-sill) has been developed. Another treatment for hyperthyroidism consists of doses of radioactive iodine. This is absorbed by the thyroid gland as though it were ordinary iodine. However, the gland is bombarded by the radioactivity. This destroys some of the gland cells. The result is similar to removing part of the thyroid gland by surgery.

If the thyroid gland is underactive, the condition is called *hypothyroidism.* The symptoms are the opposite of those for hyperthyroidism. The rate of oxidation is too slow. The nervous system is not active enough. People with this condition are characteristically physically or mentally retarded. Their heartbeat slows down and often their heart enlarges. Hypothyroidism can be treated with the thyroid extract we mentioned above. Both overactivity and under-

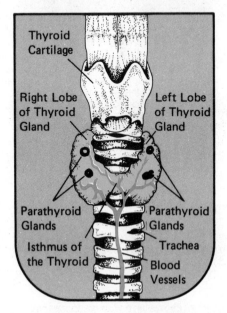

46-4 | The location of the thyroid and parathyroid glands in relation to the trachea and throat cartilage.

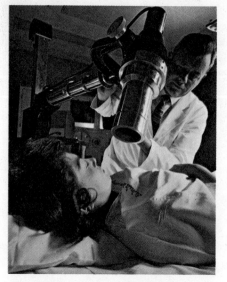

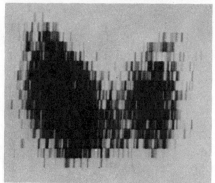

46–5 | Measurement of uptake of radioactive iodine in the thyroid gland of a patient. The detector records the areas of concentration of iodine in the gland. *(top: Brookhaven National Lab; bottom: Percy W. Brooks)*

activity of the thyroid can be detected by measuring the rate of basal metabolism.

Thyroid disorders can cause different conditions depending on the age of the person. Lack of thyroxin during infancy results in *cretinism*. This condition causes stunted growth, both physically and mentally. The face may become bloated, the lips enlarge, and the tongue thickened. If a cretin grows into childhood without being treated with thyroid extract, the dwarfism and mental retardation cannot be corrected. Treatment must occur during critical stages early in development.

Occasionally the thyroid slows down in adulthood. This condition is called *myxedema* (MICK-suh-DEE-muh). Facial features become coarse, and the eyelids swell. Mental ability is often affected. Like cretinism, myxedema can be corrected with thyroid extract if the person is treated early.

Sometimes the thyroid gland enlarges. The major cause of this is iodine deficiency. This enlargement is called simple *goiter*. People who live near the seacoast and who eat seafood rarely have this condition. Seafood contains iodine. This condition occurs more often in residents of the mountains and near the Great Lakes. In these areas, there is not much iodine in the soil. Iodine can be added to the diet through the water supply and in iodine compounds such as table salt. These measures have lowered the occurrence of goiter in the Midwest.

The Parathyroid Glands

here are four **parathyroid glands** embedded in the back of the thyroid, two in each lobe. The parathyroids secrete *parathyroid hormone*. This hormone regulates the levels of calcium and phosphate ions in the blood. These two ions are important in promoting proper bone growth, muscle tone, and nerve activity. Vitamin D also plays a part in regulating calcium and phosphate ion levels.

The Pituitary Gland

The **pituitary** is a small gland, about the size of a small pea. It is located at the base of the brain. **The pituitary was once called the "master gland" because its secretions affect the activity of all other glands.** It is now known that other glands in turn affect the pituitary.

The Function of the Pituitary Gland   Two lobes, anterior and posterior, make up the pituitary gland. The *anterior lobe* secretes several different hormones. One of these is the *growth hormone*. Growth hormone controls the growth of your skeleton, your whole body frame work. Other secretions of this anterior lobe are called *gonadotropic* (goe-NAD-uh-TROP-ick) *hormones.* They influence the development of your reproductive organs. They also affect the hormone secretion of the ovaries in the female and the testes in the male. The gonadotropic hormones work together with the sex hormones to produce the changes in your body during adolescence. In the female, the gonadotropic hormones regulate the menstrual cycle.

The anterior lobe of the pituitary gland secretes still other hormones. One, *lactogenic hormone,* stimulates the secretion of milk in the mammary glands. Another, *thyrotropic hormone,* stimulates the thyroid. A third, *adrenocorticotropic hormone (ACTH),* stimulates the cortex of the adrenal glands (another endocrine gland).

ACTH has been used in some interesting clinical ways. Some success has been reported with certain types of arthritis. Good results in the treatment of asthma and other allergies with ACTH have also been reported. Even if ACTH does not cure these diseases, it may lead to the discovery of their actual causes.

The *posterior lobe* of the pituitary gland releases two hormones. One is *oxytocin,* which helps regulate your blood pressure and stimulates your smooth muscles. During childbirth, oxytocin is secreted in large amounts. Sometimes it is given to help make the uterus contract. Oxytocin also causes milk to flow from the mammary gland when an infant nurses.

The second hormone made by the posterior lobe of the pituitary is *vasopressin.* This hormone controls water resorption in the kidneys. Vasopressin is also called *antidiuretic hormone (ADH).*

Pituitary Disorders The most common disorder of the pituitary gland involves the growth hormone. If the pituitary secretes too much of this hormone while a child is growing, the bones and tissue grow too fast. A giant may result. Some giants have been known to grow over 2.5 meters (8 feet) tall and wear size 30 shoes. Sometimes too much growth hormone is secreted in an adult. The bones of the face and hands become thick, but they cannot grow longer because the bones are fully formed in an adult. Organs and soft tissues also enlarge a great deal. This condition is called *acromegaly* (ack-roe-MEG-uh-lee). Victims of this disorder have greatly enlarged jaw bones, noses, and hands and fingers.

Deficiency of the growth hormone slows down a person's growth. These people are pituitary dwarfs called *midgets.* They are perfectly proportioned people, but very tiny. Their minds are not affected so they have normal intelligence. This is quite different from a thyroid dwarf.

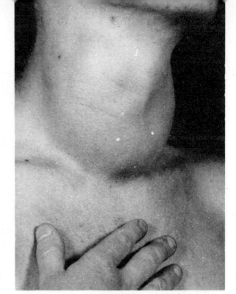

46–6 | Simple goiter can be prevented by the addition of iodine to the diet. *(Percy W. Brooks)*

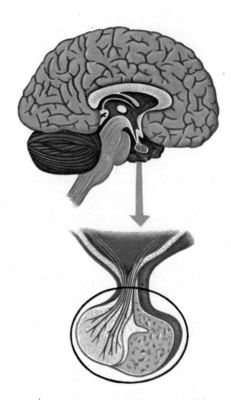

46–7 | The pituitary gland is connected by a stalk to the hypothalamus. The hypothalamus regulates the anterior pituitary through blood vessels. The posterior pituitary is connected by nerves to the hypothalamus.

ad = towards
renes = the kidney

epi = upon
nephros = the kidneys

The Adrenal Glands

One **adrenal** gland is on top of each kidney. These glands have an outer layer called the *cortex*, and an inner part called the *medulla*.

The medulla secretes a hormone called **epinephrine** (ep-uh-NEFF-reen), or adrenalin. This hormone can cause sudden body changes that give people startling strength during anger or fright. Because the adrenal glands have this effect, they are called the glands of "fright or flight." When epinephrine, or adrenalin, suddenly pours into your bloodstream, this is what happens.

- You get pale, because the blood vessels in your skin constrict. If you have a surface wound, you will lose less blood because the mucous membranes shrink and slow up bleeding. At the same time, more blood is supplied to your muscles, brain, heart, and other vital organs.
- Your blood pressure goes up, because the blood vessels in your skin have constricted.
- Your heart beats faster.
- Your liver releases some of its stored sugar. This provides material for increased body activity and oxidation.

Unlike the adrenal medulla, the adrenal cortex is essential for life. The adrenal cortex secretes a complex of hormones called *corticoids*. These hormones control certain phases of carbohydrate, fat, and protein metabolism. They also affect the balance of salt and water in your body. The adrenal cortex releases other hormones that control production of some types of white corpuscles and the structure of connective tissue.

If the adrenal cortex is damaged or destroyed, a person develops *Addison's disease*. This also occurs as a result of tuberculosis. Such people get tired easily, feel nauseous, and lose weight. Their circulation fails and their skin color changes. They can be helped by treatment with a corticoid called *cortisone*.

The Pancreas

You know that the **pancreas** produces pancreatic fluid to help digestion. This is only one function of the pancreas. There are also special groups of cells in the pancreas called **islets of Langerhans.** The islets of Langerhans secrete the hormone insulin. **Insulin enables the liver to store sugar in the form of glycogen. This hormone also controls the oxidation of sugar.**

A person who does not have insulin is unable to store or oxidize sugar properly. Therefore the tissues are deprived

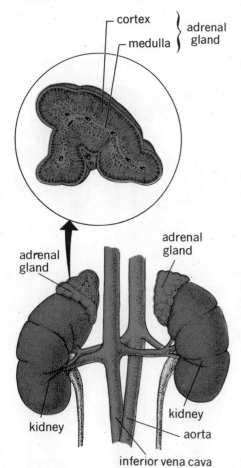

cortex
medulla } adrenal gland

adrenal gland

adrenal gland

adrenal gland

kidney

kidney

aorta

inferior vena cava

46-8 | The adrenal glands are situated above the kidneys. Name the two hormones they secrete.

of food, and sugar collects in the blood. Some of the extra sugar in the blood is excreted in the urine. Doctors call this condition **diabetes mellitus** (MELL-uh-tuss). Diabetes mellitus is probably caused by a combination of factors. It is not just the failure of the islet cells of the pancreas to make insulin. The disease is also affected by the activity of the pituitary, thyroid, and adrenal glands, as well as the liver. **People who are overweight are more likely to develop this problem. Diabetes mellitus is hereditary.** If it is in your family, your doctor should check the level of your blood sugar regularly.

dia = through
baites = to go
mellis = honey

If too much insulin is produced, the result is a conditon called *hypoglycemia*. Literally, this word means "low blood sugar." Excess insulin makes the liver store sugar that should be delivered to cells. Hypoglycemia makes a person tire easily. It can be controlled by regulating the amount of carbohydrates in the diet.

hypo = under, beneath, less than usual

The Thymus

The **thymus** may also be a ductless gland, but it is not clear if it secretes a hormone. It grows under the breastbone, just above your heart. It is large at infancy and doubles in size by the time you enter your teens. From then on, it gradually becomes smaller. Cells called lymphocytes are produced in the thymus. The thymus is an important organ in the development of antibodies early in life. More research indicates that the thymus plays a role in the auto-immune system of the body.

The Ovaries and the Testes

The *ovaries* of the female and the *testes* of the male have dual functions. We usually think of these as the organs for producing eggs and sperms. However, certain cells of both the ovaries and the testes serve as ductless glands. The ovary cells secrete female hormones called **estrogen** (ES-truh-jin) and **progesterone** (proe-JES-tuh-rone). Cells in the testes manufacture a male hormone called **testosterone** (tes-TOSS-tuh-rone). This particular hormone can now be made artificially. It is used to help disturbances of sex hormones in both males and females. Minute amounts of male sex hormones are also produced by the cortex of the adrenal glands in both males and females. A female's ovaries normally secrete enough estrogen to neutralize the effects of the male sex hormones from the adrenal glands. If estrogen secretion in the ovaries is reduced, the female may become masculine. In the same way, low testosterone production in the testes may result in feminine tendencies. As

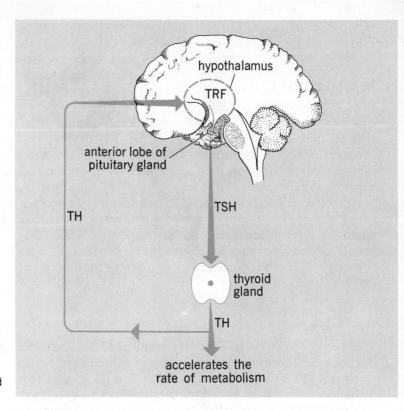

46–9 | The relationship of the pituitary gland to the uterine cycle.

you can see, people develop within a wide range of maleness and femaleness.

The Function of the Sex Glands. **Sex hormones affect the development of secondary sex characteristics.** These changes appear at the time of the change from child to adult. They begin with the maturation of the ovaries and testes during the stage of life called *puberty.* Among animals, the changes may appear as the large comb of the rooster, the bright feathers of most male birds, and the antlers of deer. Many secondary characteristics are appearing or have appeared in your own body. As a boy approaches puberty, his voice gets deeper. His beard appears, with a general increase in body hair. The chest broadens and deepens. Rapid growth of the long bones add to his height.

As a girl matures, her breasts develop and her hips get broader. Fat deposits form under the skin in those areas. Around the same time, menstruation begins.

Testosterone is also responsible for the normal sex drive in males. If the testes of an animal are removed by *castration,* its behavior changes. It becomes more docile and easy to manage. Of course, castration causes the animal to be sterile. If the male animal is young when this operation is performed, it will not develop into a typical male.

The Hypothalamus

The *hypothalamus* is located at the base of the brain, just above the pituitary gland. Research has shown that the hypothalamus plays a vital role in the control of many life functions. It is important in maintaining homeostasis, or balance, in the body. **Body temperature, ion and water balance, and release of pituitary hormones are some of the functions regulated by the hypothalamus.** The hypothalamus detects imbalances in the blood passing through it. The hypothalamus directs the pituitary to release the proper amount of a needed hormone to restore the balance.

The *posterior pituitary* is regulated by direct nerve connections from the hypothalamus. For example, if the level of water in the blood is low, it is detected by the hypothalamus. The hypothalamus then directs the posterior pituitary to secrete more vasopressin. This causes the kidneys to resorb more water. The water balance is thus restored.

The connection between the hypothalamus and the anterior pituitary is more indirect. When needed, the hypothalamus secretes substances into the blood that affect the *anterior pituitary*. These substances are called *releasing factors*. There is a releasing factor for each anterior pituitary hormone. For example, there is a thyrotropin releasing factor (TRF). TRF causes the anterior pituitary to release thyrotropin, or thyroid stimulating hormone (TSH). Thyrotropin (TSH) stimulates the release of thyroid hormone from the thyroid gland.

Dynamic Balance in the Endocrine Glands

Endocrine glands usually maintain a careful balance among the different hormones secreted in the body. Each hormone has a specific function that can be modified by the effects of hormones from other glands. Hormonal balance is generally achieved by a **negative feedback** mechanism, whereby hormone A stimulates production of hormone B. In turn hormone B inhibits secretion of A as its own level in the blood rises.

Another factor to help maintain the hormonal balance is the effect of the nervous system. If needed, the sympathetic nervous system signals the adrenal medulla to produce extra adrenalin. Nervous control and negative feedback work to maintain the steady state of the body in constantly changing conditions.

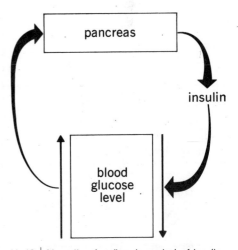

46-10 | Negative feedback control of insulin by the blood glucose level. The overall effect of insulin is to lower the blood glucose level. Increase in blood glucose level causes the pancreas to secrete more insulin.

Summary

Gland	Location	Hormone	Function of Hormone
thyroid	neck, below larynx	thyroxine	accelerates the rate of metabolism
parathyroids	back surface of thyroid lobes	parathyroid hormone	mobilizes calcium from the bones
pituitary anterior lobe	base of brain	growth hormone	regulates growth of the skeleton
		gonadotropic hormone	influences development of sex organs and hormone secretion of the ovaries and testes
		ACTH	stimulates secretion of hormones by the cortex of the adrenals
		lactogenic hormone	stimulates secretion of milk by mammary glands
		thyrotrophic hormone	stimulates activity of the thyroid
posterior lobe		oxytocin	regulates blood pressure and stimulates smooth muscles
		vasopressin	controls water resorption in the kidneys
adrenal cortex	above kidneys	corticoids	regulates metabolism, salt, and water balance; controls production of certain white corpuscles; structure of connective tissue
medulla		epinephrine, or adrenalin	causes constriction of blood vessels, increase in heart action and output; stimulates liver and nervous system
pancreas islets of Langerhans	below and behind stomach	insulin	enables liver to store sugar and regulates sugar oxidation in tissues
ovaries follicular cells	pelvis	estrogen	produces female secondary sex characteristics; affects adult female body functions
		progesterone	maintains growth of the mucous lining of the uterus
testes interstitial cells	below pelvis in scrotal sac	testosterone	produces male secondary sex characteristics

endocrine gland	islets of Langerhans
hormone	insulin
thyroid	diabetes mellitus
hyperthyroidism	thymus
hypothyroidism	estrogen
parathyroid gland	progesterone
pituitary	testosterone
adrenal gland	puberty
epinephrine	hypothalamus
pancreas	negative feedback

Biologically Speaking

Questions for Review

1. Name the endocrine glands in the human body.
2. In what ways do the pituitary and thyroid glands affect growth?
3. How does the pituitary gland affect sex glands?
4. What is ACTH? What is its function?
5. In what ways are puberty and adolescence a result of glandular activity?
6. Why does sugar appear in the urine of a person with diabetes mellitus?
7. Explain the role of the hypothalamus in maintaining homeostasis.

Applying Concepts

1. How do you account for the fact that the heartbeat of a basketball player increases a great deal before the game as well as during the game?
2. Why is a study of the endocrine glands often done at the same time as a study of the nervous system?
3. What hormone injected into the bloodstream of a male rat will often result in a mothering instinct? Why?
4. Discuss dynamic balance in the endocrine system that results from feedback control.

47

Reproduction and Development

A **EXPLAIN** the significance of sexual reproduction.

B **DESCRIBE** the male reproductive system.

C **COMPARE** the sperm cell with the egg cell.

D **DESCRIBE** the structure and functions of different parts of the female reproductive system.

E **EXPLAIN** the stages of the menstrual cycle.

F **DESCRIBE** the development of the human embryo.

G **EXPLAIN** the events of the birth process.

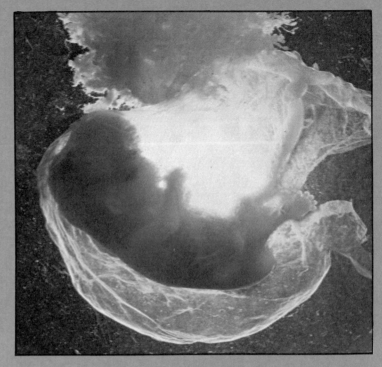

47-1 | A fetus develops inside an amniotic sac. *(Joe Baker, The Image Bank)*

Significance of Sexual Reproduction

The variety in organisms allows for adaptation to environmental changes. Organisms that produce asexually, in a one-parent system, cannot develop much variety. However, combination of unlike genes from two different parents can produce almost endless variety.

Sexual reproduction is the union of two gametes to form a zygote. The zygote is capable of growing into a mature form that resembles its parents. The word *resembles* indicates "variety." Many family characteristics such as shape of the body, head, eyes, ears, nose, and color of the eyes and hair are observed easily. Other differences, such as blood type, resistance to specific disease, and athletic ability may not be as easy to identify. Physiological and behavioral differences, as well as structural differences, are present in offspring from the same parents.

The gonads produce gametes. Cells in the gonads divide by meiosis. Thus, the gene combinations in one gamete are quite different from those in another gamete.

Beginning of Life

At the time of fertilization, the gametes unite, forming the zygote. **The zygote is diploid. The gametes from each parent have contributed a haploid set of chromosomes to the zygote. Therefore, the zygote has two of each kind of chromosome.** Now the genes function to influence characteristics in the new organism. Of course, all zygotes of a species have the broad characteristics of the particular species. The combination of genes for unlike characteristics from both parents produces offspring that vary.

Sexual reproduction produces greater variation than asexual reproduction. This variation increases the chances that a species will be able to adapt and survive.

The Male Reproductive System

The male gonads are the **testes.** These organs develop in the abdominal cavity below the kidneys. About the ninth month in the development of the male, the testes descend into a pouch of skin called the *scrotum.* The testes produce testosterone. This hormone controls the development of secondary sex characteristics. Another important function of the testes is to produce sperms.

The testes are flattened, oval-shaped bodies lying within the scrotum. Within the testes are about 500 tightly coiled tubes called the *seminiferous* (sem-i-NIFF-uh-russ)

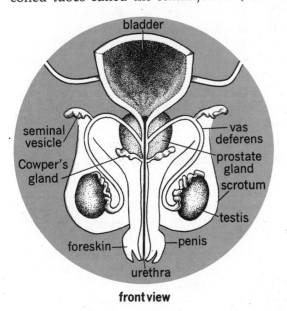

front view

47-2 | The male reproductive system.

vas = a vessel

tubules. The cells in the seminiferous tubules divide by meiosis to form haploid sperms. As sperms are produced they pass into a storage area called the *epididymus* (ep-uh-DID-uh-miss). The sperms leave the epididymus through a short duct called the *vas deferens* (VASS DEF-uh-renz). This duct carries the sperms past the *seminal vesicles.* The seminal vesicles secrete a fluid that forms a part of the semen. A short tube connects the seminal vesicle to the urethra by passing through the **prostate gland.** A small organ called *Cowper's gland* also opens into the urethra. All three of these organs release their secretions as the sperms pass by. These secretions constitute the fertilizing fluid, called **semen,** which provides the sperms with food for energy and the proper environment for survival. The male's urethra is the duct for passage of semen through the penis. The urethra also carries urine from the urinary bladder to the outside of the body for excretion. The acid of urine would be harmful to the sperms. One function of the fluids from the glands is to neutralize the acid urine.

The Sperm Cell

The human sperm cell is very small compared to the human ovum. The head of a sperm is flattened and oval. It contains the nucleus with the haploid number of chromosomes. The tail acts as a flagellum, or whip, to move the sperm. The short middle part contains many *mitochondria.* Cellular respiration occurs in the mitochondria to provide energy for sperm cells. The male gamete is a small, active cell. Its energy is obtained from the semen, which has a high concentration of the simple sugar fructose.

It takes as many as 130 million motile sperms to insure fertilization of one ovum. The sperm fertilizes the ovum by penetration. At that time the tail separates from the rest of the sperm. The head and the connecting middle part enter the ovum. **The nuclei of the sperm and the ovum unite. The zygote is formed.**

The Female Reproductive System

In the female, one pair of **ovaries** are in the abdominal cavity. They are about 3.5 centimeters (1.4 inches) long and 1.5 centimeters (0.2 inches) wide. The two ovaries are not connected directly to the oviducts, or **Fallopian tubes.** The tubes are lined with ciliated cells. When an ovum is released from one of the ovaries, the action of the cilia draws the ovum into the tube. Then the ovum moves down the Fallopian tube to the *uterus,* or womb. The uterus is a

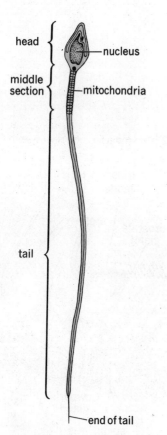

head
nucleus

middle section
mitochondria

tail

end of tail

47-3 | The structure of the sperm cell.

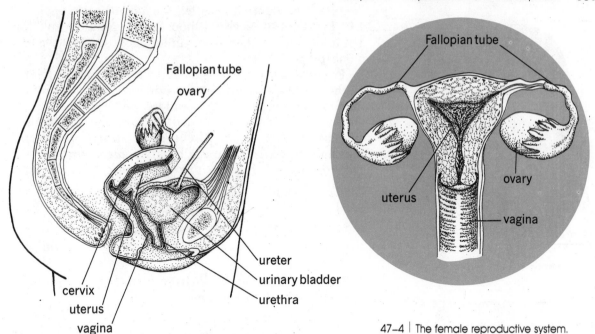

Fallopian tube
ovary

cervix
uterus
vagina

ureter
urinary bladder
urethra

Fallopian tube

uterus

ovary

vagina

47–4 | The female reproductive system.

hollow, muscular organ with thick walls. It is lined with a mucous membrane containing many small glands and many capillaries.

The ovum dies and disintegrates if it is not fertilized. Then, it is discharged through the narrow neck of the uterus, called the *cervix*. The cervix opens into the *vagina*.

cervix = the neck

Ovarian and Uterine Cycle

The development of the ovum is coordinated with the build-up of the lining of the uterus. This is controlled by hormones. Human ovaries usually produce only one egg in the course of a 28-day cycle of activity. The cycle is begun by a gonadotropic hormone produced in the anterior lobe of the pituitary gland. This hormone is called the *follicle-stimulating hormone*, or **FSH.** FSH causes a mass of ovarian cells to form a *follicle* in which the ovum is produced. As the ovum matures, the follicle fills with fluid that contains the hormone **estrogen.** The anterior lobe of the pituitary gland senses the estrogen that diffuses into the blood and stops producing FSH.

When the ovum is mature, the follicle breaks through the wall of the ovary and the ovum escapes. The release of the ovum from the follicle is called **ovulation.** The ovum is picked up by one of the Fallopian tubes. The follicle is now called the **corpus luteum.** This development is controlled by another gonadotropic hormone from the anterior lobe of

Facts & Figures

The human ovaries contain about 400,000 eggs. Only 300 to 400 are released during a female's reproductive years.

corpus = body
luteus = golden-yellow

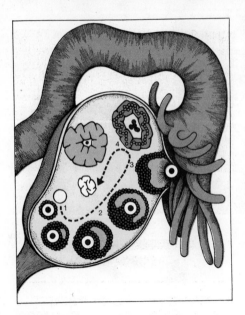

47–5 | An ovum in the ovary.

pro = before
gestro = to bear, carry

menstrualis = monthly

Facts & Figures

The time from fertilization to the formation of two cells is about 36 hours.

the pituitary gland. It is called the *luteinizing hormone,* or **LH.** LH is produced as a response of the pituitary to estrogen in the blood. The corpus luteum now secretes the hormone **progesterone.**

Progesterone maintains the growth of the mucous lining of the uterus. If the ovum is not fertilized, the corpus luteum degenerates, and no more progesterone is produced. The inside lining of the uterus detaches and sloughs off. **The breakdown and discharge of the soft uterine tissues and the unfertilized egg is called *menstruation.*** The uterine cycle has four distinct stages.

1. *Menstruation,* averaging about five days.
2. The *follicle stage,* from the end of menstruation to the release of the ovum, between 10 and 14 days.
3. *Ovulation,* the release of a mature ovum from the ovary.
4. The *corpus luteum stage,* from ovulation to menstruation, about 10 to 14 days.

The stages of ovum production are coordinated with changes in the mucous membranes of the uterus. This is an example of feedback. Endocrine glands respond to chemicals in the blood by changing their production of hormones.

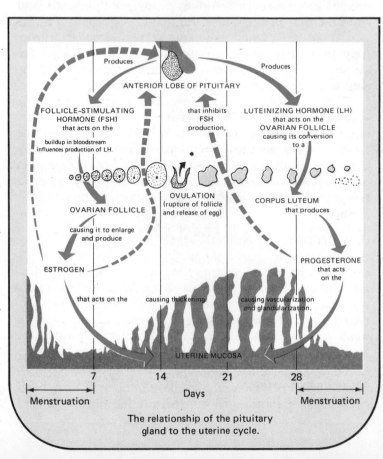

The relationship of the pituitary gland to the uterine cycle.

47–6 | The relationship of the pituitary gland to the menstrual cycle.

From Embryo to Fetus

At the time a sperm enters the ovum, a membrane immediately forms around the resulting *zygote*. This is called the *fertilization membrane*. Other sperms cannot pass into the ovum through this membrane. Fertilization usually takes place in one of the Fallopian tubes. **Fertilization causes several important changes in the female's body.**

The zygote reaches the uterus in three to five days. During this time, the zygote continues to grow. The diploid number of chromosomes has been restored. The zygote goes through a series of mitotic divisions. In a few days it has become a mass of cells. During the early stages of its development the zygote's energy comes from the nutrients stored in the ovum.

Development of the Embryo

After the fertilized ovum has divided repeatedly, it gradually becomes a sphere of cells. This sphere has a large, fluid-filled cavity. A mass of cells develops inside one pole of the sphere. Some of these cells will become the **embryo. An embryo is an organism in a very early stage of development.** It does not yet look like a member of a particular species of animal. In the human species this stage lasts from six to eight weeks after fertilization. At the end of this period the embryo is about two centimeters (0.8 inches) long. From then on its growth rate increases rapidly. The embryo then starts to take on human characteristics. From this point until birth, it is called a *fetus.*

The sphere of cells that forms from the fertilized ovum is called a *blastocyst.* The blastocyst still has not attached itself to the uterine wall. Cells from the inner mass will later form the **primary germ layers.** These cell layers are the *ectoderm*, the *mesoderm*, and the *endoderm*. **These three germ layers will form the various tissues and organs of the body.** Each of these germ layers produces different body structures.

Attachment of the Embryo

As the embryo passes down the Fallopian tube to the uterus, a part of the mass of dividing cells separates. One group of cells forms an *inner cell mass.* This mass will form the embryo. The other group of cells forms a layer that surrounds the inner cell mass. This cell mass, or blastocyst, is made of about 100 cells. When the blastocyst touches the lining of the uterus, the outer layer of cells begins to grow rapidly. The cells produce enzymes that break down the epithelium of the uterus. This embeds the blastocyst firmly in the uterine lining. The growth of the cells surrounding

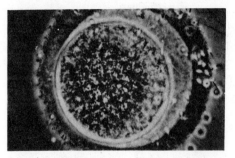

47-7 | An ovum enters a Fallopian tube. There it may fuse with a sperm. *(American Museum of Natural History)*

Table 47-1 DIFFERENTIATION OF THE GERM LAYERS

PRIMITIVE GERM LAYERS	STRUCTURES FORMED
ECTODERM	skin and skin glands; hair; most cartilage; nervous system; pituitary gland; lining of mouth to the pharynx; part of the lining of rectum; adrenal medulla
MESODERM	connective tissue; bone; most muscles; kidneys and ducts; gonads and ducts; blood, blood vessels, heart, and lymphatics
ENDODERM	lining of alimentary canal from pharynx to rectum; thyroid; parathyroids; trachea and lungs; bladder

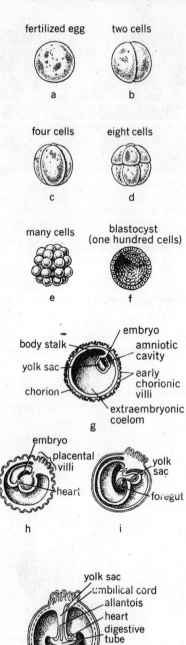

fertilized egg

a

two cells

b

four cells

c

eight cells

d

many cells

e

blastocyst
(one hundred cells)

f

body stalk

yolk sac

chorion

embryo

amniotic
cavity

early
chorionic
villi

extraembryonic
coelom

g

embryo

placental
villi

heart

yolk
sac

foregut

h   i

yolk sac

umbilical cord

allantois

heart

digestive
tube

embryo

amniotic
cavity

j

47-8 | Immediately following fertilization, the cells of the zygote divide and form the blastocyst. This resembles a hollow ball with a mass of cells located at one end; g, h, i, and j show the development of the extraembryonic membranes that accompany the development of the human embryo.

the inner cell mass results in a membrane. This is one of several membranes that will form. Since it will not become part of the embryo itself, it is called an **extraembryonic membrane.** This embedding membrane is called the *chorion* (KORE-ee-on). If forms many small fingerlike projections known as the *chorionic villi.* The villi are in close contact with the capillaries in the uterine lining. In this way nourishment is provided for the embryo. Soon another extraembryonic membrane, the *amnion,* develops.

The amnion forms a fluid-filled cavity around the developing embryo. This amniotic fluid protects the embryo from injury and keeps it moist. The third extraembryonic membrane is the *yolk sac.* The human yolk sac is small and not significant. However, for animals that hatch from eggs, the yolk provides the food for the embryo. The *allantois* (uh-LAN-toe-iss) is the fourth extraembryonic membrane. Later, this structure becomes part of the umbilical cord. In birds and reptiles, though, this membrane acts as an embryonic lung.

When the chorionic villi lodge in the uterine wall, the capillaries break down and form blood sinuses around the villi. Food, gases, and wastes are exchanged between the mother and the embryo. This exchange results from active transport and diffusion through the thin membrane of the chorionic villi. **There is no direct connection between the blood of the mother and embryo.** The area where the chorionic villi meet the maternal blood supply within the uterus is called the **placenta.**

With growth, the area that attached the embryo to the yolk sac and allantois lengthens into the *umbilical cord.* The developing embryo is connected to the placenta by two umbilical arteries, one umbilical vein, and the allantoic duct.

As the placenta grows, it also acts as an endocrine gland. It secretes progesterone to maintain the growing uterine lining. It also secretes estrogen. Remember, this causes the anterior lobe of the pituitary to produce LH. The LH, in turn, maintains the corpus luteum, and more progesterone is produced.

Childbirth

After about 40 weeks of fetal development, the child is born. Just before birth there is a rise in the blood level of estrogen and a decrease in the level of progesterone. It may be that chemical messengers from the fetus stimulate the placenta to alter its secretions to bring about birth. The smooth muscles of the uterus begin to contract. The membrane of the amnion breaks, and the amniotic fluid passes out through

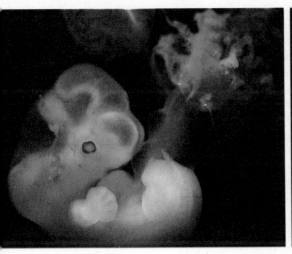 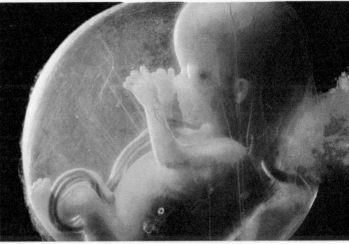

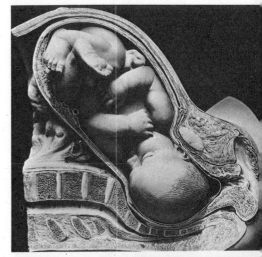

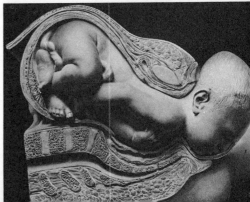

the vagina. The tissues in the cervix of the uterus relax. The size of the opening enlarges. More uterine contractions force the child from the uterus, usually head first. However, the baby is still attached to the placenta by the umbilical cord. Right after birth, the cord is tied and cut. This is done so that the child will not lose blood through the umbilical vessels. Your *navel* is the scar on your abdomen where your umbilical cord attached you to the placenta. After the child is born, the placenta and the remains of the amnion are expelled. This is called the afterbirth.

Until the baby is born, it receives both oxygen and nourishment through the placenta. As the fetus grows, the movement of its thoracic muscles draws fluid into its lungs. The lungs expand because of the fluid. The first cries of the baby remove the fluid and fill its lungs with air.

Another important change takes place at birth. **In the fetus, only a small amount of blood circulates through its lungs.** Instead, most of the blood that leaves the right ventricle goes through a vessel called the *ductus arteriosus*. This vessel takes the blood to the aorta of the fetus. The lungs are bypassed while the fetus develops. At birth, though, the ductus arteriosus closes. Now the blood must flow through the pulmonary arteries to the lungs. The new supply of blood helps the lungs expand as the baby begins to breathe air.

While the blood is circulating through the fetus, there is an opening between the atria of the heart. This opening is called the *foramen ovale*. A membrane grows over this opening, normally closing it completely soon after birth. If the opening does not close, the blood from the atria mix. Thus oxygenated blood mixes with deoxygenated blood.

47–9 | Development of the human embryo and fetus. The embryo at five weeks and a fetus of four months. *(Lennart Nilsson)*

47–10 | Some 40 weeks after fertilization of an ovum, uterine contractions begin, and a baby is born. *(Maternity Center Assoc. of New York)*

Summary

Sexual reproduction combines the genetic material from two different parents. Fertilization takes place internally. The ovum is very large when compared to the sperms. It contains the food for the early life stages of the zygote. The production of several hormones by the female coordinates the development of the ovum and the uterine wall.

If fertilization does not occur, the female body sheds the soft uterine lining materials. This process is called menstruation. If fertilization does occur, the zygote travels down the Fallopian tube to the uterus. It becomes a many-celled sphere surrounded by the first of four extraembryonic membranes. The fetus receives oxygen and nourishment by diffusion of these materials through thin membranes.

Biologically Speaking

testes	estrogen	embryo
prostate gland	ovulation	fetus
semen	corpus luteum	extraembryonic
ovaries	LH	membrane
Fallopian tube	progesterone	placenta
FSH	menstruation	

Questions for Review

1. What advantage is sexual reproduction to a species?
2. List the organs of the male reproductive system through which sperms pass.
3. How does the number of sperms in the human compare to the number of ova? Why is this important?
4. Describe the path of the ovum in the female reproductive system.
5. Describe the effect of the sex hormones on the reproductive cycle in the female.
6. Define the four stages in the uterine cycle.
7. Describe the changes in the formation of the embryo from the zygote.
8. Name several structures produced from each primary germ layer.
9. Describe the important changes that take place in the circulatory system after birth.

Applying Concepts

1. If an egg is fertilized, menstruation does not occur, and the lining of the uterus is prepared for implanting of the embryo. How do hormones cause this?
2. Discuss the importance of the ductus arteriosus as a bypass from the pulmonary circulation to the systemic circulation in a fetal heart.

UNIT 7

Activities

1. Suggested topics for written library reports:
   a. How would a person's digestion be affected if the stomach was removed?
   b. In what ways do athletes improve their respiratory function? How might these methods help nonathletes?
   c. Select any hormone and answer questions such as: What does it do? How does it act? Can it be synthesized outside the human body? What are the effects of too much? too little?
   d. What are the leading causes of death in the United States? How are diseases related to individual life styles?
   e. Substances such as drugs, alcohol, and nicotine will affect a fetus. What are these effects and how might they be prevented?

2. Take a poll among your friends and family. Ask those who smoke to give you reasons why they smoke. Ask the nonsmokers why they do not. Can their statements be verified by scientific research? Be sure to include your conclusions from this study.

3. Select an activity (such as throwing a baseball, swinging a golf club, or walking). Identify each motion made by the body and name the joints that are moved

4. Ask your butcher to cut a bone lengthwise. Identify the parts and make a large diagram to show to the class. Examine several long bones that have been cleaned and dried. Identify the bones. Look for bumps and ridges on the bones. Identify the places where certain muscles attached.

5. Obtain a kidney and/or beef heart from a butcher. Cut it lengthwise and identify each part. Make a diagram of your dissection and label each part.

6. Make a string model of a motor neuron using a piece of rope. Tie a knot toward one end of the rope and unravel both ends. The knot is the cell body and the threads near the knot are the dendrites of the model. The axon extends from the knot and ends in terminal branches. Put your model up on the bulletin board and label the parts.

Related Readings

Books

Girdano, Dorothy Dusek, and Daniel A. Girdano, *Drugs—A Factual Account*. Addison Wesley Publishing Co., Inc., Reading, MA. 1973. Presents a wide variety of information concerning such drugs as: alcohol, marijuana, LSD, amphetamines, barbiturates, sedatives, opiates, and nonprescription drugs.

Jenkins, Marie M., *Embryos and How They Develop*. Holiday House, New York. 1975. An easily understood survey of embryology, covering developmental processes from initial life stages to adult in animals.

Julian, Cloyd J., Elizabeth Noland Jackson, and Nancy S. Simon, *Modern Sex Education* (paperback). Holt, Rinehart and Winston, Publishers, New York. 1980. A presentation of the biological facts in relation to behavioral and psychological adjustments in young people.

McMinn, R. M. H., *The Human Gut*, Oxford Biology Reader. Oxford University Press, London. 1974. A basic understanding of the human digestive system.

Riedman, Sarah R., *Hormones: How They Work*. Abelard-Schuman Ltd., New York. 1973. A description of the hormones and of the effects they have on various parts of the body.

Surgeon General's Report. *Smoking and Health*. U.S. Dept. of Health, Education, and Welfare. Publication No. (PHS) 79-50066. 1979. This book discusses the health consequences of smoking, the behavioral aspects of smoking, and education and prevention of the smoking habit.

Articles

Bradley, Westley, "How Modern Life Can Damage Your Hearing," *U.S. News and World Report*, May 3, 1976. Considers how the society in which we live affects hearing.

Dempsey, David, "Transplants Are Common; Now It's the Organs That Have Become Rare," *The New York Times Magazine*, October 13, 1974. An interesting account of the need for organs that must meet the demands of transplantation.

Leakey, Mary D., "Footprints in the Ashes of Time," *National Geographic*, Vol. 155, No. 4, April 1979. This is an interesting discussion of the discovery of footprints more than three and one-half million years old.

Scientific American. 239: 3, September 1978. The entire issue is on evolution.

ECOLOGICAL RELATIONSHIPS

You have looked closely at all types of organisms. You have studied their food needs, their organs, their systems, and the makeup of their cells. But no organism can live completely on its own. Each is dependent on other organisms and on the physical environment.

The biosphere is the thin layer surrounding the earth where life is supported. Scientists have not yet found life on any other planet. This unit will treat this living world. You will look at its forests, grasslands, deserts, lakes, and oceans. Each of these makes up a community of living things.

Introduction to Ecology: The Biosphere

A **DEFINE** ecology.
B **EXPLAIN** interactions in the biosphere.
C **DISCUSS** interactions between the biotic and physical environment.
D **NAME** and **DESCRIBE** the major biomes.

48-1 | Seagulls have adapted to a shore existence. (Margot Conte,© Animals Animals)

The Science of the Environment

a = without
bios = life

Ecology **is the study of the relationships of living things to their surroundings and to one another.** The word *ecology* means *the study of homes.* Physical factors, or **abiotic factors,** such as temperature, weather conditions, altitude, water, and light, affect living things. Living things also affect one another. The ways in which organisms affect one another are the **biotic factors.** For example, many kinds of plants live in a tropical forest. The moist air and warm sunshine provide ideal growing conditions. The trees grow tall and form a canopy over the land. Their spreading branches expose the leaves to the light energy from the sun. However, the dense canopy allows very little light to reach the ground. In this way, the trees affect the environment of other plants below. Plants living on the tropical forest floor have large leaves. This adaptation allows them to trap the small amounts of sunlight that filters through the canopy.

Plants living in an area not only affect one another. The environment they create also affects the animals living there. The green color of many snakes and lizards hides them from enemies as well as from their prey. Many trop-ical forest animals are adapted to climb trees to catch food. Many spend their entire lives crawling among the tree branches.

Adaptations allow organisms to live in specific environ-ments. Differences in the structure of an organism are adaptive if they help the organism survive. For example, if you transplanted a large-leaved tropical forest plant to the desert, it would wilt and die. Also, if you were to trans-plant a cactus to the tropical forest floor, it would not receive enough energy to support life. It also would die. **All organisms depend on their surroundings for the activities of life.**

Patterns

The many different kinds of plants and animals are grouped according to common characteristics. These char-acteristics are the patterns that are identified by observa-tion. A biologist then forms hypotheses to reason how these patterns could have developed. As you read in Chapter 13, Charles Darwin proposed his theory of evolution to explain the basis for patterns in living things.

Ecologists work everywhere in the world. They look closely at the homes of all forms of life. Any forest, field, pond, lake, or ocean where life exists can be a laboratory to an ecologist. Ecologists also look for patterns. Then they seek explanations to show how the patterns develop.

The Biosphere

The *biosphere* is the thin layer where life exists on earth. In the biosphere, an individual organism is a fundamental unit of ecology. How does an individual fit into a larger pattern? How do we look at the entire biosphere and find a pattern? Let's begin by looking at some factors common to all life on the earth. Consider the earth as one gigantic sys-tem of interacting factors.

Three kinds of relationships occur in the biosphere: 1) Interactions take place among the biotic factors; 2) Inter-actions take place among the physical factors; and 3) Inter-actions take place between the biotic factors and the phys-ical factors. These are patterns that can be observed and studied.

Interactions Among Biotic Factors

Animals that depend on plants for food are naturally found where the plants are living. Animals that eat plant-eating

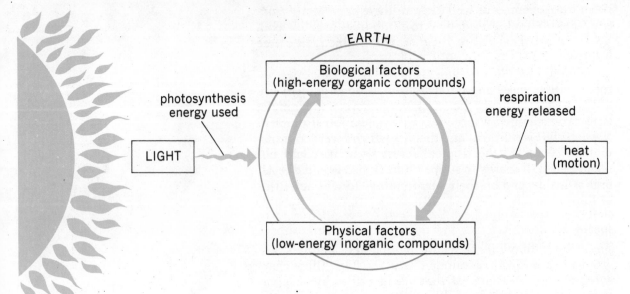

EARTH

Biological factors
(high-energy organic compounds)

photosynthesis
energy used

LIGHT

respiration
energy released

heat
(motion)

Physical factors
(low-energy inorganic compounds)

48-2 | Energy flow through the gigantic system of the earth.

animals also will be found near the plants. Lions, for example will live near their source of food, which is plant-eating animals such as gazelles. The transfer of energy from one living thing to another is called a **food chain.** The energy for this food chain came from the sun.

There are many more interactions among biotic factors other than food-getting. A lion interacts with other lions when seeking a mate. The lion family reacts among its members. Lions may react with hyenas or vultures when feeding. **Organisms use these and other reactions to increase their chances of survival and successful reproduction.**

Interactions Among Physical Factors

Some changes in the physical environment of parts of the biosphere are temporary. For example, a cloudy day will reduce sunlight. Other changes last longer. The shape and makeup of a lake, for example, can be changed when a flood carries many different materials into it. Some changes in the physical environment are permanent. An earthquake can change the course of a stream so it no longer runs into a lake. New springs may carry chemicals into the water of a lake. A volcano can erupt, sending hot lava down the hillside, completely changing the area. Water can freeze, splitting rocks as it expands.

Interactions Between Physical and Biotic Factors

Life is entirely dependent on physical factors. It is from the sun that the energy of life is dependent. Water, carbon dioxide, oxygen, and nitrogen are physical substances. The oxygen you breathe was produced by green plants. Plants synthesize organic compounds using sunlight and nutrients from soil, water, and the atmosphere.

Animals also react with the physical environment. They drink water, and their wastes and decomposed bodies return substances to the earth when they die. Humans build roads, dams, and change the courses of rivers. People add chemicals and nuclear wastes to the biosphere.

Physical factors can be *limiting factors* in that they are the materials an organism needs for growth and reproduction. These limiting factors determine where an organism can live and how well it can adapt to environmental changes. For example, animals need oxygen. Birds have special adaptations that allow them to fly in an atmosphere where oxygen is more scarce than at ground level. Physical factors are recycled so that the supply for animals and plants remains somewhat constant.

The Carbon-Oxygen Cycle   In the biosphere, materials are used over and over again. **Two basic life processes are involved in the carbon-oxygen cycle. These are respiration and photosynthesis.** Both plants and animals respire. Only green plants photosynthesize.

48–3 | The carbon-oxygen cycle.

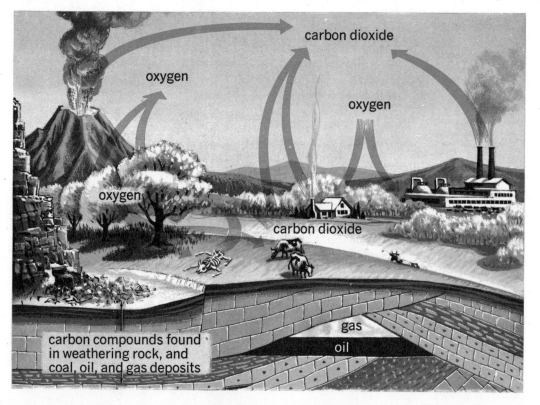

During respiration compounds containing carbon are oxidized. As a result, carbon dioxide is released into the environment. During photosynthesis, green plants take water and carbon dioxide from the environment. Using the sun's energy, water molecules are broken down. These hydrogen atoms from the water molecules combine with carbon dioxide. Then green plants use these to form carbohydrates. When this happens, oxygen from the water molecules is given off into the atmosphere. The atmosphere normally contains about 21 percent oxygen and 0.04 percent carbon dioxide.

Another part of the carbon-oxygen cycle involves the making of organic compounds. Plants use carbon dioxide to make carbohydrates during photosynthesis. The other organic compounds are made from these carbohydrates. Plant-eating animals use these organic compounds to make their own protoplasm. They, in turn, are eaten by other animals. These animals also use the same compounds. All organic compounds contain carbon. When plants and animals die, the organic compounds in them break down. The carbon leaves their decaying bodies as carbon dioxide.

Rocks and mineral fuels play a small part in this cycle too. In the geologic past the carbon of plants and animals were stored as coal and petroleum. As these fuels are burned, carbon dioxide is released into the atmosphere.

The Nitrogen Cycle Nitrogen is another chemical that is used over and over again. **The nitrogen cycle involves green plants, animals, and several kinds of bacteria.** Let's begin with the green plants. The plant's roots absorb nitrates from the soil. These compounds contain nitrogen combined with oxygen, and usually sodium and potassium. Green plants add this nitrogen to the carbon, hydrogen, and oxygen that have been combined during photosynthesis. Sulfur and phosphorus may also be added. This forms proteins.

Animals get protein by eating plants or other animals. Digestion separates this protein into amino acids. These amino acids then combine to form another protein. Proteins are used to form protoplasm. These proteins are specific to the animal in which they form.

Animals do not turn all of the protein into protoplasm. Some proteins are broken down and release energy. When this happens the animal excretes nitrogen wastes. Then bacteria in soil or water break down these compounds even further.

Bacteria also break down dead organisms. Nitrogen from a decaying organism's protein combines with hydrogen. This combination forms *ammonia*. This part of the

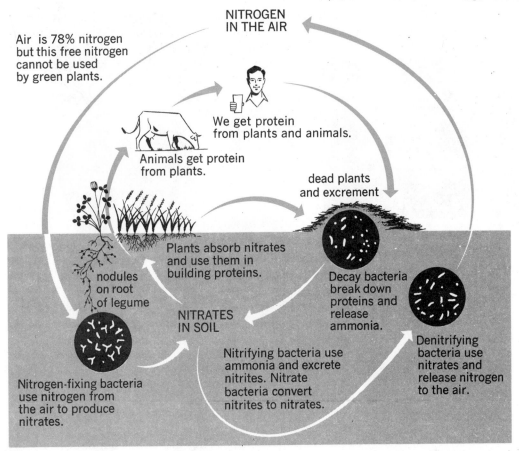

NITROGEN
IN THE AIR

Air is 78% nitrogen
but this free nitrogen
cannot be used
by green plants.

We get protein
from plants and animals.

Animals get protein
from plants.

dead plants
and excrement

Plants absorb nitrates
and use them in
building proteins.

nodules
on root
of legume

Decay bacteria
break down
proteins and
release
ammonia.

NITRATES
IN SOIL

Denitrifying
bacteria use
nitrates and
release nitrogen
to the air.

Nitrogen-fixing bacteria
use nitrogen from
the air to produce
nitrates.

Nitrifying bacteria use
ammonia and excrete
nitrites. Nitrate
bacteria convert
nitrites to nitrates.

48–4 | The nitrogen cycle.

nitrogen cycle is called *ammonification*. Other bacteria in soil oxidize ammonia to form *nitrites*. Nitrites cannot be absorbed by plant roots. Still other bacteria oxidize nitrites to form *nitrates*. This process is called *nitrification*. These nitrates can be absorbed by plant roots, and the nitrogen cycle begins again.

The nitrogen in the atmosphere cannot be used by green plants. However, two groups of bacteria can change atmospheric nitrogen into nitrates and nitrites. One group lives in the soil. The other lives in the roots of legumes. Legumes are plants such as clover and alfalfa. The bacteria get sugar from the legumes and supply them with nitrates in return. This process is called **nitrogen fixation.**

Legumes receive more nitrates than they need; the extra nitrates collect in the soil. So when farmers plant clover or alfalfa, they are building up the nitrates from atmospheric nitrogen in the soil. This makes the soil good for growing crops.

One part of the nitrogen cycle is not good for agricul-

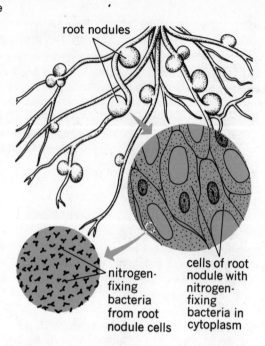

root nodules

nitrogen-fixing bacteria from root nodule cells

cells of root nodule with nitrogen-fixing bacteria in cytoplasm

48–5 | Nitrogen-fixing bacteria are found in the root nodules of legumes as shown in the photograph and the diagram. *(Hugh Spencer)*

ture. Some bacteria free nitrogen by breaking down ammonia, nitrites, and nitrates. This process is called **denitrification.** Soil can lose nitrogen this way. However, the bacteria that free nitrogen from the soil are anaerobic. That is, they do not thrive in oxygen. They are most abundant in tightly packed, waterlogged soil. Farmers with well-drained, cultivated fields do not have much trouble with denitrification.

The Water Cycle   Water is essential to life. Cells are made up largely of water. Chemical reactions essential for life require water. Chemicals dissolved in water are transported to various parts of an organism. Many organisms live in a water environment. Plants absorb water through their roots and give off water vapor from their leaves. Animals drink water and give off water when they exhale.

Water is used over and over again in a cycle. Lakes, rivers, streams, oceans, and plants serve as water reservoirs. The energy from the sun causes water to move into the atmosphere. This is called *evaporation*. Water moving from the atmosphere to the earth is called *precipitation*.

Soil   Soil is the thin outer layer of the earth. It is one of the most important factors of an environment. Soil varies greatly from place to place. So does the plant and animal life it supports.

Different types of trees grow well in different soils. Sandy soils can support pine forests in Michigan, New Jersey, Georgia, and eastern Texas. Heavy loam is good for beech and maple forests in Ohio, Indiana, Ontario, and Quebec. Bogs and swamps have waterlogged soils good for larch, white cedar, and cypress forests in southeastern United States. Certain mountain slopes have rocky, shallow soils. These soils produce the forests of redwood, yellow pine, and spruce found in the western United States and Canada.

Soil is always changing. Weathering breaks down rocks. Chemical disintegrations and plants can break down rock surfaces. Plants remove water and nutrients from the soil. When the plants die, they decompose. Bacteria, fungi, small arthropods, and worms aid in decomposition, as do termites and millipedes. These organisms return minerals to the soil. **Formation of soil is a good example of two interactions in the environment. One is an interaction between the biotic and physical factors. The other is an interaction among the physical factors.**

48–6 | Trace the steps in the water cycle shown below.

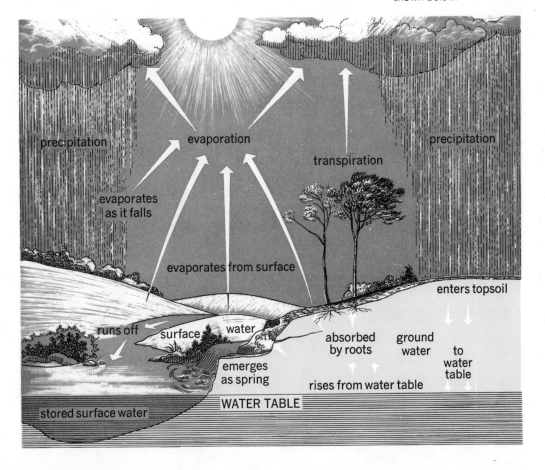

precipitation

evaporation

transpiration

precipitation

evaporates as it falls

evaporates from surface

enters topsoil

runs off

surface   water

absorbed by roots

ground water

to water table

emerges as spring

rises from water table

WATER TABLE

stored surface water

48–7 | In this redwood forest, fallen trees are broken down into substances that can be reused. What natural processes return minerals to the soil? *(Albert Towle)*

48–8 | This map of the world shows the distribution of vegetation.

Some soils can lose their richness. This can happen when minerals are removed by groundwater or by winds. It can happen when many crops are grown in the soil and the lost minerals are not replaced. Plants and animals are affected when soils change.

Biomes

Areas of the biosphere can be identified by the type of plants found there. The plants are referred to as the *vegetation*. When a group of plants dominate a region, ecologists call them the **climax vegetation.** A large geographical region identified by its climax vegetation is a **biome.**

There are three different types of biomes: terrestrial biomes, freshwater biomes, and marine biomes. Conditions that produce different climates will influence vegetation. Rainfall, temperature, air, sunlight, and shape of land are all important factors. The marine biome contains many more dissolved salts than the freshwater biome. Terrestrial biomes are the most varied.

Terrestrial Biome

The Tundra The *tundra* is a large area that encircles the Arctic Ocean of the Northern Hemisphere. There is no similar large land mass at this latitude in the Southern Hemisphere. The area of southern tundra is very small compared to the northern tundra. The tundra has a very cold and dry climate. The ground is permanently frozen about a meter (3.3 feet) below the surface. It is called the *permafrost.* Dur-

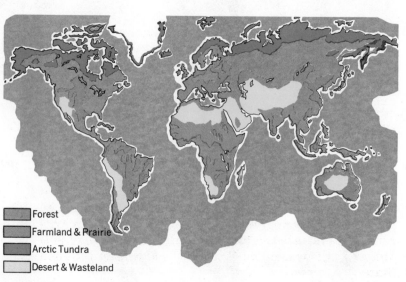

Forest

Farmland & Prairie

Arctic Tundra

Desert & Wasteland

48-9 | Very little grows on the tundra except mosses and lichens. *(Stephen J. Krasemann, © Peter Arnold)*

ing the continuous daylight of summer, the surface thaws. As a result, many bogs, streams, and ponds are formed.

Mosses and lichens, some grasses, and dwarf woody plants are the main vegetation. The plants have adapted to a rapid growing season of about 60 days of the year. Several of these plants produce large, bright flowers, even though there are periods of freezing temperatures. The birds are mostly summer visitors. Many mammals of the tundra have protective coloration. White coats that blend with the snow are found on the Arctic hares, collared lemmings, Arctic foxes, and polar bears. Insects are numerous in the summer. Most lay eggs that resist freezing. Herds of caribou wander into the tundra from areas that are farther south. They graze on mosses and lichens.

The Coniferous Forest   Just south of the tundra in Europe, Asia, and North America is another biome. It consists of evergreens, such as pines, firs, spruces, and cedars. These are cone-bearing trees. Thus the name **coniferous forest.** The coniferous forest is divided into three areas. The northernmost area is called the *taiga* (TIE-guh). The most obvious tree is the spruce. Conifers are adapted to a six-month growing season and cold winter temperatures. Their needles and cone-shaped structure allow them to shed the snow. There is a broad coniferous belt covering much of Canada. White pine, red pine, and eastern hemlock are the main conifers found here. Much of this forest was destroyed by past fires and logging. The shrubby areas of Michigan, Wisconsin, and Minnesota are the results. The *southern pine forests* are found in much of the southeastern United States.

48–10 │ A scene in a coniferous forest of the Northwest. *(Albert Towle)*

Large numbers of pine, spruce, and redwoods grow along the coastal ranges of Washington, Oregon, and California. The giant redwoods may reach a height of 60 meters (198 feet) or more. Rainfall may be heavy. Fog often covers the area providing additional moisture. Some coniferous forests are found in locations where occasional summer droughts kill other kinds of trees.

Coniferous forests have many full-time residents. Moose live in areas where they are protected or where they have not been over-hunted. Black bears roam the forests. So do martins, wolverines, and lynxes. The bobcat, fox, and wolf prey upon squirrels, chipmunks, rabbits, and mice. Beavers and porcupines are found in many of the coniferous forests. The animals are adapted for long, cold winters. Many birds breed in these forests during the summer. In the fall, however, some move south. Many insects live in the coniferous biome during the summer. They hide and become inactive during the cold winter months. As in all ecosystems, nutrients are returned to the soil and to the atmosphere by the decomposers.

The Deciduous Forest Areas of the temperate zones have a long growing season, usually lasting for more than six months. Rainfall averages about 100 centimeters (40 inches) per year. Where the soil is suitable, and summer droughts are rare or nonexistent, there are large **deciduous forests.** Oak, elm, and maple are deciduous trees. Deciduous trees lose their leaves in the winter. Deciduous forests can be found in the eastern United States, England, central Europe, and parts of China and Siberia. A similar zone is found in South America but it is limited in size by a lack of rain. There are a variety of different deciduous climax vegetations. These depend on local conditions of soil, drainage, and climate variation. Let's look at the variety of these in the United States. Beech-maple forests are found in the north central regions. Oak-hickory forests are common in the western and southern regions. Oak-chestnut forests were once common in the Appalachian Mountains, but chestnut blight disease has destroyed most of the chestnut trees. Other trees grow to replace the chestnuts. Some conifers now grow in these forests. In some areas, planted pine forests are growing where there were once deciduous forests. Other deciduous trees of the temperate zone are the sycamore, elm, poplar, willow, and cottonwood. Each of these specific forests has its typical animal species. Several animals are found in all deciduous forests. Deer are the common large herbivores. Other familiar mammals are foxes, raccoons, and squirrels. Wolves once wandered between coniferous and deciduous forests, but are now restricted to Minnesota, Canada, and Alaska. There are many tree-nesting birds, such as the woodpecker.

Deciduous forests change from season to season. Trees are green in late spring and summer. Shrubs growing in the shelter of these trees produce beautiful blooms. During the fall the leaves of many trees change to brilliant shades of red and yellow. In the winter, their bare branches stand out against the snow.

The Grasslands *Grasslands* are often found in vast areas where yearly rainfall is between 25 and 75 centimeters (10 to 30 inches). This amount is not enough to support large trees, but it is sufficient for many species of grasses. Grasslands are natural pastures. They have been used for years by huge herds of grazing animals. However, humans have allowed many of these lands to be overgrazed. Without the grass covering, the land's essential topsoil is worn away by water and wind. This erosion makes the land useless for long periods of time. We learned a sad lesson in the 1930's. Plowing, lack of shelter belts, and cultivation without returning nutrients to the soil produced the dustbowl in the western plains when a major drought occurred.

Grasses may have two growing seasons each year. The resulting accumulation of organic material produces the rich soil of the grain-growing regions on which much of the world's food supply depends. Those grasslands that receive the most water are especially important.

North American grasslands include the Great Plains and tall-grass prairies. Great herds of bison and antelope once grazed on these grassy plains. Burrowing mammals

48–11 | Deciduous forests undergo seasonal changes. During what season was each of the above photographs taken? *(top: Russ Kinne; middle: Herbert Weihrich; bottom: John King)*

48–12 | What might be the food chain in this North American grassland? *(William E. Ferguson)*

Facts & Figures

In a grassland biome, less than one fourth of the energy stored in photosynthesis is consumed. More than three fourths is returned to the soil as dead material.

48–13 | The cold desert occurs in Oregon. Note the sagebrush, characteristic of these areas. *(© Earl Roberge, Photo Researchers)*

such as hares, prairie dogs, ground squirrels, and pocket gophers are still abundant. These mammals form an important link in the food chain. They are eaten by weasels, snakes, and hawks. Locusts and grasshoppers are important members of the insect population.

The tropical grasslands of Africa are found in the Serengeti Plain. They are known for a variety of animal populations. These animals include the wildebeast, zebra, antelope, ostrich, and lion.

A *savannah* is a grassland with scattered trees. The oak-grass savannahs are found in the western United States. In Australia, the grasslands and savannahs are used by cattle, sheep, and kangaroos. South America also has large areas of savannah. African savannahs are the home of elephants, giraffe, many antelope species, and a variety of large carnivores.

The Desert *Deserts* are extremely dry areas. The rainfall may be less than 25 centimeters (10 inches) of rain per year. The largest desert is the Sahara-Arabian-Gobi desert. In many areas of this huge desert it may rain only once every few years. Death Valley is a typical *hot* desert. Its climax vegetation is the creosote bush. Did you know that there are *cold* deserts too? There are several cold deserts in the northwestern United States. They have freezing temperatures in the winter. Sagebrush is the dominant shrub in cold deserts.

Plants living in these dry environments are called *xerophytes* (ZEAR-uh-fites). They have well-developed root systems for absorbing water. Some have very long tap roots. Their leaves also are adapted to the dry environment. They are small, with thick, leathery outer layers. This helps them conserve water. Some desert plants have no typical leaves at all. The cactus, for example, has spines and use its stem for photosynthesis. Many xerophytes have thick stems adapted for water storage.

Desert animals also have special adaptations. Some excrete wastes in the form of uric acid. Uric acid may be excreted in an almost dry form. This helps animals, such as reptiles, birds, and some insects to conserve body water. Mammals cannot do this. Their wastes are urea dissolved in water. Some rats and mice obtain enough water from the seeds and fruit they eat. Others get water from cacti and other water-storing plants.

Desert herbs, grasses, and flowering plants come up very soon after a rain. Some of these plants go through a complete cycle of growth, flowering, and seed production in just a few weeks.

The Rain Forest Life flourishes in a *rain forest.* The conditions for life are similar in all rain forests. These areas have an abundant water supply and a long growing season. They have a high productivity because of the interactions of the biotic and physical factors of the environment. The warm temperature speeds up growth. In the rain forests, seasonal temperatures vary less than the temperatures between day and night. If areas in the tropical rain forests are farmed, though, the nutrients may be lost rapidly. The soils are usually loose and sandy. Nutrients wash out of them with the rains. Also, since farming removes the natural vegetations, the nutrients are not added.

48–14 | Vertical climatic regions of the earth are similar to horizontal climatic regions. Life zones on a high mountain can be compared to those found from the equator to either pole.

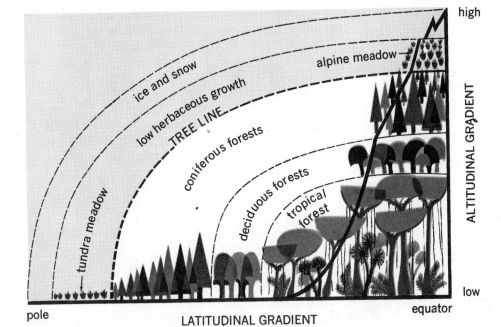

high

ice and snow

alpine meadow

low herbaceous growth

TREE LINE

coniferous forests

deciduous forests

tropical forest

tundra meadow

ALTITUDINAL GRADIENT

low

pole   equator

LATITUDINAL GRADIENT

Temperate rain forests are found on the northwest Pacific Coast. *Tropical rain forests* are found on and near the equator all around the earth.

Rain forests are rich with plant life. Short trees grow beneath tall trees. Together, they produce a thick canopy. Because of the shade, few plants can grow on the ground. Many smaller plants have adapted to this environment. Some grow as long vines. These grow roots in the moist ground and have leaves high up toward the light. Most tropical rain forest plants have very large leaves. This is also an adaptation to the reduced light. The large leaves trap more light energy than would small leaves. Conservation of water is not a problem for them. The critical problem is to find a place with enough light in which to grow.

Animal life is plentiful in a rain forest. Most of the animals live high in the trees. The rain forest is quiet in the daytime, but toward evening, everything seems to come alive. Ants, beetles, termites, and other insects are numerous. They supply many other animals with food. Crickets and tree frogs begin singing. Birds make noise as they search for food. Tree-dwelling monkeys chatter and howl before settling down for the night. Nocturnal carnivorous cats begin to hunt for monkeys, deer, and other animals. These cats include the jaguar in South America, the leopard in Africa, and the tiger in Asia.

A rain forest is not a jungle. Trees of a rain forest are usually climax vegetation. A jungle is very dense ground growth found along river banks. It also occurs on land once cleared by humans or by some natural event like a flood or fire. Left alone, most jungles usually become rain forests. A jungle, then, is a kind of immature rain forest.

The Marine Biome

The Oceans Oceans cover about 71 percent of the earth's surface. The average depth of the oceans is 3.7 kilometers (2.2 miles). Some places are as deep as 11.5 kilometers (6.9 miles). Life is found throughout the oceans. The marine biome is made of salt water. It can be divided into two zones. There is the bottom, or *benthic zone,* and the ocean water, or *pelagic zone.* The benthic zone is divided by the continental shelf into the *littoral zone* and the *deep sea zone.* In the ocean, the depth at which light penetrates is the most important factor. Some light passes through the waters above the continental shelf and the pelagic zone. The light passes down about 180 meters (198 yards). This is the most productive region of the marine biome since nutrients are usually more abundant. Here the microscopic suspended algae and the large drifting algae grow. These ocean plants

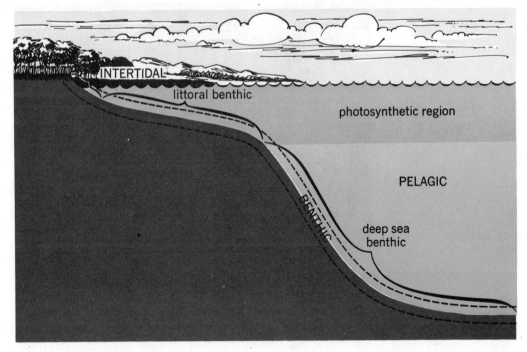

48–15 | The ocean may be divided into several zones. Each zone has characteristics that determine the types of organisms it can support.

are important in energy production, but they do not influence the physical environment as much as land plants do.

The basic food of the pelagic zone is *plankton*. Plankton includes diatoms, dinoflagellates, unicellular algae, protozoans, and the larval forms of many animals. Many copepods, small shrimp, small jellyfish, and worms are also part of the plankton. However, tiny unicellular algae are the most important food producers in the ocean. The copepods feed on the microscopic algae. In turn, the copepods are eaten by small shrimp, called krill. The krill forms the major food of the whale.

How do the animals beneath the light-penetrating level get their energy? They depend on sinking plankton, dead animals, and the swimming organisms that pass between the two levels. Many animals have recently been discovered living on the deep-sea bottom. For food, these scavengers depend on dead animals falling from above. Bacteria live in the soft ooze on the ocean bottom. The bacteria break up the dead organisms that have settled there.

As on land, mineral exchange occurs in the ocean. Food would soon be depleted if it weren't for currents and *upwelling*. Currents and differences in water temperature cause upwellings of deeper waters. This brings minerals and essential substances to the surface. Here they can be used

48–16 | Life abounds in a tide pool even though these organisms often have to withstand wave action and periods of drying out. (Anne Wertheim, © Animal Animals)

by the algae. The upwelling also brings colder waters to the surface. In areas of upwelling there are also many fish attracted to the area by a greater abundance of food. There are important fishing areas caused by upwelling near the coasts of Morocco, southwest Africa, California, and Peru.

The Shore Region At the shore area of oceans the changing tides produce a rhythmic rise and fall of water. The shore area covered and uncovered by water is called *intertidal zone.* It is exposed at low tide and covered at high tide. Life is abundant in the intertidal zone. Temperatures vary greatly. Wave action and drying out is a problem for the organisms living here. Growing space is limited. Algae and tiny colonial animals attach themselves to rocks and to the shells of other animals. Snails, periwinkles, and barnacles can be found high on rocks. Here they are exposed to air for long periods of time. They stay moist by clamping down tightly when the tide is out. When covered by the tide, they feed on algae. Other herbivores in the intertidal zone are shrimp, small fishes, and copepods. Clams, mussels, oysters, and sponges filter microscopic organisms from the water. The carnivores include the starfish, sea anemone, larger fishes, octopus, and squid. Sea urchins "graze" on algae. Familiar scavengers of the intertidal zone include worms, crabs, and hermit crabs. Other worms and bacteria break down waste materials and dead organisms for the recycling of essential nutrients.

Estuaries An *estuary* is an area where fresh water flows into the sea. The estuary then, is, a zone between the freshwater and marine biomes. **The physical factors vary**

greatly in an estuary. Tidal changes cause variations in the salt content of the water. Shallow estuaries experience a great temperature range. This is especially true if incoming water is flowing slowly. Mud or sand flats, tidal marshes, or mangrove swamps are all estuaries. Long, shallow bays can form estuaries in which the physical factors of the environment vary also. Estuaries are often rich in available nutrients. The nutrients are circulated by the back and forth tidal motion and the incoming freshwater so they are easily available to plants. Primary producers vary greatly among different estuaries but are usually tall grasses.

Many animals live in estuaries. Oysters, clams, fishes, crabs, and shrimp are adapted to estuaries and use the highly productive conditions to grow quickly. Estuaries are productive in producing food for humans. However, human activities such as construction, storm drains, and sewer discharges often destroy the organisms living in estuaries.

The Freshwater Biome

Lakes and Streams   The *freshwater biome* includes bodies of relatively still water such as lakes, ponds, and inland swamps. It also includes bodies of moving water such as springs, streams, and rivers. Many plankton organisms found in lakes and ponds do not survive in running water. What determines the types of life that can inhabit a stream? The strength of its current and type of bottom are two factors. A stream bottom of shifting, sandy soil limits life greatly. Streams with sluggish currents and sandy bottoms offer more possibilities for life. Here many organisms burrow among the rooted vegetation. Stony streams are the habitat of actively swimming or clinging animals. The trout is one of the active swimmers. It feeds on the larvae of caddisflies, mayflies, dragonflies, and dobsonflies. All are common inhabitants of stony brooks and streams. Algae grow attached to rocks, stumps, or stones. In lakes there is often mixing of surface waters with deeper waters. This is due to currents, especially in large lakes, and to differences in water temperature. This mixing allows many nutrients to be redistributed in the lake.

Water temperature is important to the organisms living in a freshwater biome. It takes a larger amount of heat to raise the temperature of water than it takes to raise the temperature of land or air. Also, when water evaporates, heat is absorbed from both the water and the atmosphere. This is what happens when you come out of the water on a hot summer day. Even a warm breeze can chill you as the water evaporates from your skin.

Water becomes lighter, or less dense, as it freezes. So

when water freezes, it floats. This is very important to lake organisms. A layer of ice on a lake's surface keeps the water from freezing solidly. However, it also keeps out some light and makes it difficult for oxygen to dissolve in the water. Because of this, lake organisms sometimes suffocate during the winter.

The Poles

The Antarctic
Many people think of the North and South Poles as large frozen wastelands, with extremes of light or darkness during the day. This is only partly correct. In fact, there are a number of differences between the two poles. The continent of Antarctica is at the South Pole of the earth. It is a very large continent. It is almost as large as the United States and Canada combined. The Antarctic land is covered by ice. Its average depth is more than a kilometer. Over 90 percent of the world's ice is found here. Antarctic winds have been measured at more than 300 kilometers (180 miles) per hour. The mean temperature doesn't go above freezing in any month. Because of this, the water is always frozen. So, in a strange way, Antarctica is as dry as a desert. It was not always like this. It is believed that this continent was connected to Africa and South America. Scientists have found fossil leaves and coal deposits in Antarctica. This suggests that it once had a tropical climate.

Only three types of flowering plants exist here, and they are on the very tip of the Antarctic peninsula. Even simple types of plants such as lichens and mosses are rare. As you might imagine from the lack of food producers, there are

48-17 | Parts of the Antarctic are not always covered with ice and snow. There, a few kinds of vegetation exist. *(Des and Jen Bartlett, Bruce Coleman)*

not many animals. The animals of the Antarctic are the penguins, a few visiting birds, mites, a wingless fly, and a rare insect that lives at the tip of the peninsula. About 50 percent of these small invertebrates are parasites. If so, where are the producers that supply even these animals? They are the phytoplankton of the marine biome surrounding Antarctica.

The Arctic The Arctic is surprisingly different from the Antarctic. More than 100 species of flowering plants have been identified here. Many types of mosses, lichens, insects, birds, and mammals live in the Arctic. About a million people also live within the Arctic. They are mostly Eskimos and reindeer herders from northern North America, Europe, Asia, and Greenland.

There are several differences between the two polar regions. The Arctic has less land mass than the Antartic and it is spread among several continents. The ice-sheet that covers most of the Arctic is seldom more than five meters (16.5 feet) thick. Stored heat from the ocean below the ice keeps the temperature within a certain range. The Arctic averages 17° C (62.6° F) warmer than the Antarctic. Ninety percent of the Arctic's land loses its ice covering in the summer. Temperatures may rise higher than 25° C (77° F). As the upper layers thaw, many flowering plants are supplied with water. Some of the tundra biome extends into the Arctic. However, as in Antarctica, most of the producers for the Arctic are in the marine biome. Many of the land creatures, such as polar bears and Arctic foxes, actually derive most of their food from the sea.

The sun's energy reaches the earth and provides energy for all life. The energy is converted to complex organic compounds by the plants. Changes also occur in the physical environment where low energy inorganic substances may be changed. Interactions between the biotic and physical factors allow some substances, such as nitrogen, carbon dioxide, oxygen, and water to be used over and over again. Energy enters the system, flows through it, and is released through respiration and heat. Energy, however, cannot be recycled.

A large geographical region identified by its climax vegetation is called a *biome*. Climate and water are important factors in determining the kinds of plants that live in the various biomes.

Summary

Biologically Speaking

ecology	coniferous forest
phyical factor	deciduous forest
biotic factor	grassland
biosphere	savannah
food chain	desert
limiting factor	rain forest
nitrogen fixation	intertidal zone
denitrification	estuary
climax vegetation	
biome	
tundra	

Questions for Review

1. Why can the biosphere be considered as one gigantic system?
2. What are some interactions that take place among the biotic factors of the environment?
3. Summarize the carbon-oxygen cycle and its value to living things.
4. How is the nitrogen cycle important to life?
5. In what ways is the water cycle important to life?
6. Why can soil be described more as a biotic factor than a physical factor?
7. Where are the coniferous forests, deciduous forests, and grasslands in the United States?
8. What adaptations to desert climates are found in mammals? in birds? in reptiles?
9. What environmental conditions are found in a rain forest?
10. What extremes of environmental conditions occur in the intertidal zone?
11. What furnishes the food for organisms living in total darkness in the depths of the ocean?

Applying Concepts

1. What patterns do ecologists search for in the environment?
2. How do organisms interact with the various biotic factors in the recycling of materials vital to life?
3. What environmental factors differ in a coniferous and a deciduous forest?
4. Discuss the adaptations of organisms in the intertidal zone.

The Ecosystem

A **DEFINE** ecosystem as a unit of the biosphere.
B **UNDERSTAND** the function of the various trophic levels in an ecosystem.
C **DESCRIBE** food chains in an ecosystem.
D **DIAGRAM** an ecological pyramid.
E **DESCRIBE** each of the biotic relationships.

49–1 | A pond is an ecosystem, a small part of the entire biosphere. (© Steve Solum, Bruce Coleman)

Ecosystems: Units of the Biosphere

You have been learning about the biosphere as though it were one large system. Now, think of the biosphere as being made of many smaller parts, or units. An ***ecosystem*** is a unit of the biosphere. In an ecosystem, living and nonliving things interact with one another and, as in the biosphere, materials are used over and over again. An ecosystem is smaller than the biosphere. Examples of ecosystems are forests, lakes, rivers, ponds, and meadows. The boundaries of a river system, though, may not be as easy to define as those of a lake. As ecosystems are units of the biosphere, they are dependent on one another and on an important physical factor, energy. **All the basic energy of an ecosystem is provided by the sun.**

A Lake is an Example of an Ecosystem

The boundary of a lake is the land surrounding the water. Many different kinds of organisms live in a lake. **The organisms that live together in an ecosystem make up the *biotic***

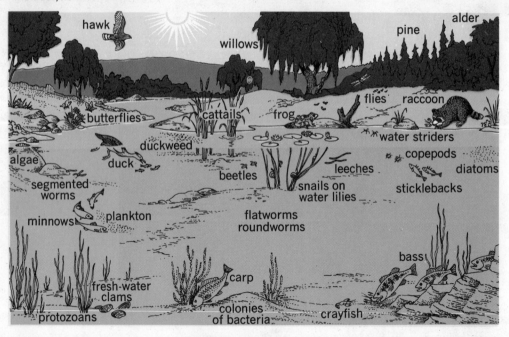

49-2 | A freshwater lake is an example of an ecosystem.

community. Can you identify members of the biotic community in the lake represented by figure 49–2?

A group of organisms of the same kind within a biotic community is called a *population.* In a lake there are many species of fish that make up the total fish population. Can you name the three kinds of fish that make up the total fish population? Although the diagram doesn't show it, an even greater number of insect species would make up the insect population of a lake. **Each population has a special function in the ecosystem.**

The nonliving part of an ecosystem is the *physical environment.* These factors have just been discussed in relation to the biosphere. Can you identify the parts of the physical environment in the lake ecosystem? As in the biosphere, interactions occur in the ecosystem: within the biotic community; between the biotic community and the physical environment; and within the physical environment.

The Biotic Community of the Lake

You have read that the organisms in the lake ecosystem depend on each other. How? You first might observe food relationships in the biotic community. The snails eat the water lilies; fish eat the snails; ducks eat the fish; and a hawk eats the duck. Bacteria of different kinds feed on the carcasses of these creatures and their waste products. Nutritional relationships are important interactions within the biotic community of the lake, but there are others. The plants, for example, serve as hiding places for young fish. Sticklebacks must find mates and build nests. How many more examples can you find in the diagram?

Perhaps you have thought of competition for food within the biotic community. Organisms may require similar things from the environment. Food is only one. Light, oxygen, carbon dioxide, and growing space are others. Organisms in the same population usually compete with each other more than with organisms of other populations. This is because similar organisms have similar needs. A good example is the cattails growing near the shore. They need the same soil and soil depth for growing. So they must all compete for the same living space. However, cattails do not compete very strongly with duckweed. The duckweed grows on the surface of the water. It does not need the same living space as cattails.

The Biotic Community and the Physical Environment of the Lake

Three aspects of the physical environment are extremely important to the biotic community. These are sunlight, nutrients, and temperature. Green plants that grow in the lake need the sun. This means that they must grow close enough to the water's surface to get the sun's rays. How deeply the sunlight will pass through the water depends on how clear the water is. A heavy growth of algae or stirred-up mud, for example, makes the water cloudy. In the clearest lakes, light can pass to depths of 25 meters (82.5 feet).

The remains of dead plants and animals build up more rapidly than decay reduces them. Thus, over many years the size of the lake may be reduced.

Water temperature is important to many organisms living in the lake ecosystem. This is especially true of temperature changes from day to day and season to season.

Humans are biotic community members, too. Their interactions may have important effects on the ecosystem of the lake. Of course, people do not live in lakes, but they sometimes pollute lakes. Water pollution by industrial waste or sewage affects an ecosystem.

Changes in the Physical Environment of the Lake As you have already read, changes in the physical environment may be temporary or permanent. Temporary changes include decreasing light by clouds, and mud washing into the lake during storms. Rains can wash chemicals into the lake and temporarily change the nature of the water. Seasonal changes also affect lakes. Water levels may fluctuate between summer and winter. Temperatures may be high in summer and below freezing in winter. When the temperature of water is near freezing, it becomes less dense. Therefore, ice forms at the surface. If the lake ecosystem is not shallow, water remains unfrozen below the surface.

Now you can see that freshwater lakes in different parts of the biosphere have similar *patterns* in the kinds of changes that occur. Yet, each of these ecosystems is unique.

Nutritional Relationships in an Ecosystem

As you know, the green plants make their own food by using the sun's energy. Inorganic nutrients are synthesized into organic compounds. Green plants are called **autotrophs.** Animals get their food by eating plants or other animals. Thus, animals are called **heterotrophs.** Find the autotrophs in the lake ecosystem represented by figure 49–3. They are the cattails and submerged water plants. They also include suspended algae that form *phytoplankton.* Perhaps you have already looked at a drop of pond water under the microscope. You probably have seen many kinds of one-celled algae.

Phytoplankton serves as food for small crustaceans like ostracods and copepods. These organisms are called **herbivores** because they feed on plants. A snail feeding on a cattail would be an herbivore. Minnows feeding on the small crustaceans are **carnivores.** They are flesh-eating animals. The minnows are called *first-level carnivores* because they feed on the herbivores and use their energy. A bass feeding on a minnow is a *second-level carnivore.* Young fishes can feed on both herbivores and minnows. So they can be either first- or second-level carnivores. Some animals are **omnivores.** They eat plants as well as other animals.

Scavengers feed on dead organisms. They are important in the cycling of chemicals. In lakes, these "garbage collectors" include crayfish, some snails, and many fishes. Scavengers also transfer energy to the animals in the ecosystem that feed on them.

Bacteria and yeasts are a lake's **decomposers.** They break down the tissues and excretions of organisms into simpler substances. We call this process *decay.* Still other bacteria change decayed matter into nitrogen compounds. Decomposers and these bacteria return nitrogen, phosphates, and other substances to the soil or water. The autotrophs can then use them to begin the cycle again. Without these bacteria, matter could not be reused in the ecosystem.

aut, auto = self
trophos = one who feeds
hetero = other, different

Facts & Figures

Omnivores do not confine their feeding to one trophic level.

Facts & Figures

Only herbivores are adapted to live on a diet high in cellulose.

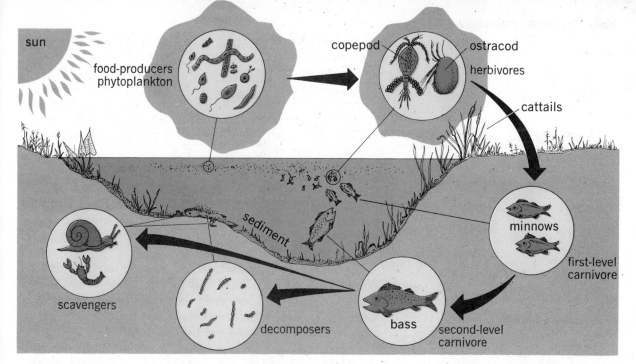

49-3 | A lake provides an interesting example of nutritional relationships.

The transfer of energy from the autotrophs to the herbivores, and through several levels of carnivores makes a *trophic pattern*. Energy flows through each level such as producer, first-level carnivore, and so on. These are called **trophic levels.**

Food Chains

Autotrophs are the ***food producers*** of the ecosystem. All the heterotrophs are ***food consumers.*** In our example of the lake ecosystem the consumers were divided into several levels. What happens to the energy each time it is passed on to another trophic level?

Let's look at the first food consumer, the herbivore. Energy is used when the herbivore moves, when it eats, when it digests its food, when it respires, and when it reproduces. Thus, most of the energy in food is not stored. **Most energy is used up in maintaining life's processes.** Let's say, for example, that a copepod in the lake ecosystem uses 85 percent of the energy it actually takes in for maintainence activities. Therefore, 15 percent of the energy is accumulated in the ecosystem. This accumulation is called ***productivity.* Only the accumulated energy is available to the next trophic level.** Herbivore productivity, then, is 15 percent of the energy it has taken in from the plants.

Now consider the first-level carnivore, a minnow in our example. The minnow is able to store about 15 percent of

Facts & Figures

Most plants transpire 1,000 grams of water for about every 2 grams of production.

the energy it actually takes in. Again, it is only this stored energy of the minnow that is available to the next trophic level. This would represent only 2¼ percent of the plant production. (15 percent of 15 percent equals 2.25 percent.)

If the bass also uses up most of the energy it takes in, it may also store about 15 percent. The energy in the bass would be only 0.3375 percent of the original energy in the green plants.

In our example of this lake ecosystem, there was no animal to eat the bass. The bass is the *top carnivore.* When it dies, it will probably serve as food for the crayfish. This transfer of the sun's energy through many organisms is called a *food chain.*

Of course, this food chain could be extended further. You might catch the bass and take it home to eat. How much of the original energy in the plants would you store? Also, in the lake, a bullfrog might eat the crayfish. Or, a raccoon might catch and eat the crayfish.

Ecosystems such as the lake have more than one food chain. Food chains overlap because many organisms eat more than one type of food. You could list every organism in the lake and draw arrows to show which organisms were used for food by others. This diagram would show all the biotic relationships involving energy transfer. There are many possibilities. Your diagram would look more like a web than a chain. For this reason, food chains are sometimes called *food webs.*

Ecological Pyramids

Food chains in an ecosystem are often shown as pyramids. Food producers form the base. The top carnivore forms the tip. Figure 49–5 shows the trophic structure of the food chain. This represents a *pyramid of productivity.*

Another method of observing an ecosystem would be to make a *food pyramid* of numbers. Consider the numbers of individuals involved in each link of a food chain. A count like this was made of a bluegrass field. There was an average of 5,842,424 food producers in an acre. The next link averaged 707,624 herbivorous invertebrates. These provided food for an average of 354,904 ants, spiders, and predatory beetles. An average of three birds and three moles formed the top of the pyramid. Studies like this help us understand the energy relationships in ecosystems. They even help us predict future changes.

Another way of studying food chains is to determine the mass in each link. All the organisms from a food chain in a selected area are removed. They are separated and weighed. Let's consider the difference between a food pyr-

49–4 | A food chain showing energy transfer, or the sequence of trophic levels. Where would you place scavengers and decomposers?

sun

green plants — producers (autotrophs)

herbivores — (first consumer)

first level carnivore (second consumer)

second level carnivore (third consumer)

Top carnivore (forth consumer)

carnivores

heterotrophs

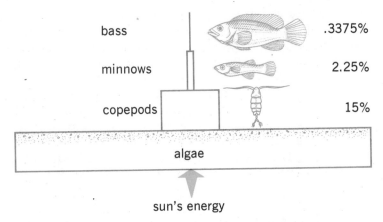

bass   .3375%

minnows   2.25%

copepods   15%

algae

sun's energy

49–5 | An ecological pyramid showing pro-ductivity of each trophic level in the ecosys-tem. If each level uses 15% of the energy it takes in, the figures represent the percent of energy used from the autotrophs.

amid based on number and one based on mass. In a food pyramid based on number, the number of trees is much less than the number of caterpillars. Obviously, one tree can support many caterpillars. Consider a pyramid based on the mass of the organisms. The mass of the tree is greater than the mass of the caterpillars. The pyramid of mass is more like an actual pyramid. Such a study might give a clearer picture of the biotic relationships.

Both of these pyramids show a condition found in an ecosystem at any given moment. However, conditions in an ecosystem are always changing. The number and mass of a group of organisms depends only in part on food supply. It really depends more on how quickly that supply can be renewed.

Understanding food pyramids may help us solve a human social problem. This is the problem of the popula-tion explosion. Remember that each level of a food chain uses up some of the energy that first came from the sun. About 85 percent of the energy moving from one level of the food pyramid to the next is lost. The energy is lost to res-piration, excretion, heat, and movement. There is always more food energy at the base of the food pyramid. If we can find ways to get ourselves closer to the base, that is, be herbivores more often than first- or second-level carni-vores, there will be more food energy for us. That way a larger population could be fed from the same amount of original sun-energy.

Special Nutritional Relationships

Most animals, including humans, are *bulk-feeders*. This means that they eat the whole organisms or parts of the organism. The *saprophytes* are another group of hetero-trophs. They absorb nutrients from dead tissues or prod-ucts of organisms. These include the bacteria that decom-pose plant and animal bodies. They also include the molds

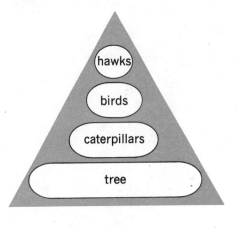

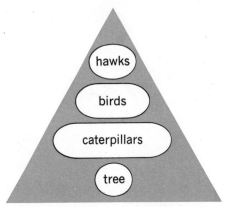

49–6 | A pyramid based on numbers (bot-tom) and a pyramid based on mass (top).

sapros = putrid
phyta = plant

49-7 | A hermit crab with sea anemones living attached to its shell. What do biologists call such a relationship? (© S. C. Bisserot, Bruce Coleman)

that live on bread, fruit, and other organic materials. They include the yeasts that ferment sugars and the fungi that live on dead trees. Some of these organisms are destructive, but others are very useful. Their relationship to dead tissues or products of organisms is a *saprophytic* one.

Symbiosis is another kind of biotic relationship. Symbiosis means "living together." Sometimes the relationship is only for a space to live. Orchids, for example may grow on trees in a tropical forest. Such relationships may not be nutritional. There are three different kinds of symbiosis that do involve food: **parasitism, mutualism,** and **commensalism.**

Parasitism In *parasitism*, the parasite lives in or on another organism, called a *host*. The parasite gets its food and a place to live from this situation. However, the host suffers. Parasites include certain insects, worms, disease-causing bacteria, mildews, rusts, and smuts.

Parasites do not usually kill their hosts. If the host dies, the parasite loses its habitat and its food supply. A successful parasite takes just enough food from the host to grow and reproduce. This is true of ticks, fleas, mosquitoes, and the fungus that causes athlete's foot.

Every free-living organism seems to have its parasites. Many parasites have parasites of their own. In fact, in terms of numbers, there are more parasites than there are free-living organisms.

Mutualism In *mutualism*, two different kinds of organisms benefit from living together. In some cases, they cannot live without each other. Termites, for example, can chew and swallow the cellulose in wood, but they cannot digest it. Protists living in their digestive tracts digest the cellulose for them. The termite is provided with a means of digestion. In return the protist is given a place to live. There are many other examples of mutualism. The association of an algae and fungus in lichens is one. The fungus provides moisture and a place to live for the alga. The alga makes food for itself and the fungus. Insects that pollinate flowers as they take nectar from them is another example of mutualism. In fact, mutualism is such a common biotic relationship that you can probably give many more examples. You have already learned about the relationship of nitrogen-fixing bacteria in nodules of the roots of legumes. How does each organism benefit in this relationship?

Commensalism In *commensalism*, one partner benefits and the other neither benefits nor is harmed. A good example is the relationship between the remora and a shark. The remora is a small fish in which the dorsal fin forms a suc-

49–8 | The wrasse feeds on scraps of food left by the moray eel. *(Animals Animals)*

tion pad. After attaching this pad to the lower side of a shark, it rides along. When the shark feeds, the remora detaches itself long enough to collect fragments of food. The shark does not benefit from this relationship. The remora does not remain permanently attached to the shark. Nor does its suction pad damage the shark's skin. Thus, the shark is not harmed by this association.

Summary

All life is maintained from an equilibrium with physical forces. To do this requires energy. Energy passes from the sun to autotrophs through a series of heterotophs until it reaches the top carnivore. Most energy is lost as it passes from one trophic level to the next. Scavengers and decomposers use energy from waste products and the dead bodies of all living things. This returns much inorganic material to the environment.

Food chains representing the various trophic levels can be identified and represented as ecological pyramids. Pyramids of numbers, mass, and energy are three different ways of showing nutritional relationships.

Biotic relationships can be identified in several kinds of symbiosis. Among these are parasitism, mutualism, and commensalism.

Biologically Speaking

ecosystem	omnivore	food chain
biotic community	scavenger	food web
population	decomposer	symbiosis
autotroph	trophic level	parasitism
heterotroph	food producer	mutualism
herbivore	food consumer	commensalism
carnivore	productivity	

Questions for Review

1. How can a freshwater lake be observed as a unit of the biosphere?
2. What is meant by a trophic pattern? Give an example of each.
3. Starting with the food-producers, name and define the various types of organisms in a food chain.
4. In what different ways may ecological pyramids be made? What do they demonstrate?
5. What is meant by symbiosis? Describe each of the three symbiotic relationships.

Applying Concepts

1. Describe an ecosystem near your home.
2. Make a diagram of a food web that exists in your local area. Can you use this to make an ecological pyramid? Explain.
3. What are some food chains of coniferous forests?

50

Biotic Communities

A **DESCRIBE** the organization of biotic communities.

B **DEFINE** habitat and niche.

C **DESCRIBE** alternating periods of activity in organisms.

D **EXPLAIN** how biotic communities change.

E **DESCRIBE** natural succession.

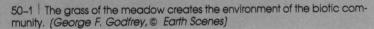

50–1 | The grass of the meadow creates the environment of the biotic community. *(George F. Godfrey, © Earth Scenes)*

Communities

When you play on your school's basketball team, you are representing the school community. When you collect newspapers for a paper drive, you are helping your community. Your home, neighborhood, school, city, state, and country are organizations of human populations. Ecologists think of ecosystems as being organized into communities too. A **biotic community is a naturally occurring group of animals and plants living in the same environment and interacting with one another.** You have already read about some of these interactions in food chains and several chemical cycles.

Recall the lake ecosystem discussed in Chapter 49. All the organisms of the lake were considered as the *biotic community*. Within the biotic community environmental conditions may be different. For example, during the summer, the temperature near the shore may be higher than at the bottom of the lake. The amount of light will also vary. Also, as you have read, different kinds of organisms live in these environments. **The place in which an organism lives is its *habitat*.** The lake ecosystem has many habitats. The

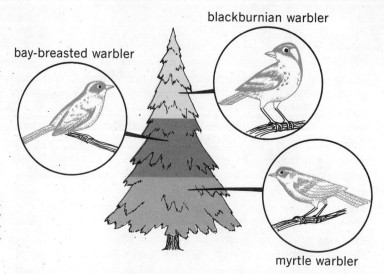

bay-breasted warbler

blackburnian warbler

myrtle warbler

50-2 | Three species of warbler hunt for insects in coniferous trees in the same New England forests. But the three species do not compete for food because they usually hunt from different parts of the tree.

habitat of the bullfrog, for example, is quite different from that of the bass. Yet, both contribute to the ecosystem. Bass and bullfrog habitats may overlap. Then the bullfrog may be eaten by a bass.

The "occupation" of an organism is its *niche*. There are many ways to "earn a living" in a biotic community. Think about the many species of *plankton* in a lake. Remember, plankton are tiny organisms suspended in the water. The niche of many small fish is to feed on the plankton. These small fish may share their habitat with larger fish, but the larger fish have a different niche. Their niche is to feed on the smaller fish.

No two species can occupy the same niche at the same time. If they did, they would compete for exactly the same food and space. A good example of this is found in three species of birds that nest on the Galapagos Islands. These are the blue-footed, red-footed, and white boobies. They all dive into the water and feed on the same kinds of marine fishes. However, the blue-footed booby always feeds close to the shore. The red-footed booby catches its fish many miles away. The white booby fishes about a mile away from the islands. The differences in feeding areas reduces competition among these birds.

What about space for nesting? The blue-footed boobies nest in the open, level spaces. Nests may be made of only a stone or two. The red-footed boobies build nests of twigs in shrubs or trees. The white boobies prefer to build their nests on cliffs or hillsides. They may use small clearings between dense shrubs and trees. Their colonies are not as dense as in the other bird species. Thus, these three species of birds share the environment. At first glance they appear to occupy the same niche, but studies have shown that feeding and nesting behaviors are different.

Patterns within Communities

In the springtime, you may waken to the sounds of hundred of birds announcing the new day. At the same time, creatures such as snails, slugs, and sowbugs are seeking protected spots where they will remain throughout the day. Somewhere a hawk is soaring in the morning sky. It spots a mouse on the ground and dives after it. At night, the attacker would have been a barn owl. **Alternating periods of activity allow for different kinds of food.** There may be an overlap in the time of hunting for the owl and the hawk. They both occupy a predatory niche. However, their niches are not the same in time. **An organism that is active during the day is called** *diurnal* **(di-URN-al).** *Nocturnal* **(nock-TURN-al) animals are active at night. Alternating periods of activity are called** *periodicity.* **When an organism's periodicity is regular, it is called rhythmic.** An early bird getting its worm every morning shows rhythmic behavior. Biologists have studied rhythmic behavior in organisms for many years, but many of their questions about this behavior are still unanswered. What, for example, causes certain insects, birds, or mammals to migrate? What causes hibernating animals to wake up in the spring? Some animals have been described as having "internal clocks."

Light seems to be important to these rhythms. Many rhythms are based on daily, seasonal, and annual light variations. Some rhythms are also based on changes in the phases of the moon. As you will see, factors other than light will affect rhythms of plants and animals. Animals and plants appear to "remember" their rhythms. Biologists have raised plants in a darkened room under a constant temperature. These plants had the same responses they would have had in normal periods of daylight and darkness. This "memory" of a rhythm has also been shown in chickens, lizards, and *Drosophila.* Different species may show slight differences in the length of their active and resting periods. Most seem to have a 22- to 26-hour cycle. Having alternating periodicity allows organisms to occupy the same *habitat* without occupying the same *niche.*

To survive, organisms must be able to adjust to environmental changes. Organisms adjust to these changes. Various populations have synchronized patterns of behavior. These behavior patterns help the species survive.

Daily Rhythms

All forests have similar environmental conditions. The tall trees provide areas of shade under which the shrub layer of the forest floor grows. In sunny spaces, grasses grow in

50–3 | The hawk is a diurnal predator, while the owl is a nocturnal predator. *(Allan Roberts)*

50–4 | (top) A night-blooming cactus. (bottom) A morning-glory. Why do you think these flowers bloom at such separate times of the day? (top: Fritz Henle, Photo Researchers; bottom: Manuel Rodriguez)

meadows. Ferns cover the banks of streams. A summer morning finds birds, chipmunks, and ground squirrels searching for food. Deer browse in the meadows. By noon, however, this activity slows. These rhythms provide different food resources for the animals living in the forest.

As evening approaches, many of these diurnal animals become active again for a short time. Dragonflies and bats dart over streams and ponds. Here they search for both diurnal and nocturnal insects. This is a period of time between day and night. The sounds of cicadas and birds gradually fade. Now crickets begin chirping. Foxes, raccoons, skunks, owls, and mountain lions begin the nocturnal search for food.

When plants bloom, their flowers may open and close at regular times of the day. This is an adaption for different pollinators. The petals of the poppy, for example, open in the morning and close at night. The poppy depends on diurnal insects for pollination. Many cacti bloom only at night. They depend on nocturnal insects for pollination.

Day-night rhythms are also found in the oceans. Many copepods and shrimp move close to the surface at night. Here they can feed on plankton. These herbivores sink to a lower level during the day. Some may be found as far down as 100 meters (330 feet). Small carnivorous fish follow the daily movements of these plankton feeders.

Tidal Changes

Many marine organisms live along the coastline. The rhythmic rise and fall of tidal water affects the lives of these organisms. They must continuously adjust to the changing tides. The greatest problem is the danger of drying out at low tide Small fishes and crustaceans find protection in tidepools. These are small areas of water left behind when the tide goes out. Many limpets and snails keep from drying out by clamping down tightly to rocks. Mussels and barnacles close their shells tightly. This keeps moisture in. Some sessile sponges and tunicates live under rock ledges covered by seaweed. The seaweed covering protects them during low tide.

Organisms living in tidal areas have other problems. Summer and winter tides cause wide variations in temperature. Fresh water from rains changes the salt content of tidepools. You can see that intertidal organisms must be able to adjust to a great variety of changes.

Adaptations to Temperature Changes

Animals meet the problems of seasonal change in many ways. When they are exposed to snow and freezing temperatures, they must be able to adjust or to move away. Most adult insects have completed their life cycles before the beginning of autumn. Many of these insects are killed by the first frosts. How do the species survive? That depends on the insect. Most have special over-wintering stages that can tolerate below-freezing conditions. Many moths spend the winter as pupae in silk-insulated cocoons. Grasshoppers, crickets, and cicadas lay eggs in the ground or in the bark of trees. In these places they are protected from extremely cold temperatures. The eggs remain dormant until the warmer temperatures of spring. Then they begin to develop. Stoneflies, mayflies, and dragonflies spend the winter in a nymph stage in the water. Here they are sheltered beneath the water's frozen surface.

Honeybees find winter protection in numbers. They feed on the honey stored during the spring and summer. This gives them energy to keep active in their hives all winter. This activity produces heat. On a very cold day, the temperature in a hive can be as much as 24° C (75.2° F) higher than the outside temperature.

Some mammals and birds live in the same region all year. Among these are the eastern cottontail rabbit, the white-tailed deer, the cardinal, and the bluejay. During very cold weather they find protection in woods and thickets. Their biggest problem is finding food when snow covers the area.

Bacteria also show changes in response to the freezing temperatures of winter. They form thick-walled spores. The spores become active with the warmer temperatures of spring.

Deciduous trees lose their leaves as temperatures fall and daylight length shortens with approaching winter. The sap is stored in the roots underground to prevent it from freezing. In spring, sap rises and new leaves form.

Some animals go into *hibernation* during cold weather. These include squirrels, chipmunks, woodchucks, and many reptiles and amphibians. The hibernating animal finds a protected place and remains inactive for the winter. Its body metabolic rate slows down. So does its heartbeat and respiration. Eventually, the animal loses consciousness. The decrease in activity reduces its energy needs. This drop in activity is important since the animal is living off stored fat. Hibernating animals do not wake until the temperature rises again in the spring. Only then do their body processes speed up enough for normal activity.

Some animals such as the bear enter a period of *dormancy* during the winter. Dormancy is similar to hibernation. Body activities slow down and the animal lives on stored fat during its *winter sleep*. However, the animal's body temperature remains normal. Unlike the hibernating

50–5 | Hibernation. Many animals, such as the jumping mouse, pass the winter in a dormant state in underground nests. *(Allan Roberts)*

animal, it may be awakened during the dormancy period. The bear, for example, may leave its shelter on a mild winter day. Skunks, raccoons, and opossums have similar winter sleeps.

Organisms also adapt to the seasonal temperature changes of summer. Many animals become dormant during hot weather. This summer dormancy is called **estivation.** A frog may estivate in the cool mud at the bottom of a pond. The box turtle often buries itself in leaves to escape the heat. Estivation can last for several days or several weeks.

Migration

Many animals migrate to warmer regions in winter. When you think of **migrations,** you usually think of birds. Some mammals and insects also migrate. These seasonal journeys may cover thousands of kilometers. Some animals migrate to find food. Others migrate to a better climate. Still others make seasonal journeys to regions where they can produce their young under the best conditions.

Mammal Migration The bighorn sheep is a mammal that migrates. It spends summers in high meadows near the summits of the Rocky Mountains. When winter comes, it moves down into the protection of the forests on the mountain slopes.

The fur seal also migrates. During winter the females, young males, and pups swim in the waters of the Pacific Ocean. The older males spend the winter in the cold waters near Alaska and the Aleutian Islands. The breeding season is in the spring. Then the males migrate to the Pribilof Islands, north of the Aleutians. They arrive several weeks before the females, and then battle for a territory. At the same time the female seals start their long journey to the Pribilof Islands. They travel more than 4,800 kilometers (2,880 miles) and arrive in June. A herd of 50 or more females gathers around each male. Pups from the past year's breeding are born in June. Then, within a week, breeding takes place again. Now, the seals migrate southward.

Insect Migration The monarch butterfly is often called the milkweed butterfly. It is a very strong flier and makes a remarkable migration. At the end of summer thousands of them gather in Canada and begin to fly south. Some travel to the Gulf states and spend the winter. Others travel along the Pacific coast. Between mid-October and November, most of them arrive in Mexico and on the Monterey peninsula. They seek shelter in a specific grove of pine trees. Here

50-6 | The bighorn sheep spends summers in the summits of the Rocky Mountains. It moves down to the forest slopes in the winter. *(Phil Farnes, DPI)*

they hang from the branches and needles in such large numbers that the trees appear to be solid brown. On warm sunny days throughout the fall and winter, they may fly around gardens gathering nectar.

In March the monarchs begin their northward journey. They lay eggs on milkweed plants as they travel north. Most of the monarchs die after their eggs are laid. After the eggs hatch, the larvae feed and then form pupae. The butterflies that emerge from the pupae continue the flight north. These butterflies also lay eggs on milkweed as they travel north.

By late summer the butterflies begin to gather for another migration south. It is not known how these insects find their way to the same trees in which their ancestors spent the previous winter.

Bird Migration   Many birds migrate long distances in the spring. They nest and raise their young in a new home. In the fall they return to warmer climates. It is difficult to understand why some birds leave food and warmth in the tropics to breed in the far north. It is much easier to explain why insect-eating birds fly south when cold weather kills their prey. We can also see why water birds fly south before northern ponds and lakes freeze. Surely birds migrate to

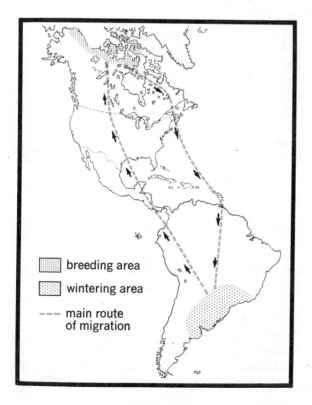

breeding area

wintering area

--- main route
    of migration

50-7 | The migratory route of the golden plover. Flying more than 13,000 kilometers (7,800 miles) each way, it breeds in northern Canada during the summer and flies to South America to spend the winter.

take advantage of food supplies. How do birds know when to migrate? Several factors are involved. As seasons change, temperature changes. Also, the ratio of daylight to darkness changes. In response to the environmental changes, the periods of feeding are altered. Fat deposits and metabolic rates are affected.

Some species of birds migrate at night. Some migrate by day. How do they know where to go? It is thought that they may be directed by the angles between the sun or stars and the horizon. Perhaps you have heard flocks of geese overhead on spring and autumn nights. Sometimes they get confused by city lights and circle about, honking noisily. You may have seen great flocks of red-winged blackbirds or grackles. These daylight-flying birds also migrate in spring and fall.

Many birds migrate slowly. They feed along the way and average only 30 to 50 kilometers (15 miles to 30 miles) a day. Others are marvels of speed and endurance. For example, the ruddy turnstone travels from Alaska to Hawaii in a single flight. The golden plover travels more than 13,000 kilometers (7,800 miles) from Canada to South America. Canada geese and other birds make several stops along the estuaries of the United States coastlines on their trip north.

Annual Rhythms

Many reproductive cycles of plants and animals are associated with seasonal changes. They also have a yearly rhythm. The female bear gives birth during the winter in the protection of her den. Birds nest and lay eggs in spring. By the time winter comes, their young are fully grown. Wildflowers bloom and produce seeds in the spring. This enables the next generation of wildflowers to develop. Deciduous trees lose their leaves in the fall. These are just a few of the annual cycles of nature. You can probably think of many more.

Changing Biotic Communities

Migration of animals can bring about a rapid change in the community. However, the changes in the plant populations of an area usually happen slowly, particularly in forests. These changes are not always easy to identify. **As plant populations change, animals find new homes. The changing of communities is called** *succession.*

Winds, fires, volcanic activity, and other natural events may destroy the organisms living in an area. This also hap-

---

Facts & Figures

The greatest distance covered by a bird during migration was 19,200 kilometers (12,000 miles).

pens when humans clear land. If the area is then left alone, succession starts. Eventually, a permanent community will take over again. This process may take longer than 100 years. Succession can also begin when humans change the makeup of an ecosystem in other ways: Putting rocks in a bay for a breakwater or sinking piles for a pier begins the process of succession.

Succession in Ponds and Lakes

As you learned earlier, the cattails and waterlilies around a lake or pond edge hold soil around their roots. More soil continues to build up over the years. As a result, the pond gradually grows smaller. Eventually the pond will be completely filled in with the same types of plants that grew around its edge. The succession of plants and animals that gradually will fill in a pond can be predicted. The organisms that grow from the pond's edge outward to the climax plants of the region must be observed closely. Other factors help determine how much of the pond will be filled. These are pond size, location, and water source. These factors also determine when and how long the succession will take.

In August 1959, an earthquake occurred in the Madison River Canyon in Montana. A new lake was formed. A large portion of the land on the mountainside was cleared when tons of soil, rocks, and trees fell into the canyon. Biologists are studying the changes occurring in the new lake and clearings. A knowledge of ecological succession helps predict changes, but an earthquake such as this gives us the opportunity to prove our theories.

The drama in nature goes on endlessly. Conditions in any given area are never permanent. Each population of plants that occupies the area changes the environment. This often makes it unsuitable for other plants of the same type. However, it may be a favorable change for plants that move in. Over a period of time these changes in plant population prepare the way for the new vegetation. The animal population depends on the plant population. Therefore, the types and numbers of animals change as plant succession occurs.

Natural Succession in a Forest

To see how the process of succession occurs, let us begin with a section of bare soil in an open area. This area might have been cleared by fire. Perhaps it was cut for trees and not reseeded. Or it might be an abandoned agricultural field. It is located in a broad-leaved forest in the eastern United States. Here beech and sugar-maple forests once grew over much of the land.

50–8 | Succession in a pond: (top to bottom) pioneer, open-pond stage; submerged vegetation stage; cattail stage; sedge meadow stage; climax forest stage.

The first organisms to appear are grasses and other open-field plants. These plants may come from seeds that are dormant in the soil, or they may be carried in by animals or winds. The first organisms to dominate an area are called *pioneers*. A meadow is produced by these pioneers. The meadow may dominate the region for several years. The life span of the pioneers is short when compared to that of the plants that follow.

Next, many seeds of elms, cottonwoods, and shrubs find their way into the meadow. This marks the beginning of a forest. The larger plants shade the shorter grasses and field plants. Thus, the environment is changing from an open field to open, low woods. These woods soon become too shady even for the seedlings of the trees and shrubs. So the area slowly continues to change.

The third stage of this succession may begin with the arrival of seeds from trees such as oak and ash. These seedlings grow well in a shady environment. Gradually, the oaks and ashes begin to take over from the elms and cottonwoods. Finally, a dense forest forms. The ground becomes moist and fertile. Beech and maple seedlings win the competition for forest space. Eventually they crowd out most of the other trees. Since the beech and maple trees are now *dominant*, we call them the **climax species.**

During these changes of succession, plants gradually have changed the environment. The biotic community has become more complex. The beech and maple trees reproduce and maintain the forest. They determine the nature of the environment. The other species in this community must adapt to the conditions created by the dominant species. Thus the *climax community* is determined by the climax species. Disturbances such as a fire or hurricane periodically may strike forest. They wipe out the climax species and force succession to begin anew.

Summary

Many habitats exist in the biotic communities. The niche is the way an organism "earns its living." No two species can occupy the same niche at the same time. Different periods of activity allow organisms to live in the same habitat.

Alternating periods of activity may cause temporal changes within the biotic community. Among these are daily, lunar, seasonal, and annual rhythms. Many of these rhythms are brought about by temperature and light variations.

In places where an ecosystem has been altered, biotic communities change slowly. As pioneers come into the area they change the environment to allow other organisms to grow. The gradual changes, called succession, occur until a climax community is reached. One or a few dominant species continue to maintain the environment. During succession, the animal populations also change because they depend on the plant populations.

biotic community   hibernation
habitat   estivation
niche   migration
diurnal   succession
nocturnal   climax species
periodicity

Biologically
Speaking

1. Why can't organisms in the same habitat occupy the same niche at the same time?
2. The owl and the hawk are both predators. Do they compete with one another? Explain.
3. What special adjustments must intertidal organisms make?
4. How do animals adjust to seasonal changes?
5. Give examples of animal migrations.
6. Of what value is periodicity to survival of some plant or animal species?
7. What methods can be used to study succession?

Questions for
Review

1. Why are human activities not governed entirely by external rhythms?
2. Discuss the senses that are well developed in nocturnal animals.
3. Review and discuss possible causes for the migration of birds.
4. What climax communities exist in the area in which you live? Identify any stages leading to this climax.

Applying
Concepts

51

Populations

A **DEFINE** population.
B **DESCRIBE** the biotic potential
of an organism.
C **DEMONSTRATE** a population
growth curve.
D **DEFINE** carrying capacity.
E **DESCRIBE** the density-
dependent and density-
independent factors.
F **DISCUSS** human population
growth.

51–1 | Sea birds are pioneer organisms on volcanic islands. *(Eric Hosking, Bruce Coleman)*

Populations

The Galapagos Islands have been of interest to biologists because they are geologically new. The Galapagos are a tiny group of islands directly on the equator in the Pacific Ocean, 600 miles off the coast of Ecuador. They were formed 2.5 million years ago by volcanic eruptions. Very gradually a succession of organisms reached its shores and began to form communities on the island.

First the sea birds probably nested on the barren rock formed from cooled lava. Their droppings would furnish nutritional energy for bacteria. Meanwhile, rain and water erosion very gradually would form soil.

Next, tropical storms probably carried other organisms to the islands. These may have included seeds, spores, small arthropods, drought-resistant eggs, and an occasional small mammal floating on an uprooted tree or debris. Many organisms reaching these islands would die, but some would produce offspring. At the very beginning there were no producers on the volcanic island so that no animal could flourish there until the arrival of plants.

Plants that reached the island and lived were the pioneers that began the events of succession. Their falling leaves were added to the developing soil. These plants could have reached the island by means already mentioned, or by wind erosion.

Isolated from their original "home," different *niches* would be available for the newly arriving organisms. All the small land birds on the Galapagos, for example, are believed to be descended from one type of small finch. Today there are several distinct species. They occupy many niches as demonstrated by their specialized bills. Some have bills like warblers, others have heavy bills, well suited for seed-cracking.

The communities of newly formed islands are *unstable*. This means that the kinds and numbers of plants and animals are changing. In the last chapter you read about an unstable condition in the forest and pond ecosystems. It is called *succession*. The major biomes of the world are much older when compared to the Galapagos. The *climax communities* of the biomes indicate a *stable* condition. What factors are involved in creating a stable condition?

Let's consider populations of organisms to understand stability in a biome. A **population** is a group of organisms of the same species that share the same habitat. What limits the sizes of populations? How do populations grow?

Population Size

Consider the life history of the housefly which has *complete metamorphosis*. A female lays about 120 eggs which hatch into maggots in one day. Within five or six days the pupa forms. Then, in a week the adult emerges from the pupa. In two-week's time, a single pair of flies produces an average of 120 offspring. If 60 offspring are females, in two more weeks, 7,200 flies could be produced.

Table 51-1 on page 684 shows the population size that would be possible from a pair of houseflies after 12 weeks. This is the **biotic potential** of houseflies. It is a hypothetical curve. The biotic potential of a species is the number of offspring that could exist if all offspring survived and produced young. Think of the biotic potential of an oyster that might shed 114 million eggs at a single spawning! It is

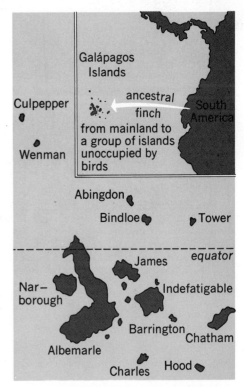

51-2 | The Galapagos Islands were pushed up from the ocean floor and have never been connected to the mainland. They offered a new environment for any organism that reached them.

51-3 | On his H.M.S. *Beagle* voyage, Charles Darwin traveled to the Galapagos where he found the finches. The finches offered Darwin an excellent example of variation and adaptive radiation. Six of the species found by Darwin are shown. (a) *vegetarian tree finch*, a plant eater; (b) *large ground finch*, a seed eater; (c) *tool-using finch*, an insect eater; (d) *large cactus ground finch*, a plant eater; (e) *warbler finch*, an insect eater; (f) *small ground finch*, a plant and insect eater.

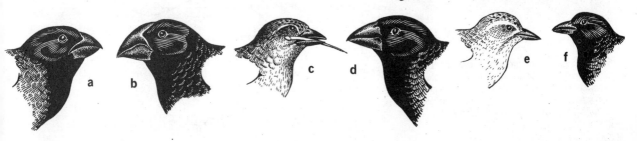

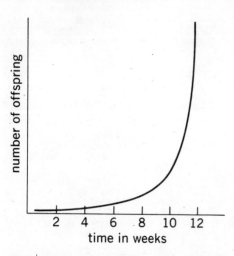

number of offspring

time in weeks

51–4 | Under ideal conditions each pair of houseflies could produce about 120 offspring every two weeks. This curve represents the biotic potential of houseflies.

Table 51-1 POSSIBLE NUMBER OF HOUSEFLIES FROM A SINGLE PAIR AFTER 12 WEEKS

2 weeks	120 (60 females)
4 weeks (120 × 60)	7,200
6 weeks (3,600 × 120)	432,000
8 weeks (216,000 × 120)	25,920,000
10 weeks (12,960,000 × 120)	1,555,200,000
12 weeks (777,600,000 × 120)	93,312,000,000
Total number after 12 weeks if all survived.	94,893,559,320

known that the size of a population does not reach the biotic potential of an organism. What limits population sizes? Let's consider another population to see what can really occur.

A farm pond, for example, may be stocked with a few bluegill sunfish. If we could count all the bluegills in the populations for several years, we could observe a pattern. The pattern of growth is called a **population growth curve.** It is an S-shaped curve. The biotic potential of the bluegills increases the size of the population. The increase is slow at first, and then becomes faster. If we continued counting the size of the population, we would find that it would level off. The population may decline slightly, and then increase again. Population counts during successive years likely would show differences within a range. A balance has been reached. The population of bluegills in the pond is *stable.* **This stable level, or the number of individuals the environment can support, is called the *carrying capacity* of the environment.** When the population size of any species reaches the carrying capacity of the environment, it becomes stable. In the bluegill population, for example, the number of bluegills being produced balances the number that die. Several factors bring about this stability.

51–5 | Population growth curve of bluegill sunfish in a farm pond. At point A, fish are introduced into the pond. At point B, the population size levels off. The dotted line indicates the carrying capacity of the environment for bluegills.

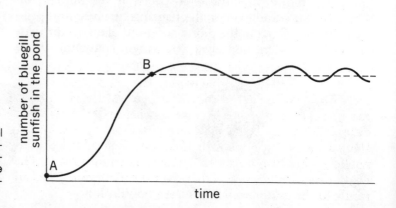

number of bluegill sunfish in the pond

time

Limits of Populations

Some factors affect populations regardless of their density. These are called *density-independent factors.* They include changes in the weather, temperature, humidity, daily and seasonal light, and available energy. Volcanic eruptions and hurricanes can destroy entire populations. However, as you might imagine, humans are the greatest factor. By building dams, breakwaters, and cities, we change many habitats. The human has exterminated entire populations of organisms.

Space, food, parasitism and disease, predation, and stress are all factors that limit the size of populations. They all act in determining the carrying capacity for the population of a particular organism in the environment. **The extent to which these factors operate on a population depends on the density of the population. Ecologists call these** *density-dependent factors.*

Space and Food The number of individual organisms in any given area is the ***population density.*** When the bluegill sunfish were first placed in the farm pond, the population density was low. Each individual fish had plenty of room to move. If the farm pond had a growth of plants and insect larvae, each fish would have plenty of food. As the population size reached the carrying capacity of the pond, the density was high. Density is a way of expressing population sizes in specific areas. In the example of the pond, energy from the sun entered the ecosystem and passed through various organisms in food chains. These energy relationships play a role in the carrying capacity of the pond for the bluegill population.

Let's consider a population of paramecia in a laboratory culture. You could place a few paramecia in a test tube containing a culture medium. At first the density would be low. If you then made density counts regularly, the results could be plotted on a graph. The results, at first, would be similar to figure 51-5 for the bluegills in the farm pond. An S-shaped curve would indicate a slow, and then a more rapid, increase in density of the animals. After a while the population density would begin to drop quickly. Why? When you first started the culture there was plenty of food. As the population size increased, the reproduction rate increased because more individuals were dividing. Soon the density could get no greater because there was not enough food and oxygen. Overpopulation turned the S-shaped curve in the opposite direction. The buildup of metabolic wastes also began to change the environment. **The death rate soon became higher than the birth rate. The end result in the culture would be zero population.**

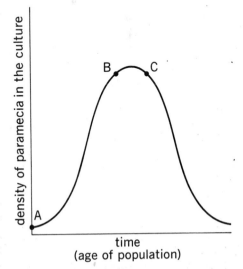

51-6 | Population growth curve for a culture of paramecia. At point A, paramecia are placed in the culture. At point B, the population size levels off. At point C, the population declines.

Just about the same things happen in large ecosystems, but space and food factors generally work to limit the population rather than to destroy it completely. What happens, for example, when the birth rate of bluegills in a pond is higher than the death rate? The bluegill population increases. This means greater competition for food. Many bluegills starve to death or become weakened from the lack of food. When enough fish die, the rest of the population again has enough food. In this way the process maintains a balance.

Space and food are also factors that limit plant populations. Grasses in a field, for example, must have room to send their roots into the soil. Their blades must be exposed to the sunlight for photosynthesis. Only a certain number of plants can occupy a given amount of space. Therefore, the size of a grass population may be limited by space.

Parasitism and Disease **Parasites and disease can be limiting factors in a population.** High density populations usually result in poor nutrition of its members. Parasites usually do not kill their hosts. However, in a weakened condition, the host organisms may die. Also, parasites are able to find hosts more easily in dense populations. Often, reproduction in a parasitized organism is affected. Death rate now becomes greater than birth rate. The population density declines, and the cycle can be repeated.

These factors also operate in human populations. You may know about the Black Death, or bubonic plague. This epidemic swept through the high density human populations of Europe in the fourteenth century. The crowded, dirty living conditions and the high density of the human population were factors that allowed the disease to spread rapidly. The parasites could find their way quite easily from host to host.

Predation The size of most populations is partly controlled by *predators* (PRED-uh-terz). A predator is one organism that feeds upon another. It is interesting to see how different populations help to keep an ecosystem in balance. Consider this situation in an open field. A meadow mouse runs through the grasses searching for seeds. You might think that this seed-eater will reduce the population of next generation of grasses. However, plants produce many more seeds than are needed to keep their population the same. It would take many mice eating seeds to change the grass population density the next season. If food is plentiful, what controls the mouse population? An owl may swoop down and catch the mouse. Without predators, mice might take over this field. If they did, two things would

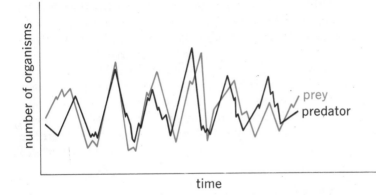

51–7 | Interaction of a predator and its prey. The size of one population is affected by the size of the other.

happen. First, they would reduce the number of grasses. Second, more mice would be competing for less food. Then, lack of food would eventually reduce the mouse population as well. This often happens when predators are removed from an ecosystem. **Wherever life is found, predators play an important part in maintaining the density of populations.** Ecologists have introduced predators into ecosystems. By doing so they have been able to control the population of certain pests. For example, a praying mantis introduced into a garden will limit insect garden pests.

Stress Scientists have studied the effects of high densities in many organisms. Overcrowding in rats, for example, leads to aggression, disease, decline in births, and many abnormal behavior problems. Perhaps you may have been able to observe similar effects in human populations. Think about the behavior of people trying to get on a crowded bus or subway train in a big city.

Stress caused by high density in a natural environment may cause organisms to move away. Crowded mice, for example, will disperse and seek new habitats.

High Density Advantages

You learned about some of the disadvantages of a large group of organisms living together in the paramecium culture. Nutrients were not added nor were wastes removed from the culture. Since the organisms could not move away, the entire population died. However, there are some advantages to a dense population. A large band of monkeys, for example, has more individuals that can look for danger and protect the group. A large flock of birds may present a confusing picture to a hawk looking for food. A large herd of deer gives each member more protection than a small group. On a warm day a large swarm of honey bees may keep their hive from melting by fanning it. A few bees could

51–8 | Starlings. This bird was introduced to New York City about 90 years ago. It is now found throughout the United States and southern Canada. *(John Markham, Bruce Coleman)*

THE POPULATION EXPLOSION

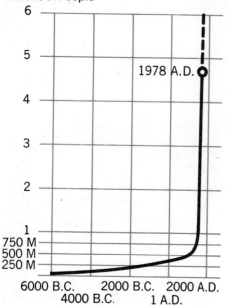

Billions of People

6000 B.C. 2000 B.C. 2000 A.D.
4000 B.C.   1 A.D.

people per square mile

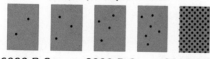

6000 B.C.   2000 B.C.   2000 A.D.
   4000 B.C.   1 A.D.

51-9 | Compare this growth curve to that of the flies, paramecia, and bluegill sunfish. The dotted line is based on growth data.

Facts & Figures

The majority of the world's population (64 percent) is concentrated in 10 countries. Arranged in order of decreasing birth rate, they are: Nigeria, Bangladesh, Pakistan, Indonesia, Brazil, India, China, Japan, USSR, and the United States.

not do this. A high population level makes it easier for the organism to find a mate. This means that the reproduction rate will probably be greater. Where would you find these conditions in the population growth curve?

Some populations, such as bees, ants, and termites, are social. Their efficiency depends on large numbers of organisms living together. A large population can sometimes change the environment to benefit the organism. **However, when the population level of a species is larger than the carrying capacity of the environment, the population will decline.**

Low Density Disadvantages

A decline in the population density of organisms sometimes leads to undercrowding. This may be harmful to the species involved. For example, blue whales have been over-hunted for centuries. The decrease in their numbers makes it harder for them to find mates. As a result, the rate of reproduction decreases and the population density is lowered even further. Eventually, the organism may become extinct.

Human Population Growth

The density factors discussed in this chapter affect human populations, too. The rate of human population increase can be determined by looking at daily births and deaths. An estimated 328,000 babies are born into the world every day. There are an estimated 134,000 daily deaths. If you subtract deaths from births, you get the estimated daily rate of population increase. It is believed that the human population increases by about 194,000 individuals each day. Of course, common sense tells us that this rate will probably increase under natural conditions. The more people there are, the more babies there are likely to be produced. In 45 years the world population could be more than eight billion people. If our present rate of food production stays the same, there will not be enough food to feed everyone. Already more than 10,000 people die from starvation or malnutrition every day. So you see that some of the same factors that control the density of other organisms also play a part in human population density.

A graph of the human population density resembles the major part of the S-shaped growth curve for populations. Human population density must be approaching the upper limit of the carrying capacity of the earth. If this is true, then we would expect the growth curve to begin to level off.

Islands, such as the Galapagos are interesting study areas for biologists. Organisms tend to disperse into newly formed areas of the earth. Successful organisms pave the way for others until climax communities develop. Methods of dispersal and succession can be compared to the existing biomes of the world.

Populations of organisms tend to become stable because various factors do not allow them to reach their biotic potential. The carrying capacity of an area for a given species involves many factors. Some are density-dependent, and some are density-independent. These same factors also affect human populations. Therefore, the human population estimates may not actually occur.

population	density-independent factor
biotic potential	density-dependent factor
population growth curve	population density
carrying capacity	predator

1. After the formation of volcanic islands, such as the Galapagos, what types of organisms would be able to live there?
2. What is a population? Give some examples.
3. Make a diagram that shows the population of an organism after stability has been reached. Label it.
4. Make a diagram to compare the population density of bluegill sunfish introduced into a pond and paramecia introduced into a culture.
5. Name several density-dependent factors that control the size of a population.
6. Name several density-independent factors that control the size of a population.

1. Compare the population of a newly formed isolated island to the population of an area in an oak-hickory forest that was burned by fire.
2. Think about the introduction of bluegill sunfishes to a newly formed farm pond. Why would this be similar to the introduction of mice to the newly formed Galapagos Islands?
3. Discuss the factors controlling human populations throughout the world.
4. How is the life history of a frog adaptive for the population?

52

Human Environmental Problems

A **DESCRIBE** the impact of human population growth on our natural resources.

B **DESCRIBE** the various resources and **EXPLAIN** conservation methods.

C **EXPLAIN** the role of fire in some ecosystems.

D **EXPLAIN** the causes and effects of water pollution.

E **EXPLAIN** the causes of air pollution.

F **STATE** a problem of radiation.

52-1 | Pioneers found fertile farmland. *(Nebraska State Historical Society)*

Increasing Human Density and Problems

When pioneers pushed westward through the North American wilderness, they found a land rich in natural resources. Stands of hardwood trees extended from the Eastern coast to the Middle West. This was the largest deciduous forest in the world. Beyond the forest were prairies and plains. Native grasses had grown on these lands for thousands of years. The land was rich and fertile. Its topsoil had been building up for centuries. All the pioneers had to do was clear the trees and plow grasses to have rich agricultural fields.

There was wildlife everywhere. Inland waters were filled with fish, waterfowl, and aquatic mammals. Large and small game roamed the forests and grasslands. Early settlers probably thought that there was no end to these natural resources.

Humans, as all organisms, change the environment in which they live. For more than a century people used the natural resources with no thought of the future. Even though the human population density was low, the natural environment was wasted and destroyed. Only a few decades ago we began to realize what was happening. In many areas the valuable topsoil was gone. It had been washed or blown away. Wildlife was disappearing. A wealth of natural resources had been used up. Today, in most of the populated areas of North America, large areas of the original climax vegetation no longer exist.

New environmental problems have developed in recent years. They have to do with human life in crowded cities. They involve the artificial environment created by science, technology, and industry. This environment includes office buildings, high-rise apartments, housing projects, apartment complexes, and residential communities. It also includes shopping centers, power plants, refineries, sprawling industries, jammed streets and highways, and dense populations. The urban environment contributes to the pollution of rivers, lakes, oceans, and the air. At the same time, many people depend on this artificial environment for their survival. Their lives also depend on resources of the land.

Natural Resources

In the last chapter you learned that the *carrying capacity* of the environment depends on the amount of energy that the species can trap. This kind of energy is food. Food for the city dweller may have come from long distances. Thus, humans are actually a part of many environments. Truly, we depend on the entire biosphere for our needs. **Resources** are the substances we take from our environment. Some resources, such as food, are **renewable.** This means that more food can be grown. Some, such as minerals and water, are **nonrenewable.** This means that no more is being produced. As our resources are used, other organisms are affected—and so are we. Let's look at the use of our natural resources.

Food

Thousands of people in the world are dying from starvation and malnutrition every day. Yet, our food is a renewable resource. So, why do people die of starvation? For one thing, food distribution over long distances is a problem. Food spoils in a short time as other organisms use the energy source in food. In undeveloped countries the food is often rich in carbohydrates and low in fats and protein. Also, the population rate is growing faster than the food production. Diets lacking protein cause retarded growth, anemia, and high infant mortality.

Scientists are working to develop new hybrid strains of corn and rice that are high in protein content. Remember the trophic levels from Chapter 49? A person eating corn and rice would be a primary consumer. In terms of biomass, more food would be available. If the producers contained more protein, then more of the human population could be supported.

In the days of the pioneers, people raised enough food for the family. Some food was used immediately, while some was stored for the winter. Today our agricultural land is supporting more and more people, and in many areas the best agricultural land has been used for housing tracts. The soil is a very important factor in primary production for all trophic levels. Soil is a renewable resource but it takes many years to form. When misused, it is lost much more quickly than it is formed. Loss of soil affects the energy available to humans.

Soil Resources

A century ago our soil contained a rich store of minerals. These minerals were built up over many centuries from the growth and decay of native vegetation. Then people settled on the land. Fields were planted year after year. No thought was given to depletion of soil minerals. This loss of soil fertility began to show in reduced crop yields. However, farmers still did not put minerals back into their fields. They just moved on to new fields. A similar practice is still used today when a field is allowed to remain unplanted for several years.

In 1896, the agricultural scientist George Washington Carver began to try to determine what treatments would be effective against worn-out Alabama soil. For years, cotton had been planted in the same area. Professor Carver concluded that continuous planting of one crop had depleted the nutrients in the soil. He introduced the idea of planting peanuts and cotton on an alternate basis. This increases the yield of both peanuts and cotton. This practice is called *crop rotation.* Many crops are rotated in a three-year cycle. The first crop may be corn. The next may be wheat or oats. Then grass or clover is planted. Clover, alfalfa, cowpeas, lespedeza, and other legumes are important in the rotation cycle. Legumes support nitrogen-fixing bacteria on their roots. These bacteria form nitrates from atmospheric nitrogen. Valuable organic matter is added when these legume crops are plowed into the soil.

Continuous farming and removal of plants from a field leads to loss of organic matter. In a natural environment,

52-2 | By inspecting plants in Alabama, George Washington Carver came up with ideas that changed crop conditions, especially in southern United States. *(The Bettmann Archive, Inc.)*

plants die and decay each season. This adds humus to the topsoil. Almost no organic matter is left in the soil after crop plants are harvested. Soil organisms die out. Many of the processes that keep the soil fertile stop.

There are ways to prevent the loss of minerals from the soil. Scientific farmers add *fertilizers* to the soil. These fertilizers contain nitrates, phosphates, and potash (potassium compounds).

Loss of Soil by Erosion   *Erosion* is a very destructive form of soil loss. It occurs when water and wind carry away the soil. Precious topsoil from millions of acres of our most productive land has been lost by erosion. This soil now lies in riverbeds and on ocean bottoms. Some has been blown thousands of kilometers by violent dust storms.

Natural erosion always has occurred. Before any land was cultivated, however, erosion was not as destructive. Soil formation generally kept up with erosion. However, farming stripped the land of its natural vegetation, and poor farming methods exposed it to the forces of water and wind. The result was a far more serious and fast-moving erosion. Soil was removed by wind and water faster than it could be formed.

The slope of the land, the type of soil, the use of the land, and amount of rainfall all influence erosion by water. Seasonal floods can cause surface water to cover exposed soil. A thin layer of soil is then dissolved in the water. When the water drains, the soil is removed. This is known as *sheet erosion*. Natural vegetation on bottomlands that flood often can help control sheet erosion.

When rain falls on the exposed soil of rolling hills, small channels develop. Each time it rains, water flows down the same rills. The rills get deeper and wider, forming *gullies*. If this erosion is not stopped, gullies can become gulchs or even canyons.

One way to prevent gully erosion is to plant trees, grasses or other vegetation on the slopes. They act as soil binders and prevent gullies from widening. Deepening can also be stopped by building a series of dams across the gully. The dams slow the flow of water. Now the settling soil will gradually fill in the gully.

There is an agricultural solution to water erosion on a slope. It is called *contour farming*. The land is plowed across the slope of a hill rather than up and down. The trench made is called a furrow. Each furrow acts as a small dam to stop the water from flowing downhill.

Terracing stops water flow on steeply sloping land. This method of preventing erosion has been practiced by humans for a long time. More than 400 years ago the Incas

52-3 | This hillside shows serious rill erosion. *(Grant Heilman)*

52–4 | In many areas the land is too steep to farm by conventional means. There, *terracing*, as seen above, is used. *(Courtesy Pan Am)*

52–5 | A dust storm. What harm can result from storms of this type? *(Grant Heilman)*

lived in the Andes mountains at 4,500 meters (14,850 feet) above sea level. They grew corn and other crops in a series of steps built on a long, steep slope. Flat strips formed the contour of the slope. Each strip was divided by another bank. Soil on the steps was held by rocks. A drainage ditch at the base of each bank carried water around the slope.

Wind erosion is especially a problem in the prairie and plain regions. Strong winds often sweep across the treeless land. At one time the climax vegetation of native grasses grew here. Their spreading roots held the soil.

In the 1930s most of the land was plowed for agriculture. Now it is known that many areas should have been left with natural grass. Many of the farmed places have climates that are only marginal for cereal grains. In the 1930s several late summer and early fall droughts hit the western plains. Strong winds blew much of the exposed topsoil away. Fine particles of soil from these great dust storms filled the atmosphere. Dust particles were in the air as far as the east coast. They were even found several hundred kilometers over the Atlantic Ocean. The dust reduced sunlight inputs to the biosphere there by interacting with other physical factors.

How can dust storms be prevented? Windbreaks or **shelterbelts** are of some help. They can be planted along the edges of fields. In addition, furrows should be plowed at right angles to the prevailing wind. The wind will blow across the furrows instead of down them. Thus each furrow will help to stop the movement of soil. In some places **irrigation** is possible. This is the running of water into the fields during the dry periods. This will check wind erosion, because moist soil does not blow away. Every centimeter of soil not cultivated regularly should be anchored firmly. This can be done by planting grasses and other *soil-binding plants*.

At this time the human population growth curve is at its greatest rate of increase. Mismanagement of our soil would be like throwing away our food. The two extremes in the water problem are floods and droughts. Both are the results of the misuse of soil and its plant cover. Rains that should soak into the ground run off at the surface. Streams flood with muddy water eroded from the nearby land. Later in the season there may be a water shortage. The wind then blows away the soil. Soil erosion, floods, and droughts form a vicious cycle.

Water Resources

Humans, as all other organisms, need water. However, humans have wasted water just as they have misused the land. With the increase in the human population and industrialization, more water is used, but everyone can waste less water. In many industries water can be used over again. Wells supply much of the water for both domestic and industrial use. The wells remove groundwater.

The amount of water in the biosphere cannot be increased. Water is nonrenewable. However, its availability for our use can be increased. What can be done to raise the water table to supply us with more water?

The amount of runoff water during heavy rains must be reduced. The loss of runoff water causes a lowering of the water table. Water conservation, then, must begin in hilly and mountainous regions. These regions are called **watersheds.** Forests and other plant cover must be returned to these areas. Vegetations breaks the fall of rain. Built-up humus and leaf litter soak up water like a sponge. Water stored in watersheds flows into springs and rivulets. These, in turn, feed rivers and streams.

Rainfall is uneven and seasonal in most parts of the country. Therefore, rivers will always have high and low water stages. A high water stage does not have to be a disastrous flood. Waters from rising rivers should spread into flood plains, sloughs, and breakwaters. As the high waters go down, these natural reservoirs should feed water back into the river. Ground and natural surface reservoirs receive excess water during rainy periods. Thus they maintain the water supply during dry periods.

Dams are another means of conserving water and preventing floods. Large dams have been built in many parts of the country. However, dams are very costly both ecologically and economically. The large reservoirs formed by dams supply water to many large cities. Hydroelectric plants are often built next to dams. This electricity supplies large areas of the nation. Dams have also raised water levels. The result is that more rivers are now navigable for long distances. The deep, clear lakes formed by dams are used for fishing and water recreation. Yet many natural river communities were wiped out completely as the reservoirs filled.

Fuel Resources

The human population growth and use of energy has created a crisis. In a natural ecosystem, the sun's energy is trapped by living plants. This energy is stored in the plant's tissue. The energy then moves through the food web. Eventually, all of the energy is released as heat. Thus, in a natural ecosystem the inflow of energy from the sun limits activities. Also, such a natural ecosystem cannot use more energy than it receives. An ecosystem must remain within these limitations in order to survive.

Human technology has taken us out of this natural energy flow. We want far more energy than can be supplied by this system. Today, average Americans use several thousand times as much energy as did their early ancestors of the nineteenth century. About six percent of the world's population lives in the United States, and the United States uses about 35 percent of the energy consumed in the world.

In 1970, about 95 percent of the total energy used in the United States came from fossil fuel. Fossil fuels include coal, oil, and natural gas. These sources are nonrenewable. The remaining energy used was from a renewable supply. This was mostly power from falling water and solar energy. A very small percent of our energy was from nuclear fuels.

Why is there an energy shortage throughout the world? One reason is that cities and surrounding areas are becoming heavily populated. As a result, fuel needs rise. The production, mining, and transportation of fuels becomes a problem. Power industries cannot respond quickly enough to these changes. Fossil-fuel generators cannot be built quickly enough. A coal mine takes four years to open. Oil fields may take up to 10 years to reach production. The power being used rose faster than was predicted. Therefore, the amount of fuel being demanded could not be supplied. Thus there was an energy shortage.

Because of such energy shortages more people are concerned with future energy needs. We are beginning to realize that our supply of natural fossil fuels is dwindling. It is believed that world energy desires are doubling every 10 years. Obviously we need other sources of energy. One solution is to explore the various renewable energy sources. These might include energy from the sun, the heat of the earth's crust, running water, tides, wind, and even burning garbage.

Nuclear fuels might also allow an increase in energy production. The first nuclear power plant in the United States began operation in 1957. A reliance on nuclear power, especially to replace fossil fuels as an energy source, has not increased as expected. The main concern most people have with regard to nuclear energy is in the waste products produced by nuclear fission reactors. These waste products are the same as those produced in a nuclear explosion. There is a safety concern as to whether there is leakage from the power plant of nuclear materials. Also, there is no guarantee that final waste products can be made safe for disposal or storage. However, with the depletion of the fossil fuels, there must be an alternative energy source.

Moving water used to produce electrical energy has

52-6 | The most prominent features of a nuclear energy park are the large cooling towers. They are needed to keep the nuclear core from overheating and emitting dangerous radiation into the environment. *(© Bill Pierce 1979, Woodfin Camp and Associates)*

already been mentioned. The energy source in the moving water and tides has not begun to be tapped. Also, at one time, and still in some parts of the world, windmills used the energy of moving air. This energy can turn large mills and perform work. Wind energy can also be changed to electrical energy.

Radiation energy from the sun can also be changed to electrical energy. You may have noticed solar heating units on homes or businesses. Large collecting units are required for solar energy use. The energy from the sun can be collected in the units and stored in solar batteries to be used when needed. Today, however, most solar energy units must be supplemented with other energy sources because of their relative unreliability. However, solar energy is a renewable energy source, and once the units are installed, they require no further cost except for possible repairs.

52-7 | Solar energy units tap a renewable energy source, the sun. *(Solar Energy Research Institute)*

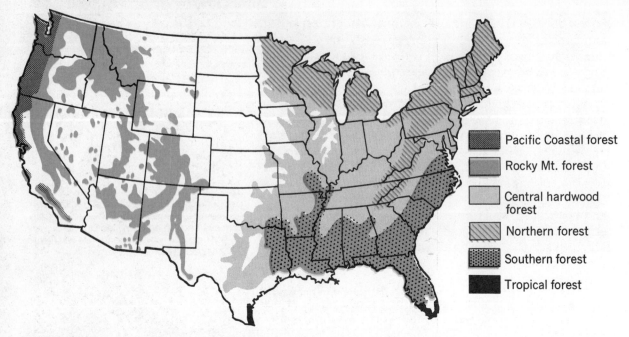

Pacific Coastal forest

Rocky Mt. forest

Central hardwood forest

Northern forest

Southern forest

Tropical forest

52-8 | The principal forest regions of the United States. These regions occupy nearly one third of the land.

Forest Resources

The two great forest belts of the eastern and western United States are divided into different types of forests. The type of forest was determined by factors such as temperature, rainfall, soil, and shape of the land.

The *central hardwood forest* covers much of the eastern and central United States. It extends all the way to the prairies in the midwest. The timber trees of this forest are valuable. They include beeches, maples, oaks, hickories, ashes, and black walnuts. The *northern forest* lies in the Great Lakes and northern states regions. It extends west to Minnesota and south down the Appalachian Mountains to Tennessee and North Carolina. This forest also covers much of Canada. It includes species of pine, spruce, and balsam fir. These trees are mingled with birch, aspen, maple, linden, and other northern hardwoods. The *southern forest* covers the southeastern and Gulf coastal states. It is a mixed forest of conifers and hardwood trees.

The *Rocky Mountain forest* covers the mountain slopes to the timberline. It is made up of species of pine, spruce, fir, and larch. The *Pacific coastal forest* is perhaps the most magnificent of all. It extends from California to Washington and far into Canada and Alaska. It forms dense and valuable stands of timber. These forests include the towering Douglas fir, coast redwood, sugar pine, white fir, and western cedar.

Forest Use In the past, the clearing of land for agriculture and housing destroyed many forests. Also, the demand for lumber has been draining our forests for more than a century. The wood of conifers is ideal for construction. It is soft and easily worked.

Forests supply an enormous amount of *pulpwood*. It is used in making many paper products. Among them are newsprint, high-quality book paper, stationery, and packaging paper. Pulpwood comes from United States and Canadian coniferous forests. Valuable distillation products come from hardwoods, such as beech, maple and birch. Some of these products are alcohol, oxalic acid, charcoal, and lampblack. Most pine products come from the southern states. These include turpentine, rosin, and pine tar. Maple sugar and tannic acid are also forest products. Tannic acid comes from the bark of hemlock, chestnut oak, and tan-bark oak.

Forest products are only a part of the value of forests. Forests are important in regulating the water supply and preventing floods. They also prevent soil loss by serving as soil binders. Trees absorb large amounts of water from the ground. Eventually, most of the water transpires from the leaves to the atmosphere. Thus, it is understandable how forests can affect the climate and all organisms living within them.

As was mentioned, it was necessary that large areas of our original forests be cleared for agriculture. This was especially true of the central hardwood forest. The soil of this forest was deep and fertile. However, this is only part of the story of forest destruction. Much of the destruction was useless waste. At one time entire forests were cut down in lumbering operations. Nothing was left but stumps and brush. Often, more than half of the removed timber was wasted. Forests were cut down in hilly regions. These areas were not suitable for farming. Thus, the land was left bare and easily eroded. Much of our forest land has been logged but not successfully reforested. Wise use could have supplied our timber demands and prevented the useless destruction of the forests.

Forest Conservation As early as 1905, officials in Washington, D.C., became concerned about the condition of our forests. As a result, Congress created the United States Forest Service under the Department of Agriculture. Large areas of timber land were set aside as national forests. Many of these areas are in the West. There are about 500 million acres of commercial forestland in the United States today. Of this, 92 million acres are owned and managed by the federal government. National forests are used for camp-

Careers

Forestry technicians work mainly outdoors. They inspect trees for disease and other problems. They help prevent and control fires, and they work in forest restoration.

To be a forestry technician requires one to two years of education past high school or comparable work experience. Forestry technicians are employed by the government and private industries such as paper companies.

52-9 | Forests are a renewable resource as long as they are maintained. *(Courtesy Weyerhauser Company)*

ing, hunting, fishing, grazing, water use, and timbering. Yet, still today, effective replanting of our forests is not keeping up with their destruction. Better methods of conservation must include ways to reduce damage from logging roads. Forest-soil nutrient loss from runoff water must be reduced.

How can people continue the use of forests without making the same mistakes of the past? Many ecologists are studying this problem. In a natural forest the climax community may comprise a dense population. A variety of species usually make up the community. The factors discussed in the last chapter operate to keep the several populations in balance with the environment. However, even our reforestation practices of the past have attempted to throw single species out of balance with these natural factors.

Reforestation takes a long time, and may be expensive, but it is an important part of the conservation program. Seedlings of many timber species are grown in large nurseries. These nurseries are maintained by the United States Forest Service and a number of private lumber and paper companies. Many hardwood forest regions are being reforested with pine. This is because pine matures rapidly. It also makes valuable construction lumber. However, the climax type of forest in the area has been changed. Habitats for all the organisms have been affected. If these areas were left alone, succession would eventually restore the original climax species.

Nature helps in the reforestation process. The Douglas fir is the main tree in the northwest, but its seedlings will not grow in the shade of other trees. In nature's succession, the climax trees are hemlocks and cedars. These grow well in the shade of the Douglas fir. Sometimes fire may destroy a large area. When this happens, Douglas fir seeds fall on open ground. Then they grow and produce a new stand of trees. In some areas controlled fires or clearcutting may actually be helpful to accelerate succession.

Fire In the past, fire has frequently been viewed as a destructive process. You may have seen many habitats destroyed and many organisms killed. It is true that deliberate destruction or carelessness of people causes most forest fires, some of which are ecologically damaging. Natural fire by lightning actually may be required by some ecosystems. Fire returns minerals to the soil. In the last section you read about the Douglas fir seeds sprouting in an area cleared by fire. Fire begins succession again. Natural grasslands of the prairies probably require periodic fires to return nutrients bound up in organic matter. Charcoal is an important material in the soil.

The pine forests of the southeastern coastal region are probably dependent on fire also. The pines are not damaged by *ground fires*. Studies have shown that when fires are exluded from these areas, deciduous hardwood trees grow up under the pines. Eventually the hardwood trees replace the pines.

Wildlife Conservation

The term *wildlife* includes all native animals and plants. Wildlife conservation problems are related directly to other environmental problems. There has been a decline in many of our wildlife populations. This is the direct result of destruction of habitats. Cities and farms cannot continue to develop without the wholesale destruction of wildlife.

Today, many species of animal and plant life are in danger of extinction, and people will be the major reason for their extinction. Perhaps the greatest single cause for the decline of any species is the destruction of its native ecosystem. The increasing demand for living space and the use of chemical poisons have destroyed many habitats. Uncontrolled hunting for sport and collection of animals for the pet trade has reduced the number of animals. Introduction of foreign species has also affected the natural environment.

Fish Dams across rivers interfere with fish migration. In some areas, *fish ladders* have been built. A fish ladder is a

Facts & Figures

As the human populated the west, more than 60 million bison were destroyed.

52-10 | Fish ladders are built to enable fish to travel upstream during spawning season. *(U.S. Department of Interior)*

channel built around a dam. It is designed to let fish travel upsteam. The fast flow of water is broken by a series of steps or plates. A fish traveling upstream can leap from one step to the next. Fish ladders are now important in salmon streams. Even so, the numbers of migrating fish have been severely reduced from the pre-dam numbers.

The fish populations in many of our natural waters have declined over the years. Many artificial lakes and ponds have been stocked with game fish. We have discussed the stocking of *farm ponds* with bluegill sunfish, for example. Small lakes have also been made from holes where earth has been removed for building highways. Many of these lakes have been stocked with bass, crappies, bluegills, and other game fish.

Artificial bodies of water may satisfy people who fish. Here, the few species of gamefish have been added with the exclusion of many other species. However, they can never replace rivers, streams, and natural environments for fish and other aquatic life.

Birds Humans have cut forests, cleared underbrush, and burned fields for their own needs. More than 2,000 acres of rural land each day is changed for urban use. In the process, many bird habitats have been destroyed. People unnecessarily have drained marshes and lowered the water in ponds. As a result, water birds and wading birds can no longer find a source of food and nesting sites. The possibility of floods in downstream areas is also increased.

In the past, many thousands of birds were slaughtered for food or feathers. State and federal laws now forbid this type of hunting. However, conservation measures came too late for some species, and birds that were once common are now extinct.

The extinction of the passenger pigeon is a common example. In the early 1800s, the naturalist John Audubon described flocks of passenger pigeons. These flocks were so large that they darkened the sky. For many years these birds were slaughtered in their roosting areas. Then they were gathered in sacks and sold for a few cents, or fed to hogs. An epidemic disease probably killed the last survivors. It never occurred to anyone to conserve this species until it was too late. It is thought that there were over two billion passenger pigeons at one time. The last survivor died in the Cincinnati Zoo in 1914.

In the last chapter some problems in low-density populations were discussed. These are important factors for the endangered bird species. Surviving birds must not only be able to find mates. They often must adapt to new food supplies and new habitats because of changed environments.

Several species are endangered. These species may soon become extinct unless conservation measures to save them are successful.

The ivory-billed woodpecker is one of these species. In fact, it may be extinct even now. The California condor numbers only about 60. There are less than 1,500 American (Southern) bald eagles. Only about 60 Everglades kites remain. Other endangered birds include the prairie chicken, the osprey, the brown pelican, and the whooping crane.

Of course, many plant and animal species have flourished and died out through the ages. Maybe it is normal that some species are becoming extinct today. Yet, it seems so unnecessary, especially if we are partially responsible and if something can be done about it.

Smaller Mammals At one time our lands were rich in small mammals. However, great numbers were killed even before the pioneers started westward. This is particularly true of the valuable fur-bearers. Early trappers set out to make their fortunes in furs. The prize catch was the beaver. It was very plentiful in the Pacific Northwest and Canada. It was known as the "empire builder," and it played a major role in the settlement of this vast wilderness. At one time the pelts of fur-bearing animals brought in more than $100 million a year to early trappers. Among these fur-bearers were beaver, mink, otter, martin, muskrat, fox, and raccoon.

Game laws today are based on ecologically sound conservation practices. A knowledge of the population density and the carrying capacity of the environment for a species is important. Then, controlled trapping or hunting can maintain the population at a level in balance with the environment. Individual animals will be healthier than if they were in an overcrowded situation. Many pelts used by the fur garment industry now come from fur farms and ranches. This reduces the demand for wild animal skins.

Protected areas, such as parks and residential communities have surprisingly large numbers of mammals. Plants serving as shelter and food create a good environment for them. Squirrels, raccoons, opossums, groundhogs, and chipmunks are found here. People often do not know these mammals are around. Many are active at night, but there is evidence of their numbers. They are often found dead on city streets and highways.

Larger Animals A century ago, many thousands of buffalo grazed on the Great Plains. Then came the buffalo hunters. Whole herds were slaughtered. They were killed

52-11 | The California condor, ivory-billed woodpecker, American bald eagle, and the whooping crane are some of our endangered birds. *(top: William Finely; middle top: Allan Cruickhank; middle bottom: National Audobon Society; bottom: George H. Harrison, Grant Heilman)*

for sport and to feed the work crews building the western railroads. At one time there were only a few hundred left. It appeared that the bison might disappear entirely.

White-tailed deer vanished from many of the eastern and central states many years ago. So did the black bear. Other large western mammals began to decline. These included elk, mule deer, and antelope.

Today, due to conservation measures, the situation has improved. White-tailed deer populations are again inhabiting many forest areas of the eastern and central states. Herds of bison, elk, mule deer, and antelope are increasing in the west. The problem now is reversed. How do we limit the large-mammal population? This requires scientific game management. Our hunting limits are based on population densities and the carrying capacity of the environment. Other larger mammals are listed as endangered by the Department of the Interior. These include eight species of whales. Conservation measures are difficult to enforce. They require international cooperation, particularly to reduce illegal trade in endangered species products.

Pollution

One of the biggest problems to all organisms is **pollution.** Pollution is the adding of impurities to the environment. Many of these impurities not only damage the environment, but they actually endanger human health. For centuries humans have put their sewage into streams or lakes. These sewage wastes were all **biodegradable.** That is, they could serve as an energy source for other organisms. However, when the human population density increased in cities, the environment became overloaded. Natural decomposition could not keep up with the waste being placed in the environment. Also, as technology developed, more and more substances were being added to the sewage. Some of these substances could not be broken down by microorganisms. These substances are **nonbiodegradable.**

Increasing technology required more energy. The use of fossil fuels increased. The burning of coal and oil produced substances that polluted the atmosphere. In the attempt to raise more food, chemicals were developed. These chemicals were used to fertilize the soil and to kill insect pests that compete with humans for food. Many of these chemicals were nonbiodegradable and were dispersed throughout the biosphere. Wind and water currents help to spread these substances. They found their way into the ground water and into the soil.

Facts & Figures

In January 1977, the Environmental Protection Agency ruled that all sludge and industrial waste dumping in the Atlantic Ocean must end by December 31, 1981.

52-12 | Is there a better way to dispose of our trash? Recycling may be a solution. *(HRW photo by Alan Mercer)*

Some polluting substances will kill organisms. Some will pass through trophic levels unchanged. They may then build up in a higher-trophic-level organism where they cause damage.

Water Pollution

Many of our streams, lakes, and rivers are polluted. Even the oceans have been polluted. Water pollution is a matter of great national concern. Among the sources of water pollution are industry, domestic sewage, and agriculture.

Industrial Pollution Many industrial plants pour chemical wastes directly into streams. These wastes include toxic compounds, salts, and solvents. Some industrial wastes are biodegradable; some are not. Power plants, steel mills, paper mills, refineries, and automobile factories are examples of industries that have waste disposal problems.

Chemical wastes poison plants and animals. Heavy metals have been a pollution danger brought about by human activities. Lead used in gasoline, for example, is released into the atmosphere where it is washed into the soil. When taken into plants, lead enters the food chain. At each trophic level, the amount of lead is increased.

Lead-base paints are another source of lead pollution. Children have been reported to repeatedly eat lead-base paint off walls because of its sweet taste. Severe retardation often results in these children. Any ingestion or breathing of lead causes poisoning. Today, less lead is being used in batteries. Lead paints are not used widely, and more unleaded gas is being used.

Mercury is another heavy metal that builds up in food chains. Industrial activities such as mining, pulp and paper mills, burning fossil fuels, and manufacturing electrical equipment have increased mercury in aquatic environments. When a fish contaminated by mercury is eaten, ill-

Facts & Figures

Over half the population depends on underground supplies for drinking water.

52-13 | Industrial waste is a major source of pollution in our environment. *(A. Devaney Inc.)*

ness results. Blindness, deafness, and death can be caused by mercury poisoning.

In a recent year, it was thought that the Hudson River and the Great Lakes areas had greatly improved water quality. Then it was discovered that a nonbiodegradable substance called PCB (polychlorinated biphenyl) was at a dangerous level. PCBs are highly toxic chemicals. They are used in the manufacture of paint and electrical equipment. There is no known method for taking them out of the water. Once they get into the food chain, they stay.

Large industries are spending vast amounts of money to fight water pollution. Some plants have been given permits to allow them to dump a certain amount of wastes. In all, 26,000 permits have been issued. Two plants alone have permits to discharge 30 pounds of PCBs into the Hudson River every day. This is still too much. Federal control, however, has caused a lowering of the bacteria and organic wastes that had been pouring into our water. With public support and cooperation, the quality of our water can continue to improve.

Pollution problems are also created by oil and other petroleum products. These products come from refineries, drilling and pumping operations, shipyards, and oil spills. They have destroyed wildlife and made water unfit for use in many areas. Often this oil soaks into the feathers of ducks and other swimming birds. Many of these birds die of exposure or drown when their oil-soaked feathers cause them to lose buoyancy. Oil slicks often wash to the shore. These slicks foul the beaches and kill many of the shore and tide-pool organisms.

Thermal pollution is the addition of heat to a body of water. Power plants and other industries use water to cool their machinery. Then they pipe the returning hot water into a stream or lake. This changes the temperature of the nearby water environment and may kill many of the aquatic plants and animals.

Domestic Pollution Domestic pollution of wastes involves sewage and garbage. Home disposal appliances grind garbage and wash it into sewers. When heavy amounts of organic wastes enter a body of water, the bacteria population increases. Bacterial decomposition of organic matter consumes oxygen. As a result of the lower levels of oxygen, many aquatic organisms may die of suffocation.

In some areas, sewage treatment plants add chemicals to sewage and then allow the solids to settle. The liquid may then be aerated for purification. After treatment, the water can be recycled.

Detergents also add to the pollution problems. This is especially true of detergents containing a large amount of phosphates and nitrates. Phosphates and nitrates may stimulate the growth of algae in streams and lakes. Algal overpopulation upsets the natural balance of aquatic environments. The population may use up most of the nutrients. Then, even the algae die. A serious pollution problem results when these algae decompose at the end of the season. Government regulations now restrict the content of phosphates in detergents.

52-14 | What kind of problem is this pollution from detergents causing? *(Lillian N. Bolstad, © Peter Arnold)*

Water pollution is also a human health hazard. Water polluted with sewage may contain bacteria and viruses. These organisms can cause typhoid, dysentery, hepatitis, cholera, and other infectious diseases. It is difficult to purify polluted water for our use. Because of pollution, many cities obtain their water from distant water supplies.

It is dangerous to eat aquatic and marine animals that come from polluted waters. Cases of typhoid, hepatitis, and other infectious diseases have been traced to this cause. Certain freshwater and saltwater food fish consume and absorb harmful chemicals. These chemicals become concentrated in the fishes' bodies. Such chemicals include mercury compounds and radioactive materials. In some areas people have been warned not to eat striped bass or salmon. Some of these fish contain PCB. This health hazard is particularly serious in areas where local populations depend on fish for their food supply. Many recreational areas have been spoiled by pollution. For example, a few years ago, you could swim in the Great Lakes. Many resort and beach areas have closed because of polluted waters.

Did you ever wonder what happens to your household garbage after it is collected? These solid wastes include such items as food scraps, old newspapers, wood, lawn trimmings, glass, cans, furnace ashes, old appliances, tires, furniture, and many other items too numerous to mention. There are several ways to dispose of these solid wastes. The wastes are dumped several miles out in the ocean. They are burned in open dumps. Solid wastes are also used as landfill. These disposal means lead to additional environmental problems. The oceans, atmosphere, and ground water become contaminated.

Almost everywhere humans go, they leave a trail of wastes. There is litter on the streets, on the beaches, and along the roadsides. Littering is a costly and serious aspect of our solid waste program, but this is one thing *everyone* easily can do something about.

Agricultural Pollution Agricultural pollution mainly has been by the use of chemical poisons. Crops are grown in dense populations. Many plants have been hybridized to produce disease-resistant strains, but the insects readily feed on our crops. In our war on insects, humans have polluted the environment with sprays, dusts, and aerosols. Such chemical poisons are called *insecticides.* Unfortunately valuable insects are destroyed at the same time the harmful ones are killed. Insecticides also soak into the soil and wash into streams with ground water. There they poison fish and other aquatic animals.

Not all, but many, insecticides contain mercury, lead, and other heavy metals. Insect-eating animals absorb these chemicals into their systems. When this happens, these metals remain in the animals' tissues. The concentration builds up from animal to animal in a food chain. This buildup is called *biological magnification.* A top carnivore may have high concentrations of these deadly metals. Many insect-eating animals are undoubtedly poisoned in this manner. They include birds, frogs, and snakes. Several species of predatory fish have been found to contain dangerous concentrations of mercury compounds, PCBs, and other poisons in their tissues. Dieldrin is an insecticide that has been used to spray fields. It also builds up in the food chain. In 1974, this chemical was banned from use in the United States. Recent laws also prohibit the sale of other dangerous insecticides. Yet many companies manufacture these chemicals for sale outside the United States. Heavy use in other countries causes continued environmental contamination and the poisoning of wide-ranging species such as migratory birds.

DDT (dichloro-diphenyl-trichloroethane) was developed at the end of World War II. It was very effective in killing body lice and controlling typhus epidemics in Italy. This insecticide became popular immediately. People used it to kill mosquitoes, household pests, garden pests, and agricultural pests.

DDT has a rapid paralyzing effect on insects. Insects absorb the DDT and it remains in their exoskeletons. DDT breaks down very slowly. So its effects are long lasting. This was once thought to be beneficial, but it is now a cause for great concern. When DDT is sprayed into the atmosphere, it settles on the ground. From there, it washes into streams and is carried to the oceans. Traces of DDT have been found in ocean water as far away as the Antarctic. In an aquatic environment, DDT clings to algae and other aquatic plants. These plants are consumed by herbivorous animals.

DDT concentrations increase from one animal to another in the food chain. They may reach high concentrations in a top-level carnivore.

1 DDT sprayed over
marsh to control
mosquitoes.
(0.00005)

5 Fish-eating birds feed
on the larger fish.
(17.0)

2 Plankton
absorb DDT.
(0.04)

3 Small fish feed
on the plankton.
(.58)

4 Larger fish feed
on the small fish.
(1.70)

52–15 | Biological magnification of DDT as it passes through the food chain. DDT is measured in parts per million.

Birds suffer from the effects of DDT. When DDT concentrations build up, it affects the reproduction system and lime-producing glands. This causes the birds to lay thin-shelled eggs that are easily broken in the nest. This is particularly true of insect-eating and predatory birds. Thin-shelled eggs have been found in the nests of eagles and of the California brown pelican.

Dieldrin and DDT still are used in some parts of the world, but are banned from sale in the United States. As a result, the environmental pollution by these chemicals has gone down. DDT in migratory songbirds has decreased nearly 90 percent since 1969. In the bald eagle, however, this is not true. DDT, dieldrin, other chlorinated hydrocarbons, and PCB levels were about the same in 1974. Perhaps the reason is that bald eagles are a top predator. Also they live longer than songbirds, and they take their prey from highly polluted tidal waters.

Some countries of South America, though, still use large quantities of DDT. Birds, such as the peregrine falcon, migrate from Alaska to South America. Their population is being affected by this chemical.

How do we continue to control insect pests? One natural answer to the insect problem is **biological control.** This is a method of introducing a predator of the pest into the environment. The larvae of the lacewing, for example, feed on aphids and scale insects. Ladybird beetles, both adult and larvae, destroy tremendous numbers of aphids. Praying mantises wait motionless and suddenly grasp harmful

52–16 | Factories such as these are sources of pollution. *(Robert Perron)*

plant-eating insects. In addition to these predatory insects, there are parasitic insects. These insects lay their eggs in the bodies of other living insects. For example, a certain wasp larvae feed on the pupa. By conserving such insects, insects are used to fight insects. Fish, frogs, toads, snakes, and other small animals are also valuable in insect control, as are birds. Yet these animals are being killed with chemical poisons. This is the insecticide dilemma.

Air Pollution

It has been estimated that more than 70 billion tons of airborne wastes are poured into our atmosphere each year. Atmospheric pollution is an enormous problem. It comes from the smokestacks of industry and the chimneys of homes and apartments. It pours from the exhaust of automobiles, incinerators, and jet planes. It is all around us.

When you are in an environment with polluted air, what can be done? You must breathe it. Air pollution causes poor health and discomfort. It also affects the plants and animals that must use the same air. There is no way of knowing how much wildlife has been destroyed by our careless pollution of the atmosphere.

Sources of Air Pollution Some of the pollutants are droplets of liquids or small particles of solid materials. We see them as smoke, dust, or haze. The small particles of solid materials are called the *particulate matter.*

Various gases cause major air pollution problems. Most of them are products of combustion. Of these, *sulfur dioxide* (SO_2), is one of the most deadly. The main source of sulfur dioxide is electric and industrial plants. Their most abundant fuels are coal and oil. These fuels contain sulfur. About 65 percent of the nation's sulfur dioxide is produced in urban areas. Sulfur dioxide is a heavy gas with a choking odor. It combines with water to form sulfuric acid (H_2SO_4). You can see how this would injure the moist surfaces of your lungs when you breathe in air containing sulfur dioxide. Rain also combines with the sulfur dioxide in the atmosphere. These acid rains harm the leaves of plants. The rain washes into the soil, killing many organisms. Over a period of time the plants may die.

Automobile exhausts release another pollutant, nitric oxide (NO). When this combines with oxygen in the air, it forms nitrogen dioxide (NO_2). This is also a deadly gas. It combines with water (or the moisture in your lungs) to form nitric acid (HNO_3). Sunlight speeds up the combination of oxygen with nitric oxide. This is a **photochemical reaction.** Nitrogen dioxide is irritating to the lungs. In high concentrations, it can be fatal. When it combines with water to form nitric acid (HNO_3), it can be damaging to humans as well as to plants and animals.

Carbon monoxide (CO) is a gas that is given off when coal, charcoal, wood, oil, and gasoline do not burn completely. Automobile exhausts are the major source of this air pollutant. More carbon monoxide is released into the atmosphere of a city than any other air pollutant. It combines with the hemoglobin in your blood faster than does oxygen. Then, since it is only slowly released, it causes suffocation.

Smog   *Smog* is just what the name implies. It is a combination of smoke and fog. When you think of air pollution, smog probably comes to mind. The smog in industrial cities is usually a combination of fog and smoke containing sulfur dioxide. This smog often comes from blast furnaces, power plants, and factories.

Another type of smog comes from automobile exhaust pipes. This smog contains nitrogen dioxide, hydrocarbons, carbon monoxide, and other harmful gases. Smog has toxic substances that irritate the eyes and damage the lungs. They also damage plants and animals.

Temperature Inversions and Pollution   Under normal atmospheric conditions, warm air close to the earth rises and cools. Air pollutants rise with it. Then they are dispersed through the upper atmosphere. The air is cleansed

52–17 | Cities with large quantities of pollutants in the atmosphere are often affected by a temperature inversion.

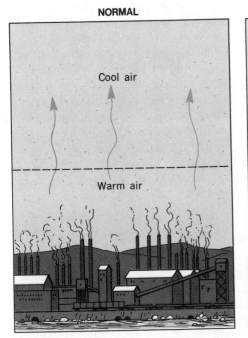

NORMAL

Cool air

Warm air

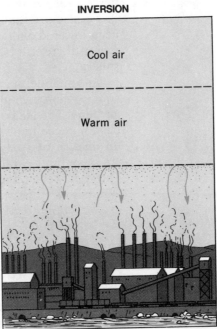

INVERSION

Cool air

Warm air

each time it rains. The rain dissolves gases and they fall to the earth. This is what normally happens.

Once in a while, there is a **temperature inversion.** A layer of cool air moves into an area below a layer of still warm air. The warm air acts as a lid on the atmosphere. It prevents air from rising. Temperature inversions are most common in the fall due to atmospheric conditions.

Temperature inversion can be disastrous in high pollution areas. Harmful gases become trapped in the lower atmosphere. These gases may remain in one place for hours, days, or even weeks. This condition can cause serious illness or even death.

Reducing Air Pollution   It is impossible to eliminate air pollution entirely from an industrial nation such as ours. However, it must be reduced well below the danger point. How? Let's start at home. Do you burn trash in outdoor incinerators or open piles? Indoor incinerators are more efficient. It is even better to have your trash picked up. Do you burn your leaves in the fall? Make a compost pile out of them, or put them in bags for collection.

Industry must do its part also. Industry has been partially responsible for the reduction of air pollutants. Some power plants, for example, are installing antismoke devices to reduce pollution. These include precipitators, cyclones, and filters.

Laws have been passed regarding almost all phases of air pollution. Sulfur dioxide has been lowered to about 75 percent of what it was in 1970. Carbon monoxide has dropped more than 50 percent. Suspended particles have been lowered about 14 percent. Even with these improvements, there still is much to do to clean our polluted atmosphere.

Automobile manufacturers have been forced to reduce compression in engines. This enables cars to burn low-test gasoline. The lead and other products of combustion have been reduced in higher octane gas. Research is being done on smaller internal combustion engines. Also, manufacturers have built catalytic converters into new car mufflers. These, however, appear to be giving off sulfuric acid. Scientists are still studying this problem to see if a danger exists. People are also investigating the possibility of steam or electric power for automobiles. The public also could reduce air pollution further by using their cars wisely.

Pollution by Radiation

Radioactive particles can also pollute the air. These particles are carried great distances by air currents in the atmosphere. They may settle to the earth as **fallout.**

Careers

Environmentalists are people who work with all environmental factors that affect the health and safety of our communities. Some work as generalists and cover all aspects of the environment. Others specialize in just one area, such as air-pollution control or proper sewage disposal.

Environmentalists help enforce health and safety laws as well as conduct health inspections in various locations. A four-year college degree in environmental health is required. A master's degree is also necessary for more specialized jobs.

52–18 | The ever-increasing number of environmental health hazards has created a need for a special profession, the environmentalist. *(Bill Shrout, EPA-Documerica)*

It is not known how long radioactive particles can remain in the upper atmosphere before they return to earth. Certain nuclear explosions in the atmosphere produce *strontium-90*. This radioactive material eventually settles on the earth. It is then taken up from the soil by plants. These plants may then be eaten by animals. If this happens, strontium-90 may be deposited in the flesh, milk, or bones of these animals. Humans may then eat the contaminated animals. As a result of this, strontium-90 is deposited in human bones. Once a certain level of concentration is reached, strontium-90 radiations can destroy tissues, cause cancer, and even cause death.

Radioactive materials have been supervised closely over the last few years. Nations have agreed not to test atomic devices in the atmosphere. If there is atomic warfare in any part of the world, radioactive pollution could be a major disaster.

Radioactivity also enters the biosphere through the piles of material left when we mine uranium. However, disposal of radioactive wastes is a more serious problem. The radioactivity will remain for thousands of years. Radioactive materials can be gathered together and placed in containers. What can be done with them? How long will they remain contained? The answers to these questions have to be answered if we are to continue the use of nuclear energy.

Summary

Wherever organisms live, the environment is affected. The more dense the population, the more there are changes. When people first settled in North America they thought the resources would never end. Now it is known that even many of our renewable resources have been wasted.

Even with present knowledge, the expanding human population has increased the demand for these resources. Dense populations gathered into cities and the development of technology have added effects on our environment.

Knowledge of the past misuse of even the renewable resources, such as food, soil, forests, and wildlife, will help us. Humans have the ability to conserve these resources and use them with more thought of the future. Also, ways of using such a nonrenewable resource as water can change. The availability of water can be increased by careful protection of the watersheds and more thoughtful lumbering and farming practices.

Human growth and the increased use of nonrenewable resources, such as fossil fuels, have caused serious pollution of the biosphere. Countless organisms have been destroyed, including humans.

Realizing that the human is affected by the biotic and physical factors of the environment is important. Yet more important is doing something to increase food production while maintaining a healthy environment for all living things. Industry and legislation have provided money to help solve this dilemma. However, every person needs to take part in restoring the soil, cleaning the water, and purifying the air.

Biologically Speaking

renewable resource	nonbiodegradable
nonrenewable resource	insecticide
crop rotation	biological magnification
erosion	biological control
shelterbelt	photochemical reaction
irrigation	smog
watershed	temperature inversion
pollution	fallout
biodegradable	

Questions for Review

1. How has an increase in human population affected our natural resources?
2. Describe three types of erosion caused by water.
3. Outline several methods of preventing erosion caused by wind.

4. What is a watershed?

5. How can we make more water available for use?

6. Are fuels renewable resources? Explain.

7. Why is fire beneficial to some ecosystems?

8. Explain the purpose of a fish ladder.

9. List eight endangered bird species.

10. List several sources of water pollution.

11. Explain how the decomposition of sewage and other organic materials in water kills fish and other aquatic animals.

12. Describe several far-reaching effects of pollution by DDT, dieldrin, and PCBs.

13. List some toxic gases associated with air pollution.

14. Describe the atmospheric conditions that cause a temperature inversion.

15. In what respect is strontium-90 a hazardous form of radioactive fallout?

---

1. Discuss the combination of contour farming and crop rotation as a conservation measure in a hilly agricultural area.

2. Discuss methods of forest management.

3. Discuss possible reasons some bird species are now endangered while others are maintaining their numbers or even increasing.

4. In what respect are many insecticides a biological dilemma?

5. What special problems are involved in the restoration of populations of the whales?

6. Discuss methods for reducing air pollution.

Applying Concepts

UNIT 8

Activities

1. Identify an ecosystem near your school. Make a list of the biotic community members and the physical factors in the environment. Identify any reactions between and among the biotic and physical factors. On the basis of your observations, can you predict what you might find if you examined the same ecosystem at another time of the year?

2. Read about how solar energy causes winds. Explain how these winds form a general pattern in the atmosphere. Explain the role of winds in forming climate.

3. Identify various kinds of soil. Dig up soil samples from different locations and try to identify each by its composition.

4. Select an area near where you live and identify a food chain. Collect data to construct a pyramid of numbers and a pyramid of mass. Write a report on your study. Explain the difficulties you encountered and why your results may not be accurate.

5. Collect samples of plant life that are characteristic of the biome in which you live. List the ways in which the environment is affected by each.

6. Select some aspect of the human population problem. Use your library to obtain information and write a report on your topic. Suggestions include *Overcrowding: zero population growth; Over-consumption of resources*, and *The energy crisis.*

Related Readings

Books

Garrison, G. A., A. J. Bjugstad, D. A. Duncan, M. E. Lewis, and D. R. Smith, *Vegetation and Environmental Features of Forest and Range Ecosystems*. Forest Service, U.S. Department of Agriculture. U.S. Government Printing Office. July, 1977. A good discussion of the major forest ecosystems, their extent, productivity, and animals associated with each one.

Hahn, James and Lynn, *Recycling: Reusing Our World's Solid Wastes*. Franklin Watts, Inc. NY. 1973. An excellent book concerning the recycling of materials and the economic values of recycling of materials.

Lauwerys, J. A., *Man's Impact on Nature*. Natural History Press, Garden City, NY. 1969. An interesting account of the relationship between people and their environment.

Leen, Nina, *And Then There Were None: America's Vanishing Wildlife*. Holt, Rinehart and Winston, Publishers, NY. 1973. Describes the long list of threatened animals, and tells why they are endangered and what is being done to save them.

Marine, Gene, and Judith Van Allen, *Food Pollution—The Violation of Our Ecology*. Holt, Rinehart and Winston Publishers, NY. 1972. States the problems created by the addition of additives to our food.

Michelsohn, David R., and editors of Science Book Associates, *The Oceans in Tomorrow's World: How Can We Use and Protect Them?* Julian Messner Publishing Co., N.Y. 1972. Explains the use of the oceans as a source of food, minerals, power and living space.

Morgan, Donald P., *Recognition and Management of Pesticide Poisonings*. Second Edition. U.S. Environmental Protection Agency, Office of Pesticide Programs. U.S. Government Printing Office. August, 1977. Presents chemical structures, common uses, and effects of many pesticides. Treatment for exposure to humans is given.

Odum, Eugene P., *Ecology*. Holt, Rinehart and Winston, Publishers, NY. 1971. A complete account of the principles of ecology.

van den Bosch, Robert, and P. S. Messenger, *Biological Control*. Intext Educational Publishers, NY. 1973. An excellent introduction to the principles, methods, and philosophies of biological control.

Articles

"Our Ecological Crisis," *National Geographic*, December 1970. The entire issue is a collection of interesting articles concerned with the problems of our environment.

Bormann, F. Herbert, and Gene E. Likens, "The Nutrient Cycles of an Ecosystem," *Scientific American*, October, 1970. A thorough and well-written description of the nutrient cycles of an ecosystem.

Horn, Henry S., "Forest Succession," *Scientific American*, May, 1975. Explains the principles of how a community of trees comes to replace another.

Palmer, John D., "Biological Clocks of the Tidal Zone," *Scientific American*, February, 1975. An interesting description of the mechanisms that control certain time-related activities of animals of the tidal zone.

Appendix

A Four-Kingdom System for the Classification of Organisms

KINGDOM MONERA

Unicellular and colonial organisms with prokaryotic cells (cells without an organized nucleus). These organisms lack chloroplasts and mitochondria.

PHYLUM SCHIZOPHYTA Mostly parasitic or saprophytic organisms; cells lacking an organized nucleus, with nucleoproteins in contact with cytoplasm; reproduction by fission, certain forms producing endospores: bacteria, Rickettsiae, actinomycetes, spirochetes.

PHYLUM CYANOPHYTA Cells containing chlorophyll and other pigments not localized in plastids; cells lacking an organized nucleus, with nucleoproteins in contact with cytoplasm; reproduction by fission and spores: blue-green algae (*Nostoc, Anabaena, Gloeocapsa, Oscillatoria*).

KINGDOM PROTISTA

Unicellular, colonial, and multicellular organisms with eukaryotic cells (cells with an organized nucleus). Protists lack specialized tissue and include both heterotrophic and autotrophic forms. Some are neither distinctly plant nor distinctly animal.

PHYLUM CHLOROPHYTA Cells containing chlorophyll and other pigments localized in plastids; food stored as starch; cells with organized nucleus; unicellular, colonial, and filamentous forms; motile, free-floating, and sessile: green algae (*Spirogyra, Protococcus, Chlorella*, desmids, *Ulothrix, Oedogonium*).

PHYLUM CHRYSOPHYTA Cells containing chlorophyll and other pigments localized in plastids; cells often yellow-green, golden-brown, or brown in color; food stored as oil and complex carbohydrates; cell walls often containing silicon; unicellular, colonial, and filamentous forms; motile and free-floating: yellow-green algae, diatoms.

PHYLUM PYRROPHYTA Cells containing chlorophyll and other pigments localized in plastids; cells often yellow-green or golden-brown; food stored as starch or oil; unicellular flagellates with two flagella, one lateral and one longitudinal; mostly marine organisms: dinoflagellates, cryptomonads.

PHYLUM PHAEOPHYTA Cells containing chlorophyll usually masked by a brown pigment, localized in plastids; food stored as oil and complex carbohydrates; multicellular; nonmotile; plant body usually large, complex, and sessile; mostly marine organisms living in shallow water: brown algae (*Fucus, Sargassum, Nereocystis, Laminaria, Macrocystis*).

PHYLUM RHODOPHYTA Cells containing chlorophyll usually masked by a red pigment, localized in plastids; food stored as a carbohydrate related to starch; multicellular; nonmotile; plant body complex, usually sessile; mostly marine, deep-water organisms: red algae (*Chrondrus, Gelidium, Polysiphonia*).

PHYLUM EUMYCOPHYTA Organisms lacking chlorophyll; parasitic and saprophytic: true fungi.

CLASS PHYCOMYCETES: Algalike fungi: black molds (*Rhizopus*), water mold (*Saprolegnia*), white "rust," downy mildews.

CLASS ASCOMYCETES: Sac fungi, usually producing eight ascopores in an ascus; many forms producing conidiospores: blue and green molds (*Penicillium, Aspergillus*), morels, yeasts, cup fungi, powdery mildews.

CLASS BASIDIOMYCETES: Basidium (club) fungi: rusts, smuts, mushrooms, puffballs, bracket fungi.

CLASS DEUTEROMYCETES: Imperfect fungi: ringworm fungi, thrush (*Candida*), athlete's foot fungus.

PHYLUM MYXOMYCOPHYTA Amorphous, slimy growths consisting of a naked protoplasmic mass creeping slowly by a flowing, ameboid motion; mostly saprophytes; spores produced in sporangia: slime fungi (slime molds).

PHYLUM SARCODINA Organisms forming pseudopodia; pellicle at cell surface lacking; reproduction principally by fission; fresh-water and marine: ameboid organisms (*Amoeba, Entamoeba, Arcella*), foraminifers, radiolarians.

PHYLUM MASTIGOPHORA Organisms that propel themselves with one or more flagella; pellicle usually present; fission longitudinal: flagellates (*Euglena, Trypanosoma, Volvox, Leishmania*).

PHYLUM CILIOPHORA (CILIATA) Locomotion by means of cilia; pellicle present; many forms with macronucleus and micronucleus: ciliates (*Paramecium, Vorticella, Stentor, Stylonychia*).

PHYLUM SPOROZOA No structures for locomotion; spore-forming; all parasitic: sporozoans (*Plasmodium*).

KINGDOM PLANTAE

Multicellular plants having tissues and organs; cell walls containing cellulose; chlorophyll *a* and *b* present and localized in plastids; food stored as starch; cell walls containing cellulose; sex organs multicellular; autotrophic.

DIVISION BRYOPHYTA Multicellular green plants living on land, usually in moist situations; alternation of generations with the gametophyte the conspicuous generation; vascular tissues lacking; reproduction by spores and gametes.

CLASS HEPATICAE: Gametophyte leafy or thalluslike, usually prostrate: liverworts *(Marcantia, Riccia, Lunularia).*

CLASS ANTHOCEROTAE: Gametophyte thalluslike, sporophyte elongated and cylindrical: hornworts.

CLASS MUSCI: Gametophyte usually an erect leafy shoot, sporophyte inconspicuous and parasitic on the gametophyte: true mosses *(Polytrichium, Sphagnum).*

DIVISION TRACHEOPHYTA Plants with vascular tissues; sporophyte plant body prominent; highly specialized roots, stems, leaves, and reproductive organs in most forms.

Subdivision Psilopsida: Leaves usually absent, if present small and simple; roots absent; mostly fossils (only four living species): *Psilotum, Tmesipteria.*

Subdivision Lycopsida: Leaves simple and usually small, spirally arranged on stem: club mosses *(Lycopodium, Selaginella).*

Subdivision Sphenopsida: Leaves small and simple and arranged in whorls; mostly fossils: horsetails *(Equisetum).*

Subdivision Pteropsida: Leaves usually large and complex; plant body often large.

CLASS FILICINEAE: Sporophyte producing a leafy frond, usually bearing sporangia; rhizome usually creeping; gametophyte plant body a small prothallium: ferns and tree ferns.

CLASS GYMNOSPERMAE: Seeds not enclosed in an ovary; mostly large, woody plants, many evergreens.

Order Cycadales: Primitive fernlike gymnosperms: cycads or sago palms *(Cycas, Dioon, Zamia).*

Order Ginkgoales: Large trees with two kinds of branches, one bearing most of the wedge-shaped leaves in clusters; mostly fossils (one genus and species remaining): *Ginkgo biloba.*

Order Coniferales: Cone-bearing gymnosperms, mostly evergreen; leaves in the form of needles or scales: pines, cedars, spruces, firs, larches, yews.

Order Gnetales: Possible forerunners of the flowering plants; two seed leaves on the embryo; wood containing vessels; mostly fossils (only three remaining genera): *Ephedra, Welwitschia, Gnetum.*

CLASS ANGIOSPERMAE: Flowering plants; seeds enclosed in an ovary that ripens into the fruit.

Subclass Monocotyledonae: Embryo with one cotyledon; fibrovascular tissues scattered through the stem tissues; flower parts in 3's and 6's; leaves parallel-veined: grasses, sedges, lilies, irises, orchids, palms (including about nine orders).

Subclass Dicotyledonae: Embryo with two cotyledons; fibrovascular tissues in a zone around a central pith tissue in the stem; flower parts in 4's or 5's; leaves with netted veins: buttercups, roses, apples, elms (including about 35 orders).

KINGDOM ANIMALIA

Multicellular animals having tissues and, in many, organs and organ systems; pass through embryonic or larval stages in development; heterotrophic.

PHYLUM PORIFERA Body in two cell layers, penetrated by numerous pores; "skeleton" formed by silicious or calcareous spicules or horny spongin; marine and fresh-water animals: sponges.

CLASS CALCISPONGIAE: Simple sponges of shallow waters; calcareous spicules forming "skeleton": ascon and sycon sponges *(Grantia).*

CLASS HYLOSPONGIAE: Deep-water sponges; "skeleton" composed of silicious spicules in open framework: Venus's flower basket.

CLASS DEMOSPONGIAE: Large sponges; often brilliantly colored; "skeleton" of spongin or a combination of spongin and silicious material; fresh-water and marine: bath sponge, finger sponge, crumb-of-bread sponge.

PHYLUM COELENTERATA Usually free-swimming animals with a baglike body of two cell layers with a noncellular substance between them; gastrovascular cavity with one opening leading to the outside; many with tentacles and all with stinging capsules; solitary or colonial forms; marine and fresh-water: hydroids, jellyfish, corals.

CLASS HYDROZOA Solitary or colonial; fresh-water and marine; reproduction by asexual buds and gametes; alternation of generations in many forms: *Hydra, Obelia, Gonionemus, Physalia.*

CLASS SCYPHOZOA: Exclusively marine; most have mesenteries; polyp stage usually absent: *Aurelia, Cyanea.*

CLASS ANTHOZOA: Marine forms; solitary or colonial; without alternation of generations; body cavity with mesenteries; numerous tentacles: sea anemones, corals, sea fans.

PHYLUM CTENOPHORA Marine animals resembling jellyfish; hermaphroditic; definite digestive system with anal pore; biradially symmetrical: comb jellies.

PHYLUM PLATYHELMINTHES Body flat and ribbonlike, without true segments; no body cavity, skeletal, circulatory, or respiratory systems; head provided with sense organs; nervous system composed of two longitudinal nerve cords: flatworms.

CLASS TURBELLARIA: Mostly free-living aquatic or terrestrial forms; many with cilia on the epidermis: *Planaria.*

CLASS TREMATODA: Parasitic forms with mouth at anterior end; intestine present; no cilia on adults: human liver fluke, sheep liver fluke.

CLASS CESTODA: Parasitic forms; body a series of proglottids; intestine lacking; hooked scolex adapted for attachment to intestinal wall of host: tapeworms.

PHYLUM NEMERTEA Body elongated and flattened; long proboscis extending through mouth opening at anterior end; circulatory system present; bilaterally symmetrical; mostly marine: proboscis worms.

PHYLUM NEMATODA Body slender and elongated; unsegmented body wall in three layers; body cavity present; bilaterally symmetrical; free-living and parasitic forms: round-worms (*Ascaris*, *Trichinella*, pinworm, hookworm, vinegar eel).

PHYLUM NEMATOMORPHA Body slender and elongated, resembling a hair; larvae parasitic in insects, adults free-living in fresh water; mouth often lacking in adults: horsehair worms ("horsehair snakes").

PHYLUM ACANTHOCEPHALA Body elongated; digestive tract lacking; anterior proboscis armed with many recurved hooks; parasitic in vertebrates: spiny-headed worms.

PHYLUM ROTIFERA "Wheel animals" with rows of cilia (around the mouth) that beat with a motion suggesting the rotation of a wheel; chitinlike jaws and a well-developed digestive system; body usually cylindrical, ending in a forked grasping foot: rotifers.

PHYLUM BRYOZOA Microscopic organisms forming branching colonies; row of ciliated tentacles at anterior end; usually marine: bryozoans (sea mosses).

PHYLUM BRACHIOPODA Body enclosed in dorsal and ventral shells resembling those of a clam; two spirally coiled arms within shell bearing a row of ciliated tentacles; simple circulatory system; marine animals; mostly fossil forms: brachiopods.

PHYLUM PHORONIDA Wormlike animals; sedentary and tube-dwelling; spirally coiled arm with ciliated tentacles at anterior end; marine: Phoronis.

PHYLUM CHAETOGNATHA Free-swimming, transparent, slender animals resembling arrows; mouth lined with curved bristles; body divided into head, trunk, and tail with finlike projections; marine: arrow worms.

PHYLUM MOLLUSCA Soft-bodied animals without segments or jointed appendages; most forms secrete a valve, or calcareous shell, from a mantle; muscular foot usually present; terrestrial, fresh-water, and marine animals: chitons, clams, snails, octopus.

CLASS AMPHINEURA: Elongated body and reduced head, without tentacles; many forms with a shell composed of eight plates: chiton.

CLASS PELECYPODA: Axe-footed with bivalve shell; gills in mantle cavity; head, eyes, and tentacles lacking: clam, oyster, scallop.

CLASS GASTROPODA: Flat-footed, with or without coiled shell; head, distinct eyes, and tentacles present: snail, slug, whelk.

CLASS SCAPHOPODA: Body elongated and enclosed in a tubular shell, open at both ends; gills lacking; marine animals: tooth shells.

CLASS CEPHALOPODA: Head large; foot modified into grasping tentacles; marine animals: squid, octopus, chambered nautilus, cuttlefish.

PHYLUM ECHINODERMATA Radially symmetrical; spiny exoskeleton composed, in some cases, of calcareous plates; most forms with tube feet for locomotion; marine animals: echinoderms.

CLASS CRINOIDEA: Five branched rays and pinnules; tube feet without suckers; most forms with stalk for attachment; many fossil forms: sea lily.

CLASS ASTEROIDEA: Body usually with five rays and double rows of tube feet in each ray; eyespots: starfish.

CLASS OPHIUROIDEA: Usually with five slender arms or rays: brittle stars.

CLASS ECHINOIDEA: Body spherical, oval, or disk-shaped; rays lacking; tube feet with suckers: sea urchin, sand dollar.

CLASS HOLOTHUROIDEA: Elongated, thickened body with tentacles around the mouth; no rays or spines: sea cucumber.

PHYLUM ANNELIDA Segmented worms with the body cavity separated from the digestive tube; brain dorsal and nerve cord ventral; body wall containing circular and longitudinal muscles: segmented worms.

CLASS POLYCHAETA: Fleshy outgrowths, or parapodia, extending from segments; marine animals: sandworm *(Nereis)*.

CLASS ARCHIANNELIDA: Similar to Polychaeta but without parapodia and with two rows of cilia: *Polygordius.*

CLASS OLIGOCHAETA: Head not well developed; setae on body wall; terrestrial and fresh-water forms: earthworm, *Tubifex*, *Chaetogaster.*

CLASS HIRUDINEA: Body flattened from top to bottom; no setae on body; suckers at both ends; mostly fresh-water forms, but may occur as terrestrial or marine organisms: leeches.

PHYLUM ARTHROPODA Animals with segmented bodies, the segments bearing jointed appendages; chitinous exoskeleton; aerial, terrestrial, and aquatic forms: arthropods.

CLASS CRUSTACEA: Head and thorax joined in a cephalothorax, usually five pairs of legs, two pairs of antennae; mostly aquatic; gills for respiration; many with calcareous deposits in exoskeleton: crayfish, lobster, crab, shrimp, water flea, sowbug, barnacle.

CLASS CHILOPODA: Body flattened and consisting of 15 to 170 or more segments; one pair of legs attached to each segment; maxillipeds developed into poison claws: centipedes.

CLASS DIPLOPODA: Body more or less cylindrical and composed of 25 to 100 or more segments; most segments bearing two pairs of legs: millipedes.

CLASS ARACHNIDA: Head and thorax usually fused into a cephalothorax; antennae lacking; four pairs of legs; book lungs and tracheae for respiration: spiders, scorpions, ticks, mites.

CLASS INSECTA: Head, thorax, and abdomen separate; three pairs of legs; one pair of antennae; usually two pairs of wings; tracheae for respiration: insects. The numbers in parentheses following the order names indicate an approximation of the number of species in that order.

Order Thysanura (700): Wingless; chewing mouthparts; no metamorphosis; primitive insects: silverfish.

Order Ephemeroptera (1,500): Two pairs of membranous wings, the forepair larger than the hindpair; mouthparts nonfunctioning in adults;

metamorphosis incomplete; adults short-lived: Mayfly.

Order Odonata (4,870): Two pairs of strong, membranous wings, the hindpair as large as or larger than the forepair; chewing mouthparts; incomplete Metamorphosis; very large compound eyes; larvae aquatic: dragonflies, damsel flies.

Order Orthoptera (22,500): Two pairs of wings, the outer pair straight and leathery; chewing mouthparts; incomplete metamorphosis: grasshoppers, cockroaches, walking stick, mantis, crickets.

Order Isoptera (1,720): Some forms wingless, others with two pairs of long, narrow wings lying flat on back; chewing mouthparts; incomplete metamorphosis; social insects.

Order Dermaptera (1,100): Two pairs of wings, forewings are short and do not cover the abdomen; chewing mouthparts; incomplete metamorphosis; cerci forming forceplike tail appendages: earwigs.

Order Mallophaga (2,680): Wings absent; chewing mouthparts; incomplete metamorphosis: chicken lice.

Order Anoplura (250): Wingless; piercing and sucking mouthparts; no metamorphosis; external parasites on mammals: human body louse.

Order Hemiptera (23,000): Wingless, or with forewings leathery at the base and folded over the hindwings; piercing and sucking mouthparts; incomplete metamorphosis: true bugs, water bug, water strider, water boatman, back swimmer, bedbug, squash bug, stink bug.

Order Homoptera (32,000): Wingless, or with two pairs of wings held in a sloping position like the sides of a roof; piercing and sucking mouthparts; incomplete metamorphosis: cicada, aphids, leaf hopper, tree hopper, scale insects.

Order Neuroptera (4,670): Four membranous wings of equal size, netted with many veins; chewing mouthparts; complete metamorphosis; larvae of some forms aquatic: dobson fly (hellgrammite), aphis lion, lacewing.

Order Coleoptera (276,000): Four wings, the forepair hard and shell-like, the hindpair folded and membranous; chewing mouthparts; complete metamorphosis: beetles, ladybugs, firefly, boll weevil.

Order Lepidoptera (112,000): Four wings covered with colored scales; mouthparts modified into a coiled, sucking proboscis; complete metamorphosis: butterflies, moths, skippers.

Order Diptera (85,000): Forewings membranous, hindwings reduced to knobbed threads; mouthparts for piercing, rasping, and sucking; complete metamorphosis: housefly, bot fly, blowfly, midge, mosquitoes, crane fly, gall gnat.

Order Siphonaptera (1,100): Wingless; piercing and sucking mouthparts; complete metamorphosis; legs adapted for leaping; external parasites on mammals: fleas.

Order Hymenoptera (103,000): Wingless or with two pairs of membranous wings, the forewings larger; forewings and hindwings hooked together; chewing and sucking mouthparts; complete metamorphosis; many members living in social colonies: bees, ants, wasps, hornets, ichneumon fly.

PHYLUM CHORDATA Notochord present at some time, disappearing early in many forms; paired gills slits temporary or permanent; dorsal nerve cord.

Subphylum Hemichordata: Wormlike chordates; body in three regions with a proboscis, collar, and trunk: acorn worm (tongue worm).

Subphylum Tunicata (Urochordata): Marine animals with saclike body in adult; free-swimming or attached: sea squirts and other tunicates.

Subphylum Cephalochordata: Fishlike animals with a permanent notochord: lancelet (*Amphioxus*).

Subphylum Vertebrata: Chordates in which most of the notochord is replaced by a spinal column composed of vertebrae and encasing the dorsal nerve cord: vertebrates.

CLASS CYCLOSTOMATA (AGNATHA): Fresh-water or marine eellike forms without true jaws, scales, or fins; cartilaginous skeleton: lamprey, hagfish.

CLASS CHONDRICHTHYES (ELASMOBRANCHII): Fishlike forms with true jaws and fins; gills present but not free and opening through gill slits; no air bladder; cartilaginous skeleton: sharks, rays, skates.

CLASS OSTEICHTHYES (PISCES): Fresh-water and marine fishes with gills free and attached to gill arch; one gill opening on each side of body; true jaws and fins; bony skeleton: bony fishes.

Subclass Ganoidei: Mostly extinct forms with armoured body; heterocercal tail; air bladder with duct: amia.

Subclass Teleostomi: Tail rarely heterocercal; air bladder present or absent: trout, eel, perch.

Subclass Dipnoi: Air bladder connected with throat and used as a rudimentary lung: lungfish.

CLASS AMPHIBIA: Fresh-water or terrestrial forms; gills present at some stage; skin slimy and lacking protective outgrowths; limbs without claws; numerous eggs, usually laid in water; metamorphosis: amphibians.

Order Apoda: Wormlike amphibians; tail short or lacking; no limbs or limb girdles: caecilians.

Order Caudata: Body elongated and with a tail throughout life; scales lacking; most forms with two pairs of limbs: salamanders, newts, sirens.

Order Salientia: Body short and tailless in adult stage; two pairs of limbs, the hind limbs adapted for leaping; gills in larval stage, lungs in adult stage: frogs, toads, tree frogs.

CLASS REPTILIA: Terrestrial or semiaquatic vertebrates; breathing by lungs at all stages; body scale-covered; eggs provided with a leathery, protective shell; fertilization internal: reptiles.

Order Testudinata (Chelonia): Body enclosed between two bony shells, covered with scales: turtles.

Order Rhynchocephalia: Skeletal characteristics of the oldest fossil reptiles; lizardlike in form; parietal eye in roof of cranium: tuatara *(Sphenedon)*.

Order Squamata: Body elongated; with or without limbs (vestigial in snakes); body covered with scales: lizards and snakes.

Order Crocodilia: Large, heavy, scaled body; muscular tail; heart approaching four chambers: alligators.

CLASS AVES: Body covered with feathers; forelimbs modified into wings; four-chambered heart: birds.

Order Gaviiformes: Loons: common loon.

Order Pelecaniformes: Tropical birds: white pelican, brown pelican, cormorant.

Order Ciconiiformes: Long-legged wading birds: heron, bittern, ibis, spoonbill, flamingo.

Order Anseriformes: Short-legged gooselike birds: duck, goose, swan.

Order Falconiformes: Large birds of prey: hawk, falcon, eagle, kite, vulture, buzzard, condor.

Order Galliformes: Fowllike birds: pheasant, turkey, quail, partridge, grouse, ptarmigan.

Order Gruiformes: Cranelike birds: crane, coot, gallinule, rail, limpkin.

Order Charadriiformes: Shore birds: snipe, sandpiper, plover, gull, tern, auk, puffin.

Order Columbiformes: Pigeons and doves: mourning dove, white-winged dove.

Order Psittaciformes: Parrots and parrotlike birds: parrots, parakeet, macaws.

Order Cuculiformes: Cuckoos: cuckoo, roadrunner.

Order Strigiformes: Nocturnal birds of prey: owls.

Order Caprimulgiformes: Goatsuckers: whippoorwill, chuck-will's widow, nighthawk.

Order Apodiformes: Swifts: chimney swift, hummingbird.

Order Coraciiformes: Fishing birds: kingfisher.

Order Piciformes: Woodpeckers: woodpecker, sapsucker, flicker.

Order Passeriformes: Perching birds: robin, bluebirds, sparrow, warbler, thrush.

CLASS MAMMALIA: Body covered with hair; warm blooded; four-chambered heart; mammary glands.

Order Monotremata: Egg-laying mammals: duckbilled platypus, spiny anteater.

Order Marsupialia: Pouched mammals: opossum, kangaroo, koala bear.

Order Insectivora: Insect-eating mammals: mole, shrew.

Order Chiroptera: Flying or hand-winged mammals: bat vampire.

Order Edentata: Toothless mammals: armadillo, sloth, great anteater.

Order Rodentia: Gnawing mammals: squirrel, woodchuck, prairie dog, chipmunk, mouse, rat, muskrat.

Order Lagomorpha: Rodentlike mammals: rabbits, hare, pika.

Order Cetacea: Marine mammals: whale, porpoise, dolphin.

Order Sirenia: Aquatic mammals: sea cow.

Order Proboscidea: Trunk-nosed mammals: elephant, fossil mammoth, fossil mastodon.

Order Carnivora: Flesh-eating mammals: bear, raccoon, ring-tailed cat, weasel, mink, otter, skunk, lion.

Order Perissodactyla: Odd-toed hoofed mammals: tapirs, rhinoceroses, horses.

Order Artiodactyla: Even-toed hoofed mammals: hippopotamuses, camels, llamas, deer, giraffes, cattle, sheep, goats.

Order Primates: Erect mammals: monkey, lemur, marmoset, gibbon, orangutan, gorilla, human.

Glossary

A

abdomen   in arthropods, the body region posterior to the thorax; in mammals, the area of the body between the thorax and the pelvis.

abdominal cavity   a body cavity that contains the viscera. It is separated from the thoracic cavity by the diaphragm.

abiotic factors   nonbiologic factors, such as temperature, weather conditions, altitude, water, and light, that affect living things.

aboral surface   the surface opposite the mouth or oral surface in pentaradial animals, e.g., starfish.

abscission layer   the two rows of cells near the base of the leaf petiole that are involved in the natural falling of the leaf.

acoelomates   animals that lack a coelom.

activation energy   the energy that is needed to change potential energy into kinetic energy.

active site   that portion of a molecule at which interactions with other molecules can occur.

active transport   the passage of a substance through a cell membrane requiring the use of energy.

adaptation   the process in which a species slowly or rapidly becomes better suited to survive in an environment.

adaptive radiation   the pattern in which different species develop from a common ancestor.

addiction   the body's dependence on a drug caused by use over a period of time.

adhesion   the force of attraction between unlike molecules; a factor aiding the support of the water column in plants.

ADP (adenosine diphosphate)   a low-energy compound found in cells that performs an important function in energy storage and transfer.

adrenal glands   endocrine glands located at the top of each kidney.

adventitious root   one that develops from the node of a stem or from a leaf.

aerial root   one that is grown by a plant that lives on a tree and absorbs water from dew, rainwater, and damp air.

aerobic   requiring free atmospheric oxygen for normal activity.

air bladder   a thin-walled sac that permits a fish to remain at a particular level in water.

air sac(s)   in humans, thin-walled divisions of the lungs; in insects, the enlarged spaces in which the tracheae end; in birds, cavities extending from the lungs.

airborne infection   infection that is spread from one person to another by means of the respiratory tract.

alcohol psychosis   a form of mental illness caused by drinking excessive amounts of alcohol over an extended period of time.

alcoholic fermentation   the production of ethyl alcohol from carbohydrates.

alcoholism   a disease in which an individual comes to depend on alcohol.

alimentary canal   those organs that compose the food tubes in animals.

allantois   an extraembryonic membrane that aids in respiration and excretion of nitrogenous wastes in birds, reptiles, and some mammals.

allele   one of a pair of genes responsible for contrasting traits.

alternation of generations   a type of life cycle in which an asexual reproductive stage alternates with a sexual reproductive stage.

altricial birds   birds that are helpless when hatched.

alveoli   microscopic sacs, located in the lungs, in which gases are exchanged.

amebocytes   amebalike cells in sponges that function to absorb food and excrete wastes.

amino acids   the basic building blocks of protein molecules.

amniocentesis   a test done during pregnancy to detect genetic defects.

amnion   the innermost fetal membrane which forms the sac that encloses the fetus.

amniote egg   an egg, laid on land by a reptile or bird, having an amnion, other membranes, and a shell.

AMP (adenosine monophosphate)   the lowest energy compound in the building of the higher energy ADP and ATP.

amphetamine   a drug that acts as a stimulant.

amplexus   the clasping of the female frog by the male frog that causes the female to eject her eggs.

anaerobic   deriving energy for life activity from chemical changes which do not involve oxygen.

anaerobic stage of cellular respiration   the first stage of cell respiration; during this stage glucose is broken down into pyruvic acid.

anal fin   a single fin that grows along the midline on the ventral side of a fish.

anal pore   the structure in the paramecium through which undigested particles are released.

analogous structures   those that are similar in function and appearance but not in origin.

anaphase   the phase in mitosis in which the chromatids separate and move to opposite poles of the spindle.

anatomy   the science of the structure of the animal body and the relation of its parts.

angiosperms   a division of seed plants that includes all flowering plants.

annuals   plants that live for one season only.

antennae   organs of touch, taste, and smell in insects and certain other animals.

antennules   the anterior pair of appendages in the crayfish and other arthropods.

anther   the part of the stamen that bears pollen grains.

antheridium   a sperm-producing structure found in some plants.

anthocyanin   a pigment that causes red color in plants.

anthropology   the study of all primates, fossil evidence of prehistoric human cultures, and all present human cultures.

antibiotics   germ-killing substances produced by a bacterium, mold, or other fungus.

antibodies   immune substances in the blood and body fluids.

antigens   substances, usually proteins, that stimulate the formation of antibodies in the body.

antitoxin   a substance in the blood that counteracts a specific toxin.

aorta   the large artery that leads from the heart to the rest of the body.

aortic arches   structures in the earthworm that keep blood flowing through the body.

apical cell   the terminal, or tip, cell of a growing plant.

appendage   an outgrowth of the body, such as a leg, a fin, or an antenna.

appendicular skeleton   those portions of the skeleton that form the limbs in vertebrates.

arterioles   tiny arteries eventually branching into capillaries that carry blood away from the heart.

artery   a large muscular vessel that carries blood away from the heart.

artificial resuscitation   an emergency process of forcing air into and out of the lungs.

ascospores   spores produced in a saclike structure called the ascus in Ascomycetes.

asexual reproduction   reproduction without the joining together of two cells.

aster   the fibrils that form from the centriole during cell division.

astral rays   protein fibers that form around each centriole during prophase.

atom   the smallest unit of an element.

atomic mass   the total number of protons and neutrons in an atom.

atomic number   the number of protons in the nucleus of an atom.

ATP (adenosine triphosphate)   a high-energy compound found in cells that performs an important function in energy storage and transfer.

atrium   a thin-walled upper chamber of the heart that receives blood from the veins.

auditory nerve   the nerve leading from the inner ear to the brain.

autonomic nervous system   a division of the nervous system that involuntarily regulates the internal organs.

autosome   any paired chromosome other than the sex chromosomes.

autotroph   an organism capable of organizing organic molecules from inorganic molecules.

auxin   a plant hormone that regulates growth.

axial skeleton   the backbone and the skull, in vertebrates.

axon   a fiber that carries impulses away from a nerve cell body.

B

bacillus   a rod-shaped bacterium.

bacteria   a group of microscopic, one-celled prokaryotic organisms.

bacteriophage   one of several kinds of viruses that can destroy bacteria.

barbiturate   a drug that acts as a tranquilizer.

barrier   anything that prevents the spread of organisms to a new environment.

basal disk   a structure in hydras which secretes a sticky substance that permits attachment to rocks or water plants.

basidia   club-shaped hyphae found in the club fungus which bears the spores.

basidiospore   a spore produced by basidia.

benthic zone   the bottom part of the marine biome.

biennials   plants that live two seasons.

bile   a brownish-green fluid secreted by the liver.

binary fission   a form of asexual reproduction in which one cell splits into two cells of equal size.

binomial nomenclature   the system of naming in which each organism is given a two-word name.

biogenesis   the biological principle that life arises from life.

biological control   a method of introducing predators into an environment in order to control insect pests.

biological magnification   the buildup in concentration of a substance as it moves from animal to animal in a food chain.

biology the science that deals with the phenomena of life and living organisms in general.

biome a large, geographical region identified by its climax vegetation.

biosphere the thin layer where life exists on earth.

biosynthesis the building of organic molecules by living organisms.

biotic community a naturally occurring group of animals and plants living together in the same environment.

biotic factors biological factors such as viruses and bacteria that affect living things.

biotic potential the number of offspring of a species that would exist if all offspring survived and produced young.

bivalve a mollusk possessing two shells that are hinged together.

blastopore a cavity that forms in a blastula.

blastula an early stage in the development of an embryo in which cells have divided to form a hollow sphere.

blood the fluid that circulates through the heart, arteries, capillaries, and veins, carrying nutrients and oxygen to body cells.

bond energy the energy needed to break a chemical bond.

brain stem an enlargement at the base of the brain where it connects with the spinal cord.

breathing the movement of air into and out of the lungs.

bronchioles small subdivisions of the bronchial tubes within a lung.

bronchus any of the larger air passages of the lungs.

bud an undeveloped shoot of a plant; developing offspring forming at the bases of some coelenterates.

bud scale a small, modified leaf that protects the inside of the bud.

budding a form of asexual reproduction in hydra and yeast.

bulb an underground stem composed of a short, central stem and bud surrounded by layers of thick, fleshy leaves.

bundle scar a tiny bump or dark dot which marks the place where the vascular bundles entered the petiole.

bundle sheath a collection of small- and medium-sized veins in a leaf.

C

calorie (food) used to measure food energy, the amount of heat needed to raise the temperature of one kilogram of water one centigrade degree.

calyx the sepals of a flower.

cambium a ring of cells beneath the bark of woody plants.

capillarity a force causing water to move upward through a small tube.

capillary a small, thin-walled vessel through which exchanges occur between blood and tissue fluid.

capillary water the water held in the small spaces around soil particles.

capsule a thick slime layer surrounding some bacteria; the spore case of mosses.

carapace the hard covering on the back of an animal, such as a crab, lobster, or turtle.

carbohydrate an organic compound made of carbon, hydrogen, and oxygen.

cardiac muscle the muscle that makes up the heart wall.

carnivore a meat-eating animal.

carotene an orange pigment found in chloroplasts.

carrying capacity the number of individuals an environment can support.

cartilage a pliable supporting tissue in vertebrates.

catalyst a substance that accelerates a chemical reaction without being altered chemically itself.

caudal fin a structure that forms a fish's tail.

cell the basic structural and functional unit of life.

cell specialization the differentiation of cells where each is suited for a different activity.

cell wall the outer, nonliving cellulose structure around plant cells.

cellular respiration all of the chemical reactions that release energy for the support of cell life.

cellulose a carbohydrate that forms the skeleton of plant cells.

central nervous system the brain, spinal cord, and the nerves that arise from each.

centriole a cytoplasmic body located just outside the cell nucleus.

centromere a single cell body to which a pair of chromatids attach following replication.

centrosome a small oval area of cytoplasm appearing outside the nuclear membrane.

cephalization the concentration of receptors and nerves at the anterior end of an organism.

cephalothorax a body region in certain animals consisting of a joined head and thorax.

cerebellum the region of the brain concerned with balance and muscular coordination.

cerebrum the largest region of the human brain, the seat of emotions, intelligence, and voluntary nervous activity.

chalaza a band of albumin extending from

either end of the yolk of a bird's egg to the shell.

chelicerae the first appendages of the spider, serving as poison fangs.

cheliped a claw foot in crayfish and other arthropods.

chemical change a change in which matter is altered from one substance to another.

chemical elements the basic building blocks that combine in many different ways to form all living and nonliving matter.

chemistry the science of the composition of matter and how it can change.

chemosynthesis the synthesis of carbohydrates from carbon dioxide and water as a result of energy derived from chemical reactions, rather than from absorbed light.

chemotherapy a form of therapy in which specific chemical compounds destroy pathogenic organisms without harming the host.

chlorenchyma plant cells that contain chlorophyll.

chlorophyll the green pigment in plants without which photosynthesis could not occur.

chloroplast a cell plastid containing chlorophyll.

choanocytes flagellated cells of the sponge.

chordate an animal having a notochord, nerve cord, and gill slits at some time in its development.

chorion a membrane that attaches to the uterine wall, in mammals; in birds and reptiles it lines the inside of the shell.

chromatid a strand of replicated DNA material formed during prophase.

chromatin a complex of nucleic acids and proteins found in the nucleus.

chromatophores pigment-containing structures in the skins of fishes, frogs, and other animals.

chromosome a rod-shaped structure located in the cell nucleus, which contains the genes for inherited traits of future generations of cells.

chromosome mutation a change occurring in an organism's genetic material.

chrysalis the hard covering of the pupa of a butterfly.

cilia tiny, hairlike projections of cytoplasm.

circulation the movement of nutritive fluids, waste materials, and water through the body.

cirrhosis a disease of the liver, which can be caused by excessive use of alcohol over an extended period of time.

citric acid cycle a series of reactions that occur in the mitochondria of a cell during the aerobic stage of cellular respiration.

class a taxonomic category subordinate to a phylum and superior to an order.

climax species a group of plants which dominate a region.

climbing root a root that clings to a tree or wall.

clitellum a structure on the earthworm which swells during the reproductive cycle.

cloaca a chamber in certain vertebrates at the end of the digestive, urinary, and/or reproductive systems through which substances pass out of the organism.

cloning a method of asexual reproduction in which a single cell can be placed in a nutrient and eventually develop into a complete identical organism.

closed circulatory system a circulation system in which the blood stays within specific vessels and does not bathe the organs directly.

coccus a sphere-shaped bacterium.

cocoon a strong casing of silk which covers moth larvae.

codon one or more groups of base triplets of messenger RNA that code for a specific amino acid.

coelom a fluid-filled cavity that contains digestive organs.

coelomates animals that have a coelom.

coenzymes nonprotein molecules that work with enzymes in catalyzing reactions.

cohesion attraction between like molecules; a factor in the movement of water up a plant stem.

coleoptile the first leaf of a monocotyledon which forms a protective sheath around the plumule.

collar cells see choanocytes.

colloid a gelatinous substance, in which solids are dispersed.

colon the large intestine.

color blindness an inability to distinguish certain colors; a sex-linked genetic trait.

commensalism an association in which one partner benefits and the other is not harmed.

companion cells small cells that lie alongside the sieve tubes in phloem tissue.

compound a substance in which two or more elements are combined chemically.

compound eye an eye composed of numerous lenses.

compound microscope a microscope that has more than one lens.

conditioned reaction a form of learned behavior in which a specific behavior response always follows a particular stimulus.

conidia a type of spore produced by certain molds.

conidiophore   the branch of a fungus that produces conidia.

coniferous forest   a biome that is characterized by evergreen trees.

conjugation   a primitive form of sexual reproduction in which the contents of two cells unite; an exchange of nuclear substance in the paramecium.

connective tissue   tissue that binds together and supports other structures.

conservation   the preservation of natural resources.

contact infection   infection that spreads from one person to another through physical contact.

contractile vacuoles   organelles found in one-celled organisms which help to keep a healthy water balance within the cell.

control   a standard against which experimental observation may be evaluated.

convergent evolution   the pattern in which organisms with different ancestors become more alike because they share the same environment.

cork   tissue, formed by the cork cambium, that has a protective function.

cork cambium   a layer of cells in the outer bark of a woody stem that produces cork tissue.

corm   a shortened underground stem in which the leaves are reduced to thin scales.

corolla   the petals of a flower.

coronary circulation   movement of blood within the coronary vessels of the heart.

corpus luteum   the ruptured follicle after the ovum has been discharged.

cortex   in roots and stems, a storage tissue; in organs such as the kidney and brain, the outer region.

cotyledon   a food reservoir present in the embryo of a plant.

covalent bond   the sharing of electrons at the highest energy level.

cranial cavity   a cavity, in the skull, that encloses the brain.

cranial nerves   in vertebrates, the 10 or 12 pairs of nerves that extend from the brain.

cristae   membranous in-folded structures located on the inner membranes of mitochondria.

crop   a food-storing organ of the alimentary canal in earthworms, birds, and other animals.

crop rotation   the practice of planting different crops each year on the same piece of land.

crossing over   the exchange of segments of chromosomes that occurs when the two chromosomes are in synapse.

cuticle   a thin, waxy film that covers the epidermis of a leaf; the outer covering that protects a parasite from being digested by its host's intestines.

cuttings   pieces of a plant used in vegetative propagation.

cyst   a resting stage of a less complex animal, enclosed by a protective wall.

cytokinins   plant hormones that influence cell division.

cytolysis   the swelling and bursting of cells when put in a hypotonic solution.

cytoplasm   the protoplasm of a cell excluding the nucleus.

D

dark reactions   those reactions in photosynthesis during which light is not required.

daughter cell   a newly formed cell resulting from the division of a previously existing cell, the mother cell, or parent cell.

deciduous   woody plants that shed their leaves seasonally.

deciduous forest   a biome characterized by oak, elm, and maple trees, which lose their leaves in winter.

decomposers   bacteria and yeasts that break down the tissues and excretions of other organisms.

dehydration synthesis   the formation of more complex compounds by the removal of one molecule of water.

dendrite   a nerve process that carries impulses toward a nerve cell body.

denitrification   the process in which bacteria break down ammonia, nitrites, and nitrates, liberating free nitrogen.

depressant   a drug that has an anesthetic effect on the nervous system.

dermis   the layer of tissue that lies under the epidermis.

desert   a geographical area that has less than 10 inches of rainfall each year.

development   the process in which a zygote grows into a complete multicellular organism.

diaphragm   a muscle that separates the abdominal and thoracic cavities in mammals and is involved in the process of breathing.

diastole   the second phase of the complete cycle of heart activity in which the ventricles of the heart relax and receive blood from the atria.

diatomic molecules   molecules that are made of two atoms of the same element.

dicot   a seed plant with two seed leaves, or cotyledons.

diffusion the movement of molecules from an area of greater concentration to one of lesser concentration.

diffusion pressure the force that results from differences in molecular concentration, temperature, and pressure and thereby affects diffusion.

digestion the process in which foods are broken down into small, water-soluble molecules.

dihybrid cross a cross that involves parents differing in two pairs of traits.

dipeptide two amino acids held together by a peptide bond.

diploid a condition in which there is a double set of homologous chromosomes.

disaccharide a sugar formed by the union of two simple sugars.

dissociation the splitting of ion pairs, such as the dissolving of salt in water.

DNA (deoxyribonucleic acid) a molecule consisting of alternating units of nucleotides in the shape of a double helix.

dominance a principle, observed by Mendel, that one gene may prevent the expression of another gene in an allele.

dormancy a period of inactivity.

dorsal surface the upper surface of an animal.

Down's syndrome a condition associated with chromosomal abnormality, usually trisomy of chromosome 21.

droplet infection an infection that is spread from one person to another through the discharge of thousands of tiny droplets into the air.

drug any chemical substance that alters either the mind or the body.

E

ecology the study of the relationships of living things to their surroundings and to one another.

ecosystem a unit of the biosphere in which living and nonliving things interact.

ectoderm the outer layer of cells of a simple animal body; in vertebrates, the layer of cells from which the skin and nervous system develop.

ectoplasm a clear, watery substance found outside the cell membrane.

egg a female reproductive cell.

electron microscope a microscope that uses a stream of electrons to magnify the image.

elongation region the area behind the embryonic region of a root or stem in which cells grow in length.

embryo an early stage in a developing organism.

embryonic membrane one of the delicate coverings in an amniote egg.

endocrine glands ductless glands that secrete hormones directly into the bloodstream.

endocytosis the passage of large molecules and particles through the plasma membrane into the cell.

endoderm the inner layer of cells of a simple animal; in vertebrates, the layer of cells from which the linings of the digestive system, liver, lungs, and other internal organs develop.

endodermis a single layer of cells located at the inner boundary of the cortex of a plant root.

endoplasm the inner portion of cytoplasm.

endoplasmic reticulum a network of folded membranes in the cytoplasm of a cell.

endoskeleton internal framework of bones and/or cartilage.

endosperm in some seeds, the tissue that contains stored food.

endosperm nucleus the body formed by the fusion of a sperm with the polar nuclei during double fertilization.

endospore a resting stage of some types of bacteria that is resistant to adverse environmental conditions.

endotoxins poisons produced by certain bacteria that are released when the bacterial cells are destroyed or die.

energy the capacity to do work or cause change.

energy levels the different distances from a nucleus at which electrons constantly move in an atom.

entomology the study of insects.

environment outside forces of all types that act upon an organism.

enzyme a protein that acts as a catalyst.

enzyme-substrate complex a temporary combination of an enzyme with its substrate which allows a reaction to proceed rapidly.

epicotyl in a seed, the part of the plant embryo that lies above the attachment of the cotyledons and from which the stem and leaves develop.

epidermal hair an outgrowth of epidermal cells that gives a leaf surface a velvety, fuzzy, or woolly nature.

epidermal tissue the covering layer on the surfaces of roots, stems, and leaves.

epidermis in plants, the outer tissue of a young root, stem, or leaf.

epiglottis a flap of cartilage located at the upper end of the trachea.

epithelial tissue   a type of tissue that covers the body organs and the body surface.

erosion   the loss of surface material by the action of water and wind.

erythrocytes   red blood cells.

esophagus   the food tube, or gullet, that connects the mouth and the stomach.

estivation   a period of summer inactivity in certain animals.

estrogen   a female hormone secreted by the ovaries.

estuary   a zone between the fresh water and marine biome.

eukaryote   a cell that contains a nucleus.

Eustachian tube   a canal that connects the pharynx with the middle ear.

evolution   the process of slow change by which organisms have acquired their distinguishing characteristics.

excretion   the process in which metabolic wastes are removed from living cells or from the body.

excurrent pore   a hole in the sponge through which water is forced out.

excurrent siphon   the structure in a mollusk through which water passes out of the body.

exobiology   a field of biology that explores the possibility of life in the universe other than Earth.

exocytosis   the passage of large molecules through a plasma membrane to an area outside the cell.

exoskeleton   a hard external skeleton.

exotoxin   a soluble toxin excreted by bacteria and absorbed by the tissue of the host.

experimental factor   the single condition to be tested in an experiment.

expiration   the discharge of air from the lungs.

external respiration   the exchange of gases between the atmosphere and the blood.

extraembryonic membrane   a membrane that functions during reptile, bird, and mammal development, but does not become part of the embryo.

eyespot   the sensory structure in euglenas and planarians that is sensitive to light.

F
_____

facultative bacteria   bacteria that can live in either anaerobic or aerobic conditions.

Fallopian tubes   oviducts.

fallout   radioactive particles which pollute the air.

family   a taxonomic subdivision subordinate to an order.

fatty acids   chains of carbon atoms and hydrogen atoms which are insoluble in water.

feces   masses of undigested food bulk that pass out of the body through the anus.

fermentation   an anaerobic glucose oxidation that forms lactic acid or alcohol.

fertilization   the union of two gametes.

fetus   a mammalian embryo after the main body features appear.

fibrous root   secondary root that grows from the primary root and spreads out widely.

fibrovascular bundle   a strand containing xylem and phloem.

filterable viruses   viruses capable of passing through pores through which bacteria cannot pass.

fission   the simplest form of asexual reproduction, in which one organism splits into two or more organisms.

flagella   tails, or whiplike strands, used by bacteria for movement.

flower   the portion of the plant that specializes in sexual reproduction.

follicle   a mass of ovarian cells that produces an ovum; an indentation in the skin from which hair grows.

food   any substance taken into an organism for work, repair, and maintenance of life processes.

food chain   the transfer of energy when one living thing consumes another.

food consumers   heterotrophs of the ecosystem.

food producers   the autotrophs of the ecosystem.

food pyramid   a quantitative representation of a food chain, with the food producers forming the base and the carnivores at the apex.

food web   a complex system of food chains existing within an ecosystem.

formula   a symbol that represents a compound.

fossil   the remains of an organism that lived in the past.

fragmentation   an asexual form of reproduction in which pieces of an organism break off and regenerate into a new organism.

fraternal twins   individuals that develop at the same time from two different eggs, each fertilized by a different sperm.

fronds   the leaves of a fern.

fructose   a simple sugar made by green plant cells.

fruit   the portion of the flower that contains the seeds.

FSH (follicle-stimulating hormone)   a hormone secreted by the anterior pituitary gland and which stimulates the growth and maturation of the ovum.

G _____

gall bladder   a sac in which bile is stored and concentrated.

gamete·   a male or female reproductive cell.

gametophyte   the stage of a plant in the alternation of generations that produces gametes.

gastric caeca   pouchlike extensions from the midgut of a grasshopper.

gastric fluid   a secretion of the stomach.

gastritis   a painful swelling of the stomach lining.

gastrodermis   the inner layer of cells in coelenterates.

gastrovascular cavity   the central cavity in coelenterates.

gastrula   that stage in embryo development during which the primary germ layer forms.

gemmae   tiny flat structures found at the surface of the gametophyte of liverworts.

gemmule   a coated cell mass produced by the parent sponge and capable of developing into another sponge.

gene   the basic unit of heredity; that portion of a DNA molecule that through replication and mutation, passes a trait from one generation to another.

gene frequency   the extent to which a gene occurs in a population.

gene linkage   the assemblage of genes in a linear arrangement on a chromosome.

gene mutation   a mutation that arises when the code of a DNA molecule is changed.

gene pool   all the genes present in a given population.

generative nucleus   one of the two nuclei present in a pollen cell.

genetic code   the sequential arrangement of a DNA molecule's bases that controls traits in an organism.

genetic drift   the increase or decrease of a certain trait in succeeding generations of a population due to chance.

genetic engineering   a method for introducing new genes into an organism.

genetic equilibrium   a condition in which the gene pool is not evolving.

genetics   the science of heredity.

genotype   the genetic makeup of an organism.

genus   a taxonomic category subordinant to a family.

geotropism   the growth response of plants to gravity.

germ mutations   mutations that occur in reproductive cells and may be passed on to offspring.

germination   the growth of a seed when favorable conditions occur.

gestation period   a period of uterine development, called pregnancy, in mammals.

gibberellins   growth-regulating substances that promote cell elongation in plants.

gills   organs that absorb dissolved oxygen from the water.

girdling   cutting the phloem all the way around a tree, which causes the death of the tree.

gizzard   an organ that grinds food in the digestive system of earthworms and birds.

glottis   the upper opening of the trachea in land vertebrates.

glucose   a simple sugar made by green plants; it provides fuel for both plants and animals.

glycerol   a fundamental building block of fats.

glycogen   a complex carbohydrate that is stored in an animal's liver and can be reconverted to glucose when additional fuel is needed.

Golgi apparatus   a cell organelle that prepares protein secretions of a cell.

grafting   the union of the cambium layers of two woody stems, one of the stock and the other of the scion.

grasslands   an area in which yearly rainfall is between 10 and 30 inches.

green glands   excretory organs in crayfish and other crustaceans.

guard cells   modified epidermis cells located around stomata.

gullet   the passageway to a food vacuole in paramecia; the food tube or esophagus in more complex animals.

gymnosperms   a division of seed plants that includes cycads, gingkos, and conifers.

H _____

habitat   the place in which an organism lives.

half-life   the time it takes half a radioactive isotope to reach its stable form.

hallucinogens   chemical compounds that affect the mind and sensory perceptions.

haploid   a condition in which there is one chromosome of each homologous pair.

hard palate   the bony roof of the mouth.

Haversian canals   numerous channels penetrating the layers of a bone.

hemoglobin   a protein substance in red corpuscles that contains iron.

hemophilia   a sex-linked trait that produces a condition in which a person's blood does not clot properly.

hemotoxin   a poison that destroys red blood cells and breaks down the walls of small blood vessels.

herbaceous stem   an annual stem with little woody tissue.

herbivores   animals that feed on plants.

heredity   the transmission of traits from parents to offspring.

hermaphroditic   having the organs of both sexes.

heroin   an opiate that has an addictive property.

heterogametes   male and female gametes that are different in appearance and structure.

heterotroph   an organism that is unable to synthesize organic food molecules from inorganic molecules.

heterozygous   refers to an organism in which the paired genes for a specific trait are not identical.

hibernation   a period of winter inactivity in certain animals.

hilum   an oval scar on a seed where it was attached to the pod wall.

holdfast cells   special cells at the bases of algae which anchor them to a substrate.

homeostasis   the self-regulating and self-maintaining system of internal stability of an organism.

homologous chromosomes   chromosomes having similar and paired genes.

homologous organs   organs or body parts that are similar in structure and origin but have different uses in different species.

homozygous   refers to an organism in which the paired genes for a specific trait are identical.

hormone   the chemical secretion of an endocrine gland, which produces a physiologic reaction.

host   in a parasitic relationship, the organism from which the parasite derives its food supply.

humus   decaying organic matter of soil.

hybrid   the offspring of parents differing in one or more traits.

hybrid vigor   the desirable qualities, such as increased size, that hybrids often possess.

hybridization   a form of controlled breeding, opposite to inbreeding, in which two different but related strains of plants or animals are crossed and yield a new, or hybrid, strain.

hydrolysis   the chemical breakdown of a substance by combination with water.

hyperthyroidism   a condition caused by an overactive thyroid gland.

hypertonic solution   a solution of a higher concentration of solutes and a lower concentration of water molecules than another solution.

hyphae   threadlike filaments found in fungi.

hypocotyledon   the lower end of the plant embryo from which the root develops.

hypothalamus   a gland located at the base of the brain which interacts with the pituitary gland.

hypothesis   a working explanation or trial answer to a question.

hypothyroidism   a condition caused by an underactive thyroid gland.

hypotonic solution   one that contains a lower concentration of solutes and a higher concentration of water molecules than another solution.

---

identical twins   genetically similar people who develop from a single fertilized egg.

immunity   the ability of the body to resist disease by natural or artificial means.

inbreeding   the mating of plants or animals that have similar genetic makeups.

incomplete dominance   a blend of two differing traits.

incubation   the warming of an egg so that it can mature to hatching.

incurrent pore   a hole in a sponge through which water passes.

incurrent siphon   the structure in a mollusk through which water passes into the body.

independent assortment   a law based on Mendel's hypothesis that the separation of gene pairs on a given pair of chromosomes is entirely independent of the distribution of other gene pairs on other pairs of chromosomes.

initiator codon   a base that marks the point where a protein chain will begin to form.

innate behavior   behavior that is present from birth; not learned.

inorganic compounds   compounds that do not contain the element carbon.

insecticide   a chemical used to kill insects.

insectivorous plants   plants that have leaves adapted to capture and digest insects.

insertion   the attachment of a muscle at its moving point.

inspiration   the taking of air into the lungs.

instinct   unlearned, involuntary actions animals make without deliberate decision.

insulin   a substance, secreted by the pancreas, that regulates the uptake of glucose from the blood into the cells.

intelligent behavior   a complex nervous activity that involves problem-solving, judgment, and decision-making.

interdependence the dependence of cells on other cells, or of organisms upon other organisms, for complete functioning.

interferon a cellular chemical defense against a virus.

internal fertilization a feature of sexual reproduction in which sperm cells are transported into the oviducts of the female.

internal respiration the exchange of gases between the blood or tissue fluid and the cells themselves.

interphase the period of growth of a cell that occurs between cell divisions.

intertidal zone the shore area of an ocean that is exposed at low tide and covered at high tide.

intestine an organ in which food is digested and absorbed by the bloodstream.

invertebrate an animal without a backbone.

involuntary muscle one that cannot be controlled at will; smooth muscle.

ion an atom that carries a positive or negative electric charge.

ionic bond a bond formed by the transfer of one or more electrons from one atom to another.

ionic compound a compound formed by ionic bonds.

irritability an organism's ability to respond to a stimulus.

islets of Langerhans specialized groups of cells in the pancreas that secrete insulin.

isogametes gametes that are similar in size, form, and ability to move.

isolation the confinement of a population to a certain region, due to physical barriers.

isotonic solution a solution that contains an equal concentration of solutes and of water molecules as another solution.

isotopes different forms of the same element caused by differences in the number of neutrons.

J

Jacobson's organs tiny pits in a snake's mouth that contain nerve endings that are very sensitive to odor.

joint the area where two bones meet.

K

kidney an organ of excretion in vertebrates that filters wastes from the body and forms urine.

kinetic energy energy that is doing work or causing changes.

kingdom the division of living organisms on which the system of classification is based.

Klinefelter's syndrome a condition associated with an abnormality of the sex chromosomes.

L

labium the lower mouthpart of an insect.

labrum the two-lobed upper mouthpart of an insect.

large intestine an organ of the digestive system that begins at the small intestine and ends at the rectum.

larva an immature stage in the life of an animal.

larynx the voice box.

lateral bud a tiny bud, located immediately above each leaf scar, that contains embryonic structures which emerge in the spring.

lateral line a line of sensory cells along each side of a fish.

layering a method of artificial vegetative propagation.

leaf the portion of a plant that is usually the chief organ of photosynthesis.

leaf scar a mark on a twig that indicates the attachment of a leaf stalk in a previous season.

leucocytes white blood cells.

LH (luteinizing hormone) a hormone of the anterior pituitary which acts with FSH to cause ovulation of the mature follicles and secretion of estrogen; also concerned with corpus luteum formation.

ligament a tough strand of connective tissue which holds a joint in position.

light reactions those reactions in photosynthesis during which light is required.

limiting factors the materials an organism needs for growth and reproduction that determine where an organism can live and how well it can adapt to environmental change.

lipids fatty substances made of carbon, hydrogen, and oxygen.

liver a large organ that secretes bile; located in the upper right area of the abdomen.

loam a type of rich soil valuable for growing crops.

lymph the clear, liquid part of blood which enters the tissue spaces and lymph nodes.

lysis dissolution or destruction.

lysosome in a cell, a rounded organelle that contains digestive enzymes.

lytic cycle the stage of a virulent phage resulting in destruction of a bacterial cell.

M

magnification the extent to which a microscope enlarges an image.

Malpighian tubules a series of tubes that collect wastes in the grasshopper; small ducts in the kidney of vertebrates.

mammary glands glands in female mammals that secrete milk.

mandibles arthropod jaws that crush and chew food.

mantle a covering of the visceral hump in mollusks.

mantle cavity a space formed by the mantle hanging down over the sides and back of the mollusk body.

marsupial a pouched mammal.

mass selection the selection of ideal plants or animals from a large number of individuals to serve as parents for further breeding.

matter the material from which everything living and nonliving is made.

maturation region the area of a root or stem where embryonic cells differentiate into tissues.

maxilla a mouthpart of an arthropod; the upper jaw of vertebrates.

maxilliped in crayfish and other arthropods, appendages that hold food while it is being chewed.

medulla oblongata the region of the brain that controls the activities of the internal organs.

megaspores four cells formed in the plant ovary, three of which disintegrate and one of which develops into the embryo sac.

meiosis a type of cell division in which the number of chromosomes in the daughter cell is reduced to half the number in the parent cell.

meninges three membranes that cover the brain and spinal cord.

menstruation the breakdown and discharge of the uterine tissue and unfertilized ovarian egg.

meristematic tissue small, actively dividing cells that produce growth in plants.

mesentery a folded membrane that connects to the intestine and the dorsal body wall.

mesoderm the middle layer of cells in an embryo.

mesoglea a jellylike material that separates the two cell layers in coelenterates.

mesophyll photosynthetic tissue composed of chlorenchyma cells located between the upper and lower epidermis of a leaf.

mesothorax the second segment of an insect's body to which the first pair of wings and second pair of walking legs are connected.

messenger RNA the type of RNA that receives a code for a specific protein from the DNA and acts as a template for protein synthesis on the ribosome.

metabolism the sum of the chemical processes of the body.

metamorphosis a marked change in the structure of an animal.

metaphase the second phase of cell division during which the chromosomes line up at the cell equator.

metathorax the third segment of an insect's body to which the second pair of wings and the jumping legs are attached.

microbiology the field of modern science that studies organisms at the microscopic level.

micron microscopic measurement equal to 0.000001 meter (1/25,000 inch).

micropyle the opening in the ovule wall through which the pollen tube enters.

microspores four cells that develop into pollen grains.

midrib the large central vein of a palmately veined leaf.

migration seasonal movements of animals from one environment to another.

milt the sperm-containing discharge of the male fish.

mitochondria rod-shaped organelles in cell cytoplasm that release the energy that supports all cell activity.

mitosis the division of chromosomes preceding the division of cytoplasm.

mixture a substance that results when two or more substances are mixed together with no chemical change taking place.

molecular formula a formula that represents a molecule.

molecules units of matter where the atoms share electrons in covalent bonding.

molting in arthropods, the shedding of the outer layer of exoskeleton; in reptiles, the shedding of a scale layer.

monocotyledon a flowering plant that develops a single seed leaf, or cotyledon.

monohybrid cross a cross involving parents differing in one pair of traits.

monosaccharide a simple sugar; a carbohydrate that cannot be decomposed by hydrolysis.

monosomy the presence of a single homologous chromosome in all body cells.

monotreme an egg-laying mammal.

motor neuron one that carries impulses from the brain or spinal cord to a muscle or gland.

motor unit the nerve cell and the muscle fibers it stimulates to contract.

mucus a lubricating solution secreted by mucous glands.

mucous membrane   a form of epithelial tissue that lines the body openings and digestive tract and secretes mucus.

multicellular organism   a complete living thing that consists of more than one cell.

multiple alleles   more than a single pair of genes that produces a trait.

muscle tissue   a type of tissue that functions in movement.

mutagens   agents that cause mutation.

mutant   an organism in which a mutation has occurred in its genetic makeup.

mutation   a sudden genetic change resulting in a new characteristic that can be inherited by future generations.

mutualism   a form of symbiosis in which two organisms live together to the advantage of both.

mycology   the study of fungi.

N ─────────────────────────────

NAD (nicotinamide adenine dinucleotide)   a hydrogen acceptor active during the anaerobic stage of cellular respiration.

narcotics   a group of drugs that have a strong effect on the nervous system and can cause addiction with continued use.

nastic movement   turgor movements in plants, such as the daily opening and closing of flowers.

natural selection   the result of survival in the struggle for existence among organisms possessing those characteristics that give them an advantage.

negative feedback   a mechanism of the endocrine system by which change in the concentration of a hormone balances the production of another.

nematocyst   a stinging cell in coelenterates.

nephridia   the excretory structures in worms, mollusks, and certain arthropods.

nephrons   filters of the kidney that control the chemical makeup of blood.

nerve   a bundle of nerve cell fibers.

nerve cord   part of the central nervous system in chordates.

nerve impulse   an electrochemical stimulus that causes changes in a nerve fiber.

nerve net   a primitive type of nervous system which allows coelenterates to react strongly to a stimulus.

nervous tissue   specialized tissue that functions as the communication system in the body.

neuron   a nerve cell body and its processes.

neurotoxin   a poison that affects the nervous system.

niche   the particular role played by organisms of a species.

nicotine   in tobacco, a substance that has an irritating effect in the human body.

nictating membrane   a thin covering that keeps the eyeballs of certain vertebrates such as frogs, reptiles, and birds moist.

nitrogen cycle   a series of chemical reactions in which nitrogen compounds change form.

nitrogen fixation   the process by which certain bacteria in soil or the roots of legumous plants convert free nitrogen into nitrogen compounds that are usable by plants.

node   a growing region of a stem from which leaves, branches, or flowers develop.

nondisjunction   the failure of homologous chromosomes to segregate during meiosis.

notochord   a rod of specialized cells running along the length of the dorsal side of lower chordates and present also in the embryonic stage of all vertebrates.

nucleolus   a small, spherical body within the nucleus.

nucleoplasm   the dense, gelatinous, living content of the nucleus.

nucleotide   a unit composed of a ribose or deoxyribose sugar, a phosphate, and an organic base; many such units make up a single RNA or DNA molecule.

nucleus   the part of the cell that contains chromosomes; the center of an atom that contains protons and neutrons.

O ─────────────────────────────

obligate aerobes   bacteria that require oxygen and cannot survive without it.

obligate anaerobes   bacteria that cannot grow in the presence of oxygen.

olfactory lobe   the region of the brain that registers smell.

olfactory nerve   the nerve leading from the olfactory receptors to the olfactory lobe.

omnivores   animals that eat plants as well as other animals.

ootid   a cell that matures into an egg.

open circulatory system   a type of circulatory system in which blood is not contained in vessels, but bathes body organs directly.

operculum   the gill cover in fishes.

optic lobe   the region of the brain that registers sight.

optic nerve   the nerve leading from the retina of the eye to the optic lobe of the brain.

oral groove   a deep cavity along one side of paramecia and similar protozoans.

order   a taxonomic category between a class and a family.

organ   a structure composed of several tissues working as a unit to perform a function.

organ system   a collection of several organs working as a unit to perform a function.

organelles   organized structures found in the cytoplasm of a cell, each with a specific function.

organic compounds   carbon-containing compounds produced by all living organisms.

organism   a complete and entire living thing.

origin   the attachment of a muscle at its nonmoving point.

osculum   the opening in the central cavity of sponges through which water enters and leaves the animal.

osmosis   the diffusion of water through a selectively permeable membrane from an area of greater concentration of water to an area of lesser concentration.

osmotic pressure   the pressure created by the movement of water molecules in the process of osmosis.

ossification   the process of forming bone in which cartilage cells are replaced by bone cells.

ovary   a female organ of reproduction; also the basal part of the pistil containing the ovules.

oviduct   a tube in the female through which eggs travel from an ovary.

oviparous   producing offspring from eggs hatched outside the body.

ovipositor   an egg-laying organ in insects.

ovoviviparous   producing offspring from eggs, but bringing forth young already hatched.

ovulation   the release of the ovum from the follicle.

ovule   a structure in the ovary of a flower that can become a seed when the egg is fertilized.

P

palisade mesophyll   a layer of elongated cells that stand side by side directly beneath the upper epidermis.

palmate   a pattern in which leaflets branch out from the base at the petiole.

pancreas   an organ located near the stomach and duodenum that has both endocrine and digestive functions.

parasite   an organism that lives in or on the body of another.

parasympathetic nervous system   a division of the autonomic nervous system.

parathyroid glands   four endocrine glands, embedded in the back of the thyroid gland, that play an important role in bone growth, muscle tone, and nerve activity.

parenchyma   the thin-walled, soft tissue in plants that forms cortex and pith.

parent cell   a cell that has undergone growth and reaches a point at which it is ready to divide into daughter cells.

parietal eye   in the tuatara, a third eye which is covered by thin, small scales, yet is sensitive to the sun's radiation.

passive immunity   the immunity acquired by introducing antibodies into the body.

passive transport   the movement of molecules by their own energy during diffusion.

pathogenic   disease-causing.

PCP (angel dust)   a dangerous drug that acts on the central nervous system.

pectoral fin   a structure in fish that is homologous to the front legs of other vertebrates.

pectoral girdle   the framework of bones that supports the forelimbs in vertebrates.

pedipals   the second pair of appendages of the spider.

pelagic zone   the open ocean part of the marine biome.

pellicle   the thick, outer membrane that surrounds the cell membrane of the paramecium.

pelvic fin   a structure in fish that is homologous to the hind legs of other vertebrates.

pelvic girdle   the framework of bones that supports the hind legs of vertebrates.

pentaradial   the body type of echinoderms, which have five sections.

peptide bond   a bond that links amino acids to form polypeptides.

perennial   a plant that lives more than two seasons.

pericycle   the tissue in roots from which secondary tissue arises.

periodicity   alternating periods of activity.

peripheral nervous system   the cranial and spinal nerves.

permanent wilting   damage to a plant due to the plant not getting enough water.

permeable membrane   one that allows substances to pass through it.

petals   the brightly colored leaflike parts of a flower.

petiole   the stalk of a leaf.

PGAL (phosphoglyceraldehyde)   a product of photosynthesis that can be used directly as an energy source for cell activity.

phage   a bacteriophage or virus that reproduces in a bacterium.

phagocytes   cells within the body that engulf bacteria and digest them by means of enzymes.

pharynx   the throat cavity, extending up over the soft palate to the nasal cavity; the food tube in planarians.

phenotype   the outward appearance of an organism as the result of genetic makeup.

pheromones   secretions that act as a chemical language between animals of the same species.

phloem   the tissue in leaves, stems, and roots that conducts dissolved food substances.

photochemical reaction   a chemical reaction accelerated by sunlight.

photoperiodism   a response of plants to varying periods of light and darkness.

photoreceptors   receptors, located on the retina of the eye, that are stimulated by light.

photosynthesis   the process by which certain plant cells combine carbon dioxide and water in the presence of chlorophyll and light, thereby forming carbohydrates and releasing oxygen.

phototropism   the response of plants to light.

phyla   a main division of the animal or vegetable kingdoms.

physical change   a change in which states of matter are altered but the particles that make up the matter are not changed.

physics   the science of matter and motion.

phytoplankton   the minute plant organisms that are free-floating on or near the surface of bodies of water.

pinocytosis   the engulfing of large particles in fluid-filled vacuoles at the surface of a cell.

pistil   the female reproductive part of a flower.

pith   storage tissue of roots and stems that consists of parenchyma cells.

pituitary gland   a small endocrine gland, located at the base of the brain; its secretions affect the activity of all other glands.

PKU (phenylketonuria)   a genetic disease due to lack of an enzyme.

placenta   a large, thin membrane in the uterus that transports substances between the mother and the developing young by means of the umbilical cord.

plankton   a collective name for the minute, free-floating organisms that live in water.

plasma   refers to the liquid portion of blood; the blood without the blood cells.

plasma membrane   a thin, living membrane located at the outer edge of the cytoplasm that separates one cell from another and from surrounding fluids; also called the cell membrane.

plasmids   small elements of genetic material found in some bacteria.

plasmodium   the body of a slime mold; a mass of protoplasm with many nuclei and no cell walls.

plastids   organelles often containing pigments in the cytoplasm of plant cells.

plastron   the lower shell of the turtle.

platelets   the smallest of the solid components in blood that play an important role in blood clotting.

pleural membrane   a double membrane that covers the lungs.

plumule   the part of a plant embryo that consists of the first pair of leaves.

point mutation   a gene mutation.

polar bodies   three haploid cells that die at the final stage of meiosis and are absorbed by the organism during egg development.

polar nuclei   the two nuclei in the embryo sac in flowers that fuse with one of the sperm nuclei to form the endosperm nucleus.

pollen   grains that contain the male sex cells, produced by the anther of a flower.

pollen cone   a type of cone, found in conifers, that forms at the tips of branches.

pollination   the transfer of pollen from an anther to a stigma.

pollution   the adding of impurities to the environment.

polypeptide   a large molecule made of amino acid subunits and linked by peptide bonds.

polyploidy   the condition in which cells contain more than twice the haploid number of chromosomes.

population   a group of organisms of the same kind within a biotic community.

population sampling   the study of a population to determine the present ratio of genetic traits.

portal circulation   an extensive system of veins that lead from the stomach, pancreas, small intestine, and colon, then unite and enter the liver.

potential energy   energy that is available to do work, but such work or change is not actually taking place.

precocial birds   birds that are active immediately after birth.

predator   an organism that feeds upon another.

primary germ layers   the ectoderm, endoderm, and mesoderm.

primary root   the first root pushed down into the soil from the lower end of the plant embryo.

primary tissues   the first tissues that develop in a young root and add length to the root.

primates   the order of mammals that have the most highly developed brains as their most prominent trait.

prismatic layer   the middle layer of an oyster; made of calcium carbonate crystals.

productivity   the amount of energy that is accumulated in an ecosystem.

progesterone   a female hormone secreted by the ovaries.

proglottid   a segment of the tapeworm's body.

prokaryotes   cells that lack nuclei.

prop roots   roots that push into the ground to help the underground root system support the stem.

propagation   the multiplication of plants by vegetative means.

prophase   the stage in mitosis in which chromosomes contract and spindle formation occurs.

prostate   a gland located near the upper end of the urethra in the male.

prostomium   a type of upper lip in the earthworm.

protein   a complex chain of amino acids essential in cell structure and function.

protein synthesis   a phase of cell activity in which protein molecules are built up from amino acid molecules.

prothallus   the tiny, heart-shaped gametophyte that develops from the spore of the fern.

prothorax   the first segment of an insect's thorax to which the head and first pair of walking legs are attached.

protonema   a filamentous gametophyte structure produced by a spore in mosses.

protoplasm   a complex system of substances organized into a special state of chemical activity that establishes the living condition.

protozoa   microscopic, unicellular, animallike organisms.

pseudopodia   the "false feet" of the ameba or amebalike cells.

pulmonary circulation   movement of the blood from the heart to the lungs and back to the heart.

pulse   regular expansion of artery walls caused by the pumping of the heart.

Punnett square   a grid system resembling a checkerboard used in computing possible results of various genetic crosses.

pupa   the stage in an insect having complete metamorphosis that follows the larva stage.

purines   organic molecules that are two of the four types of bases that occur in DNA.

pus   a substance formed from the buildup of fluid, dead phagocytes, dead bacteria, and dead tissue due to an infection.

pyloric caeca   pouches extending from the upper end of the intestines in fishes.

pyloric valve   a valve at the intestinal end of the stomach that regulates the passage of substances to the duodenum.

pyrenoid   a small protein body that serves as a center for starch formation in *Spirogyra*.

pyrimidines   two of the four types of nucleotide bases that occur in DNA. They are thymine and cytosine.

Q

quill   the cylinder that originates from the follicle and produces a feather.

R

radicle   the embryonic root in a seed.

radiocarbon method   a process of radioactive carbon measurement used to indicate the age of a fossil.

radula   a tonguelike structure in a snail which has a "scraperlike" quality.

rain forest   a biome characterized by abundant water supply and a long growing season.

RDP (ribulose diphosphate)   a five-carbon sugar molecule which functions as a carbon dioxide acceptor.

receptacle   the end of the flower stalk that bears the reproductive structures.

receptors   special sense organs that receive stimuli.

recessive   a gene or characteristic that is masked when a dominant gene of an allele is present.

recombinant DNA   the new DNA that results from combining DNA from one or more sources.

rectum   the end of the large intestine; the lower end of the rectum forms the anus.

red corpuscles   disk-shaped blood cells that contain hemoglobin.

red marrow   a type of marrow found in flat bones and at the ends of long bones; it forms red corpuscles and certain white corpuscles.

reflex   an automatic response to a stimulus.

reflex action   a nervous reaction in which a stimulus causes an involuntary muscular response.

regeneration   the ability of certain animals to regrow missing parts.

renal circulation   movement of blood to the kidneys and back to the heart.

replication   the process in which a DNA molecule builds an exact copy of itself, allowing the cell to pass its code from one generation to the next.

reproduction   the process by which organisms produce offspring.

research method   a system of following logical and orderly steps in order to solve a problem or answer a question.

resolution   the capability of a microscope to transmit a visible image with clear detail.

resources   the substances available from the environment.

respiration   the exchange of oxygen and carbon dioxide between cells and their surroundings, accompanied by oxidation and the release of chemical energy.

response   the reaction of an organism to a stimulus.

retina   the innermost membrane of the eye that receives the image from the lens and is connected with the brain by the optic nerve.

Rh factor   a type of protein found in red blood cells which may cause a problem in childbearing.

rhizoid   vertical hyphae of a mold; a rootlike structure that absorbs water.

rhizome   a horizontal underground stem which stores food and can propagate vegetatively.

rhythmic   having regular periodicity.

ribosomes   tiny, grainy structures, attached to the endoplasmic reticulum, that contain enzymes that control protein synthesis.

RNA (ribonucleic acid)   a nucleic acid in which the sugar is ribose; a product of DNA, it serves in controlling certain cell activities, including protein synthesis.

root   the portion of a plant that holds it to the ground, absorbs water and minerals, and conducts them to the stem.

root cap   a tissue at the tip of a root that protects the tissues behind it.

root hair   a tiny fingerlike extension in a young root.

root pressure   the pressure that is built up in the root which aids in maintaining the column of water and moving water up the plant.

roughage   foods that are helpful in digestion in that they stimulate muscle contractions of the intestine walls.

ruminants   hoofed mammals that have specialized digestive systems.

S _____

saliva   a fluid secreted into the mouth by the salivary glands.

salivary glands   a group of secretory cells that produce saliva.

saprophyte   an organism that lives off dead or decaying organic matter.

saturation   the point at which no further solute can be dissolved in a solution.

savannah   a biome characterized by grassland with scattered trees.

scavenger   an animal that feeds on dead organisms.

scientific method   a logical, orderly way to solve a problem or answer a question.

scion   the portion of a twig grafted onto a rooted stock.

sclerenchyma   a strengthening tissue in plants.

scolex   a knob-shaped head with hooks or suckers in certain parasitic flatworms.

secondary roots   roots that grow out from the primary roots.

secondary tissues   those produced by the vascular cambium, a lateral secondary meristematic tissue, of a root or stem.

seed   a complete embryo plant surrounded by an endosperm and protected by seed coats.

seed cone   a woody type of cone found in conifers that takes months or years to develop.

segregation, law of   a pair of genes are segregated or separated during the formation of gametes.

selectively permeable   the ability of a cell's plasma membrane to allow certain substances to pass through more readily than others.

self-preservation   a basic instinct in which an animal will react by "fight or flight" when in danger.

semen   fluid that contains sperm.

seminal receptacles   in certain animals, structures that receive sperm cells.

seminal vesicles   in certain animals, structures that store sperm cells.

sensory system   that part of the peripheral nervous system made up of neurons which carry impulses toward the central nervous system.

sepal   the outermost part of a flower.

serum   the liquid part of the blood that is left after the blood clots; a substance that produces immediate passive immunity, used in treating disease.

sessile   in a leaf, lacking a petiole; in an animal, living attached to another object.

setae   bristles on the earthworm, used for locomotion.

sex chromosomes   the two kinds of chromosomes (X and Y) that determine the sex of an offspring.

sex-influenced trait   a trait that is dominant in one sex and recessive in another.

sex-linked trait   a recessive trait that is carried on the X chromosome.

sexual reproduction   a form of reproduction involving two parents.

shell membrane   a double lining around the albumin and inside the shell of a bird's egg.

shelterbelts   planting trees along the edges of fields.

shoot   the stem and the leaves; the visible portion of the plant as it rises into the air.

sickle-cell anemia   an inherited blood disease in which red blood cells exhibit the shape of a sickle.

sieve tube   a conducting tube of the phloem.

sieve-tube elements   cells that form the phloem in angiosperms.

simple eye   a small, photosensitive organ in certain lower animals.

simple microscope   an early microscope made of a single-lens magnifying glass.

sinoatrial node   a small mass of tissue located in the wall of the right atrium of the heart, in which the heartbeat originates.

skeletal muscle   a type of striated muscle that functions voluntarily.

slime layer   a layer that surrounds a bacterium.

small intestine   an organ of digestion; the digestive tube.

smog   a combination of smoke and fog.

smooth muscle   the type of muscle that functions involuntarily and is found lining the walls of the intestines, stomach, and arteries.

social insects   insects that develop societies, such as bees, ants, certain wasps, and termites.

soft palate   the soft area that forms part of the roof of the mouth.

solute   the dissolved substance in a solution.

solution   a homogeneous mixture of two or more substances where one is dissolved in another.

solvent   the dissolving component of a solution.

somatic mutation   a type of mutation that occurs in the body cell of a plant or animal but is not passed on to its offspring.

sori   the asexual reproductive bodies of a fern.

spawn   the mass of eggs discharged by a fish; to discharge gametes directly into the water.

specialization   the adaptation of a cell for a particular use.

speciation   the development of a species.

species   a group of organisms that are similar in structure and can mate and produce fertile offspring.

species preservation   an animal instinct that directs reproduction and care of the young.

sperm   a male reproductive cell.

spicule   the material that forms the skeleton of certain sponges.

spinal cord   the main nerve of the central nervous system that extends down the back.

spinal nerves   large nerves connecting the spinal cord with other parts of the body.

spindle   the fine threads formed between the poles of the nucleus during mitosis.

spiracle   a tiny opening on an insect's body that leads to the trachea.

spirillum   a spiral-shaped bacterium.

spongy mesophyll   loosely constructed leaf tissue that contains many spaces.

spontaneous generation   the belief that certain nonliving materials can change directly into living organisms.

spore   a small asexual reproductive cell.

sporophyte   the stage at which spores are produced in an organism that has alternation of generations.

stamen   the male reproductive part of a flower.

starches   complex carbohydrates made of glucose units organized into chains.

statocyst   the balancing organ of the crayfish.

stem   the portion of a plant that conducts water and minerals from the roots up to the leaves and other nutrients back down.

stigma   the part of a pistil that receives pollen grains.

stimulant   a drug that has an effect of increased activity on the nervous system.

stimulus   a factor or environmental change capable of producing activity in an organism.

stipule   a leaflike structure at the base of many leaf petioles.

stock   the plant on which a scion has been grafted.

stolons   transverse hyphae of a mold; a horizontal, creeping underground stem.

stomach   an organ of digestion that receives ingested food and prepares it for digestion by churning it and secreting gastric fluid.

stomata   pores that regulate the passage of air and water to and from a leaf.

structural formula   a diagram of the atoms and bonds in a molecule.

substrate   the material upon which an organism lives.

succession   the process where plant and animal populations of an area change in a specific manner.

sugar   a type of carbohydrate that provides the basic fuel for plant and animal life.

survival of the fittest   a process in nature in which organisms best adapted to an environment will survive while others die.

suspension   a mixture formed by particles that are larger than ions or molecules

suture   an irregular joint at which bone edges are united.

swimmerets   appendages on the abdomen of a crustacean.

symbiosis   the relationship in which two organisms live together in close association.

symmetry   the general form of an organism.

sympathetic nervous system   a division of the autonomic nervous system.

synapse   the space between nerve endings.

synapsis   the coming together of homologous pairs of chromosomes during meiosis.

syrinx   the song box of a bird.

systemic circulation   movement of oxygen-rich blood from the heart, through the aorta, to all body tissues except the lungs, and back to the heart.

systole   the first phase of a complete cycle of the heart activity in which the ventricles of the heart contract and force blood into the arteries.

T
_____

taproot   the main root of a plant, often serving as a food reservoir.

taste buds   tiny bumps located on the surface of the tongue with nerve endings at their bases.

taxonomy   the science of classifying living things.

tegument   a thick layer of cells that surrounds a parasite.

telophase   the last phase of mitosis during which two daughter cells are formed.

telson   the posterior segment of the abdomen of certain crustaceans.

temperate phage   a phage that injects its DNA material into a bacterium without causing new phages to be created.

temperature inversion   an atmospheric phenomenon in which a layer of cool air moves below a layer of warm air.

template   a specific sequence of bases in the messenger RNA molecules that acts as a pattern for the building of amino acids into proteins.

temporary wilting   drooping in a plant due to a decrease in water that does not lead to permanent damage.

tendon   a thick band of connective tissue to which skeletal muscles attach.

tendrils   part of some plants modified for climbing.

tentacle   a long appendage of certain coelenterates; a "feeler."

terminal bud   the end, or top bud, of the twig.

terrapin   a hard-shelled, freshwater turtle.

testa   the outer coat of a seed.

testes   the male reproductive organs.

testosterone   a male hormone manufactured in the testes.

tetrad   a group of four cells.

thallus   a plant body that lacks differentiation into stems, leaves, and roots and does not grow from an apical point.

theory   a hypothesis that is supported by experimental evidence.

thoracic cavity   a body cavity that contains the lungs, trachea, heart, and esophagus.

thorax   the middle region of an insect's body; the chest region in mammals.

thymus   an endocrine gland located under the breastbone.

thyroid   a large endocrine gland, located in the neck, that regulates metabolism.

tissue   a group of cells that are similar in structure and function.

tone   the state of slight contraction in muscles, caused by the opposition of the flexor and extensor muscles.

tortoises   turtles that live on land, have hard shells, and are slow-moving.

trachea   the windpipe; an air tube in insects and spiders.

tracheids   thick-walled conducting tubes which strengthen wood tissue.

tracheophyte   a plant that has vessels for the conduction of fluids.

transcription   the process in which a molecule of DNA codes for the creation of a molecule of RNA.

transduction   a process in which a bacteriophage picks up part of the genetic material of a host cell and transfers it into another cell.

transfer RNA   a form of RNA that delivers amino acids to the template formed by messenger RNA on the ribosomes.

transformation   the transfer of genetic information in which a small portion of the total DNA of a lytic bacterium enters another bacterium and is incorporated into its genetic constitution.

translocation   the movement of water, minerals, and food within a plant.

transpiration   the process in which water is lost from plants.

transpiration pull   a negative pressure in the

water column of a plant as water evaporates due to transpiration.

trisomy   the presence of three homologous chromosomes in an organism's body cells.

trochophore   a larval stage in mollusks.

trophic levels   the transfer of energy from autotrophs to several levels of heterotrophs.

tropism   a directional growth response to an environmental stimulus.

tube feet   movable suction discs on the rays of most echinoderms.

tube nucleus   one of the two nuclei present in a pollen cell.

tuber   a swollen area of a stolon.

tundra   a biome encircling the Arctic Ocean characterized by very cold and dry climate; its ground is frozen permanently.

tympanic membrane   a membrane in certain arthropods serving a vibratory function; the eardrum.

tympanum   a membrane-covered cavity in the first abdominal segment of a grasshopper.

U

ungulates   hoofed mammals.

ureter   a long narrow tube that leads from the kidney to the bladder or cloaca.

urethra   a tube leading from the urinary bladder to an external opening of the body.

urinary bladder   the sac, at the base of the ureters, that stores urine.

urinary ducts   structures in the excretory system of frogs.

urine   the liquid waste filtered from the body.

uropod   a flipper or developed swimmeret at the posterior end of the crayfish.

uterus   the organ in which young mammals develop; in many less complex animals, the long coiled tube where the many eggs are stored.

V

vaccination   a method of producing immunity by inoculating with a vaccine.

vaccine   a substance used to produce immunity.

vacuoles   fluid-filled cavities in the cytoplasm of plant cells.

variation   a characteristic of all living things such that no two offspring are exactly like each other nor are they exactly like their parents.

vascular bundles   strands of phloem and xylem found in the roots, stems, and leaves of plants.

vascular cylinder   the innermost region of a root that contains the xylem and phloem.

vascular rays   sheets of parenchyma cells which radiate from the pith through the xylem into a woody stem.

vascular tissue   fluid-conducting tissue characteristic of the tracheophytes.

vegetative organs   the organs of a flowering plant, each with a specific role, e.g., the root, stem, and leaves.

vegetative propagation   the process of asexual reproduction which occurs during a plant's growing stage.

veins   vessels that carry blood toward the heart; strengthening and conducting structures in leaves.

venation   the arrangement of veins in a leaf.

ventral surface   the lower surface of an animal.

ventricle   a muscular chamber of the heart; a cavity in the brain.

venules   small branches of veins.

vertebrae   the bony parts of the spinal column in vertebrates.

vertebrate   an animal with a backbone.

vessel   a tube made of vessel elements that forms the xylem in angiosperms.

vessel elements   thin-walled conducting tissues in angiosperms.

vestigial organs   structures that appear to have no function.

viability   the ability of a seed to germinate.

villi   fingerlike projections in the small intestine that participate in the process of absorption.

virulence   an organism's ability to cause disease.

virulent phage   a bacteriophage that produces a lytic cycle of destruction.

viruses   particles that are noncellular, have no nucleus, no cytoplasm, no surrounding membrane, and reproduce in living tissue.

visceral hump   a structure of an adult mollusk that contains the digestive organs, reproductive organs, excretory glands, and heart.

visible spectrum   the colors of the rainbow that are capable of being seen.

vitamin   an organic substance necessary for the maintenance of normal body activity.

viviparous   refers to mammals that bear live young and nourish their young during development.

vocal cords   the structures within the larynx which vibrate to produce sound.

W

walking legs   in the crayfish and other arthropods, appendages located behind the claws.

water cycle   the continuous movement of water from the atmosphere to the earth and from the earth to the atmosphere.

water-vascular system   the system of tubes connecting the tube feet in certain echinoderms.

waterborne infection   infection spread from one person to another by means of sewage, ground water, and so on.

watershed   a hilly region, usually extending over a large area, that conducts water to streams.

white corpuscles   colorless cells that have nuclei and are important in defending the body against infection.

wood fibers   tissue in angiosperms that strengthens and supports.

X

X chromosome   a sex chromosome present singly in human males and as a pair in females.

Y

Y chromosome   a sex chromosome found only in males.

yellow marrow   found in the central cavity of long bones; primarily composed of fat cells.

yolk   a special food in the egg that nourishes the developing embryo.

yolk sac membrane   an embryonic membrane that provides food for the embryo.

Z

zoospores   flagellated cells that leave the parent cell and then develop into new organisms.

zygospore   the dormant form of some organisms during which the zygote forms a thick protective wall.

zygote   a fertilized egg.

xanthophyll   a yellow pigment found in chloroplasts.

xylem   the woody tissue of a root or stem that conducts water and dissolved minerals upward.

Index

Page references for illustrations are printed in **boldface.**